A History of
Domesticated
Animals

A History of Domesticated Animals

FREDERICK E. ZEUNER

Professor of Environmental Archaeology, University of London

HARPER & ROW, PUBLISHERS

NEW YORK AND EVANSTON

Contents

CONTENTS

Acknowledgements for Illustrations

I should like to thank many friends and colleagues for their kindness in supplying me with photographs and allowing me to use illustrations. Some are mentioned in the text and others include: Mr R. Carrington (Fig. 11 : 16), Mr C. Crisler (Figs. 2 : 4, 2 : 5 and 4 : 6), Mrs Nina de Garis Davies (Fig. 24 : 12), Mrs Dorey (Fig. 10 : 13), Mrs Gabrielle Keiller (Fig. 4 : 11), Dr R. Mertens (Fig. 4 : 10), Dr J. Papadimitriou (Figs. 16 : 4, 16 : 5 and 22 : 5), Mr N. Teulon Porter (Fig. 16 : 8), Dr E. Ripoll (Fig. 27 : 1), Mrs Liselotte Selbiger (Fig. 12 : 22), Mr C. R. Stonor (Fig. 9 : 8), Dr A. Sutcliffe (Fig. 11 : 2), Miss Veronica Tudor-Williams (Fig. 4 : 27) and Dr F. Windels (Fig. 12 : 9).

I am also indebted to many museums and other institutions for permission to reproduce illustrations of material in their collections: the Directors of the Rheinisches Landesmuseum, Bonn (Figs. 6 : 12, 8 : 14, 10 : 3 and 22 : 8), the Landesmuseum, Trier (Fig. 14 : 2), the Niederösterreichisches Landesmuseum, Vienna (Fig. 22 : 7), Museo Archeologico Nazionale di Napoli (Figs. 16 : 7 and 24 : 11), Museo Nazionale G. A. Sanna-Sassari (Fig. 8 : 43), Syracuse Museum (Fig. 4 : 29), Museo Canario, Las Palmas (Figs. 6 : 16, 6 : 17, 6 : 18), Metropolitan Museum of Art, New York (Figs. 4 : 17, 4 : 30 (Rogers Fund, 1947), 12 : 12 (Rogers Fund, 1915) and 21 : 1), City Art Museum, St Louis (Fig. 7 : 24), Oriental Institute, University of Chicago (Fig. 20 : 14), the Conservatoire en Chef, Musée du Louvre, Paris (Figs. 4 : 12 and 24 : 5), the Trustees of the British Museum (Figs. 1 : 14, 2 : 6, 4 : 25, 10 : 4, 11 : 19, 12 : 11, 14 : 3, 14 : 4, 14 : 5, 14 : 6, 16 : 3, 20 : 6, 24 : 6, 24 : 10, 27 : 5), Victoria and Albert Museum (Figs. 12 : 27 and 25 : 2), the Science Museum (Fig. 15 : 5), the Ashmolean Museum, Oxford (Fig. 6 : 7), the Zoological Society of London (Figs. 11 : 1 and 14 : 1), the Dorset Natural History and Archaeological Society (Fig. 4 : 15), the Canadian Wild Life Service (Fig. 2 : 16), the East Africa Office (Figs. 2 : 9 and 2 : 10), the Tourist Office of Morocco (Fig. 6 : 2), the Swedish

ACKNOWLEDGEMENTS FOR ILLUSTRATIONS

Institute for Cultural Relations (Figs. 2 : 7, 5 : 1, 5 : 2 and 5 : 3), the Editor of *The Times* (Fig. 13 : 1), the Directors of Fremlins Brewery (Fig. 12 : 19), Walt Disney Productions, Ltd. (Fig. 5 : 5), J. Allan Cash, Ltd. (Fig. 15 : 3), Messrs Nigh and Sons (Fig. 15 : 6), Polar Photos, Ltd. (Fig. 5 : 7), Ronald W. Clark (Fig. 6 : 11), Frank Lane (Figs. 17 : 1 and 20 : 1) and Paul Popper (Fig. 4 : 14).

Preface

Animals of past ages have attracted the interest of the inquiring since early times. There has always been in man a desire to obtain knowledge of what happened before the inquirer himself came into existence and to find out how things came to be as they are. This desire is deeply rooted in man's natural relation to his environment. The animal world was an important source of food and raw material for primitive man, and as his conceptions of magic and religion developed, the animal world was naturally drawn into them. The two most obvious contacts between man and animal, therefore, are economic and religious, in the widest sense. But though this may be true broadly speaking, man cannot ignore the natural environment in which he exists, and little thought is required to appreciate that all processes of the evolution of man, as well as of his cultures, are governed by biological processes.

Ever since man assumed the habit, at least 10,000 years ago, of living in more or less permanent settlements, his relationship to the animal world has undergone changes. As a hunter and food collector he felt essentially a part of nature, but once permanent settlement had become the rule, his attitude to animals was profoundly changed. The outcome of this process was the domestication of certain species, with most of which we are familiar at the present day. How the processes that led to domestication were themselves partly due to the interplay of biological phenomena and not wholly to deliberate acts of man will be shown in this book.

The lack of a textbook on the history of domesticated animals has been felt for a good many years. None has ever been published in the English language, and the three German books by Antonius, Hilzheimer and Keller are out of date and unobtainable. The present work is intended to fill this gap. Originally, it was planned as a somewhat technical, palaeontological treatise, which could be a help in identifying osteological material from archaeological sites. It was soon realized, however, that it would be premature to make such an attempt in view of the extremely uneven state of our knowledge. On the other hand, the archaeological information available

9

is considerable, and a worker's knowledge of it is usually confined to his own immediate area. An attempt has therefore been made to draw together this information
and to present it as a whole. At the same time, a vast amount of biological information both from actual finds and from general zoological considerations had to be
incorporated, and it is hoped that the fusion of the different spheres has been carried
out with some degree of success.

In view of its many aspects, it is hoped that this book will be of interest not only
to the student of archaeology, but to palaeontologists and animal-breeders, not to
mention those who like to know more about the early history of their favourite
pets.

It was felt necessary to incorporate a large number of illustrations since these
help substantially in the appreciation of the written word and save the reader endless
trouble in looking up sources. It should, however, be pointed out that many represent original material. In preparing this book a considerable amount of original
research was carried out, which is perhaps not everywhere apparent. In addition,
every effort has been made to provide reliable information only, and to present carefully considered deductions. Although thirteen years have been spent in the production of the book, it has proved impossible to cover the enormous field in the
time.

I am sadly aware of the fact that I have not succeeded in levelling out the
differences which are due to the varied dates when chapters were completed. As the
book grew, the factor of size, too, became an important consideration, and much
matter had to be left out which I should have liked to include. Looking at it now it
is completed, I confess it is not what I wanted to write. I am glad that I need not
review it myself, for I should be the first to criticize it.

It may be useful to mention that throughout the book the term 'race' is used for
natural (i.e. wild) subspecies, whilst the term 'breed' is restricted to products of
domestication. A distinction also has to be made between tamed animals which co-
operate with man, though they breed in liberty, and domesticated animals, which
breed under the control of man. Sometimes differentiation is recommended between
domesticated animals (the breeding of which is controlled by man, as has just been
said) and *domestic* animals, i.e. those that have voluntarily associated themselves with
man. In the latter category should be included the house-mouse and the house-
sparrow. This distinction, however, is not in general use, and the two terms are used
interchangeably by most authors. I myself have therefore preferred to remain
similarly inconsistent in this respect.

Furthermore, it is worth pointing out that the use of capital letters for archaeological terms is a complicated matter and the apparent inconsistencies in the text
usually have a reason; adjectives such as 'early', 'middle', 'late', are spelt with a
capital if they constitute a definable chronological period, but not otherwise.

Measurements are given throughout in the metric system since this is universally adopted in all scientific books.

A glance at the Bibliography will convince the reader that the number of books consulted is large (about 580). Even so, many papers have not been referred to so as to avoid overloading the text with references. In particular, I have become very interested in the evidence provided by classical writers such as Herodotus, Aristotle and Pliny. Their works deserve very close study when considering animal domestication, but naturally the number of references to their views is not large. In the Bibliography the chief interest of the book or paper is indicated in parentheses, unless obvious from the title. Needless to say, the international system of abbreviations for periodicals is used throughout.

Apart from original research on fauna from archaeological sites, in which I have been much helped by some of my students, various journeys have been undertaken, partly to collect material, and partly to study the results of excavations and to obtain essential biological information in the very countries concerned. In addition to most European countries, North and East Africa were visited, as well as the Middle East (where the writer has undertaken the investigation of the fauna from prehistoric Jericho) and India.

I am most grateful to the Curators and Directors of many museums in these countries for the help they have afforded me in connection with my studies. Among them I should like to mention the following places: Amsterdam, Tervueren, Paris, West Berlin, East Berlin, Bonn, Frankfurt, Hamburg, Munich, Trier, Basle, Vienna, Prague, Brno, Madrid, Rome, Palermo, Piazza Armerina, Syracuse, Athens, Rabat, Tangier, Tunis, Algiers, Tebessa, Oran, Cairo, Jerusalem, Amman, Delhi, Bombay, Melbourne, Sydney, the Metropolitan and Natural History Museums, New York, and various museums in London and the counties of Britain.

In the preparation of my manuscript I have received help from many friends and colleagues. First and foremost I wish to put on record my grateful thanks to Miss Joan Sheldon, who has carried a fair share of the burden of straightening out many an unevenness due to the various periods of writing and circumstances under which the chapters were prepared, and for much technical help. Others who have helped by supplying me with information or clarifying various points, as well as with technical matters, are: Mrs O. Brogan (Oxford), Mr R. Carrington (London), the late Professor V. Gordon Childe, Dr I. W. Cornwall (London), Mrs E. Coult (London), the late Mr O. G. S. Crawford, Dr P. E. P. Deraniyagala (Ceylon), Mr G. C. Dunning (London), Miss M. Eden (London), Professor Eve Edwards (London) Père Fleisch (Beirut), Miss Frances Gibbs (London), the late Sir William Gowers, Dr P. Graziosi (Florence), Miss A. Grosvenor-Ellis (Lindfield), Dr Heinz Heck (Berlin), Dr Lutz Heck (Munich), Dr W. Herre (Kiel), the late Mr W. H. Johnson, the late Dr L. Keimer (Cairo), Miss D. Kirkbride (Jerusalem), Dr L. Leschi (Algiers)

Professor M. E. L. Mallowan (London), M Serée de Roch (Tebessa), Dr O. Samson (London), Mr Walter Shepherd (London), Professor Sydney Smith, Miss J. du Plat Taylor (London), Miss P. Wallace (London).

Special thanks are due to Mr Hubert Pepper for the expert way in which he has drawn the vast majority of black-and-white illustrations. A few others were drawn by Mrs M. Eastham, Dr F. G. R. Payne, Mr H. Stuart and Dr G. J. Wainwright, to whom I am most grateful.

Many others are mentioned in the text at the appropriate places and to all these colleagues and others unnamed I extend my sincere gratitude.

Finally, I wish to stress that from the studies made in the preparation of this book there emerges an urgent need for further osteological work. The mere identification of specimens found on archaeological sites is no longer enough. They require detailed investigation and comparison with finds from other sites, and monographs on the osteology of the various species are urgently required. But to understand and interpret correctly the results of osteological studies from the archaeological point of view, some ground on which to stand is essential. In other words, a summary of our present knowledge, incomplete though it is as yet. This book is intended to provide such a starting point. Its publication will, I hope, stimulate further work, and I am looking forward to learning from my critics.

F. E. ZEUNER

London, 1962

PART ONE

The Origins and Evolution of Domestication

I

The Conquest of Environment

I T IS only to be expected that the domestication of animals should be considered
by many in the same manner as other human activities, namely as a deliberate
process of exploitation of environment. To one who has found his way to archaeology
from a background of historical biology (palaeontology) and the study of environmental changes, however, the idea comes more naturally that the beginnings of
many such processes were unintended and not conscious. The domestication of
animals may well be derived from the social relationships of animal species, man
being one of them. This is the view put forward in this book. Domestication is
rooted in the natural contacts of man with beast which, in the early stages, were
provided mainly but not exclusively by hunting.

It is widely held that early man did not influence his natural environment to
any noticeable degree. This is true of the Palaeolithic and Mesolithic periods during
which man was a pure *food-gatherer* who relied on hunting, fishing and collecting
shell-fish, grubs, fruit and wild vegetables. This stage, as we now know, lasted for
several hundred thousand years and was hardly more than a direct development
from the food economy practised by our ape-like ancestors.[1] It must not be overlooked, however, that, though few in number, these men may have interfered with
the stability of their environment at least temporarily, and on a scale which was out
of proportion with the scantiness of the population.[2]

---

[1] Ancestors who changed into human beings by adopting the practice of planned hunting of animals, thus
reverting to a partly carnivorous diet.

[2] The density of human population during the Palaeolithic is often underrated, and one writer has put the
number for Britain as low as 250. This is certainly a serious underestimate; a few thousand would be nearer the
mark. In some Palaeolithic sites, especially in Africa and India, the evidence from living sites, even of Lower
Palaeolithic Age, suggests that the human population was by no means scanty.

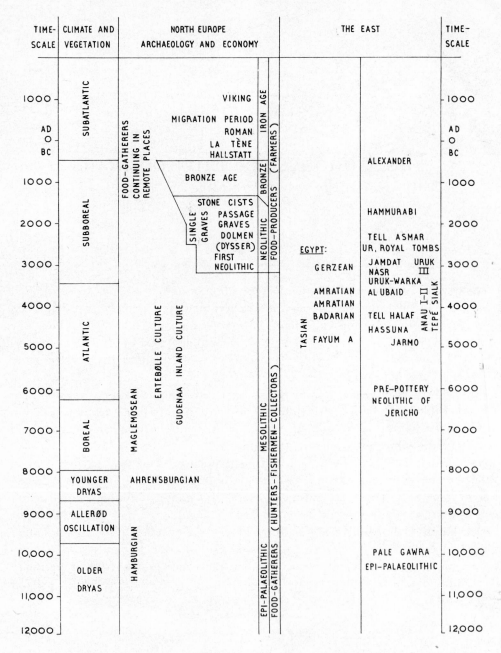

FIG. I : I. Table of prehistoric and climatic periods for the time since the end of the Ice Age

One means by which interference with his environment was possible even for Palaeolithic man was fire. Burning woods and grasslands is a method of hunting widely employed in the present day. It may have been learned from accidental fires in very early times, and there is no reason to assume that Lower Palaeolithic man should not have practised it.[1] One is probably right in assuming that early man did not, and did not want to, control steppe or forest fires he had started. The results of

Localities	Man	Age of the individuals in years			
		$\frac{1}{4}$–6	6–20	20–50	50 upwards
Mauer (*E. antiquus*)	Heidelberg Man	31·1%	26·6%	20·0%	24·4%
Süssenborn (*E. trogontherii*)	absent	—	8·6%	13·4%	78·0%
Taubach (*E. antiquus*)	Neanderthal Man	25·5%	28·8%	28·8%	16·7%
Younger Loess near Emmendingen, Baden (*E. primigenius*)	absent	—	17·2%	20·7%	62·1%

FIG. 1 : 2. Table of proportion of young and old individuals of Pleistocene elephants in prehistoric localities in Europe, contrasting those in which man was present and absent. The age determination is based on the molars. After Soergel (1922)

such activities must have been the temporary appearance of clearings in the forests, the expansion of steppe at the expense of forest or the temporary replacement of steppe by desert. In addition to changing the floral environment, such fires would have affected the mammalian fauna of the area for some time.

This is not the place to discuss primitive hunting methods in detail.[2] It should nevertheless be pointed out that some of them are extremely wasteful. The driving of herds of horses over precipices, such as was practised at Solutré in France in Upper Palaeolithic times, may well have affected the number of certain species of game.

[1] Evidence to this effect has recently be..ı put forward for the Acheulian site of Hoxne in Suffolk (West, 1956), of Great Interglacial age (about 250,000 years ago).

[2] A companion volume on prehistoric game and hunting is in preparation.

Trapping would have been much less harmful, although, where large and slow-breeding animals are concerned, it can influence the number of young and females considerably (Fig. 1 : 2). In Java, for instance, the number of rhinoceroses has in recent years been much reduced by trapping. Trapping was, moreover, practised well back in the Lower Palaeolithic, especially by Mousterian man. Fossil remains

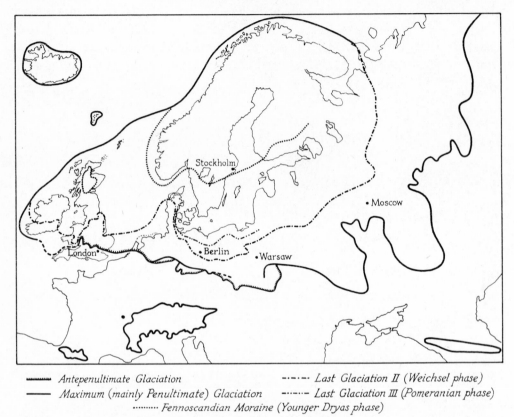

▬▬▬ *Antepenultimate Glaciation*	— · — · — *Last Glaciation II (Weichsel phase)*
——— *Maximum (mainly Penultimate) Glaciation*	— · · — · · — *Last Glaciation III (Pomeranian phase)*
·········· *Fennoscandian Moraine (Younger Dryas phase)*	

FIG. 1 : 3. Map of the glaciations of Europe showing the maximum extent and some of the stages of the Last Glaciation. After Wills (1951) and Zeuner (1958)

have shown that at the Mousterian site of Taubach more than 70 per cent of the rhinoceroses caught were young animals.[1]

Even so, however, any modifying influence that Palaeolithic man might have had on his environment was local and temporary. It is probable that his presence in a certain area disturbed members of the wild fauna sufficiently to cause them to

---

[1] It is worth remembering that the pygmies of the Congo forest have to change their abodes once every few months because they have exhausted their food supply completely by hunting and food-collecting, in spite of the fact that their communities consist of no more than family groups.

withdraw until he left again. But there is no definite evidence that Upper Palaeo-lithic man, even of the Magdalenian culture who had attained a high level of technological skill (Fig. 1 : 8), had begun to domesticate animals or to grow food plants.[1] As regards agricultural operations, these are in any case most unlikely to have been possible in the cold climate then prevailing in Europe, but a primitive type of domestication of such an easily tamed and common animal as the reindeer would have been within the range of possibility. The evidence, however, so far shows only that the reindeer was hunted by the Magdalenians and their contemporaries. In a reindeer-hunters' camp at Meiendorf, near Hamburg, Rust found that the animals were killed by shooting or throwing missiles which in some cases penetrated the shoulder blades, in much the same way as a correctly aimed modern bullet would.

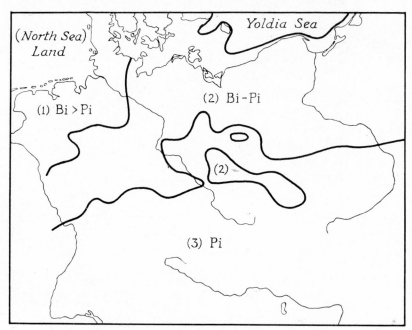

FIG. 1 : 4. Distribution of forests in the Preboreal of central Europe. After Firbas (1949). Symbols used : Bi=birch; Pi=pine. On the whole, birch/pine association is present into which the hazel is soon to move. The North Sea is still dry land

Until about 10,000 years ago, when the change of the northern climate from an arctic to a temperate type occurred, it may be assumed that man's interference with his environment was on the whole no more than temporary. In northern Europe the change of climate brought an extension of the forest, which began to cover the open

[1] Palaeolithic agriculture has mistakenly been claimed by Willvonseder on the grounds of grain found in Austrian caves.

loess steppe and tundra of west, central and eastern Europe, spreading from the 'refuge' areas in the north-western and north-eastern borders of the Mediterranean where temperate forest had survived the glacial phases (Figs. 1 : 4 and 1 : 5).

This process was a slow one, and climatic zonation was pronounced so long as the ice-sheet in the north persisted (Fig. 1 : 3). There was, therefore, tundra persisting (though all the time withdrawing north to the belt it now occupies) near the

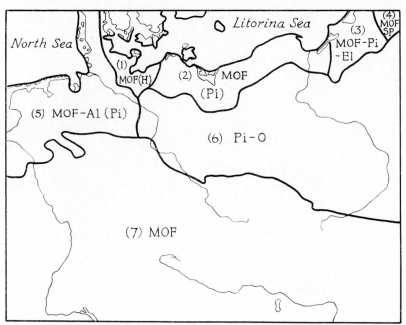

FIG. 1 : 5. Forests of the Atlantic period of central Europe. After Firbas (1949). The mixed oak forest (MOF) is now dominant, though pine is still widespread, especially in the north. Symbols used : Pi=pine; Al=alder; O=oak; H=hazel; El=elm; Sp=spruce. Coastlines now much the same as today

margin of the retreating ice, whilst at the same time forests occupied vast portions of temperate Europe.

Man of necessity adapted his economy to the new conditions. Those tribes which were reluctant to change their habits, and preferred to adhere as closely as they could to the inherited Palaeolithic mode of life, withdrew northwards with the waning tundra belt. But other tribes took the plunge and modified their mode of life in accordance with the new environment, developing a new cultural stage, the Mesolithic. Professor V. G. Childe has described how social co-operation—necessary in the open country of the late phases of the Ice Age—was to some extent given up, because in the forests it was easier for small, independent groups of food-gatherers to forage for themselves. Bone as a raw material was largely replaced by wood but stone continued to supply cutting tools.

The earliest Mesolithic peoples of Europe whose cultural remains have been dated are the manufacturers of the Lyngby axe, made of reindeer antler. This instrument is believed by some to have been designed to cope with wood, the new raw material provided by the advancing forests. The Lyngby people lived in the Jutland peninsula about 8000 B.C.

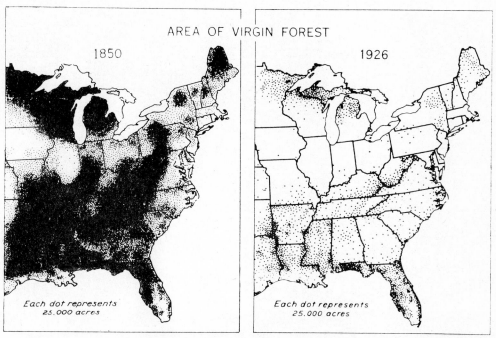

FIG. 1 : 6. The reduction of the forested area in North America as the result of the introduction of European agriculture

Another piece of Mesolithic equipment was bow and arrow. The arrows were provided with very small geometrically shaped flints, microliths, which altogether play a great part in the stone technology of Mesolithic man (Fig. 1 : 9). Apart from the hunting of the new game of the forests, Mesolithic man relied extensively on the collecting of snails, shell-fish and nuts, and it has been pointed out that the large size of many of the refuse-heaps ('Kitchen Middens', some 100 yards long and thirty yards wide) suggests a relatively sedentary life (Childe, 1944, 1947). Or at least it suggests regular seasonal visits to favourable hunting and collecting grounds. By about 2500 B.C. pottery and polished stone made their appearance in the Danish Ertebølle culture.

The Mesolithic is the oldest cultural period in which we have definite evidence of animal domestication. In northern Europe the dog had become a companion of man at the latest by about 6000 B.C. The dog was no doubt employed in hunting and proved useful as a scavenger in many ways, as the living sites of early man were

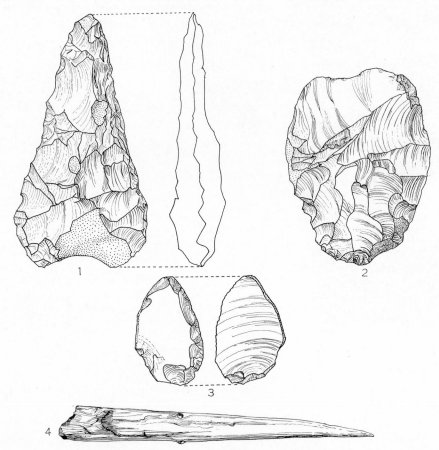

FIG. 1 : 7. Lower Palaeolithic tools. (1) An Acheulian handaxe, a universal digging and cutting tool. (2) An Acheulian cleaver, used for chopping wood and possibly meat. (3) Mousterian scraper, probably used for cleaning skins. (4) Part of a wooden spear found at Clacton-on-Sea and belonging to the Clactonian period. (1), (2) and (4) from Britain, (3) from France

littered with the remains of meals. The dog has been found also in Mesolithic deposits in the south. These finds will be discussed presently.

Whilst the domestication of the dog in Mesolithic times must be regarded as certain, some indications have come forward that a domesticated sheep was also known in the Mesolithic of western Europe. Its presence has been recorded from three Tardenoisian sites in France, namely Sauveterre (Coulonges, 1935), Cuzoul (Lacam, *et al.*, 1944) and Téviec (Péquart, *et al.*, 1937). In England only one site is known, Three Holes Cave at Torbryan in south Devon, where the writer has been excavating in recent years. The industry here is 'Sauveterrian' but it is conceivable that the British Sauveterrian is in part contemporary with the Tardenoisian of France. These sites are not likely to be earlier than the fourth millennium B.C. Whilst they suggest that Late Mesolithic man of temperate Europe had adopted the practice of keeping sheep, this does not imply a transition to life in permanent settlements. The sheep is a nomadic species and it would move and could be moved as readily as the temporary living sites of man himself. It must also be remembered that at this time the countries of the Near East were already in the possession of fully domesticated goat and possibly of sheep and even cattle, hence it is conceivable that the practice of sheep-keeping had spread to the backward tribes of the more northern countries.

The origins of domestication have therefore to be sought in the Near East rather than the north, and this is substantiated by the fact that at least the goat, and most breeds of domesticated sheep, are derived from wild ancestors which still occur in the Near East. Excavations, especially at Jericho in Jordan, Jarmo in Iraq and Belt Cave in Persia, have thrown interesting light on the question of the origins of domestication in that part of the world. On the other hand, it would be a mistake to assume that domestication started there exclusively. It is obvious, for instance, that reindeer

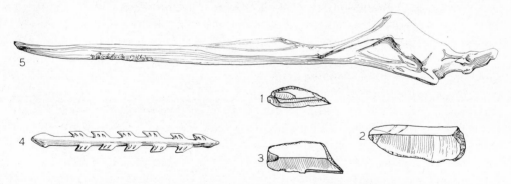

FIG. 1 : 8. Upper Palaeolithic tools. (1) A Gravettian knife-blade. (2) An end scraper. (3) An angle-burin (much used for working bone and antler). (4) A late Magdalenian barbed point or harpoon. (5) A beautifully sculptured end of a spear-thrower. All from France.

domestication has at all times been confined to the north and nobody knows whether it has chronological priority over the first domestication of goat and sheep in the Near East. The horse too was domesticated north of the great mountain ranges, though almost certainly at a very much later date. But since most evidence has become available from the Near East, it is this area that most requires discussion, and in particular the development from the Mesolithic Natufian through the pre-pottery Neolithic of Jordan.

The Natufian culture takes us to a climatic zone which is very different from temperate Europe. In the present day the countries adjacent to the Mediterranean Sea, and the Near and Middle East, are on the whole characterized by a 'dry' environment, with lack of forests, plenty of steppe—natural or agricultural—and even semi-desert. But during the cold phases of the Ice Age these countries were covered with forests resembling in many respects those of present-day Europe, though much richer in species of trees. On their southern edge the forests passed into scrublands and steppe, densely populated with herds of game animals. After the end of the Ice Age, about 10,000 years ago, the steppelands began to spread at the expense of the forest. Had man not interfered with this natural process, it would have been very slow. In the forests, moisture-loving trees might have been replaced by species that resist summer drought. It was, however, from that time onwards that man began to destroy his environment at an ever-increasing rate.

The peoples concerned in this process still belonged to the Mesolithic. Taking the Natufians of Palestine as an example, they were in many respects more advanced than the Magdalenians and Erteb⊘llians of northern Europe. There is no need here to discuss the industry (Garrod and Bate, 1937; Garrod, 1957), though it is important to note that there was no pottery. This does not mean that vessels were not used: leather bags, gourds and clay-lined baskets were efficient forerunners of fired pots. The equipment of the Natufians was not confined to utilitarian items. They were fond of ornaments, and necklaces of surprising beauty have been found.

Like the Mesolithic peoples of northern Europe, the Natufians had the domesti-cated dog. The question therefore arises whether other species had been drawn into the orbit of human habitations. Both the true horse and cattle have been found in Natufian deposits. The late Miss D. M. A. Bate, of the British Museum (Natural History), an authority on fossil mammalia from Palestine, studied these remains with great care and arrived at the conclusion that both species, horse and cattle, were members of the *wild* fauna. The investigation of the Natufian fauna from Dr K. Kenyon's magnificent excavations in the tell of ancient Jericho is being carried out under the direction of the author and has so far produced no domesticated forms. There is, therefore, no evidence that the Natufians had any domesticated animals except the dog. However, an approximately contemporary Mesolithic site in northern Persia, the Belt Cave, yielded to Carleton Coon bones of goat, which he suspects were domesticated. Should further evidence confirm his suggestion, the goat would be another animal domesticated by Mesolithic man. It is difficult to say whether his contention is correct, but at Jericho it is certain that the goat was domesticated in the period immediately following.

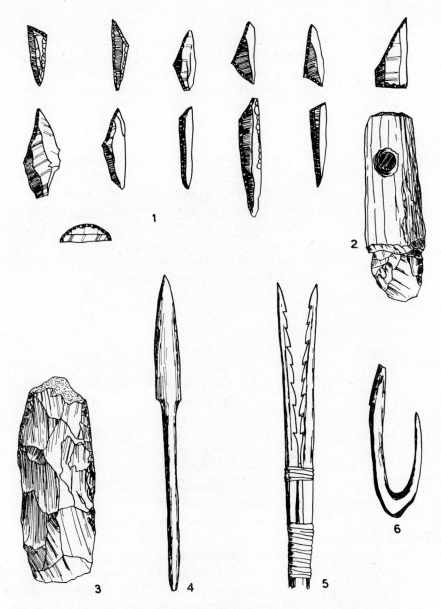

Fig. 1 : 9. Mesolithic tools. (1) Group of microliths. (2) Flint adze, hafted in antler sleeve. (3) Tranchet axe. (4) Wooden bird-arrow. (5) Leister prong made of antler. (6) Fish hook. (1) from various localities, (2)–(6) from Denmark

The most remarkable piece of equipment of the Natufians is the sickle. It was an instrument made of a bone handle with a deep furrow into which stone blades were set, serving as sickle teeth. About the use of these instruments there is no uncertainty, since the sickle teeth which have been found show the peculiar lustre that results from cutting straw or grass. However, does their presence imply that some sort of agriculture was practised by the Natufians? The view generally held is that it does not. The Natufians appear to have used their sickles to collect wild grasses, as is done even at the present time by natives of South Australia. The existence of a specialized instrument for collecting seed-bearing grasses indicates at least that it was a regular practice.

Regular harvesting, however, does not constitute agriculture, though it may continue for considerable periods of time. True agriculture consists in the preparation of the soil, deliberate sowing and storage of the harvested products. It is perfectly possible that the Natufians stored the seeds collected. In view of the steppe condition of the country and the presence of wild cereal grasses it is conceivable that the surplus was stored away to be used between seasons. But there is no evidence whatever that the soil was tilled and seed retained for deliberate sowing. This indeed was not even necessary, because the harvesting of wild grasses results in unintentional sowing. Wild grasses have brittle ears, and a certain number of seeds inevitably fall to the ground when the ears are cut off with stone tools. Since brittle ears have to be seized by the hand, the straw would have been left on the field, greatly reducing the loss of humus substance in the soil, and the seed left behind would produce another crop in the following year. The number of seeds left on the ground is not a serious problem, as plenty of seed produces many plants competing for space, whilst fewer seeds produce larger plants with a greater number of stalks, which will eventually bring forth the same amount of seed in the next generation as does a field on which a greater number of seeds has been left behind. Modern agriculture takes advantage of this by applying the practice of rolling, which encourages the growth of side shoots. It appears, therefore, that the harvesting of a natural grass steppe would not impair the yield for many generations.

The present writer inclines to the view that this practice lasted well into the Neolithic (Fig. 1 : 10), and that it will be extremely difficult to establish when agriculture in the strict sense of the word began to be practised. The evidence would have to be provided by agricultural instruments, such as hoes and ploughs.

It will be shown in this book that the domestication of animals was similarly a gradual process, so that the beginning of the Neolithic should not be regarded as the result of a revolution in thought but rather as the result of the gradually intensified control of natural processes by man. A point was reached when the food obtained was more than the minimum required to feed the population. It was then that permanent settlement became possible, that it became important to defend optimum areas against intruders, and that hands and minds could be spared for occupations not directly concerned with the basic necessities of survival. The Neolithic thus

Fig. 1 : 10. Neolithic tools and pottery. (1) Sickle used for harvesting grain. After Caton-Thompson. (2) Neolithic pot. (3) Polished axe. (4) Flaked axe with ground cutting edge. (5) Flint saw. (6) Flint arrowhead. (7) Hollow scraper. (1), (2), (5), (6) and (7) from Egypt, (3) and (4) from Denmark

emerged gradually from the Mesolithic, and the view that food production was from the beginning a deliberate act, in fact an invention leading to an economic revolution, can no longer be upheld in the strict sense of the word.

The reason why this economic change-over interests us in the present context is that it marks the beginning of large-scale interference of man with his environment, a process which has become accelerated in the course of time to such an extent that by now it is beginning to threaten the very existence of our own species.

How long ago, then, was it that man passed on to the stage of food production in the strict sense of the term? It is clear from the outset that the beginnings were localized in one or a few centres. Some peoples, like Eskimoes and Australian aborigines, have even now not yet adopted the new economic system. As we know that all the earliest true food-producing cultures discovered so far are later than the Natufian of Palestine, we may provisionally accept the Natufian stage as a *terminus ad quem* or *post quem*. Fortunately, it can now be dated fairly accurately. Recent determinations of the radiocarbon age of the Natufian layers in the tell of prehistoric Jericho gave 8940 B.C. (Zeuner, in press). This figure is substantiated by the following palaeontological and climatological considerations.

From the chronological point of view the most striking feature of the Natufian is the comparatively large number of extinct species in its fauna as was established by Miss Bate at Mount Carmel. Out of about thirty species represented no fewer than seven are extinct, including three kinds of gazelle and a hedgehog. Though the term 'species' is here used in a narrow sense, it is clear that the Natufian must be appreciably older than the Neolithic of Palestine and other parts of the Near East. On the other hand, Professor Dorothy Garrod obtained evidence from the caves of Mount Carmel that the Natufian is later than the late Upper Palaeolithic, including the Kebaran industry, which belongs to a late phase of the Last Glaciation, so that the Natufian is likely to date from the transition of the Late Glacial to the Postglacial period.

The climatic character of the Natufian fauna is mixed. There are, amongst the mammals, twelve species that prefer or require forest environment (including a squirrel, wild pig, red deer, fallow deer), compared with nine species that need open country and drier conditions (these include gazelles, the onager, a horse and the rodent mole). One would conclude, therefore, that both woodland and open country were available, and from the larger number of woodland forms one would suspect that the forest element was rather more considerable than the steppe. But when Miss Bate considered the number of *individuals* represented in the collections from the Natufian, she found that the steppe element was much greater. In one of the caves, Mugharet el Wad on Mount Carmel, nearly two thousand specimens of gazelle were counted, whilst the greatest number of any other species was only eighty-eight. This, at first glance, appears to indicate that the steppe was far more prominent in the environment than the forest, and it has been so interpreted.

It must not be overlooked, however, that the large number of gazelle bones in the cave may be the result of selective hunting. Gazelles, like most other steppe-inhabiting ruminants, live in herds and are more easily hunted than any of the forest game, which live singly or in small numbers and enjoy the advantage of the protective cover of trees. The frequency of the gazelle in the Natufian, therefore, does not mean that the climate was very dry, indeed the large number of forest species contradicts this interpretation. But even so it is apparent that in Natufian times open grasslands had begun to replace the forests of the last pluvial phase (the Mediterranean equivalent of the last glacial phase of Europe).

This observation affords a means of obtaining a tentative climatological date for the Natufian. It is believed that, while glacial conditions were reigning in northern Europe, the Mediterranean enjoyed a more humid, so-called pluvial climate than today (Zeuner, 1953c). Above all, the summers were wetter and cooler, since many of the rain-carrying depressions, which now move from the Atlantic eastwards across western and central Europe, in those days found their paths barred by heavy, cold air. They were thus compelled to move along the southern route, i.e. across the Mediterranean, bringing summer rain to many countries which are now dry. Under such conditions of climate, forests grew where there is now steppe and even desert.

The question that interests us here is: when was this type of 'pluvial' climate replaced by the modern, 'Mediterranean' type? Clearly this must have happened when the ice-sheet had melted down to so small a size that it would no longer sustain a sufficiently large mass of cold air above it capable of deviating the depressions. By a comparison of the climatic effects in modern glaciated areas, like Antarctica, Greenland, Iceland and Spitzbergen, Dr C. E. P. Brooks (1926), the Director of the Meteorological Survey of Britain, found that the diameter of an ice-sheet must be at least 700 miles in order to influence air-pressure distribution by pushing depressions out of the way.

It cannot be pure coincidence that, when the Scandinavian ice-sheet had melted down to a diameter of about 625 miles, after a brief halt at the 'Central Swedish Moraines', the climate of northern Europe became similar to that of the present day. It appears that this was due to the final breakdown of the cold anticyclone which had affected the climates both of Europe and, indirectly, of the Mediterranean.

The Fennoscandian Moraines have been dated by Professor de Geer's counts of varves (annual layers of mud from the meltwater of glaciers) at about 7900 B.C. This date has received confirmation by radiocarbon determinations of wood and peat from deposits of the Alleröd-oscillation, a mild phase which preceded the halt at the Central Swedish Moraines. The mean of four values for British and German sites is 8250 B.C., and of five values for samples from corresponding North American sites is 9450 B.C. That the re-advance of the ice responsible for the Fennoscandian Moraines occurred about 8000 B.C. thus appears reasonably well established. The halt at the moraines is known to have been brief, on the evidence of varve-counts about 300 years. It was followed immediately by the final retreat of the ice. Early in the eighth millennium B.C., therefore, the change of the east Mediterranean climate towards drier conditions must have begun.

We thus obtain another date for the Natufian and for the earliest evidence we have for reaping with sickles. By this time the dog had been domesticated. It is on geological evidence 8000 B.C., and 8840 B.C. on radiocarbon evidence. Such a date may, for the moment, be regarded as a convenient earliest time for permanent settlement and the introduction of strictly domestic treatment of animals, as distinct from control by herding only. By the beginning of the seventh millennium the hog-back brick phase of the pre-pottery Neolithic of Jericho had already begun (6935 B.C., C14 date, GL.43).[1]

It is, of course, wise not to regard Jericho as altogether the earliest settlement, or rather town. But it is certain that the early pre-pottery Neolithic exhibits relations with the animal world compatible with the view that we are there witnessing the very beginnings of 'settled domestication' of animals. And the first ruminant drawn into the human orbit was the goat. In the later pre-pottery Neolithic, changes due to domestication became recognizable in the animals. For these periods, radio-carbon dates are available, and the brief table on the next page thus summarizes what is at present known about the chronology of the domestication of animals.

While the roots of domestication lie in the natural contacts of man and beast provided often, but by no means exclusively, by hunting, its subsequent development is closely bound up with the introduction of agriculture. The conversion of the natural environment into a man-made one which set in with the beginning of the Neolithic in the Near East about 8000 years ago was on a scale which is generally underrated.

We are not here directly concerned with the widespread effects of shifting agri-culture, but it is a fact that wherever available land was claimed from the forest the land would deteriorate, and the forest would not easily grow up again (Fig. 1 : 6). The open wastelands created in this way, however, served another of man's urgent needs, for they provided pasture for his livestock. With the beginning of a settled life, the feeding of domesticated animals became a problem which had to be solved by moving the animals from one natural pasture to another. Derelict fields, there-fore, came in handy. Their existence contributed substantially to the development of early animal husbandry. This is known for a fact in Europe, and we are entitled to suggest the same with regard to other regions.

The Neolithic settlers of the 'early Danubian' of central Europe practised shifting agriculture mainly on the loess lands, and stock-raising was on a small scale. But

---

[1] The new, earlier, Jericho dates here put forward are those obtained by pre-treatment of the samples with acid and alkali. See Zeuner, in press. For standard deviations, see reports on radiocarbon dates.

by the time of the last Neolithic cultures, such as that of the Corded Ware, livestock had become a prominent part of human economy.

That Neolithic man should have taken advantage of the wastelands created by

South	Approximate Dates B.C.		North
Height of Last Pluvial, phase 3 Dog probable	18,000	18,000	Height of Last Glaciation 3 Dog and reindeer herding by Magdalenian man *possible*. Transition from hunter to nomadic herder
? Practice of herding ruminants with help of dogs		13,750[1] (W.172)	Reindeer culture of Meiendorf, Holstein
Natufian at Jericho	8840(GL.70)		
End of Pluvial	8000	8000	End of Glaciation
		7528 (C.353)	Star Carr, Maglemosian
Early pre-pottery Jericho	6935(GL.43)	7500	Senckenberg dog
Later pre-pottery Jericho with domesticated goat	{ 6840(GRO.942) { 6710(GL.41)	6000	Mesolithic man-dog association
AGRICULTURE Beginning of domesticated cattle	?5000		
		3500	?Sheep herded in Mesolithic western Europe
		2720 (K.120)	Neolithic farmers in Switzerland with goat,
		2650(GL.17)	sheep, cattle, pig
Appearance of domesticated horse in Asia Minor	2000		

[1] Radiocarbon laboratory numbers in parentheses.

his agricultural activities is natural. What he did not realize was the importance of maintaining a closed cover of vegetation on the soil, in order to prevent the disastrous effects of soil denudation. These effects are slight in the temperate forest zone, but in the Mediterranean, the Near East and in the tropics they assume colossal proportions. Land, once left open, does not revert to forest or, if it was steppe to begin with, it merely remains the desert it has become. All the time, herds are made to feed on what there happens to be in the way of plants.[1]

A simple calculation shows that this is an unstable condition that must lead to complete desert. Under natural conditions, a balance exists between the vegetation and the wild animal population. Should the latter increase unduly, starvation might reduce their numbers, and the predators take an increased share. So, as soon as man enters the picture, the vegetation begins to suffer. Agriculture takes more organic

Fig. 1 : 11. East African acacia steppe under natural conditions, not over-grazed. An example of natural environment where the growth of vegetation is balanced against the number of grazing animals. Kenya Rift Valley. Photo F.E.Z.

matter out of the soil than it puts back. Where herds are kept under primitive conditions they are allowed to eat as much as they can get (Figs. 1 : 11 and 1 : 12), whilst natural predators are severely persecuted. The manure returns only a small proportion of the organic matter to the soil, and much of it is burnt for fuel. Man uses the animals that made their bodies from the organic matter of the vegetation. In short, more is taken out by man than is put back. Whilst in advanced countries modern man does his best to slow down this process, even the best agricultural and soil-preserving methods cannot yet arrest it completely, for more organic matter disappears in the form of carbon dioxide than is returned.

---

[1] Only the effect of feeding on the environment is discussed here. Domestic animals are destructive in other ways, for example by trampling the soil and by making tracks along which soil erosion will start, etc.

Primitive man, and indeed civilized man until quite recently, was unaware of this, hence vast regions have changed their aspect completely, and always to quasi-drier conditions, since the beginnings of the Neolithic. Mesopotamia and Syria became victims of this process. In turn, North Africa (Fig. 1 : 13), Italy and Spain

Fig. 1 : 12. Heavily over-grazed steppe in Kenya Rift Valley. The result of man (in this case the Masai) keeping large herds of cattle which feed on the vegetation in addition to the natural fauna. Photo F.E.Z.

Fig. 1 : 13. Man-made desert at Sbaikia, south-east Tunisia. Under the Romans this country abounded in olive groves and cereals were grown also. Ruthless agricultural methods have removed the soil and left a desert with hardly any vegetation, on which only some goats can subsist. Photo F.E.Z.

went the same way, though to a lesser extent because of better climate. Even in temperate Europe the effects are noticeable.

Among livestock, the worst offenders are the goat and the sheep. The goat is very partial to leaves of trees and shrubs, and goats are prepared to perform arboreal antics to get at them (Fig. 6 : 2). The 'Ram in a Thicket' of Ur, really a goat eating leaves, is a popular motif in Sumerian and later Mesopotamian art (Fig. 1 : 14).

Sheep are most destructive of grasslands. The practice of driving them on to the

FIG. 1 : 14. Goat feeding on a tree. The well-known 'Ram in a Thicket' found in one of the royal tombs at Ur. This theme of a goat or pair of goats rampant with a tree in between is a common one in Sumerian art. *c.* 2300 B.C. Compare Fig. 6 : 2

fields after the harvest is perhaps wise in humid-temperate countries, but in the semi-arid zone they eat up the last vestiges of the crop that might at least have contributed some humus to the soil.

Since the goat and the sheep were the first ruminants to be domesticated, they have had a chance to destroy the natural environment for at least 8000 years. Their influence in southern countries can hardly be over-estimated, and even in the north that of the sheep has been considerable.

Similarly, though less conspicuously, the pig has taken its toll of undergrowth in the forests of the temperate zone, and domestic cattle have seen to it that trees do not grow their branches low down. They have in this way become pioneers of forest clearance in many areas.

It distinguishes man from all other animals that he, instead of adapting himself increasingly to his environment, has undertaken to subdue the environment to his purposes. This process started in the Palaeolithic, gathered speed in the Neolithic and has by now assumed gigantic proportions. But it cannot be said that man has succeeded in controlling his environment, though this is undoubtedly his aim. As to the biological environment, it must be admitted that, unwittingly, he has made rather a mess of it, by releasing natural processes of destruction the results of which he did not anticipate. Among these is the destruction or modification of the environment by domesticated animals. How, then, did domestication arise? Was it a procedure planned in order to improve the food supply? Or was it another of those uninvented changes that make up the progress of evolution? The following chapter will show that the second alternative is much the more likely.

2

The Origins and Stages of Domestication

MANY theories have been put forward attempting to explain the domestication of animals by man. Nearly all of them have in common the basic conception of a purposeful procedure, that man needed a supply of certain animals and therefore contrived to domesticate the species in question. This applies to Hahn's (1896) theory of a religious origin—the animals being first domesticated for use as sacrifices—as well as that of Hilzheimer and others that domestication was invented to satisfy economic needs, like supply of meat and skins.

But in theories of this kind the difficulty is apt to be overlooked that Mesolithic man (for it was in the Mesolithic that domestication began) would have found it far easier and more economic to obtain the necessary supplies by hunting and trapping, just as his forefathers had done, instead of embarking upon experiments of taming unwilling animals that would reward him for his efforts only after several generations.

The biological approach

The fruitful approach to the problem of domestication is the biological one. The problem resolves itself into a simple and natural process if one adopts the practice advocated here of considering man as an integral part of his physico-biological environment. It is then found that the habits of man on the one hand and of certain animal species on the other made the appearance of domestication almost inevitable.

To understand this, it is necessary to remember that the social relation called 'domestication' is by no means restricted to man and his animal subordinates. Man has applied the same practice to members of his own species, though in this case it is usually called slavery, unless a more euphemistic word is used.

36

Nor is man the only species of the animal kingdom which practises slavery or domestication. There are so many cases of the subjugation of one species by another that no more than a few examples can be given. These, however, must be regarded as truly relevant to the subject, for they clearly show, in my opinion, the way which in all probability man took when he had reached that crucial stage of his social evolution which led to the appearance of slavery in the widest sense.

Domestication presupposes a 'social medium'. As a rule the social evolution of a species must have reached a certain level before domestication becomes possible. This applies both to the domesticator and to the domesticated, though there are exceptions. In the case of domestication by man, the only notable exception is the cat. All other domesticated animals have in the wild state a social life of some kind, forming packs or herds.[1] Animals which naturally entertain social relations with members of their own species are more ready to do the same with members of other species. Mixed herds of zebra, gnu and other antelopes are commonly seen in Africa. It is therefore not surprising that the vast majority of species domesticated by man belongs to the gregarious hoofed animals. Similarly, domestication of one animal species by another occurs almost exclusively among the social insects, especially the ants.

To discuss the conditions found in the animal kingdom is well worth while, but in order to throw some light on the origins of domestication in the human species it is advisable to clarify the complex conditions observed in nature, and to introduce certain terms of social relationship. The kinds of social relations observed are linked by many intermediate cases; in fact, clear-cut divisions do not exist. Nevertheless, it is convenient to use some kind of classification.

Symbiosis

All conditions of permanent living-together of two different species are called symbiosis, provided both partners derive advantages from it. Perfect symbioses, from which both partners benefit, without suffering in one respect or another, are rare. As an example of two non-social species which enter frequently into such relationship, the well-known hermit crab with its rider, the sea-anemone, may be recalled (Fig. 2 : 1). The crab is supposed to derive protection from the tentacles of the anemone, whilst the latter obtains food morsels from the meals of the crab. The crab is careful not to lose the anemone and transplants it when it changes house and moves into a larger snail-shell. The anemone, however, is decidedly a passive partner and may, if one likes, be regarded as subject to the crab, and its position classified as one of slavery. This illustrates the rule that in a symbiosis the partners are rarely equal.

---

[1] The pig is at a very primitive level, forming merely associations of individuals which forage together. The dogs (wolves, etc.) hunt in packs, though they are quite capable of leading a solitary life. All other ancestors of domesticated animals live in herds, often with a leader.

Another example, in which equality appears to exist without reservation, was described by W. M. Wheeler (1928), the well-known insect sociologist. Two species of ant, a small *Crematogaster* (*C. parabiotica*) and a large *Camponotus* (*C. femoratus*), live together in a ball-shaped nest built round the branch of a tree, but the small

FIG. 2 : 1. A hermit crab (lobster-like crustacean), which lives in a snail shell, carrying a sea-anemone of the genus *Adamsia* on the shell. This is a common occurrence and believed to be one of the most perfect examples of symbiosis

species occupies the outer and the large one the central portion. The galleries open into one another, and the workers of both species forage together. When the nest is slightly disturbed, only the small ants come forth to defend it, whilst a severe shaking brings forth the large pugnacious *Camponotus*. As Wheeler expresses it, the *Crematogaster* seem to act as a skirmishing line for the *Camponotus*. There is clearly a mutual advantage in this arrangement, for the large species need not attend to minor disturbances whilst the small species enjoys protection by the large species when things become serious.

This case appears to be one of the very few the animal kingdom has brought forth of symbiosis on the basis of true equality.

Many more are known of unequal partnership which, however, is not sufficiently unequal to be called social parasitism. *Myrmica canadensis*, for instance, is an ant of northern North America, whose nest is occasionally found to be intertwined with that of a smaller ant, *Leptothorax emersoni*. This species can enter the galleries of the large one through minute openings, but not *vice versa*. Far from being hostile to their little neighbours, says Haskins (1945), the *Myrmica* welcome the *Leptothorax* with a sort of tolerant indifference, treating them much as dogs are treated by people who do not like dogs. But the *Leptothorax* lick the *Myrmica* and beg food from them, and are indeed willingly supplied with regurgitated drops of food juice. It cannot be said that the invaded colony suffers from the invasions of the little neighbours, though it is doubtful whether they derive advantage from them. Nevertheless, the behaviour of the *Leptothorax* almost makes them social parasites. While the going is good they live entirely by begging, though when the need arises they are capable of fending for themselves.

This case is instructive from the human point of view, for it is one of supporting another form of life, that is intrusive but is not an open enemy. There are men who feed the sparrows that have intruded into their domain, and there may well have been a stage of throwing morsels to wild dogs which invaded the camps of pre-Neolithic man, long prior to any realization of the possible economic use of dogs. Such acts are elementary manifestations of the solidarity of life, especially of related life. It is characteristic of most higher animals that have developed a social medium of some sort and which are not enemies. It finds a simple expression in animal friendships as they occur under conditions of domestication between cats and dogs, or, stranger still, between cats and tame birds. It finds a higher expression in man's desire to keep all sorts of pets, and its highest expression in the naturalist who finds supreme satisfaction in observing, understanding and feeling as one with other living creatures.

The tendency to suffer the presence of other species as pets perhaps appeared very early. Even Upper Palaeolithic man may have done this, though the form of his economy prevented him from developing this relationship to full domestication. There are tribes of Australian aborigines who illustrate this stage of pet-keeping. Except for the dog, they have never domesticated animals, but keep them as pets. Wallabies and opossums, bandicoots and rats, even frogs and young birds, are tied up in the camp, but they are not properly fed or cared for, and most of them soon die. Wallabies and opossums, and occasionally cassowaries, however, learn to fend for themselves in the camp area. It is noteworthy that the dingo is treated in the same fashion, tied up when young and released when he has got used to the human environment. Similarly, pets are kept by certain American Indians.

It cannot surprise us, therefore, that several authorities believe that the habit of keeping young animals as pets is at the root of domestication in general. In this form it is certainly an over-statement, but it is conceivable, and even probable, that pet-keeping provided one of the bases on which domestication on an economic scale developed later on. The mothering instinct of the human female may well have played a part in this process, too.

Pet-keeping is particularly likely to have played a part in the domestication of the dog. The scavenging habits of wild dogs brought them into contact with the human social medium, and the pups may occasionally have been adopted. It is very interesting to find that one of the camp-fire stories of the Africans of Calabar in southern Nigeria explains the origin of the domesticated dog exactly in this way.

According to this story, related by Yoti Lane (1946), a boy adopted a wild dog's pup, grew fond of it and brought it up in the village in spite of the attempts

of the pup's mother to rescue her child. When fully grown, the dog induced a bitch to join him, and their litter became used to camp conditions immediately. They went out on hunting expeditions with their human friends. Subsequently the inhabitants of other villages imitated the practice.

It is of course not assumed that this folk-tale is a piece of surviving tradition, but it describes the way in which, in the views of a people who are still in close contact with their natural environment, the domestication of the dog might have come about.

Another theory which supposes that domestication came about under conditions of amicable relations assumes that totem animals, which are not killed by certain groups of humans, would become tame in the area in question. There is, however, a great difference between the taming of a totem animal (in any case an unusual event) and its economic exploitation under conditions of complete domestication. Moreover, animals which are now domesticated do not appear to be chosen as totem animals. Though totemism is perhaps as old as the Upper Palaeolithic, as witnessed by the bison-hunter of Lascaux (Fig. 2 : 2), it is very improbable that it ever led to domestication (2 : 15).

Fig. 2 : 2. The bird man (bison hunter) of Lascaux Cave with his totem stick. Note that the man himself has the face of a bird. This remarkable drawing is certainly of Palaeolithic age and, since it is associated with a rhinoceros (not shown in this illustration) belonging to the temperate species *Dicerorhinus merckii*, it must be extremely early (see Zeuner, 1952). Probably the earliest example of totemism so far known

The various examples of symbiosis here discussed are admittedly not all voluntary. A certain amount of coercion, i.e. transplantation into the social medium of the more intelligent species, or expansion of the latter into the social medium of the weaker species, is common. Yet it cannot be denied that both parties derive advantages from the condition; the animal living with man, in particular, finding personal safety and an easier and more ample food supply.

Food supply appears to have played a particularly important part in the establishment of close association between animals and man. This is most obvious in the case of the scavengers.

Scavenging

Some species enter into a relationship in which one lives regularly on the food debris or other waste products of the other species. If the removal of the waste products is an advantage to the producer, scavenging might approach closely a true symbiosis. But scavengers often have the habit of preying on the host, especially on its progeny, as and when opportunity arises. Scavenging thus grades into social parasitism.

FIG. 2 : 3. A silver fish, *Atelura formicaria*, stealing a drop of food from one ant feeding another. From Wheeler (1928), after Janet

Many scavengers are, moreover, not closely bound to the host species. The jackal, for instance, can live perfectly well without man, but where human settlements are available he will enter into a loose and impermanent though nevertheless quite regular relationship with man, in which the mutual advantage is obvious enough. Though in other associations of the scavenging type the relations are permanent, the comparatively loose ones of the wild dogs are of great interest since they illustrate one of the ways in which domestication is likely to have begun.

Two social media, those of the wild dog and of man, overlap because man produces offal which the dogs will eat. There is no cause for enmity in this, unless one of the species interferes with the habits of the other or causes danger to life. This is in fact so in the case of hyaenas, for instance, which are prone to steal man's food reserves and are of too fierce a disposition for the establishment of friendly relations. They are not sufficiently sociable. The smaller species of wild dogs are in a different category. Not only are they afraid of man; their habit of associating in packs with a recognized leader affords the possibility of the transfer of allegiance to man, once he is recognized as a being of superior strength and cunning (Figs. 2 : 4 and 2 : 5). The origin of the domesticated dog will be discussed later. In the present context our interest is focused on scavenging as a possible basis for the development of actual domestication. It is, however, obvious enough that not every scavenger is a prospective candidate for domestication. The requirements of non-interference and of mental disposition have been mentioned already. In these respects all existing wild dogs are not equally suitable. Jackals head the list in so far as they are unlikely to attack man. But their social level is lower than that of the dogs that practise active hunting and for this reason would be more ready to form with man groups which, from their point of view, must be regarded as mixed packs.

The smaller races of wolves found in southern countries do a fair amount of scavenging as well as hunting. They would, therefore, appear to be the most amenable to domestication, but they also tend to regard human settlements as legitimate hunting grounds, from which they frequently steal goats, domestic dogs and even children, as for instance in India today. These propensities are most strongly

FIG. 2 : 4. Wolf becoming the companion of man. Mr Chris Crisler in 1951 having a 'howling concert' with one of the wolves he had befriended in northern Alaska

developed in the large northern races of wolves, which, therefore, are the least likely to have provided the initial stock from which the domesticated dog emerged.

The combination of scavenging and robbing is of course exceedingly common in nature, and it has often provided the conditions for the evolution of regular pests and even parasites. Thus, whilst scavenging in its pure form is an example of symbiosis, it grades imperceptibly into exploitation of the host species by the scavenger. On the other hand, where conditions are favourable to domestication, it is evident that the scavenging species will in due course be exploited by the host.

Fig. 2 : 5. Mr Crisler resting with two of his wolves. This illustrates well how quickly
confidence can be established between two quite different species

The pig is another scavenger which has been domesticated. Since it occupies a
low level on the social scale, its relations have rarely developed beyond those of an
exploited captive.

Scavenging exhibits more clearly than any other social relationship the possibilities of further developments, either in the direction of pests and parasites (the
guests exploiting the hosts) or in the direction of domestication (the hosts exploiting
the guests).

The invention of agriculture brought in its train fresh opportunities for the
development of guest-host relations, as the fields were liable to be regarded as
excellent feeding grounds by several herbivorous and gregarious animals. So long
as the fields lay fallow this condition would not be radically different from other
cases of scavenging, but while the crop was growing the same practice of the
animals constituted an act of robbery. Nevertheless, it did afford social contacts
which in all probability led to the domestication of the aurochs and related large
bovines, and perhaps other species also (Fig. 2 : 6).

The examples of scavenging and similar guest-host relationships given so far
were drawn from the social medium of man. There are many others, especially
among social insects like termites, bees, wasps and ants, which show that similar
conditions develop wherever social media overlap, and one at least may usefully be
quoted here to illustrate the point.

Generally speaking, pure scavengers are as rare among insects as they are in the
human social medium. Most of them are more or less predacious, though many

43

enter into friendly relations with their hosts by offering them exudates with a pleasant taste. Since these are very unlikely to have a significant value as food for the host, who is nevertheless eager to obtain it, biologically unhealthy conditions have developed in many insect societies as a result of the presence of predacious scavengers, conditions which may be described as selling the child for a tin of tobacco. I am alluding to the fact that many scavengers, which have become adapted to ants' nests, feed on the larvae of their hosts, who nevertheless suffer their presence and

FIG. 2 : 6. Domestication of the crop-robbers: bovine cattle. Painting of the cattle of Nebamen of Thebes, Egypt, c. 1400 B.C.

even enjoy it because of the flavour of their exudates. These practices are due to an error, since ants are used to licking the exudates of their own larvae.

The biologically disadvantageous perversion has therefore arisen independently many times over. Since this condition of scavenging and robbing combined with the offer of a reward has no parallel in the social relations of man and beast, it suffices to refer the interested reader to textbooks on social insects, such as W. M. Wheeler's.

There are, however, examples of straightforward scavenging in ants' nests, the scavengers living there without receiving any attention from the ants. A white woodlouse (*Platyarthrus*), for instance, feeds on the small pellets which the ants disgorge from pockets inside their mouths.

Other true scavengers are the beetles of the genus *Antherophagus*, the larvae of which feed on refuse in the nests of bumble bees, whilst the adults live on flowers. From these and many other cases a series of increasingly intimate relations with the host lead to those extreme cases mentioned, in which the scavenger becomes a robber and a thief, though he is not recognized as such by the host.

It is evident that scavengers of the robber kind may be regarded as parasites of the social medium on which they depend. But the ant world has produced instances of social parasitism on a grand scale, which find a parallel in certain examples of man-animal relationships, and which have innumerable counterparts in the relationships of human social groups to one another.

The various possibilities inherent in the guest-host relationship can be roughly summarized as follows:

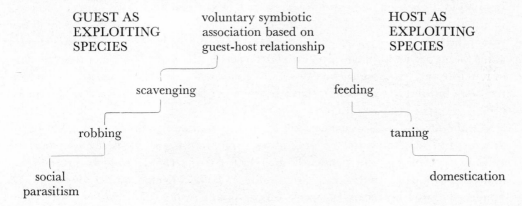

Social parasitism

The condition of social parasitism, in which one organized community is exploiting another, has developed from the condition already described of the small *Leptothorax* ants living in symbiosis with the much larger *Myrmica*. The American ant, *Solenopsis molesta*, invades the dwellings of larger ants, which it pillages, the advantage being again its small size. It is so adaptable that it frequently substitutes human dwellings for the nests of the larger ant. In much the same way *Carebara*, another thieving ant, builds its small galleries in the mounds of African termites, which it exploits.

In these cases the females of the social parasite breed in their own quarters, which are inaccessible to the host community. There are more extreme associations, however, in which the breeding is transferred to the premises of the host community which even feeds and brings up the progeny of the social parasite. The young queens of *Strongylognathus testaceus* enter the nests of *Tetramorium caespitum*, another ant. They succeed in being accepted by the workers that feed them and tend their eggs and larvae in the usual way. Only a small proportion of the colony consists of the invading parasite species. This condition finds many a parallel in the history of mankind, wherever numerically small invading races have imposed themselves upon the much more numerous natives.

Domestication of the reindeer as a case of social parasitism

There appears to be one example of domestication of an animal by man which may be regarded as falling into the category of social parasitism. It is that of the domestication of the reindeer.

For several reasons the reindeer represents a particularly interesting example of domestication by man. Both the domesticators and the domesticated have remained in the state of nomadism (Fig. 2 : 7).[1] Nevertheless, the activities of man in relation to the reindeer can only be described as those of a social parasite. Like so many guests of ants and termites, the human species has even supplied a delicacy which the host species is eager to obtain. In so far, however, as the exploiting species gains the upper hand in this process and the exploited species degenerates, the case of reindeer and man might equally well be discussed under the head of 'true domestication', but since it appears to have begun as ordinary social parasitism it is more usefully treated at this point.

Of the several theories concerning the domestication of the reindeer, that which attributes its beginnings to the practice of decoy-hunting is the best-founded. This view was developed independently by Hatt (1919), the Danish anthropologist, and Sirelius (1916), the Finnish archaeologist. Hatt collected numerous records of reindeer-hunting by means of decoy animals and has reported on them with care. Only three variants of these may be quoted to illustrate the method. According to Pallas, the eighteenth-century traveller, the Samoyed hunt reindeer in the following manner: The hunter selects four or five tame reindeer, usually from the hinds and fawns. Holding them on ropes he approaches the herd of wild reindeer under their cover and against the wind, until he is near enough to shoot his arrow.

Another method is practised by the Tungus. It consists of leaving, during the rutting season, a few tame hinds on a feeding ground of the wild deer. The wild stags will associate with the hinds and are killed when the hunter returns after a day or two and approaches the group cautiously. Both the Tungus and the Samoyed employ strong tame stags during the rutting season. Ropes or thongs are tied round their antlers and they are sent off when a wild herd with a stag is in sight. The tame stag begins a fight with the wild one and the latter's antlers become entangled. He is held in this condition until the hunter arrives.

Tame deer which had proved their worth would naturally be protected and looked after by the hunter. Since tame hinds would mate with wild stags, fawns would be born in due course, and any hunter owning some decoy reindeer would

[1] Late developments are irrelevant in this context.

FIG. 2 : 7. A reindeer herd in Lapland illustrating primitive primary nomadism in which the animals are allowed to run wild for most of their lives, though they are rounded up from time to time. Of those that were domesticated by man, it appears that only reindeer, goat and sheep passed through this stage

almost unintentionally become a reindeer-breeder. The ease with which domestication of reindeer could be effected is largely due to the fact that the social state of man and of deer was the same, namely nomadism, and that neither was compelled to adopt any profound change of habits. Thus, to the present day the reindeer, both wild and domesticated, have remained a nomadic species, and so has man who follows the herds, preying on the wild and controlling and exploiting the tame.

In doing so he takes his toll of the species in much the same way as wolves do, and the only advantage that accrues to the domesticated reindeer is a very limited amount of protection from these and other predators. From the biological point of view this is a doubtful advantage, since the reindeer as a community have to pay heavily in individuals which, instead of being devoured by wolves and bears, are killed by man. The fact that man has adapted himself to the habits of the reindeer, as well as his numerical inferiority, make him a social parasite of the deer. The hunting of wild reindeer was not ended as a result of domestication. The more elaborate forms of exploitation of the domesticated deer, like use as a draught-animal, for riding, and as a milk-supplier, are of comparatively recent date, and evidently influenced by familiarity with cattle and horse.

At the onset of the process of domestication, man appears to have taken advantage of the greediness with which reindeer lick up salty matter. Human urine is regarded by them as the greatest delicacy, and it is this substance which attracts and binds reindeer to human camps. This craving is probably due to the lack of salt in the water available to reindeer, which is mainly derived from melting snow, though all ruminants are attracted by salt-licks. The reindeer nomads of course take full advantage of it, even today, so that the supply of a delicacy provides the meeting ground on which the social media of the two species 'overlap'. This is indeed a remarkable parallel to the conditions under which societies of social insects are invaded.

The attraction of salt-licks has been used by man in a few other cases of domestication. An example is the case of the mithan, believed by some to be a cross of the gaur with domesticated humped cattle. The gaur is a large bovine of India, not closely related to cattle, and the crosses are produced in Assam. The wild animals are, in this case, allured by salt-licks placed by man in suitable localities.

It should further be noted that deer are easily tamed when young and that it is not difficult to obtain fawns of any species. As young red deer were tamed as decoys in Germany until the Middle Ages, it is evident that the method of transforming fawns into decoys has been practised in widely distant areas. Nor is decoy-hunting with the aid of tamed young animals restricted to deer. Apart from birds, with which we are not concerned here but which have given the name to the method, both aurochs and bison appear to have been hunted in this manner. Reinhardt relates the ancient Frankish, Alamannic and Langobardian laws on decoy-hunting. The practice was common with red deer, but aurochs and bison were tamed also. Hatt rightly emphasizes the potential significance of this fact as follows:

'May we suppose that the use of tamed oxen as decoys in the hunt was a feature characteristic of the initial stages of the domestication of oxen, although it persisted until the Middle Ages? In that case, the hunter's culture has been of greater importance to the early development of the domestication of animals, than has been supposed by leading philosophers.'

Though this possibility has to be taken seriously, some difficulties arise when the decoy method is regarded as the only way in which the aurochs was transferred into the state of domestication. It is one proposition to tame specimens and to train them for special tasks. The circus director succeeds in doing so today with the most unusual kinds of animals. But to cause them to breed freely in captivity, and to make them forget their personal freedom, so that they stay with man without cage, fence or chain, is a very different matter. We shall have to return to this point shortly.

Other domesticated species which may have gone the way of the reindeer, and subsequently been compelled even to renounce their migratory habits, are the sheep, the goat and the horse. This is put forward as a suggestion. In the case of sheep and goat it is based on their natural habits; they are shy and fond of mountainous country and far less likely to invade fields than, for instance, pig or wild cattle. As to the horse, a pronouncedly nomadic species, it is likely to have been domesticated by nomadic peoples.

The social parasite Lomechusa

Whenever man imposed himself as a social parasite on an animal species, it was he who succeeded in domesticating the host species. In insect societies the opposite is more common, namely that the host species succeeds in domesticating the invading parasite. These cases are of interest as they show how initially similar social relationships may evolve along very different lines. A particularly interesting example is a beetle, *Lomechusa strumosa*, which has been studied with care by Wasmann (Fig. 2 : 8). It lives with a European slave-making ant, *Formica sanguinea*. The segments of its abdomen are provided with scent organs which are eagerly licked by ants. These beetles are literally reared by the ants, very much to the detriment of the colony. From the sociological point of view they are simply domesticated animals producing a secretion for the benefit of the ants. This is the position as seen from the ant's point of view. From the point of view of the beetle, however, the situation represents a case of social parasitism.

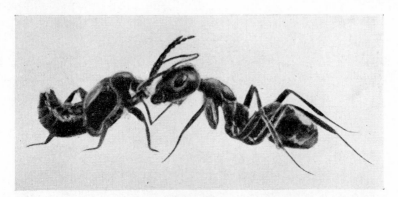

FIG. 2 : 8. The guest beetle *Lomechusa strumosa* feeding from a worker of the European slave-making ant *Formica sanguinea*. From Wheeler (1928), after Donisthorpe

Lomechusa lays its eggs in the nests of the ants. These eggs (or the young larvae) are collected by the ants and placed in their own brood chambers alongside the ant larvae. It appears that the beetle larvae produce an exudate which the ants regard as pleasant, for they treat the beetle larvae better than their own. As the beetles are themselves, so are their larvae regularly fed by the ants with regurgitated food. In addition, however, the beetle larvae eat many of the ant larvae present in the brood chambers. When mature, the ants treat the ungrateful beetle larvae exactly like their own, covering them with earth to enable them to spin a cocoon. The beetle cocoons are again treated like those of the ants, but it is at this point that the beetles suffer very considerably from the care which the ants lavish on them. For the ants expose the pupae to the sun, a practice which is deadly for the beetle. It appears, therefore, that the survival of the beetle population depends mainly on the survival of cocoons which the ants overlooked.

In strongly infested *Formica* nests the beetles tax the ant brood so heavily that abnormal specimens begin to appear and eventually the reproduction of the ant state may be so seriously interfered with that it dies. The later stages of this process may almost be regarded as a case of successful domestication of the ants by the beetles, though the process is liable to lead to a complete destruction of the 'domesticated stock'.

The case of *Lomechusa* and *Formica* is exceptionally instructive because it shows

FIG. 2 : 9. Secondary nomadism. Herds of Masai cattle kept only for blood-letting, a small amount of milk and mainly as currency

that there are two points of view, if one may say so, to every case of domestication, according to the two species involved. The social relationship established may appear advantageous from both points of view, though its biological effects usually favour one of the species decidedly. Which of the two this is cannot be predicted in any such experiment carried out by nature. In the case of man, we believe that it is our own species which invariably maintains the upper hand.

True parasitism

In insect societies social parasitism has repeatedly developed into true parasitism, the guest living exclusively on the body fluids of the host. Since there is hardly any parallel to this among mixed societies of the man-animal group, there is no need to go into details. The only case which could be placed in this category is that of

FIG. 2 : 10. Masai tapping the jugular vein of a cow by means of an arrow in order to obtain blood, which serves as food. This is an extreme case of secondary nomadism where man has become almost entirely dependent on one particular type of food supplied by his herds

the Masai, cattle-breeding nomads of East Africa who drink the blood of their cattle without killing them (Fig. 2 : 9). An arrow is shot at close range into a vein in the neck, and the wound is closed with a plug after a certain quantity of blood has been obtained (Fig. 2 : 10).

It is impossible to sort the various possibilities of social relationships between different species into hard and fast categories, and the classification adopted here is arbitrary in several respects. On the whole the examples so far discussed belong to cases in which the host species remains in control of the environment. Nevertheless, the balance occasionally shifts so much to the advantage of the guest (man-reindeer, *Lomechusa*) that the host is ruled by the guest. True domestication seems to have arisen more than once in this manner.

Taming

There are many other cases in which a guest-host relation does not exist in the strict sense of the term, but where one species, whose social medium overlaps that of another, proceeds to limit the freedom of movement of the latter. This is, of course, a conspicuous feature in many cases of domestication by man. The meeting ground of the social media of two species is a purely geographical one, as they both inhabit the same area. The absence of the guest-host relationship presupposes systematic subjugation of one species by the other and compulsory incorporation in the social medium of the domesticator. One would expect this condition to be characteristic

Fig. 2 : 11. The honey ant with replete specimens hanging from the roof. In this species certain members of the community gorge themselves with sugar juice and subsequently suspend their bodies to serve as food-storage vessels. A case of self-enslavement. Common in the arid regions of the tropics. Based on Wheeler

of man, which indeed it is, but it is not exclusive to man as it is very common among social insects. In both types of animal (i.e. in man and the social insects), however, this condition is not primitive and it appears only in the more highly developed social groups.

It is convenient first to give a few examples from the social insects. The ants of the genus *Polyergus* are keepers of slaves and their entire economy is adjusted to the presence of slaves in their colonies, hence slave-making is a necessity. The species *P. rufescens*, for instance, raids the nests of *Formica fusca* and other species of this genus. According to Haskins, the raids are carried out with great precision and brilliance. A powerful excitement pervades the raiding army which takes advantage of the moment of surprise when it attacks a *Formica* nest. Resisting *Formica* workers are killed and the young, especially the pupae, are carried away to the raiders' nest with great celerity. On arrival home the victims of the raid are handed over to the slaves already present who bring them up to become faithful servants of the colony. *Polyergus* has become so dependent on its slaves that all the domestic life of the mixed colony is conducted by the slaves, even the building of the nest. The slave-keepers themselves have restricted their activities to conducting wars and to loitering.

Many other varieties of slavery among social insects could be quoted (Figs. 2 : 11 and 2 : 12). It will be noticed that the closest parallels exist between these

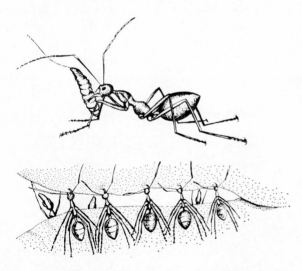

FIG. 2 : 12. Enslavement of the larvae of the spinning ant. Spinning ants use their own maggots. Above: a spinning ant holding a larva spinning a thread. Below: ants spinning the edges of two leaves together. After Hesse and Doflein (1914)

examples among insects and cases of human slavery. We are not here concerned with these intra-specific examples, however. The inter-specific cases, in which man tames or enslaves another animal species, are those which fall under the heading of domestication.

Just as the ant communities of the *Polyergus* type have passed through stages of more primitive conditions of slave-keeping, it is more than likely that the taming of animal species which would not voluntarily enter into a guest-host relationship with man can only have occurred after man had already gathered experience in the keeping of domesticated animals. Such cases, therefore, are to be regarded as of a higher level of domestication. The guest-host relationships discussed earlier represent a more primitive and possibly more ancient condition. Once man was familiar with the practice of keeping animals like the dog or sheep, he might have conceived the idea of trying to keep other species which he was in the habit of hunting.

It is extremely difficult to visualize this happening prior to the beginnings of agriculture, because the initial social contact between man and the animal in question can only have been an unfriendly one. For example, elephants are utilized as slaves of man on the *Polyergus* principle. Sociologically independent ('wild') specimens are caught and compelled to work for man. The process of taming is much helped by the presence of previously tamed elephants, a remarkable parallel to the conditions under which *Formica* slaves enter into the social medium of the *Polyergus*. Nevertheless, the domestication of elephants has usually not proceeded beyond the stage of taming, for they are mostly allowed to breed in freedom and only captured from time to time. The reason for this is undoubtedly the large size of the animal.

It is very probable that the domestication of the large bovines also proceeded along similar lines. This is, of course, not meant to imply that bovines were originally caught in order to perform definite jobs for man, as is the case with the elephants today. But the first contacts of settled communities with large bovines which might have made them think of the possibilities of domestication, with which they were already familiar from the dog, goat and sheep, may well have been established by herds of wild animals robbing the fields, a habit of wild bovines today as much as of elephants. Attempts to tame young individuals of the bovine species may have been made at an early date in the Neolithic.

For some time a condition intermediate between taming and true domestication is likely to have existed, in which the tamed animals were allowed to interbreed with their wild relations. This practice is known to exist among certain reindeer-breeders, and among bovines it is illustrated by the mithan of Assam, already mentioned. The mithan are allowed to interbreed regularly with wild gaur, and this is considered a necessity in order to maintain the qualities of the domesticated stock. A serious obstacle to the incorporation of any large animal species within the social medium of man is the greater or lesser fierceness and intractability of its individuals. In this respect, however, man derives, quite 'unintentionally', considerable advantage from keeping animals under unfavourable conditions.

The conceptions of stock-breeding which early Neolithic man may have had are not likely to have been of an advanced kind. In fact, his sole interest was to keep the animals subjugated, to make them docile and to use them to his own advantage. To give them the best possible living conditions and to provide them with the most suitable food were ideas not likely to have entered the minds of a race of men who were modest in regard to their own requirements of feeding and housing. Inevitably, therefore, animals kept in captivity must have deteriorated. Their progeny would have been smaller and weaker than their wild ancestors, and hence presumably more docile. I am inclined to think that the outcome of this process was the development of the so-called *Bos longifrons* type of cattle. Cattle of small size and great docility, in fact, must have been essential under early Neolithic conditions, and man obtained such cattle quite unintentionally by keeping them in, or near, his settlements.

Once the domestication of the species had been thoroughly effected, however, the idea of increasing the body size is likely to have been regarded as useful, in order either to increase the meat supply or the working strength of the animals. Since under primitive conditions interbreeding with wild individuals was an easy matter, it is conceivable that this would at times have been regarded with favour by the breeders of the age. It is with the intention of improving the domesticated stock that the mithan and reindeer are allowed to interbreed with wild individuals today.

With increasing experience in the keeping of domesticated stock, it would also have occurred to prehistoric man from time to time to restart the entire process from fresh wild stock, which process, as well as that of allowing cattle to interbreed with wild individuals, is likely to have played a decisive part in the appearance of some of the so-called *primigenius* breeds of domesticated cattle.

Systematic domestication

It was only after man had gained considerable experience in the keeping of animals that he became capable of deliberately domesticating animals within short periods of time. It appears, however, that the majority of animals which are important from the economic point of view had been domesticated under conditions of scavenging, social parasitism and the like, before planned domestication was first undertaken. By that time the domesticated animals had proved their worth and played their part in the economic revolution of the Neolithic, and there was, therefore, little cause left to domesticate other species which would be no better than those already subjugated.

Nevertheless, it appears that many such experiments were made in Egypt in Old Kingdom times. Pictorial representations, such as those in the grave of Mereruka at Sakkhara, show animals like gazelles, ibex, addax antelopes with collars round their necks, not to mention monkeys and even carnivores like hyaenas. Hyaenas in particular appear to have been kept and stuffed like geese to make them fat (Fig. 20 : 6). Many attempts were made by civilized man to tame or, by allowing them to propagate themselves in captivity, fully to domesticate animals (Fig. 2 : 13). But most were given up sooner or later, other than experiments with the well-known standard stock of domesticated beasts.

There is only one species regarding which it is difficult to construct a case of overlap of social media leading to domestication, and which does not fall into the category of crop-robbers already mentioned. This is the domestic fowl, and it may therefore be suspected of having been domesticated by peoples who were already familiar with the possibilities of domestication. The fowl may originally have attracted man by its fighting habits and not so much as an economic proposition. Jungle fowl are shy birds and would hardly associate themselves voluntarily with man.

Animals domesticated by man

At this point it is advisable to refer briefly to the more important species that man has succeeded in domesticating. Broadly speaking, and in accordance with a practice prevalent also among social insects, it is likely that the individuals on which domestication was tried were nearly always immature. Youngsters are less fierce than adults and adapt themselves more readily to changed conditions.

It has been repeatedly emphasized in these pages that the groupings made are inevitably arbitrary and that it depends greatly on point of view to which category one is apt to assign a species. This must be borne in mind in connection with the following attempt to classify domesticated animals according to their social relationship to man.

There is a group of categories of early date, comprising scavengers and social parasites, which is likely to have arisen under very primitive conditions. This group does not necessitate agricultural activities and everything points to the cases in question having arisen while man was a nomad. The category of scavengers comprises the dog, the pig and the duck. That of social parasitism contains the reindeer, the sheep and the goat. Since many human communities have continued a nomadic life up to the present day, the time when domestication occurred need not always be particularly remote. But it is in these two categories that pre-Neolithic domestication is likely to be found. For the dog this has been established as a fact, for sheep and goat it is highly probable.

A later group comprises the categories of crop-robbers, the systematically domesticated and the pest-destroyers. These categories cannot be earlier than the beginnings of agriculture. The crop-robbers comprise cattle, buffalo, elephant, rabbit and goose. In the systematically domesticated category come fowl, hyaena, ostrich and recent acquisitions like domestic mouse, rat and canary. Thirdly, among the pest-destroyers which invade the social medium of man in pursuit of a prey that happens to be a pest, the cat, the ferret and the mongoose are prominent species.

Finally, one more group appears to exist which is of considerable historical interest. These are the animals domesticated by secondary nomads. Secondary

FIG. 2 : 13. Mr Raymond Hook of Nanyuki, Kenya, feeding an eland antelope on his farm. One of the few experiments now being made to develop new domesticated species. Photo F.E.Z.

nomadism occurs in regions where agriculture is no longer profitable because of deterioration of the soil. These nomads needed transport, and they domesticated the horse and the camel.

In the following paragraphs this classification will be discussed in some detail.

The process of domestication
It is possible to generalize to some extent the process of domestication. In any particular instance there must have been an initial stage when our animal species had but loose ties with the social medium of man. Interbreeding with the wild forms must still have been common and kept the species close to the wild ancestor from the morphological point of view.

The second stage was one of completing the process of domestication, that is of subjugating large numbers of the species and of making these individuals wholly dependent on the social medium of man. This period was one of comparatively strict captivity, during which the domesticated beasts cannot have had much opportunity of interbreeding with their wild relations. The outcome of this process was a stock with distinct characters of domestication, such as different colour, reduction of body size and horns (if any) or the appearance of a frontal eminence in the *brachyceros* breeds of cattle, a reduction of the chewing apparatus in dogs and cats,

57

and many other features. It was with domesticated stock which had successfully weathered the second stage that Neolithic man settled in Europe. He came with small and distinctive breeds of sheep, cattle and pig. Similarly, it appears that in Mesolithic times the domesticated dog came into Europe as a ready-made breed.

The third stage is marked by the beginning of intentional development of certain characters in the stock. There was an economic consideration in the size of domesticated animals as it was advisable to have large animals where these could be maintained, provided that they did not revert to the fierceness of their wild ancestors. For this reason one may suspect that Neolithic and Bronze Age man from time to time allowed interbreeding of the domesticated stock with wild animals. This applies to cattle in the first instance, but it appears that it also provided a means of developing more aggressive breeds of dogs from Maglemose times onwards.

This third stage passes imperceptibly into a fourth stage when man, the breeder, began to pay increasing attention to the qualities of the beast, both economic (milk and meat production, wool and so on) and morphological (horn shapes, drooping ears, colour and so forth). In the Middle East this fourth stage had been entered long before 3000 B.C., a time when very well-marked breeds of sheep, goat and cattle were already in existence.

During the fourth stage the domesticated stock was becoming standardized, and so different from the wild ancestral species that interbreeding with the wild must have been highly undesirable, for interbreeding would have spoilt the qualities which had been obtained laboriously through selection.[1] For this reason the wild species is likely to have come to be regarded as an enemy and this fifth stage, therefore, spells the doom of the wild ancestor. In fact, when a specialized stock, suiting man's purposes and well adapted to his social medium, was available, the inroads of wild relations into the domain of man would have been regarded as a serious nuisance. Since the domesticated beasts would supply all the economic needs the species in question could satisfy, except purely for sport, the wild relations were no longer wanted even for hunting. There are many medieval reports of the extermination of wild cattle, and the tarpan, the wild horse of south-east Europe, was exterminated by the local peasants partly because the tame mares were apt to elope with wild stallions.

As the wild species became rarer, the absorption of its last remnants into the domesticated stock is bound to have happened frequently. It is known, for instance, that the last wild horses in the great game park of Count Zamoyski, situated at Zwierzyniec, near Bilgoraj, Poland, were caught and given to the peasants in 1812. Similarly, the Przewalskii horse of Mongolia has by now been almost completely

---

[1] A firm belief in the causal connection of characteristics helped in this process. Hair colour or horn shape and milk production, for instance, may have been believed to be linked, with or without reason. In any case, such views speeded up the standardization of breeds considerably.

absorbed into the domesticated stock of the nomads of the country. At an earlier date, this must have happened to the dromedary of Arabia. The process of extermination of the wild form has, however, everywhere been much accelerated by the destruction of its natural environment, either by deforestation or the spreading of plots of cultivation.

Probable date of the earliest domestication

It is widely held that the domestication of animals is closely linked with agriculture, so much so that the development of animal husbandry without crop-raising is by some regarded as impossible. This view is in part based on evidence from excavations which show that animal husbandry and agriculture occur together, even in early Neolithic sites. There is, however, a psychological element present, namely a reaction to the earlier hypothesis that nomadic herding of animals preceded the agricultural stage, a hypothesis for which archaeological evidence had been scarce or missing. Before discarding it, however, it must be remembered that it may have a considerable element of truth.

First of all, the dog is an obvious and undoubted exception. From it one learns that, even under the less settled conditions of Mesolithic food-gathering, a symbiotic association of some animals with man might well have developed by way of scavenging, social parasitism or in some other way. In the case of the dog, evidence from prehistoric sites has actually been found, and it is fortunate that the dog remains from the Maglemose and other Mesolithic sites were recognizably domesticated. We owe a debt of gratitude to the dog species for developing domestication characters so rapidly. Had this not been the case, and it is probable that other species responded more slowly, we should hardly have hesitated to regard the specimens in question as coming from races of wild wolves, and might even have construed a theory that these species were hunted.

Considering further the information provided by modern reindeer nomadism, it is evident that at the Mesolithic stage it would have been quite possible for man to attach himself to certain social ruminants, in the same manner as the Lapps and the Siberian reindeer nomads have attached themselves to that species. The only evidence which might be produced in support of such a view would be the concentration of the bones of the species in question in Mesolithic food refuse. In this respect, however, the evidence does not suggest the domestication of any species other than the dog. Nor could it be conclusive if such were found, since specialized hunting would produce a similar effect.

One comes, therefore, to the point of admitting that (quite apart from the dog) a social relationship, which may be described as a primitive condition of domestication, is at least conceivable in the Mesolithic. The species to which this would have been applicable would have been nomads themselves, or one should perhaps rather say seasonal migrants. There are several modern domesticated species which may be regarded as possible candidates for pre-Neolithic domestication, namely reindeer, goat, sheep, horse and camel. Of these, sheep and goat are known from the Belt Cave in Persia to have been domesticated since the earliest Neolithic, and the goat at Jericho since 6710 B.C. at least. The initial stages of their domestication may well lie much further back in prehistory, i.e. in the Mesolithic. Moreover, the scarcity of evidence for nomadic animal husbandry, which at present is taken too seriously, is perhaps no more than a result of the scarcity of prehistoric nomads' sites, especially in those areas of western Asia where the domestication of several of our important animal slaves is likely to have begun.

FIG. 2 : 14. 'Man becomes wolf.' Red Indians hiding under wolf skins and thus approaching a buffalo herd in disguise with bows and arrows. This extraordinary scene was depicted by Catlin in 1844

In fact, the simple conditions of reindeer domestication, which are believed to have arisen by way of decoy-hunting, do not even exclude the possibility that the very first step towards domestication may actually have been taken in Upper Palaeolithic times. The first steps are bound to have been slow and made at considerable intervals. The suggestion that the reindeer-hunting economy of the

Magdalenian and related cultures was perhaps supported by some primitive domestication has occasionally been timidly put forward. It has always been emphatically rejected. But we should be clear in our minds that the absence of evidence does not mean that the idea is wrong. Whilst hunting was still the dominant practice, it was after all not above the mental level of Upper Palaeolithic man, as we know him from other activities, to keep reindeer as decoy animals. It is really a small step from stalking in the disguise of a deer, whose horns and skin are worn by the hunter himself, to approaching the quarry hidden behind some live animals. But whilst I am not prepared to regard it as probable that Magdalenian man had already taken the first step towards domestication by keeping decoy animals, I do consider the question as sufficiently serious to deserve attention in the hope of finding some definite evidence either for or against. Even Lower Palaeolithic evidence for man's assumption of a 'personal' relation to animals is not lacking (Fig. 2 : 15).

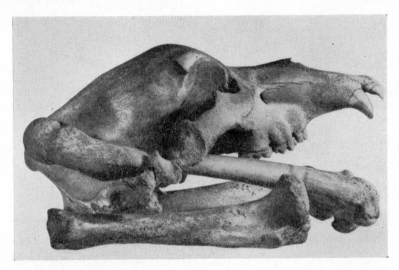

FIG. 2 : 15. Skull of cave bear with long bones as found in a stone cist, Drachenloch Cave, northern Switzerland, of Mousterian Age. Earliest evidence of bear cult, though by no means unique in the Palaeolithic. Surviving to present day in Siberia and among the Ainu in Japan

There is one factor which, viewed in the light of the biological approach here advocated, supports the hypothesis of pre-agricultural domestication of ruminants. It is the sheepdog's performance. Evidently, if the dog joined man in the Mesolithic at the latest, why should it not retain its habits and continue to drive animals as wolves are wont to do? Fig. 2 : 16 shows a wolf driving reindeer. A tamed wolf would do the same. I therefore suggest that the comradeship between man and wolf led to a driving of certain nomadic animals, especially sheep and goats, and that

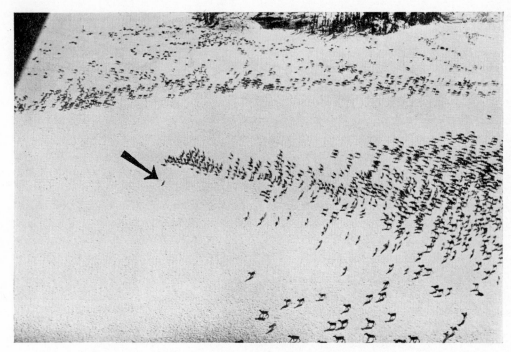

Fig. 2 : 16. A wolf driving caribou in northern Canada. It is easy to see how he is trying to isolate the deer at the top of the lower herd as a potential victim. It is important to note that only the deer in the more immediate neighbourhood are paying attention to the happenings. This air photograph shows that the wolf knew how to round up ruminants long before man thought of doing so

Mesolithic man had already joined in this operation. The domestication of sheep and goats would thus have begun while the Mesolithic was still in full swing.

It must be admitted, then, that agriculture is not a prerequisite of domestication as such, and the domestication of certain species may well date far back into pre-Neolithic times. On the other hand, there are species which, for biological reasons, are not likely to have come into the orbit of man before agricultural operations had begun. Chief amongst these are cattle (Fig. 2 : 6). Furthermore, the Neolithic revolution was a change that placed an enormous economic premium on the art of animal domestication, which in consequence became established as a universal practice. On the other hand, the advanced state of domestication, in which movements of animals were completely controlled by man, was clearly impossible in pre-Neolithic times. So long as man was moving with the animals he might have been able to develop domestication to the level exemplified by the reindeer today. But to proceed to the stage of confining animals to restricted spaces man would have had to change his economic system, for the sake of an experiment the outcome of which would have been extremely uncertain. It is most unlikely that Upper Palaeo-lithic or Mesolithic man would ever have been willing to do this.

Restricted number of domesticated species
The curious fact that, out of an enormous number of available mammalia, only very few have been domesticated has already been mentioned. It is known that others were tried by the Egyptians and probably similar experiments were made at earlier periods elsewhere. The lake-dwellers of Switzerland, for instance, appear to have domesticated foxes. But as soon as man adopted the Neolithic settled mode of life, restrictions of mobility, space and climate imposed themselves upon him which made it increasingly difficult to try out new species. Moreover, once a sufficient number of species had been domesticated to satisfy the needs of human life, providing man with food and raw material, nothing was to be gained from undertaking the difficult task of reducing additional species to a state of domestication (Fig. 2 : 13). It is economic considerations as a rule, therefore, that prevent further experiment.

Conclusion
To summarize the discussion of this somewhat complex subject it may be helpful to present the results in a concise form. Two sequences have emerged: one comprising the stages of intensity of domestication through which a species would pass in the course of time, and the other being the probable order in which species were domes-ticated one after the other.

The stages of domestication are as follows:

(a) Loose contacts, with free breeding.
(b) Confinement to human environment, with breeding in captivity.
(c) Selective breeding organized by man, to obtain certain characteristics, and occasional crossing with wild forms.
(d) Economic considerations of man leading to the planned 'development' of breeds with certain desirable properties.
(e) Wild ancestors persecuted or exterminated.

The order in which species were taken into domestication is shown in the follow-ing list:

1. *Mammals domesticated in the pre-agricultural phase:*
    Dog, reindeer, goat, sheep.
2. *Mammals domesticated in the early agricultural phase:*
    (The crop-robbers. Mainly used for food.)
    Cattle, buffalo, gaur, banteng, yak, pig.

3. *Mammals subsequently domesticated primarily for transport and labour:*
   - (a) Domesticated by agriculturalists in the forest zone: elephant.
   - (b) Domesticated by secondary nomads; horse, camel.
   - (c) Domesticated by river-valley civilizations; ass, onager.
4. *The pest-destroyers:*
   Mongoose, ferret, cat.
5. *Various other mammals:*
   - (a) The small rodents: rabbit (medieval), dormouse (Roman).
   - (b) Experimental domestication: hyaena (Egyptian), fox (Neolithic), gazelle (Egyptian), ibex (Egyptian).
   - (c) New World species: llama (American Indian).
   - (d) Pets: mouse (modern European).
6. *Birds, fishes, insects* (not classified chronologically).

3

The Effects of Domestication on Animals

THAT domestication affects the physical characters of the animals concerned is well known. In spite of considerable variation both of conditions and their results, certain generalities can be deduced. Since the effects of domestication on characters of a species will be touched upon frequently, they may be summarized briefly here in so far as they affect size, colour, skeleton and soft parts. Some of the aspects in question have recently been discussed by Herre (1954) from the angle of evolution.

Size

On the whole, the size of the early types of domesticated animal[1] is smaller than that of their wild relations. This is well illustrated by most dogs, cats, cattle, sheep, goats, pigs and others. In fact, small size is used as a diagnostic character in prehistoric deposits where wild and domesticated forms are liable to occur together. But this rule does not apply without exception. The camels, for instance, both of the Old World (dromedary, Bactrian) and of the New (llama, guanaco, vicuña) are about the same in body size as their wild ancestors. On the other hand, some mammalian species have developed a tendency to larger size under conditions of domestication, such as the rabbit and the horse. Domesticated birds, too, are as a rule larger than the wild forms from which they are derived.

But since in all species a variation of body size is observed greater than that found under natural conditions, giant as well as dwarf forms have been selected by man and developed into special breeds on many occasions. The only group to which this does not apply are the camels already mentioned, but even goats and sheep, which show comparatively little variation in size, have developed giant and

[1] i.e. excluding modern developments.

dwarf races. In cattle, horses, and most of all in the dog, this tendency is even more conspicuous. Apart from the variations in over-all size which do not affect the proportion of the parts of the body, there are dwarfs and giants due to the modification of body proportions, most noticeable perhaps among the dogs with the short-legged dachshund and the deerhound as extremes. But since these are due to modifications of the skeleton, they are not strictly comparable with the variation of over-all size. The study of body proportions on skeletal material is a complex matter. The interested reader may consult papers by Röhrs (1959) and Meunier (1959).

Colour
The most conspicuous characteristic of domesticated animals is often their coloration. It is uncommon for wild coloration to be preserved completely. In the dromedary and the two-humped camel wild colour is by far the commonest, but dark-coloured —'black'—and very light-coloured—'white'—specimens are found and often highly valued. Among the elephants the colour of the skin is often patchy, marbled with white, which in extreme cases results in the appearance of white elephants so notable for their rarity. But this variability is hardly due to domestication, since elephants are not normally bred under controlled conditions.

The ass has, in the majority of individuals, retained the wild grey coloration with a dark eel-mark on the back, although black races are regularly bred in certain areas and white individuals occur occasionally.

In all other domesticated animals, wild coloration is the exception. It is not completely absent in any of them and is usually preserved in particular breeds, among which it is regarded as a desirable character. The Alsatian among the dogs, the 'Belgian Hare' among the rabbits and the striped tabby among the cats may be quoted as examples. Among horses wild colours are very exceptional, namely the yellow-dun of the Mongolian wild horse and the mouse-grey of the tarpan. It appears that the reddish-brown shade has always been popular and hence selected for preference by man. In cattle the wild colour is preserved in some breeds of south-west Europe and north-west Africa, such as the Camargue breed of the Rhône Delta, the Spanish fighting bull and the common domestic breeds of Morocco. In the latter it is clearly seen how some of the characteristic domestic coloration arises from the wild. The bulls are usually blackish with a cream-coloured stripe on the back and a patch on the forehead. The cows are often more reddish, and a lighter colour develops from the light line on the back in the form of a saddle. The plain red or reddish brown so common among cattle is due to the retention of juvenile coloration. But other colours like black, plain white and piebald seem to be due to ordinary mutations.

The colours just mentioned are not entirely new, since the black, white and red pigments are usually present in the hair of the wild races. A study of the hair of a wild cat or rabbit (Mikulicz-Radecki, 1950) or a wolf will show that this is so. The mutations, therefore, are often characterized by the absence of one or more pigments. Piebaldness,[1] a matter of distribution of the pigments on the body, is a character which is very common in domesticated breeds, but very rare in nature. There are very few wild species known to me which are piebald, one of which is *Lycaon pictus*, the Hyaena Dog. Piebaldness in the animals depicted by early man is, therefore, definite evidence of domestication.

Sheep and goats have, on the whole, been less ready to discard their wild colour scheme until comparatively recent times. Among the sheep there are a number of hairy races surviving in which the moufflon coloration, brown with a white patch on the side of the rump, is still preserved, mainly in north-west Africa, as, for instance, in the Fezzan race. It is the domination of the woolly undercoat over the hair that tends to make sheep single-coloured, but, as suggested by the Soay sheep, this is likely to have appeared on the body long before it spread to the legs, neck and head. It is extremely unlikely that Neolithic farmers were already in possession of white-wool sheep, such as have occasionally been shown in reconstructions of Neolithic environment.

Changes in the skull

The most important effects of domestication are exhibited by the skull, important mainly because they are easily recognizable in fossil material from ancient dwelling sites. There is again a general rule which is liable to exceptions. The rule is that the facial part of the skull tends to be shortened relative to the cranial, which is but little affected. This tendency, which incidentally is present in man also, occurs in domesticated animals to a varying degree. It is virtually absent in horses and asses, and also in camels, though it might, after all, prove to be present if careful measurements were made. It is very conspicuous in the pig, where the shortening of the face is extremely pronounced and connected with an upward bend of the plane of the palate in relation to the plane of the occipital. A similar condition is observed in dogs like the bulldog, the boxer and the Pekinese. The same tendency, though less conspicuous, is present in cattle, sheep and goats; and it is also found in the domesticated cat, as measurements have revealed to the author. Generally speaking, these changes are correlated also with changes in the size of the braincase (and therefore the brain) as has been so clearly demonstrated by Herre. These changes, in turn, affect the bones of the ear, as was shown by Herre (1953) for the llama.

Although this has proved to be a widespread tendency inherent in domestication, it is occasionally replaced by the opposite tendency—a lengthening. It has become the fashion with modern dog-breeders, and many breeds like sheepdogs,

---

[1] Piebald denotes black and white, skewbald denotes brown and white. Both occur together occasionally, but no term exists for this condition. 'Piebald' therefore is here used in a general sense.

terriers and dachshunds have changed in appearance in recent years owing to intensive selection of long-faced specimens. Strictly speaking, however, even the most long-faced domesticated dog has a face which is shorter than that of the large races of wolves, and the effect of a long face is produced mainly by the narrowing of the skull across the zygomatic arches, and by the reduction of the supra-orbital eminences.

The dentition is inevitably affected by changes in the proportion of the skull. At a very early stage of domestication the teeth became smaller than they are in wild forms, though this is not always easy to show. In dogs, for instance, the fourth pre-molar of the upper jaw and the first molar of the lower jaw, which together form the bone-cutting pincers so characteristic of carnivores, are smaller than in the European wolves. With progressive shortening of the face, teeth which are already in the state of reduction may disappear entirely, such as the first pre-molars and third molars. With extreme shortening, the position of the teeth in a single row may be replaced by a partly overlapping oblique arrangement, as in bulldogs and some kinds of pigs.

Very considerable changes occur in the skulls of species which have horns in the wild condition. On the whole, domestication tends to reduce the size of the horns, as exemplified by the small horns of prehistoric cattle of the *brachyceros* breed and the sheep and goats of the Neolithic lake-dwellings. Hornless cattle are known from Old Kingdom Egypt onwards. Domesticated buffalo also have smaller horns than the wild species. But there are many exceptions, and it appears that man has sometimes indulged in producing breeds with abnormally shaped horns, which have no economic use whatever. Four-horned sheep have been bred, and the shapes of horns of cattle, sheep and goats vary astonishingly. In cattle, the Hungarian steppe breed, the Ankole cattle of East Africa and the Bechuana breed of South Africa have horns of enormous length, and incidentally of an outward curve not normally present in wild species. In sheep and goats the shape of the horns varies even more. The horns may be rolled up into a more or less close spiral near to the head, or drawn out into open spirals, and even straight, twisted horns occur in certain breeds. That such variation is basically present in the group is amply shown by the wild races and species, such as the markhor goat of India. In modern breeds, however, economic considerations are paramount, and the oddly shaped horns are fast disappearing.

Changes in the skeleton of body and limbs
At one time it was widely held, under the influence of Rütimeyer, that the bones of the body and limbs of domesticated animals were distinguishable from those of the wild forms. But Antonius and many others have since found that the characters which Rütimeyer considered reliable have a very restricted value, and that single bones of dogs, cats, horses and camels cannot reliably be recognized as domesticated or wild, unless they belong to races with abnormal legs. Even in sheep and goats this

is usually impossible, except where size provides evidence. In domesticated cattle, however, weak muscle-ridges and poorly defined facets of the joints make it comparatively easy to recognize specimens of domesticated origin, and also in the domesticated pig, where the epiphyses of the limb bones do not fuse with the diaphyses until long after maturity is reached, and the same applies to the sutures of the skull.

The number of bones is not affected by domestication except in the tail. The number of tail vertebrae may be reduced or increased. It is reduced in the Manx cat and in some breeds of dogs. In some cases abnormal twisting of the tail occurs, due to irregular growth, and occasionally also oblique fusion of the vertebrae. The pig's tail may be mentioned in this context, but more remarkable are the angular or knotty tails of certain bulldogs and some cats, such as certain Siamese. The spiral tail of some breeds of dogs, notably the ancient Egyptian greyhound, also appears to be due to some structural modification of the tail vertebrae.

Long tails are most notable in the sheep. In sheep the increase in the number of tail vertebrae beyond twelve is a virtually certain character of domestication, present in nearly all domesticated breeds. Long-tailed wild sheep have but rarely more than ten tail vertebrae, whilst domesticated sheep with thirteen vertebrae are regarded as short-tailed, and the number may rise to thirty-five.

The bones of the limbs vary considerably in domesticated breeds (Bantje, 1958). They may be longer, but are usually shorter, than in the wild form, and they are frequently less straight and sometimes even curved in a manner which can only be described as pathological. The limbs of bulldogs and dachshunds are the most obvious examples.

Hair

Apart from the changes in size, shape and colour which appear as a result of domestication, many modifications occur in the soft parts of the body. Of these the most striking are those of the length and texture of the hair and skin.

As regards the hair, the greatest variability is observed in the dog (Brunsch, 1956). No obvious changes appear to have occurred in cattle. The sleek hair of the ordinary cattle is almost certainly directly inherited from the wild forms, and other types, such as the thin hair coat of some southern races and the curly coat of certain park cattle, are most easily interpreted as characteristics of southern and northern geographical races, respectively. In the horses both mane and tail hair have become longer, and the falling mane of domesticated horses, as distinct from the upright mane of wild horses, is usually regarded as a good diagnostic feature. Although in general this appears to be correct, it has occasionally been mentioned in literature that the mane of the Przewalskii horse in its winter coat is not upright. Since this horse has long and shaggy hair all over the body in winter, this is possible. On the other hand, the crossing with domesticated horses may easily have introduced the hanging mane into some members of the wild stock. The shaggy winter coat was present in the European wild horses depicted by Upper Palaeolithic man, the pattern of streaks on the ivory carving from Mas d'Azil showing it clearly. Among the asses, shaggy coats occur occasionally, as for instance in the Poitou breed. Long hair has further appeared in many cats and dogs.

Whilst in some cases domesticated breeds have been developed in which the hair is longer than in the wild forms,[1] the opposite, namely hairlessness, has been favoured in others. The most obvious example of this kind is the pig.

FIG. 3 : 1. Hairless sheep, a breed from Tiringueo, Huerrero, Mexico. Photo Arturo Romano

Hairlessness occurs in other species, for instance the dog and the sheep. A hairless sheep has made its appearance in Mexico since the Spanish Conquest (Fig. 3 : 1); it has been bred for the production of milk, the lack of hair being an incidental character without economic significance.

The profoundest changes have, however, been produced in the woolly undercoat, especially in species which have a large amount of wool in the wild forms. In most cases the connection between wool-bearing domesticated animals and the production of human garments is evident, and it would be worth while to investigate in detail the connection between the making of felt and wool cloth and the keeping of wool-producing animals. On the borderlands of the western Asiatic mountains, wool-

[1] This is often restricted to certain portions of the body. Herre (1935) discovered a horse with a moustache.

producing sheep appear at an early date, whilst they are absent from Egypt until the Middle Kingdom. Although the sheep is the wool-producer *par excellence*, hair sheep with large manes on the necks of the males have been developed also. Similarly, goats have been bred for hair, like the Mamber goat, whilst wool is obtained from the Angora goat and the Kashmir goat. In the yak, too, the woolly undercoat is heavily developed in domesticated races, and the camels are good natural wool-producers.

Occasionally, the distribution of the hair on the skin is uneven, so that tufts (locks) appear. These are usually connected with particular growth forms of the hair, as for instance in the *karakul* sheep (Persian lamb), which has been studied in detail (Herre and Langlet, 1936; Herre and Rabes, 1937; Herre and Wigger, 1939; Hornitschek, 1938).

Correspondingly abnormal distribution and growth form of feathers is observed in birds. Domestic fowl with bare skin are well known. Requate (1959) has studied the formation of tufts of feathers.

Soft parts

The skin itself is frequently modified as the result of domestication; it tends to become more flabby. Folds like dewlaps appear and skin folds, which are normally characteristic of young animals only, are retained by the adults as, for instance, in certain breeds of dogs.

The development of the skin which, as pelt or leather, is one of the most important products provided by the animal world, is intimately connected with the development of fat. But apart from the deposition of fat under the skin, it is often concentrated in and around certain muscles in such a way that the shape of the animal is much affected by it. The most obvious cases in point are the Old World camels, the humped cattle and the fat-tailed sheep. But there are several species which were never domesticated and yet had the same character, namely the mammoth, the woolly rhinoceros and the bison. Fat concentration in certain parts of the body seems to be connected with life in an environment in which the climate comprises a regularly recurring lean season, which may be either a dry season (as exemplified by the camel, humped cattle and fat-tailed sheep) or a cold one (as exemplified by the mammoth, woolly rhinoceros and bison).

Under conditions of domestication this development of fat accumulations has usually been favoured. In the camels, individuals which lead a life comparable with the wild state have small humps, otherwise humps develop sometimes to an enormous size in well-fed specimens kept in close confinement. It appears to be simply a function of food supply and muscular activity. One wonders, therefore, whether the bronze image of a camel found at Khurab (Fig. 13 : 29), which shows no hump at all, does not after all represent a wild specimen.

The hump of the humped cattle or zebu raises an interesting question. It is so characteristic of the Indian cattle and their African derivatives that one is inclined to trace it back to some wild ancestor. Indeed it has been claimed that these cattle have some gaur blood, the gaur being a wild species of *Bos*, indigenous to India. It has been pointed out, however, that the hump of the gaur is supported by the enlarged dorsal spines of the vertebrae, which is not the case in the humped cattle. The humped cattle are, moreover, of considerable age, since the Indus civilization of about 2500 B.C. was familiar with them and distinguished them sharply from the *primigenius* type of cattle. It is conceivable, therefore, that there was a wild race of cattle in the drier parts of India which was already in possession of the hump, and this may have been related to, or identical with, *Bos namadicus*.

A very peculiar fat-storage system has been adopted by certain sheep, namely in the tail. It is particularly strange since the wild sheep show no tendency to increase the size of the tail for its fat content. Until contrary evidence comes forth, therefore, the fat-tailed sheep must be regarded as a pure product of domestication which has led to hypertrophic forms in which the tail is so long and heavy that it has to be supported by rollers (Fig. 7 : 6).

That the brain is affected by domestication was shown by Klatt (1954 and Herre) (1955). When studying dogs Klatt found that under the influence of domestication the brain as a whole becomes smaller in proportion to the body. But the parts of the brain are not all equally affected (Volkmer, 1956). It is mainly those containing the centres of sensual perception which suffer, whilst those carrying the centres of the complex psychic processes are affected little or not at all. Antonius suggested that it would be worth while to study the brains of breeds of dogs which have become specialized in using their noses (bloodhounds, for instance) and those which depend on other senses like hearing or seeing. The greyhound, for instance, is a breed which relies mainly on sight. Herre (1956), Lunau (1956) and Rawiel (1939) have shown that the brains of pigs are much influenced by domestication.

That the development of musculature is, as a rule, an effect of use, need hardly be mentioned. It is, however, not unimportant to point out that many domesticated breeds have been bred so as to excel physically their wild relations. This applies, among the horses, to the racing breeds which have much stronger shoulder muscles than the wild horses; to the heavy draught horses; and, of course, to many breeds of dogs. There are also the many kinds of cattle bred for beef.

Reduction of musculature as a result of domestication is equally common. The chewing muscles of domesticated carnivores, for instance, are inferior to those of their wild relations, with the result that the shape and size of the muscular ridges on the skull and even the shape of the lower jaw are affected.

The blood is apt to be modified under conditions of domestication (Jaeschke and Vauk, 1951), and that testicles and ovaries are affected is to be expected (Metzdorf, 1940; Voss, 1952; Lüdike-Spannenkrebs, 1955; Boye, 1956).

Examples of modifications of the soft parts resulting from domestication may easily be multiplied. Only one more, however, need be mentioned in this context. It is the length of the digestive tract, which has increased considerably in domesticated carnivores. This applies not only to the dog and the cat but, according to Antonius, even to the otherwise but little modified ferret. The length of the gut is undoubtedly connected with the change-over from a more or less pure flesh diet to one which includes quantities of vegetable matter.

Some general considerations

In spite of the great variety of modifications observed under conditions of domestication, some general rules appear to emerge. Except in very exceptional cases, new characters are not produced but existing ones selected. Pathological characters are often favoured and the withdrawal of animals from natural selection makes it possible to develop such characters in domesticated breeds, especially when the breeding communities are small. Under natural conditions large populations make it difficult for recessive genes to establish themselves and natural selection eliminates pathological types. Hence domesticated animals, which have become feral, tend to revert to standard forms more or less resembling their wild ancestors. This was pointed out by Hilzheimer long ago and has since been made use of by Lutz and Heinz Heck in their attempt to redevelop horses and cattle of the wild type from domesticated forms.

Many domestication characters are in reality juvenile characters persisting to the adult stage. This phenomenon, called neoteny by palaeontologists, is very apparent, for instance, in the skull shapes of domesticated dogs. Even cattle are in this category since *Bos brachyceros* owes its short face and small horns to the retention of the juvenile shape of the skull. Skin folds of adult dogs are another example.

An important rule is that under domestication the growth rates of organisms are affected. The parts of the body develop at rates which are not the same as in wild species. The heads of cattle are, on the whole, smaller in proportion to the body than they were in the aurochs. But the most conspicuous growth-rate changes are exhibited by the horns of sheep. In the geographical races of wild sheep which are likely to be ancestral to the domesticated breeds, the horns formed a comparatively wide but low spiral, the tip remaining fairly close to the head. In some domesticated breeds, growth in the direction away from the head is much accelerated, so that in extreme cases the horns assume the shape of a straight, twisted stick.

Many other modifications are due to changes in the physiological equilibrium of the species. It is, in fact, probable that this is the basic cause of most changes observed, since it is known that the activities of certain glands have a profound influence on the rate of development of certain organs.

In the selection of types man has often followed economic considerations. In the earliest stages of domestication it is doubtful if much intentional selection took place, but as soon as the animal had proved its economic worth things became different. Geographical races, where physiological make-up made them particularly suitable to withstand certain environmental conditions, would very naturally have been preferred. When milk production became an economic proposition it was obvious that selection of the most prolific females for breeding would rapidly lead to the establishment of a reasonably productive stock.

Apart from economic considerations, standards of beauty must have appeared at an early date. As early man was wont to adorn himself and to conform to a certain standard of outward appearance, he would also, at an early date, have taken an interest in the appearance of his domesticated stock. For this reason bizarre forms of no economic significance may have been favoured. Whilst it is certainly an advantage to have cattle with small horns, there is no economic difference between those that have tiny horns like certain *brachyceros* breeds and those that have no horns at all. In the case of the straight-horned sheep, and the very large horns of the Hungarian and of the Ankole cattle, there are practical disadvantages connected with the presence of such bizarre features. In most of these cases it appears that the whim of the breeders has been at play. In some extreme cases, however, it is possible that a suggestion made by Hilzheimer applies, namely that physical and mental abnormalities made the wild life of such breeds impossible and thus eased the task of keeping them under supervision.

Finally, it must not be forgotten that psychological characteristics are profoundly affected by domestication. The dog in particular has been well studied in this respect, among others by Grzimek (1940, 1943) and by Lorenz (1942).

PART TWO

Domesticated Animals

GROUP I

Mammals Domesticated in the Pre-agricultural Phase

AT ALL times man has regarded the animal world as a source of supply of food and of raw materials. The domestication of the dog constituted an exception, for man and dog joined to form a hunting team. The acquisition of food and raw materials (skin, bone, fat, sinews, etc.) was thus made less laborious, since the team hunted more efficiently than its members alone. The alliance between man and dog led in the course of time to the subjection of the dog, and this was the primary act of domestication.

Once the dog had become a member of human society, the control and later domestication became possible of certain small ruminants which had always constituted an important part of the diet of the dog's ancestors. These are the goat, the sheep and the reindeer. It is in the nature of the process that evidence for the domestication of these species by pre-agricultural man is scanty. Sites of prehistoric nomads controlling such ruminants are bound to be found only in exceptional circumstances, and the osteological remains of the animals would be indistinguishable from the wild forms. One such site at least has been made known, Belt Cave in northern Persia, to which we shall have to refer in due course.

4

The Dog

SCIENTIFIC NAMES—VILLAFRANCHIAN DOGS—*Canis falconeri* Maj., *C. etruscus* Maj. (*C. majori* Del Camp., *C. olivolanus* Del Camp., *C. avus* Aym.), *C. arnensis* Del Camp., *C.* spec. from Siwaliks, India.

PLEISTOCENE AND RECENT WILD DOGS—WOLVES—*Canis lupus* L. (wolf; Pleistocene and Recent), *C.l. suessi* Woldrich (loess wolf), *C.l. pallipes* Sykes (Indian wolf), *C.l. hodophylax* Temm. (Japanese wolf).

JACKALS—*Canis aureus* L. (golden or common jackal; Recent), *C. lupaster* H. and E. (Egyptian jackal; Recent), *C. neschersensis* Croizet (Pleistocene; France, perhaps a jackal).

DOMESTICATED DOGS—*Canis familiaris* L. (specific name applied, for convenience's sake, to all domesticated dogs), with *C. indicus* Fitzinger (pariah dog).

PREHISTORIC SHEEPDOGS AND HOUND-LIKE RACES—*C.f. inostranzewi* Anutschin, *C.f. poutiatini* Studer, *C.f. matris-optimae* Jeitteles (? forerunner of sheepdogs), *C.f. intermedius* Woldrich (? forerunner of hounds).

SMALL PREHISTORIC 'HOUSE'-DOGS—*C.f. palustris* Rütimeyer, *C.f. ladogensis* Anutschin, *C.f. spalleti* Strobel.

PREHISTORIC AND EARLY HISTORIC GREYHOUNDS—*C.f. grajus* L., *C.f. leineri* Studer.

NORTH AFRICAN DOMESTICATED DOGS, UNDATED—*C.f. latifrons* Pomel, etc.

Many others have been named, a full account being available in Hauck (1950).

T HE formidable list of scientific names given here, which is by no means complete, illustrates the complexity of the problem of the prehistoric dogs. The members of the genus *Canis* are very closely allied to each other. They interbreed without difficulty, and there are many transitional forms to be found even under natural conditions. Broadly speaking, it is possible to divide the true wild dogs of the Old World into two groups: the wolves and the jackals; but the distinction is not sharp, and there are species such as *Canis doederleini* Hilz. from north-east Africa, about the classification of which authors have disagreed.

The palaeontological record of the species of true dogs
The recent wild dogs being so closely related to each other, it is not surprising to find it well-nigh impossible to sort out the fossil remains. In them the same variability —mainly in regard to size—is observed. In the Villafranchian deposits of Italy, two kinds of dog have been found. The larger (*Canis falconeri*) resembles in size and preserved characteristics the modern wolf (*Canis lupus*) but, unfortunately, the molar and premolar teeth of the upper jaw are all that are known. The other kind is a dog intermediate in size between the jackal and the wolf, for which Stehlin prefers to retain the old name *Canis etruscus*, the splitting into four species suggested by Del Campana not being justified by the morphological differences. Only the small *Canis arnensis* of Del Campana appears worthy of being retained. Stehlin also holds that the teeth of a 'wolf' described by Newton from the Red Crag of East Anglia resemble this small species. Three kinds of dogs thus appear to have existed in Europe at the commencement of the prehistoric era: one of wolfsize (*C. falconeri*), an intermediate form (*C. etruscus*) and one of jackal size (*C. arnensis*).

This is, of course, an unhappy condition, since even the ancestral forms present the whole size range from wolf to jackal. In the Pleistocene the smaller forms dominate in the three interglacials, and those of the size of the modern wolf do not become frequent until the Last Glaciation, when they are met at the Magdalenian sites of Kesslerloch and Schweizersbild, and elsewhere. There is even a wolf of a size larger than the modern *C. lupus lupus*, *C.l. suessi* from the loess of Austria. All these, including the small interglacial forms known from the Cromer Forest Bed and Crayford in England, Montsaunès and Lunel-Viel in France, the Wildkirchli in Switzerland, Püspökfürdö and Villany in Hungary, are yet, in Stehlin's opinion, wolves rather than jackals.

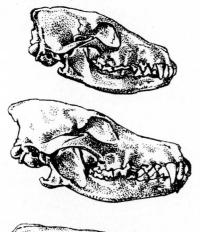

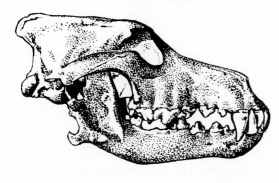

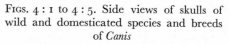

Figs. 4 : 1 to 4 : 5. Side views of skulls of wild and domesticated species and breeds of *Canis*

(1) Jackal (*C. aureus*). (2) Egyptian jackal (*C. lupaster*). (3) Indian wolf (*C. lupus pallipes*), the most likely ancestor of the domesticated dog. (4) Persian wolf (*C. lupus*), female. (5) Galician wolf (*C. lupus*), male. All these are on the same relative scale, No. 5 being approximately 25 cm. overall length

The wolf and the jackal

With the end of the Pleistocene, the modern distribution of wild dogs must have established itself. It is worth while to describe it briefly, for it forms the background on which the prehistory of the domesticated dog unfolds itself. The wolf occurred from Ireland and Spain throughout Europe and Siberia to Japan. In the south, its area extends to peninsular India, and wolves are found in North and Central America also. In this enormous area numerous local races developed.

Generally speaking, the northern races are larger than the southern and have a thicker fur, and there is much variation in colour. But, in the skeleton, the different races cannot be distinguished, except according to their absolute size (Figs. 4 : 1 to 4 : 5). According to Hilzheimer, the length of the base of the skull varies from 172 to 236 mm. Jackals are on the whole smaller, measuring less than 200 mm. and down to 148 mm. This leaves an awkward overlap of small wolves and large jackals. The skulls of wolves have as a rule the stronger jaws and larger teeth, and in particular the upper carnassial tooth is usually longer than the two molars taken together. There are some subtle differences in the teeth which only an expert can recognize. The various rugosities and crests serving as insertions for the musculature are also more strongly developed on the bones of the wolf than of the jackal.

Of the various races of wolves, the small wolves of southern Japan (*C. lupus hodophylax*), of India (*C. lupus pallipes*) and the Syrian wolf deserve mention. The Indian and Syrian wolves are less gregarious than the northern races. Of the 'Indian' wolf, which plays a great part in speculations on the origin of the domesticated dog, Blanford (1891) relates that it is rarely, if ever, heard to howl, and that it sometimes barks like a pariah dog. With local variants it populates Mesopotamia and Arabia also and, being small, is extremely difficult to distinguish from the dog (Lawrence, 1956; Clutton-Brock, 1962a).

It is well known that the whole of Europe was populated with wolves until quite recently. The species survives in the Iberian peninsula and in eastern Europe. In the British Isles it had disappeared from England by the reign of Henry VIII, i.e. about 1500. In Ireland wolves were extinct by 1766. The last Scottish wolves seem to have lingered on till about 1756, for Buffon, the writer of the famous *Histoire naturelle* which was a standard work in the first half of the nineteenth century, tells us that Lord Morton, President of the Royal Society, had assured him that wolves still lived in Scotland in that year. Until the advent of firearms, and the reduction of uncontrolled woodlands and waste places, wolves were frequent everywhere in Europe. Since the war, they have again penetrated into Germany west of the Elbe. Though they prey on the livestock of man, it is known that young wolves are easily tamed and become attached to man.

Jackals have at all times been restricted to more southerly countries than the wolves. The 'golden jackal', a small beast, is familiar to most oriental travellers; it occurs from Sumatra through India to the Caucasus, to Asia Minor, Syria and south-western Europe, where I observed it in Dalmatia thirty-five years ago and where it had advanced as far north as Hungary. The jackal of that country is the so-called reed-wolf, a beast of which many stories are told but which was identified by Ehik as a jackal as recently as 1937. There is no evidence, however, that it penetrated to central and western Europe in Postglacial times, but it is possible that some of the small dog-bones known from interglacial deposits belong to the jackal. This applies particularly to *Canis neschersensis*, a species usually, but erroneously, attributed to the Villafranchian. According to Stehlin, no Villafranchian deposits occur at Neschers (a locality in south France); on the contrary the site yielded a Pleistocene fauna. Professor Boule of Paris regarded this dog as closely related to the jackal.

Apart from the golden jackal, the Eygptian or wolf-like jackal (*C. lupaster*) must be mentioned, an essentially North African animal. There are several varieties of jackal distributed over the whole of Africa, but these are not likely to have contributed to the domesticated dog to any great extent.

Domestication of the dog

This brief survey of the geographical distribution of wild dogs closely related to the domesticated dog shows clearly that prehistoric man was, everywhere and throughout the period of his existence, surrounded by wild dogs. That both man and wild dog were hunters is not likely to have brought about any close association, since then, as today, the dogs would keep away from hunting men, and men would keep away from hunting wolves. Yet the habits of wolves and jackals would have ensured their contact with prehistoric man. Both wolves and jackals are carrion-eaters, and whenever prehistoric man had killed a large animal it was natural for the wild dogs to appear with the intention of snatching a share. This habit was, of course, not likely to establish bonds of friendship between man and the wild dogs, and the beginnings of actual domestication cannot have been due to encounters of this kind. How they may have come about has been described elsewhere (p. 39), but there is no doubt that certain habits and qualities of wild dogs must have favoured a sort of symbiotic association.

The wild dog's habit of clearing away food debris, particularly highly developed in the jackal, which readily eats even vegetable matter, is well known. Neither the wolf nor the jackal is afraid of entering the domain of man. Wolves have often entered villages to obtain live prey, such as sheep, goats, tame dogs or even children. That this would not ingratiate them with man of any period whatever is obvious enough, and for this reason it is improbable that the domestication of the dog was first accomplished in the area of the large ferocious races of wolves found in northern latitudes. The jackal, on the other hand, is not an aggressive animal, and without being asked to do so, and without any favours from man, it has taken over the job of scavenger in most oriental villages and towns. I have seen some walking about in full daylight in the flower-beds of the Government House of one of the largest cities of India. The advantage which accrued to early man from the removal of food debris, which otherwise would have accumulated in or near the camps and villages, must have been noticed at an early period.

Furthermore, jackals and even wolves are easily tamed when young. One cannot expect them to become as pacific as a lap-dog within one generation, but young wolves have been reared in captivity many times. Buffon, as long ago as 1797, related that in Persia wolves were trained for shows, being taught to dance and exhibit a number of tricks. He himself reared several, and found them very docile and even 'courteous' during the first year. They never attempted to seize poultry or other animals when properly fed, until they were about eighteen months old, when they began to do mischief. According to Blanford, the young of the Indian wolf are born with drooping ears, have all the habits of domesticated dogs and are readily tamed, and Mr Cris Crisler has recently tamed them in Alaska (Lois Crisler, 1959). It is therefore easy to imagine conditions in which the domestication of wild dogs might have been carried out in more or less permanent living sites, such as camps or villages. But it is known that the dog had been domesticated in Mesolithic times when man was still exclusively a hunter and food-collector.

Assuming that the presence of wild dogs was suffered in the camps of Mesolithic man because of their usefulness as scavengers,[1] the habits of dogs afford a possible explanation of the development of closer association between dog and man. All wild dogs exhibit the beginnings of a social life, in so far as they associate with each other to form packs for the purpose of hunting as well as for defence. The individuals of each pack are tied together by bonds of friendship, they help one another and often, in their operations, work in unison according to what one might almost call plans designed to meet certain situations. Their intelligence is far superior to that of other carnivores, including the large cats who simply rely on strength and surprise but often display a clumsiness in their attack which is astonishing. The cunning of the dog and his concerted efforts on hunting expeditions are not unlike the hunting practices of early man. It is, therefore, not impossible that young wolves or jackals or other wild dogs, which grew up in or near the temporary camps of Mesolithic hunters, would quite naturally regard the men, who provided part of their food supply, as members of their pack, an association which the hunters would not have failed to turn to their advantage.

That an association of wolf and man is perfectly conceivable, especially when pups are taken, is confirmed by the most interesting experiences of Mr and Mrs Crisler in northern Alaska (1956, 1959). These explorers, while working on films of caribou, adopted wolf pups which grew up in human company and revealed their social propensities. It is evident from Lois Crisler's report that hunters on the Mesolithic (and indeed Upper Palaeolithic) level would have found it easy to associate with wolves. (See Figs. 4 : 6, 2 : 4 and 2 : 5).

To sum up, it is probable that the association of wild dogs with man began on the basis of scavenging and was firmly established by the formation of hunting packs in which the two species co-operated. Whilst it is thus easy to understand how the domestication of the dog came about, it is impossible as yet to say with certainty when it was first effected and which of the wild races is the ancestor of the domesticated dog. It is conceivable that there are several.

That the dog was already domesticated in the late Palaeolithic is possible, though not established with any degree of probability. According to Narr (1959), Russian workers have found coprolites (fossilized faeces) in the Crimea, as well as in Siberia.

---

[1] Ashley Montague (1942) described the scavenging function of the dingo in camps of the native Australians.

At Timonovka on the Desna River, coprolites and fragments of jaws of a *Canis* occur in a 'Gravettian' context. Another of the late Palaeolithic sites where the presence of dogs is suspected is Afantova Gora on the Yenisei. Narr holds that the presence of canine coprolites in a human occupation level would carry some weight if their occurrence in an undisturbed condition could be established. Even then, however, the site may have been temporarily abandoned by man, when wolves

FIG. 4 : 6. 'Mr Arctic', a wolf tamed by Mr and Mrs Crisler and kept for months in northern Alaska. See also Figs. 2 : 4 and 2 : 5

would have entered it for scavenging purposes. These are precisely the conditions under which domestication of the dog must have begun, but they do not amount to proof that it was achieved in the Palaeolithic and under glacial conditions.

Mesolithic dogs

The earliest archaeologically dated evidence for the presence of domesticated dogs comes from various Mesolithic sites, ranging from north Europe to Palestine. In addition, the remains of an apparently domesticated dog were found in the Senckenberg bog in Frankfurt-on-Main (Figs. 4 : 7, 4 : 10a). They were associated with the skeleton of an aurochs, and Mertens (1936) believes that traces of gnawing found on the bones of the ox were due to the activities of this dog. No evidence, however, has been found for the presence of man. The investigators of this dog, Mertens and Baas, have satisfied themselves that it was a real dog, in the sense of *C. familiaris*, and not a wolf. Its osteological characters refer it to a type that resembles the Australian dingo to a surprising extent. For this reason it has been compared with *C. familiaris poutiatini*, the type of which, however, appears to be of later age. The date given for the Senckenberg dog is about 9000 B.C. and is based on the determination of tree pollen found with the aurochs skeleton.

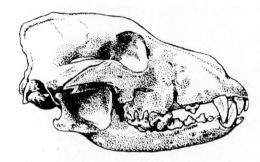

FIGS. 4 : 7 to 4 : 9.   More skulls of domesticated dogs

FIG. 4 : 7. A domesticated dog resembling *C.f. poutiatini*, from the Senckenberg bog, Frankfurt-on-Main, West Germany, of early Postglacial Age.

FIG. 4 : 8. *C.f. matris-optimae*, type specimen, a primitive sheep-dog

FIG. 4 : 9. *C.f. intermedius*, type specimen, a primitive hound. Size of Senckenberg dog approximately that of a dingo, the two others approximately fox-terrier size. (Illustrations 1—8 (excluding 6) after Antonius and Mertens)

Pine was the dominating tree in the forest (86.5 per cent), but birch (7.5 per cent), hazel (6 per cent), oak (2.5 per cent), willow (2 per cent) and elm (1 per cent) were present also. This composition of the flora corresponds to the early Boreal in the climatic sense. It is not impossible that in a climatically favoured area, such as that of Frankfurt, the vegetation had reached the Boreal stage rather earlier than elsewhere, and a date of 9000 B.C. could be defended on these grounds. A later date is more likely, however, such as one between 7500 and 8000 B.C., which is suggested by the Danish chronology of peat bogs. Such a date would bring Senckenberg into line with the oldest Danish dogs to be discussed presently. The Swiss peat-chronology, established by Welten (1944), would place the Senckenberg dog even later.

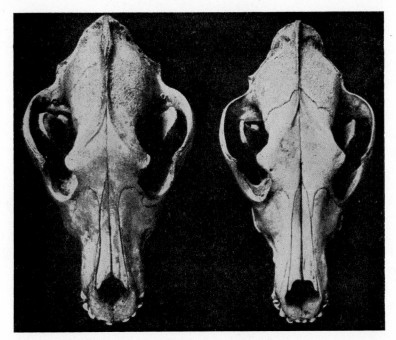

FIG. 4 : 10. (a) Skull of Senckenberg dog seen from above (left) and
(b) that of the dingo (on the right). Note broader muzzle of the former.
After Mertens

Thus, whilst it is undoubtedly one of the earliest known dogs and at that the most completely known, since the whole skeleton is preserved, it is possibly the earliest known of all. Its age is so close to that of the Fennoscandian Moraines, which mark the end of the Ice Age in Europe, that it becomes probable that the domestication of the dog dates back at least to Late Glacial times. It is very unlikely, however, that the centre of domestication was in the neighbourhood of the waning ice-sheet of Europe. This is borne out by finds from the Maglemose period of Denmark.

The Maglemose dogs of Denmark were investigated by Brinkmann, Degerbøl and others. From the very beginning two races are present, a large and a small one, though even the large one is smaller than the wolf. The presence of two distinct races in archaeological deposits which date from 6500 B.C. to nearly 8000 B.C., and in an area which was exclusively inhabited by a large race of wolf, points clearly to a foreign, i.e. more southerly, origin of the domesticated dog and to its domestication at a time when northern Europe was still in part glaciated.

The large Maglemose dog has been compared with *C.f. inostranzewi* by Degerbøl. It was found in the Lundby and Svaerdborg bogs of Denmark and apparently in Oban, Scotland, also. This type of dog exhibits many characters of the wolf which some authors regard as evidence of direct descent, whilst others consider them as the result of the crossing of a dingo-like dog with a wolf. But from the same period the Mullerup site, and Svaerdborg itself, have yielded small dogs, which appear to be akin to the turbary dog (*C.f. palustris*) of the Swiss lake-dwellings.[1]

In the following period, the Ertebølle or Kitchen Midden phase, partly equivalent to the Campignian of French writers, the same two breeds of dog are known. Brinkmann (1924) referred the larger ones to the *inostranzewi* type, whilst the smaller ones with a basal length of less than 150 mm. are assigned to *C.f. palustris*, more especially to a form of the latter, *ladogensis*, described by Anutschin (1882) from the 'Early Neolithic' deposits of Lake Ladoga. A large type *C.f. inostranzewi* comes from the same locality and also from Bologoye (Nowgorod). What is here called 'Early Neolithic' is in all probability the Ertebølle period, through which, therefore, the two types of dog would have persisted.

To the same Ertebølle or Kitchen Midden period may belong *C.f. poutiatini*, a dog described by Studer (1901) from Vysokye near Moscow. There had been some doubt about its age, though it is certainly not Mousterian, as had at one time been assumed. Gandert (1930) considers a Neolithic Age possible. This dog was exceptionally well preserved. The basal length of the skull is 169 mm. and according to Antonius the dog resembles the Australian dingo to a high degree.

Antonius regarded *C.f. poutiatini* as the earliest-known domesticated dog and related to the dingo. The dogs of the *inostranzewi* type were for him original *poutiatini* strains which had been crossed or had interbred with wolves. Now that *inostranzewi* dogs are known to be older than the *poutiatini* forms, it is not necessary to assume interbreeding with wolves, as it would be simple to attribute the wolf-like features of the large Maglemose dogs to their direct descent from wolves. Moreover, Gandert regards *poutiatini* as an unsatisfactory subject for phylogenetic speculation. Yet, since Degerbøl has stressed that the Maglemose dogs must be regarded as imported domesticated animals, it is still possible that Antonius is right. The dingo problem will have to be discussed later.

Dogs of the Neolithic and Metal Ages

In the European Neolithic proper, somewhere about 3500–2000 B.C., the small turbary dog is almost the only one found in the Swiss lake-dwellings. Similarly, dogs of the *palustris* type, though often of somewhat larger size than the Swiss variety, have been found in Neolithic sites in southern Britain, such as Windmill Hill (a well-preserved skeleton; Fig. 4 : 11), Whitehawk Hill and Trundle.

Kuhn (Hescheler and Kuhn, 1949) is right in stressing that, in view of the large number of finds made, this cannot be due to an accident of the palaeontological record. For some reason or other the lake-dwellers did not want large dogs, perhaps because a small house-dog was more convenient in the restricted space of the pile-

---

[1] Another occurs at the Maglemose site of Star Carr in Yorkshire, *c.* 7528 B.C., teste Degerbøl.

dwellings. On the contrary, very small dogs (basal length of the skull 125 mm. or less), the so-called *C.f. spalleti*, have been recovered from the lake-dwellings of Ripač in Bosnia, Terramare in Italy, Sipplingen in Baden, at Egolzwil 2 in Switzerland, and in Austria.

Evidence for the presence of dogs larger than the turbary dog, however, is not missing either. Both at St Aubin on Lake Bienne and Sipplingen on Lake Constance, a few large dogs have been recorded, from the former locality by Reverdin (1927), from the latter by Vogel (1932). In the late Neolithic, therefore, large dogs existed,

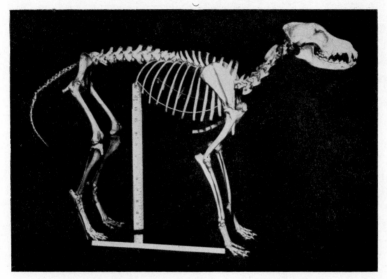

FIG. 4 : 11. Skeleton of a Neolithic dog from Windmill Hill, Wiltshire.
C.f. palustris group

though in very small numbers. Outside the lake-dwellings, they have been found at Schwabsburg in Rhenish Hesse and other localities in the Rhine Valley. Schoetensack, who described them, emphasized the scarcity of dog remains in Neolithic sites of the Rhine Valley. This scarcity may be connected with the mainly agricultural preoccupation of the Neolithic tribes concerned.

In the Bronze Age a moderately large dog is frequently found which, in many respects, is like some of the primitive breeds of sheepdogs[1] still to be found in parts of Europe. The modern collies, Alsatians and others with their elongated skulls are products of very recent systematic breeding. The basal length of the skull of the Bronze Age dog varied from 171–189 mm. It has been called *C.f. matris-optimae* by

[1] Hilzheimer makes a careful distinction between sheepdogs, which take herds to and from the pasture, and shepherds' dogs, which keep guard against robbers, both human and animal. Here, the sheepdog proper is under discussion.

FIG. 4 : 12. Limestone statue of eighteenth-dynasty dog from Egypt, in the Louvre Museum, resembling in several respects the modern Alsatian

Jeitteles (1872). But whilst such a kind of dog has indeed been found in a very large number of Bronze Age sites, the type specimen (Fig. 4 : 8) on which Jeitteles based his description, and which he believed came from the Bronze Age of Olomouc in Moravia, is likely to be as recent as the Middle Ages. In view of the palaeontological material now available, this means that the sheepdog group can be traced back to the Bronze Age. It is not easy to separate it on osteological grounds from the modern pariah dog. The pariah dog (Fig. 4 : 13) being much like a dingo (Fig. 4 : 14), Antonius was inclined to derive the *matris-optimae* dog from *C.f. poutiatini*. Its frequent occurrence in Bronze Age sites may be connected with the increasing importance of sheep-breeding in the economy of Bronze Age Europe.

Thus the forerunners of the modern sheepdogs can so far be traced back to the Bronze Age only. Fresh evidence might extend their lineage into early prehistoric periods. Whether or not recognizable breeds of sheepdogs existed, however, it is highly probable that dogs helped man in controlling sheep from the earliest stages of domestication onwards (p. 61).

Another Bronze Age breed is *C.f. intermedius*, a dog with a basal skull length of 164 mm. The type specimen (Fig. 4 : 9) came from the Bronze Age of Lower Austria, but Studer recorded finds from the late Neolithic of Switzerland, which

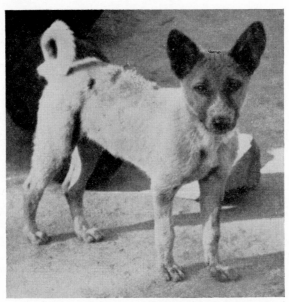

FIG. 4 : 13. Young dog of pre-agricultural Chenchu tribe—an example of pariah dogs of India which closely resemble dingoes in many respects. This specimen has a curly tail—a domestication feature much fancied by ancient Egyptians. Photo F.E.Z.

FIG. 4 : 14. Australian wild dog or dingo. For skull see Fig. 4 : 10(b)

appear to link this breed with *C.f. poutiatini*. It has since been found at Brüx in Bohemia, in a *Kammkeramik* (Neolithic) context. It may have survived into the last centuries B.C. Hilzheimer and Antonius agree that the modern descendants of *C.f. intermedius* are to be found among the hounds as used for hunting. Apart from these dogs of the *matris-optimae* and *intermedius* groups, other breeds occurred in the Bronze Age which were related to *C.f. palustris*, the turbary dog, both on the Continent and in Britain (Easton Down). Again, some like those from Zürich-Utoquai are larger than the Neolithic *palustris* forms from the lake-dwellings. *C.f. palustris*, thus, appears to become increasingly variable.

As regards the Iron Age, little need be said. Amschler found a very large dog of wolf-size in the Hallstatt site of Bludenz, on the Austrian shore of Lake Constance, which he believed to have been used for the control of herds of cattle and sheep. Smaller breeds of dog are also known from Hallstatt sites. Remains of dogs from the La Tène period are attributed to the *matris-optimae*, *intermedius* and *palustris* races, but in this late period the distinctions became increasingly arbitrary, being almost entirely based on size. By this time so many races of dog must have been in existence that no author has yet succeeded in sorting them out with certainty on osteological characters.

According to van Giffen (1929), the dogs of the late Iron Age of Holland display a variety of breeds. Large dogs resembling bulldogs and hounds appear to have been most commonly kept, but greyhound-like forms (resembling *C.f. leineri* and betraying admixture of wolf-blood) were present also. Van Giffen compared statistically his Dutch material, which came from occupation mounds called 'Terpen', with earlier prehistoric and also with modern dogs. The gradual increase in the diversity of

FIG. 4 : 15. Iron Age dog found buried under the east entrance of Maiden Castle, Dorset

breeds from the Mesolithic and Neolithic through the Bronze Age and the Iron Age to modern times is very apparent in his results.

The dogs from British Iron Age sites exhibit equally wide diversities. One of the most interesting comes from the eastern entrance to Maiden Castle. D. M. S. Watson (1943) compared it with the Chow and regards it as an unspecialized dog derived from the *palustris* group (Fig. 4 : 15).

What breeds are the early dogs of Europe?

Briefly, then, there were four major types of dog in early Europe. Of these:

C.f. inostranzewi has been regarded as a wolf-like polar or Eskimo dog, and it has even been suggested that this breed was used to draw sledges;

C.f. matris-optimae is believed to have been a primitive sheepdog;

C.f. intermedius appears to be the ancestor of various breeds of hounds; whilst

C.f. palustris was a small house-dog from which the later Pomeranians, terriers and so forth would be derived.

Prehistoric and early-historic dogs from Asia and Africa

Turning now to the Mediterranean countries, it is noteworthy that a Mesolithic dog from Palestine has been described by Miss Bate. It was found in the Natufian layers of Mugharet-el-Wad, one of the Mount Carmel caves excavated by D. A. E. Garrod. The basal length of its skull is 205 mm., which makes it a very large dog. Miss Bate states that she found no skulls of recent dogs which can be said to resemble it at all closely. She compared it with *C.f. matris-optimae* in spite of the very great difference in geological age, but does not stress the resemblance as proof of close phylogenetic relationship. On the contrary, she was surprised to find in the Natufian dog characters of the Egyptian jackal, *C. lupaster*, and points out that Hilzheimer held the view that certain jackals have been domesticated. The re-investigation of this specimen by Clutton-Brock (1962a) has, however, shown that the jackal features are, to say the least, very doubtful and due to faulty reconstruction of the skull from its fragments. It is in all essential features identical with the Arabian wolf. Moreover, its relatively broad muzzle does suggest incipient domestication. It shares this feature with the Natufian dog from Kebarah and it thus appears probable that the Arabian wolf had been taken into domestication by the ninth millennium B.C. (corresponding radiocarbon date at Jericho, 10,800 B.P. $\pm$ 180; GL. 70).

The earliest 'dog' that has ever been claimed is from the Belt Cave in Persia (Coon, 1951), radiocarbon dated at 11,480 years B.P. = *c*.9500 B.C. It has, however, not yet been studied in detail.

Both the pre-pottery Neolithic and the pottery Neolithic of Jericho have yielded the remains of domesticated dogs (Zeuner, 1958a). Apart from the published finds more are awaiting description. It is certain already that there was considerable variation in size which suggests the presence of several breeds. One was of fox-terrier size, another of that of the pariah dog. This earliest evidence for differentiation comes from pre-pottery Neolithic B (about 6710 B.C.=8670 B.P. $\pm$ 150; GL. 41).[1]

About Jarmo in Iraq, another important site with pre-pottery Neolithic, Reed (1959) says that he has not yet been able to convince himself that dog bones are present, though figurines which can only be intended to represent dogs are there. Revised dates for this site obtained from Dr Braidwood's samples at the Geochronological Laboratory in London are 4970 B.C. (6930 B.P. $\pm$ 120; GL. 48) and

FIG. 4 : 16. Man with two dogs from tomb of Mereruka
(sixth dynasty). Note exceptionally small curled tails.
After Rechinsky

4790 B.C. (6750 B.P. $\pm$ 120; GL. 50). By this time, domesticated dogs were well established in northern Europe, as has been related earlier (p. 87).

Other domesticated dogs, such as *C.f. latifrons*, were described by Pomel from prehistoric sites in Algeria (period not known precisely).

Many domesticated dogs are known from Egypt where at least three breeds can be distinguished in predynastic times. It is noteworthy that on the white-painted pottery of the Amratian phase (fifth millennium B.C.) indubitable greyhounds are depicted beside dogs of other, unidentifiable, breeds. (Fig. 4 : 16). The bones, however, have with few exceptions not been studied in detail yet. On the other hand, innumerable pictorial representations show that, apart from types resembling

[1] A C13 check, kindly made by Dr Vogel, Heidelberg, has shown that there is no evidence for isotopic fractionation at Jericho. The dates obtained after pre-treatment with hydrochloric acid and sodium hydroxide are, therefore, more probable than those published previously. The new dates are given here and should replace the somewhat younger HC dates published previously.

Pomeranians, hounds (Fig. 4 : 17), mastiffs and greyhounds, mongrels existed in numbers in Old Kingdom times (Fig. 4 : 18). In the so-called grave of Menes at Naqada, a hound is shown which Hilzheimer believed to be assignable to the *intermedius* group. The most striking early Egyptian dog, however, is a greyhound with erect ears, which had occurred already in predynastic times (prior to 3000 B.C.)

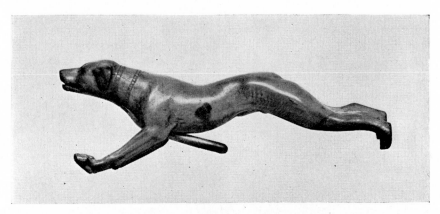

FIG. 4 : 17. Ivory toy hound with movable jaw, late eighteenth dynasty, *c.* 1375 B.C. *c.* 7 inches long. Metropolitan Museum of New York, No. 40.2.1

FIG. 4 : 18. Egyptian mongrel bitch, Beni Hassan, twelfth dynasty, *c.* 1900 B.C. After Carter *et al* (1900)

and which appears to have been regarded as particularly pure bred if it could boast a tail curled up in a spiral over its hind quarters.

These dogs very closely resemble certain greyhounds of eastern Spain (Fig. 4 : 20). In Spain, including the Balearic Isles, and north-west Africa, and even the Canary Islands (Fig. 4 : 21), such dogs are frequently seen, those with drooping ears being almost identical with a predynastic dog from Hieraconpolis (Fig. 4 : 19) as well as

Rekhmere's dogs, whilst those with erect ears remind one of the 'thoroughbred' Egyptian greyhound (Figs. 4 : 22, 4 : 23), though their tails are not clearly twisted. The spiral tail, however, is occasionally found in modern breeds, as in the Basenji of central Africa, and in the elkhound. Whippets also tend to have semi-curled tails.

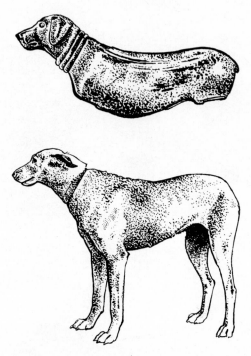

FIG. 4 : 19. The greyhound descendant with drooping ears and hanging tail (broken off). Another Egyptian breed with shorter snout. Both types of Egyptian greyhound survive, especially in the western Mediterranean, in large numbers. From Hieraconpolis, pre-dynastic.

FIG. 4 : 20. Similar greyhound (a bitch, hiding her tail), with drooping ears, from Spain

Not all greyhounds, however, had the curled tail. In the grave of Rekhmere (eighteenth dynasty), for instance, a high-legged dog with drooping ears and a long-haired unrolled tail is shown. It may be compared almost with Irish setters, but this is probably a superficial resemblance.

There are many transitions in existence which link the greyhounds with the pariah dogs of the East, from which both Studer and Antonius are inclined to derive

FIG. 4 : 21. Cross of two kinds of Egyptian greyhound, from Fuerteventura, Canary Islands. Note slender head. These dogs, having become popular in antiquity in the western Mediterranean, were introduced by the Spanish into all their dependent territories. They reached Peru very early and have mistakenly been believed to be indigenous there. Photo O. G. S. Crawford

FIG. 4 : 22. Egyptian greyhound with slender head, upright ears and curled tail, from Beni Hassan, twelfth dynasty, c. 1900 B.C. After Carter et al (1900)

FIG. 4 : 23. Coin showing Egyptian-type greyhound. From Segesta, Sicily, diameter 2·3 cm. After Head (1959)

FIG. 4 : 24. Queen Elizabeth I as Diana with a grey-
hound. Painting by Cornelius Vroom in Hatfield House,
Hertfordshire. Reproduced by kind permission of the
Marquess of Salisbury

them. The existence of such intermediate forms at the present day may well be due
to mongrel breeding. Osteologically no suggestion regarding the origin of the greyhound can as yet be substantiated. The greyhound is remarkable because it hunts
with the eyes rather than the nose. A greyhound-like dog, *C.f. leineri*, was described
by Studer from the lake-dwellings of Bodman on Lake Constance. Antonius regarded
it as a greyhound crossed with the descendants of wolves.

Apart from the Egyptian dogs already mentioned, there occurs a smooth-
haired, somewhat short-muzzled dog (Fig. 4 : 26) with erect ears, which Duerst
regarded as a relative of the Anau dog to be mentioned presently. Mummified
skulls were identified by Jeitteles as *C.f. matris-optimae*, the prehistoric sheepdog.
This breed, therefore, appears to have been present in Egypt, although the dogs of
the ancient Egyptian shepherds are shown mostly as greyhounds. It is important to
note that the sheepdog group, which is closely related to the pariahs, existed in
ancient Egypt.

FIG. 4 : 25. Terracotta tablet from Babylon, now in the British Museum, representing a very heavy mastiff or bloodhound. Such animals were bred in ancient Mesopotamia and used in wars. They were believed to have originated in India. According to Herodotus the revenues from four cities were used to support the kings' dogs. After Layard

FIG. 4 : 26. Sculpture of ancient Egyptian dog with erect ears and heavy forelegs. Considered as related to the dog of Neolithic Anau in Turkestan. Perhaps used in hunting and related to our hounds. Roman period, sculptured in basalt, Louvre Museum

In ancient Mesopotamia[1] a large and powerful mastiff and a greyhound were in use and are frequently shown on monuments (Fig. 4 : 25). In addition, a large dog with drooping ears is shown on the cylinder seal of Bel-Bin (Duerst, 1908, pp. 352, 354) acting as a shepherd's dog. It is too large and heavy to be regarded as a member of the *matris-optimae* group. These dogs may indeed have been shepherds' dogs rather than sheepdogs in Hilzheimer's sense. This author altogether derives the shepherd's dogs from the mastiffs.

Last but not least, the dogs from the famous sites of Anau in Turkestan and of the Indus Valley civilization must be mentioned. The former belongs to the second cultural period of that locality, the 'copper culture,' and was recovered from the layers between + 28 and + 36 feet. Duerst studied it with great care, taking numerous measurements and comparing them with those of other dogs. Studer also saw the specimen. The basal length of the skull was 164 mm.; it was therefore of the size of a dingo. Studer was struck by the resemblance of its skull to the pariah dog and the dingo. Duerst emphasized its close relationship to the primitive sheepdog, summing up his conclusions as follows: 'The domesticated dog of Anau belongs to the subspecies of *Canis familiaris matris-optimae* in a form which stands craniologically very near to the dingo and to *Canis poutiatini* Studer, but which is distinguished by a rather broad muzzle.'

The dog from the Indus Valley civilization at Mohenjo-Daro was described by Sewell (Sewell and Guha, 1931) as a type very closely resembling the Anau dog. He, too, stresses the difficulty of separating these dogs from the dingo-pariah group. The Mohenjo-Daro dog thus suggests that dogs very like the modern pariahs existed in north-west India in the third millennium B.C.

Similar dogs were described by Prashad (1936) from Harappa. Their relationship with the pariah-dingo group is indicated by Prashad's comparison with *C. tenggeranus* Kohlbrugge, which is said to be found in Pleistocene deposits in oriental countries. The name, however, is that of the Javanese pariahs. Their skulls suggest affinity with the Indian wolf, *C.l. pallipes*, which is the most dog-like of the true wolves. The domestication characters of the Harappa dogs lie in the direction of greyhounds, though slender-legged dogs may well have arisen independently in more than one place.

A hound is represented by a steatite figure from Mohenjo-Daro (Marshall, pl. XCVI, f.17), so that the Indus Valley civilization had a dingo-pariah, a greyhound and a hound, the last two probably derived from the first. The importance of what is here called the dingo-pariah group is thus becoming more and more obvious.

This result illustrates that the differences between the breeds mentioned are comparatively small. That *C.f. poutiatini* is virtually a dingo has been emphasized by Studer, and the Anau dog, although comparable with the *matris-optimae* group, is in reality still very close to the former.

[1] See van Buren (1939) for an enumeration of finds.

Dingo and pariah

It seems that the dingoes of Australia (Fig. 4 : 14) and the pariah dogs of southern and western Asia (Fig. 4 : 13) have indeed preserved numerous primitive characters. Both are medium-sized dogs, smaller than the wolf but larger than the jackal. The coat is variable, but mostly reddish, fawn or yellowish, diffused with grey or brown, or wolf-coloured, and the hair is short or moderately long (changing seasonally). The ears are upright. The tail is often carried as in domesticated dogs, namely raised, though from memory I believe it is correct to say that it is more often carried wolf-fashion, hanging and protecting the tender parts of the hind quarters, than is the case in modern European breeds.

Most palaeontologists have recognized the close relationship between pariah dogs and the dingo. I was particularly struck by this resemblance when I saw the pariah dogs in remoter parts of northern Gujarat in north-west India. These dogs are in almost every respect like dingoes: fawn-coloured, sleek-haired and of medium size and with upright ears. They breed remarkably true to type, for there are very few specimens which deviate, and this is usually in coloration only. Pariah dogs are found from the Balkan peninsula, Asia Minor and North Africa to India, Java (if the extinct Tengger dog belongs here) and Japan, though in many districts they vary owing to the admixture of numerous other breeds.

It is not difficult to understand how early man might have taken such dogs to Australia, where they established themselves rapidly 'pariah'-fashion, in part even becoming independent of man, since the Australian environment offered them plenty of food in the numerous species of marsupials unadapted to the presence of a true carnivore. This introduction of the dingo into Australia is not very recent. Howchin says that neither its living presence nor its remains are known to occur in either Kangaroo Island or Tasmania. It is moderately certain, therefore, that its advent was subsequent to the separation of these islands from the mainland, and, by inference, later than the occupation of the island of Tasmania by its aboriginal population. The bones of the dingo are found associated with those of some extinct marsupials, but this need not imply a very great antiquity, as some such extinctions have occurred at no great distance of time, and these animals were probably the contemporaries of the existing aborigines. Wood Jones (1921) inclined to the belief that aborigines brought their dogs with them when they arrived in the country. For geological reasons this advent is likely to be at least as remote as the last phase of the Last Glaciation, when the sea-level was low, so that the dingo has a fair chance of being older than the Mesolithic dogs of Europe and Asia.

The fact that the dingo and pariah dogs are relatively constant in their characters, in spite of innumerable opportunities of interbreeding with both wild and domesticated relations, coupled with the fact that their morphological characters are very like those one would expect to find in the ancestors of the domesticated dogs, has induced several authorities to regard them as the ancestors of all domesticated races. This view was held above all by Studer, the great Swiss monographer of the dogs of the lake-dwellings, and it is followed also by the Austrian school of Antonius.

Prehistoric dogs of America

The domesticated dog is known from prehistoric America also. Nehring (1884) described three types from mummified skeletons prepared by the Incas of Peru. One was somewhat like a sheepdog, the second a 'dachshund' and the third a 'bulldog'. Later on, Noack (1916b) described a fourth which resembled closely the larger varieties of the European *C.f. palustris*, and Antonius regards it as possible that the 'roe-hound' of South America, which appears to have been in the possession of the natives when the first travellers visited that subcontinent, is an indigenous breed. Disregarding the dachshund, bulldog and greyhound races as the products of special breeding, one is once more led back to forms resembling *C.f. palustris* and *C.f. matris-optimae*, and these would have been brought from Asia by early immigrants. Ueck (1961) is convinced that the great variety of breeds in South America is the result of local differentiation and that it could well be derived from pariah-like ancestors.

Nehring thought of an independent centre of domestication in America, the presumed ancestor being the small Mexican wolf. But Antonius regarded it as more likely that the domesticated dog was brought either by the original immigrants from Asia, or at a later date by one of the waves of arctic tribes like the Eskimoes who invaded America. This view is supported by Ueck, who notices resemblances between certain Eskimo dogs and pariahs. Hybridization with coyote or fox is excluded as a possibility by experiments which proved negative, and other wild South American Canids (Haltenorth, 1958) are even less likely. The Mexican wolf, however, cannot be excluded as it belongs to the species-group of *Canis lupus*.

Characters of domestication

Primitive domesticated dogs resemble their wild relations to such an extent that it is necessary to enumerate some of the characters which enable investigators to distinguish them. This is particularly important in regard to the dingo.

In doing so, it goes without saying that deformities, like short-leggedness as in the dachshund, the Beni Hassan dog (Fig. 4 : 18) and the Inca dog, are reliable proof of domestication. They are apt to occur independently in different localities and similarity due to the presence of such characters need not imply close relationship.

Comparing a sheepdog, or a pariah, with a wolf, one notices that the dog's back is straighter and shorter than that of the wolf, and that the cross-section of its chest is barrel-like, not keeled. This feature results in an outward-turned elbow, a conspicuous feature of highly domesticated dogs. It, in turn, influences the gait, for the dog puts the hindfoot beside the forefoot, whilst the wolf places it into the print of the forefoot.

The dog, especially the male, further carries his tail preferably in the erect position, showing his anus. A wolf never does so. This is perhaps more than a habit and caused by a change in the shape of the tail vertebrae. The spiral roll-tails of

FIG. 4 : 27. The Basenji dog of the Congo. A dog of the natives which has preserved several features characteristic of ancient Egyptian dogs, notably the large upright ears and curly tail. It does not bark. Specimen bred by Veronica Tudor-Williams and illustrated in the *Journal of the Society for the Protection of the Fauna of the Empire*, vol. 54 (1946)

some breeds both ancient (like the Egyptian greyhound) and living (like the Basenji, an African breed, Fig. 4 : 27) suggest this.

Variations in hair length and colour also are due in part to domestication. The smooth hair, which is present in so many domesticated forms, may however be an original character of the ancestor of the dog. Hair characters are altogether unreliable except that single-coloured coats are rare in nature, and piebaldness is almost non-existent in wild animals.[1] Another proof of domestication is the lop-ear, which is

---

[1] An exception is the Hyaena Dog (*Lycaon pictus*) of South and East Africa. It is, incidentally, a member of the hyaena family, and not a dog.

present only in the pups of the wild species. The retention of juvenile characters by the adults, a phenomenon called neoteny, is extremely common in domesticated animals.

Finally, the shape of the head affords criteria to be mentioned presently in connection with the skull. They concern the position of the eyes, which are somewhat more lateral and slit-like in the wild dogs, especially wolves, giving them what one might call a slightly mischievous expression. In the domesticated breeds the eyes are 'round' and directed a little more forward. This is clearly noticed when a dog looks at a person while begging for food. The difference is evidently in the proportions of the skull, and in all probability it has played a part in modifying the habits of some breeds which appear to be using their eyes rather than their noses. Nevertheless, the cause of this difference is far from clear. Whilst Studer and other early investigators believed that the frontal bones have expanded by a greater development of the sinus, modern workers like Dahr (1942) and Hauck (1950) favour the idea that it is due to the position of the post-orbital processes, in other words to shape and position of the eye-sockets.

Changes in the skeleton are indeed many. Wolfgramm (1894), for instance, found that a reduction in size occurs in the first generation of wolves bred in captivity; and it is a rule which applies to all thoroughly domesticated species in the early stages that they are smaller than their wild ancestors. Examples are provided by numerous remains of sheep, cattle, pigs and dogs from Neolithic sites.

Extreme short-leggedness and, more rarely, long-leggedness, find their expression in the leg bones and may in some cases be taken as evidence of domestication.

The most important changes, however, occur in the skull, for the measurement of which the Swiss palaeontologist Studer elaborated a complicated system. In *Canis*, as in other domesticated genera, domestication tends to shorten the facial part of the skull. Conspicuous examples are the bulldog and the pig. But this tendency is by no means universal, and lengthening of the face is observed also. The shortening of the face occurred, according to Wolfgramm, in the first generation of captive wolves, but Antonius found, also in the first generation, a wolf with an elongated, greyhound-like snout. Whilst, therefore, shortening and broadening of the face is more usual than the opposite in domestication, increased variability of skull proportions is the essential feature.

The most significant change is best described as a raising of the anterior part of the cranium (the brain case) above the bridge of the nose. It is accompanied by an enlargement of the frontal sinuses and a broadening across the cheekbones. Moreover, the facial portion, including the upper jaw, is inserted lower at the bridge of the nose, the tip of the nose being proportionately raised. These modifications show clearly when the skulls are placed on a table (Figs. 4 : 1 to 4 : 5 and 4 : 7 to 4 : 9). A wolf's skull then rests on the auditory bullae and the canines, whilst that of a well-domesticated dog rests on the bullae and the carnassials, the row of the teeth rising from the table. Moreover, Noack maintains that the auditory bullae become smaller and irregularly shaped under the influence of domestication. Furthermore, experimental work by Herre and Stephan (1955) has shown that the size of the brain is reduced in captivity. The effect of this important change on the cranium remains to be studied.

In the primitive breeds of dogs, however, these differences from the wolf are by no means constant, and sometimes the only character that indicates domestication is the smaller size of the preserved portions of skull and of the teeth, compared with the wolf.

The teeth of dogs are on the whole smaller, especially the canines and the carnassials. In the upper jaw of a northern wolf the carnassial is usually longer than the two molars which follow it taken together, whilst in the dog it is shorter. This change illustrates a change in feeding habits: the dog is more omnivorous and uses his molars more than the wolf does, whilst the wolf lives mainly on flesh and hence needs an efficient carnassial. Correspondingly, the muscular ridges on the skull are less strongly developed in the dog, and the lower jaw is narrower.

On the whole, the length of the upper carnassial is a good character of the domesticated dog. But Hauck and Dahr stress that the wolf is the most carnivorous of the genus *Canis*, and the descendant of less carnivorous ancestors whose teeth should have been more like those of the domesticated dog. They do not believe in a return to a more 'primitive' type of dentition and therefore hold that the domesticated dog is not descended from the wolf.[1] This argument is interesting but not conclusive, since similar changes have occurred in the domestication of the cat. In fact, there is a fair measure of plasticity in the skeleton of the head of a young mammal, which in nature is reduced by the young all leading the same kind of life. I was able to demonstrate this for rhinoceroses (Zeuner, 1934), and there is no reason to suspect that dogs should behave differently. Life in the domesticated state could, therefore, have influenced the relative growth rates of the carnassials and the molars.

The origin of the domesticated dog

The characters indicating domestication are distinct only in the highly bred forms, whilst the primitive races resemble the wild forms to such an extent that a sharp line can hardly be drawn. The dingoes and pariahs among the living forms, and *C.f. poutiatini* and *C.f. inostranzewi* among the fossil, are hardly distinguishable from the wild dogs. What then is the ancestral species?

At first sight, this question appears to be easy to answer: it is the wolf. Not only are the characters of the earliest European dogs of the *inostranzewi* group very close

[1] Recent investigations by Dr J. Clutton-Brock show that the Indian wolf has small carnassials, like the dog.

to wolves, but many sheepdogs have preserved wolf-like characters. Moreover, Miller (1912), when studying the osteology of the mammals of western Europe, noticed that all the dogs' skulls which he had seen, including pug, fox-terrier, blood-hound, mastiff, ancient Egyptian, ancient Peruvian, Greenland and Alaskan Eskimo, and American Indian, all have teeth strictly of the wolf-type, 'never showing any approach to the jackal'.

There are, however, some difficulties involved in accepting the wolf as the ancestor without qualification. It is a fact that all primitive breeds of dogs tend to be of a size intermediate between wolf and jackal. Breeders have noticed that this particular size is the easiest to produce. The pariahs and the dingoes are in the same category, and so are the Mesolithic dogs. It seems, then, that the original dog was smaller than the Palaearctic wolf. One might explain this simply as size-reduction owing to domestication. The majority of workers have, however, accepted it as an indication of the size of the wild ancestor and looked for the latter among the small southern wolves, especially as some of these approach the fawn colour which is so characteristic of pariahs and dingoes.

The Indian wolf (*C. lupus pallipes*) has more than once been quoted as a suitable candidate. According to some, it does not even howl, but barks occasionally like a dog. In body size and in certain proportions of the skull it is intermediate between wolves and jackals. Duerst pointed out that a small wolf like the Indian race occurred in the Culture-level I of Anau, i.e. below the Anau dog. But measurements show that the skull of the Indian wolf is so much more slender than that of the Anau dog, that, instead of an imperceptible passage, a large and conspicuous change would have to be assumed at the beginning of domestication. Duerst, therefore, prefers to think that the Anau dog was imported by the first breeders of cattle and camel who came to the area.

From time to time, other fossil dogs have been described as related to *C.l. pallipes*. Nehring even described a fossil Indian wolf from the Heppenloch Cave in south Germany, though on fragments of lower jaws—material too scanty to be reliable. It occurred in association with the remains of the dhole (*Cuon alpinus*, a wild dog not belonging to the genus *Canis*, which still occurs in India and central Asia but reached Europe only once, namely during the Last Interglacial), and with a monkey indistinguishable from the Gibraltar macaque.

Noack (1916a) thought he had found a domesticated Indian wolf in the supposedly Neolithic filling of the Popenburgklippe near Hildesheim. These skulls, as well as one from the Steinau Cave in Hesse, are not, however, regarded as evidence for descent from *C. pallipes* by Hauck.

If the Indian wolf is the ancestor of some breeds of domesticated dog, one would expect the dingo to be closely related to it. On this point it would be worth while to carry out some detailed research.

Studer found that the Japanese wolf is very close to the primitive domesticated dog, but did not accept it as ancestor for geographical reasons. Neolithic dogs from Japan were described by Hasebe (1924), who considers them as resembling the European *palustris* and *intermedius* groups, i.e. the house-dogs and the hounds. Kono (1934), another Japanese worker, however, has raised the question of relationship with the Japanese wolf, *C.l. hodophylax*, without attempting an osteological comparison.

Antonius holds that similar small races of wolves, such as the Syrian or the Spanish ones, might have supplied the first domesticated dogs, but again no osteological studies have yet been made to test this possibility.

In spite of Miller's statement about the lupine character of the teeth of domesticated dogs, some evidence that the jackal has had a hand in the game has to be refuted before the derivation of the dog from the wolf only can be accepted. That a mummified Egyptian jackal was described by Hilzheimer as *C. lupaster domesticus* is not necessarily proof of actual domestication, for the ancient Egyptians kept many animals captive. More recently, Degerbøl (1933), after an exhaustive study of the prehistoric dogs of Denmark, has agreed that 'with our present knowledge, we cannot entirely reject the possibility that at least some dogs have originated from the jackal'. The Natufian dog from Mount Carmel, Palestine, was regarded by the late Miss Bate as showing relationship to the Egyptian jackal (*C. lupaster*) in the following characters: the skull rises gradually from the muzzle backwards, having a low forehead; the interorbital portion is flat; and the shape and size of the upper carnassial and the pattern of the upper molars are as in *C. lupaster*. Recent studies by Miss Clutton-Brock, however, have compelled her to modify this interpretation of the Mount Carmel specimen. It is a relative of the Arabian wolf, and it shows slight evidence of domestication (see p. 93).

So far, then, there are four alternatives: The domesticated dog is descended (1) exclusively from the wolf, (2) exclusively from the jackal, (3) from both, with a dominance of a small race of wolf, or (4) from a wild dingo. Of these, (4) is the best-founded theory, (1) the second best, whilst (2) is no longer seriously considered probable.

The fourth alternative relies on the dingo and pariah group with their curiously constant characters. Studer was convinced that these dogs are the descendants of an originally wild dog, a *Canis ferus*, a species related to both wolf and jackal but originally distinct. It has become more likely that this wild dingo was a geographical race very closely related to the Indian wolf. Where it would have occurred in the wild state is open to conjecture, though the lands from Syria eastwards to north India would be the most probable. Duerst followed Studer's views on the whole, and so does Hauck among recent workers. The sense of unity which is so characteristic of the dog world has often been quoted in support of this alternative.

Altogether, one comes to the conclusion that the arguments in favour of the fourth alternative are weighty, but the difficulty remains of explaining why a form so closely related to the wolf should have been able to maintain itself within the area inhabited by the Indian wolf. Evidently the last word has not yet been spoken.

Breeds of dogs

The breeds of dogs are too many to be discussed here; but in the past there were few outside the great civilizations, and they were mainly utilitarian. It is likely that

FIG. 4 : 28. Pekinese dog in imperial cloisonné enamel, Ch'ien Lung period, China, A.D. 1736–1795. This and similar Chinese effigies are probably symbolic of the lion, but actually represent Pekinese dogs

polar dogs and Alsatians stem from the *C. inostranzewi* group, and that the terriers are descended from *C. palustris*. From *C. poutiatini* would come both the sheepdogs and the hounds (Fig. 4 : 29). Personally I am inclined to regard the sheepdogs as a composite group containing some very primitive elements.

The Egyptians of the eighteenth dynasty had apparently already established the dog as a companion of man in every walk of life. That they should have bred dogs for a variety of utilitarian purposes, and that there should be mongrels in the streets, is only to be expected. But dogs were pets also, much as they are today. They wore collars for practical reasons as well as for identification, the name of the animal often being inscribed on it. Names such as 'Ebony', 'Grabber' and 'Cooking-

FIG. 4 : 29. Boar-hunting scene with hound from third century B.C. of Sicily. Part of a sarcophagus in Syracuse Museum

pot' have come down to us. Fancy breeds appeared retaining juvenile characteristics and were valued greatly (Fig. 4 : 30).

More than this, the personal attachment to the dog as a friend and comrade is frequently attested. Faithful dogs were buried with honours and grave-goods in

FIG. 4 : 30. Small bronze dog with gold collar, late eighteenth dynasty, c. 1350 B.C. Probably representing a tiny lap-dog. The reproduction is twice actual size; height of original only 15 mm. Metropolitan Museum, New York, 47.58.1

special tombs by pharaohs of the Old Kingdom. An eighteenth-dynasty officer stationed on the Palestine border wrote home complaining bitterly about the fierce street-dogs of the garrison town and relating how a little wolfhound protected him from the dangerous packs.

Conclusion

To sum up: the evidence so far available suggests that the domesticated dog sprang from one of the geographical races of the wolf. The possibility of an originally wild, dingo-like form now completely absorbed into the domesticated stock cannot be excluded, but such form would have been extremely close to the Indian wolf. In any case, however, the Mesolithic dogs of northern Europe already were introduced stock which appears to have been dingo-like (*C.f. poutiatini*) and which interbred with northern wolves (*C.f. inostranzewi*). These large dogs, from which Eskimo or other polar-dog breeds are ultimately derived, continue through the Neolithic. *C.f. poutiatini* gave rise to the sheepdogs of the Bronze Age and later (*C.f. matris-optimae*), and to the hounds (*C.f. intermedius*).

But as early as in Mesolithic times a small dog, perhaps a house-dog, makes its appearance. It gives rise to the turbary dog (*C.f. palustris*) of the Neolithic and survives in many modern breeds, like terriers, Pomeranians, etc. The following table summarizes the position on the basis of present knowledge.

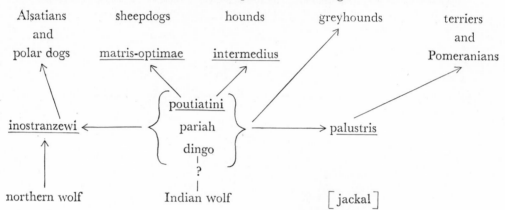

Until the beginning of the Iron Age the number of breeds is small in Europe, but with the La Tène period the finds show so much variation that, in view of their close relationship, the breeds can no longer be easily disentangled on osteological grounds. The La Tène *oppidum* of Manching in Bavaria, which has yielded four hundred and forty bones of dogs, contained three distinguishable breeds of dog (Oberdorfer, 1959), namely a hound of the *C.f. intermedius* group, a small breed of the *C.f. palustris* type, and a group of large-size animals which can be classified as *C.f. inostranzewi* or *C.f. matris-optimae*, which appears to include the sheepdogs of the township but which is very variable. In addition, two bent long bones have been found which raise the possibility of dachshund types being represented, though they can be explained as the result of injury or pathological change. Oberdorfer is careful to stress that the only real distinction that has been possible in this material is into size-groups. Incidentally, some bones have cut-marks which may suggest that dogs were occasionally eaten.

The history of the dogs as here presented is inevitably tentative. The same material could undoubtedly be made to support other theories. This is not surprising in a group in which the wild forms are so closely related as in the genus *Canis*, in which fertile interbreeding of all species is still possible, and whose members vary both geographically and individually. These were, however, precisely the factors that enabled man to produce various domesticated types suitable for different economic needs, such as shepherding, hunting and house-watching. That the dog was, and still is, very occasionally eaten in addition, is known from Sipplingen on Lake Constance, the Swiss lake-dwellings, the Hildesheim sites and elsewhere. But the case of the dog differs from that of other domesticated animals in so far as that food was not man's concern when he domesticated the species. Indeed, man has associated himself with the dog, another mammal, for mutual advantage, and on the whole the companionship of man and dog has been respected. Most people today would be disgusted at the idea of eating dogs, and to the Moslem the species is unclean. That this symbiosis led to the ultimate dominance of the human partner is, of course, the result of the latter's superior intelligence.

5

The Reindeer

SCIENTIFIC NAMES—*Rangifer tarandus tarandus* L. (Scandinavian vjell reindeer; Scandinavia to north Russia). *R.t. fennicus* Lönnberg (European forest reindeer; Finland, Russia, Siberia). *R.t. platyrhynchus* Vrolik (Spitzbergen). *R.t. sibiricus* Murray (Siberian and east European tundra reindeer). *R.t. pearsoni* Lydekker (Novaya Zemlya). *R.t. valentinae* Flerov (forest reindeer of Siberia, south to northern Mongolia and Altai Mountains). *R.t. arcticus* Rich. (North American tundra reindeer). *R.t. caribou* Gmelin (caribou, North American woodland reindeer).

THE reindeer was one of the most important species in the economy of Upper Palaeolithic man. There is no doubt that Palaeolithic man hunted reindeer on a large scale, but whether there was any association approaching domestication is not known. The species survived in enormous numbers in the high latitudes of the northern hemisphere, and even today there are many tribes, from the Lapps in northern Scandinavia through Siberia to the Eskimoes of North America and Greenland, for whom the reindeer is a most important supplier of food and raw material (Figs. 5 : 1 – 5 : 3). Over this wide range, however, the species now appears, except in the New World, as a partly domesticated animal. Domestication has in some areas remained at a primitive level, i.e. neither reindeer nor men have given up their nomadic habits. In others, the reindeer has been fully domesticated, being used as a draught animal, for riding and milk production. But it is certain that this was achieved by adopting at a late date the practices applied to cow and horse. These late stages are here left out of consideration.

The reindeer belongs to the group of cervine deer in which the lateral toes are reduced in such a way that the lower ends only are preserved. This group is mainly American, for all American deer (except the wapiti) belong to it; in the Old World

FIG. 5 : 1. Two Lappish reindeer which, though allowed
to run wild, are in fact controlled by man

all deer belong to a group in which the reduction has affected the lower parts of the lateral toes so that their upper ends have remained, with the exception of the roedeer, the elk and the reindeer. This clearly points to an American origin for the three last-named species. Indeed, the reindeer is rare in deposits earlier than the Last Glaciation, and no fossil ancestor has been found in Europe. The earliest European reindeer are of approximately Antepenultimate Glaciation age.

For a member of the deer family, the reindeer has many peculiar features. Like the elk it carries its head low. Both sexes have antlers, though those of the female

FIG. 5 : 2. Catching reindeer with lasso during the
annual round-up, Lapland

are usually small. The nose is covered with fur, an adaptation to intense cold encountered in many Arctic mammals. The toes are broad and splayed. It is well
adapted to a life on soft and boggy ground.

Many races of reindeer have been distinguished and some authors even regard
them as distinct species. What emerges from the various attempts at subdividing the
reindeer is that there are two main types, the woodland and the tundra deer. The
former is the larger. Its antlers are branched in a complicated way, the beam being
comparatively short, stout and flattened. There is nearly always a back tine present
about half-way between the bez and the terminal branches of the main beam.

The tundra variety, on the other hand, has long antlers with a rounded and
slender beam, and the back tine is often absent, especially in North American
races. The brow tine is usually palmated and broad. It is much larger on one side
than on the other, usually the left, that of the other antler being sometimes reduced
to a mere knob. The woodland variety is best represented by the Canadian caribou,
the tundra race by the Barren Ground deer of arctic North America. Corresponding
races exist in the Old World. There are ecological differences, too, for the forest form
is confined to the woods, where it feeds on branches, grasses, water-weeds and lichen
which grow abundantly on the trees.

The tundra race is the more gregarious. It spends the summer in the tundra and
comes to the northern edge of the forest in winter, where it enters the domain of the
caribou. It feeds on the carpets of lichen called 'reindeer moss' which are often several
feet thick, as well as many other tundra plants. In winter the males enter deeper into
the woods than the females, but there is little chance of their meeting the caribou
which tends to move inland into the mountain forests at that time of the year. Moreover, the tundra reindeer breed later than the woodland reindeer.

The interesting question arises as to which of these two groups the Old World
reindeer can be assigned. Jacobi (1931) holds that the European group of reindeer
in the main belong to the tundra race of North America (*R. tarandus arcticus*) but
Scharff, Sandford, Ritchie (1920) and the author do not share this view. As regards
the modern race of Europe (*R. tarandus tarandus*), it extends from the mountains of
southern Scandinavia into northern Russia. Its antlers are of the subcylindrical and
elongated type. In this respect they resemble the American *R.t. arcticus*. But it is
open to question whether the distinction drawn by Jacobi, that the antler of the
Lapland race is kinked in the beam whereas that of the American tundra race is
regularly curved, is valid. It appears that in the antlers no constant differences can
be found between these two tundra forms, except that in the European races the
back tine is normally present whilst it is commonly absent in the North American.

The fossil reindeer of Europe is found from the Riviera and north Spain to
Britain, northern Germany and Russia, though not penetrating south of the Alps.
They are in several respects intermediate between the woodland and tundra races.

Fig. 5 : 3. A great round-up of domesticated Lapland reindeer for the purpose of selecting animals for slaughter. On this occasion the young are branded with property marks

This is evident, for instance, from the Magdalenian engraving of Kesslerloch (Fig. 5 : 4) in Switzerland and from those of Limeuil in the Dordogne. The animals shown are clearly tending towards the woodland type, since the brow tines are strongly palmated and the antlers generally heavily pronged. On the other hand, the engravings from Petersfels (Middle Magdalenian, south Germany) are distinctly of the tundra variety, as indicated by the long and slender beam and the absence of the back tine, and the same applies to the painting from Font-de-Gaume. Some of the reindeer from the British Isles approach the woodland type, such as the magnificent head from Ashbourne, County Neath, Ireland, preserved in the National Museum in Dublin, but others from Ireland usually have the long rounded beams of the tundra race. In Ireland this type seems to be the dominant one. In Scotland and England, however, the intermediate type appears to be the common form in the Pleistocene. Antlers from the Thames gravels near Staines, collected by the writer, are flattened and provided with a back tine, but they appear to have been rather less branched than the forest form.

Plenty of reindeer remains are found in Scotland in Postglacial deposits as well as in the Pictish forts called 'brochs' of Caithness, Sutherland and the Orkneys. According to Ritchie all these are of the intermediate type and bear a close resemblance to the modern Scandinavian race. From this evidence it appears that the tundra and forest reindeer cannot be so clearly distinguished in Europe as is possible

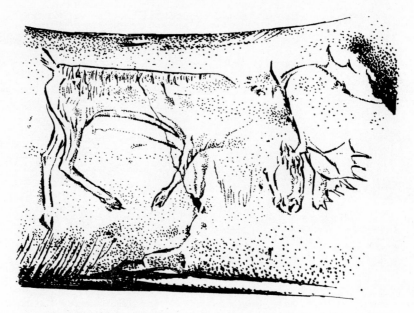

FIG. 5 : 4. Engraving of male reindeer on a piece of reindeer antler, Magdalenian of Kesslerloch Cave near Schaffhausen, Switzerland. Original in Rosgarten Museum, Constance

in North America. Nevertheless, hardly any systematic work has been done on the characters of the fossil European reindeer, and an investigation of stratigraphically dated material might produce interesting results.

The race which occurs in Spitsbergen is related to the Lapland deer. This is natural, since the European tundra type extends through northern Russia into western Siberia. East of the River Lena, it appears to be replaced by a variety of the American *R.t. arcticus*, if indeed a clear distinction can be drawn at all between these two tundra races.

The Finnish reindeer (*R.t. fennicus*) belongs to the woodland group. Since woodlands exist in that area, this is not surprising from the biological point of view, though the race is much less extreme in the structure of its antlers than the caribou. Connected with the Finnish race appears to be a group of north Russian forest reindeer about which little is known. The woodland types, however, extend from here right across northern Asia to the New World. Curiously enough, the race occupying Novaya Zemlya resembles the caribou. This is the only exception to the general rule that antler formation varies according to the environment in which the reindeer races live.

From the evidence afforded by modern reindeer, two conclusions may be drawn regarding the Pleistocene reindeer of Europe, namely (a) that the European reindeer

116

was neither a typical forest nor a plain tundra form, although variations tending towards these extremes occur occasionally, and (b) that the north European races, i.e. the intermediate 'Lapland race' and the 'Finnish forest race' may be regarded as the survivors of the fossil European population. This was apparently made up mainly of animals that showed no distinct preference for either forest or tundra, and of small numbers of specially adapted animals that preferred either the forest or the tundra. Altogether it appears that according to environmental conditions the reindeer tends to produce ecotypes which cannot be regarded as different species.

From the biological point of view the reindeer is extremely well adapted to cold conditions; there are virtually no northern limits to its distribution, at least in summer. In Postglacial times, but before the arrival of modern agriculture, the southern boundary of the reindeer appears to have coincided with the occurrence of a regular snow winter. It is doubtful whether it still occurred in Germany in Roman times, since the reference to the reindeer in Caesar's *De Bello Gallico* cannot be regarded as reliable. It must be admitted that the statement that both males and females have horns, as well as the observation that 'velut palmae rami quam late diffunduntu-' would fit the reindeer. But it is said to have only a single horn! It is possible, however, that the reindeer still occurred at that time in the forests of eastern Germany, whence it would since have withdrawn to Finland.

Similarly, it has been held that the reindeer survived into the Middle Ages in northern Scotland. From the biological point of view this is conceivable, since, even prior to the extensive deforestation from which Scotland has suffered, there must have been plenty of tundra-like environment available in the bogs and on the mountains. Moreover, there is plenty of snow in the winter on higher ground and lichens occur plentifully in the woods and on rocks. Among writers on the subject, the view prevails that the reindeer survived from the Pleistocene into the historical period or at least into the Roman period. The evidence is believed to be supplied by large numbers of bones found in drained lochs and in the brochs of northern Scotland which are dated from about 50 B.C. to about A.D. 400. Ritchie points out that at the time of their erection, however, the reindeer was already on the decline and restricted to Sutherland, Caithness and the Orkneys.

There is, moreover, evidence that the reindeer existed in Scotland during the Middle Ages. An historian, Torfaeus, in his *Rerum Orcadensium Historia* which was published late in the seventeenth century, says that the Orkney Jarls used to visit Caithness in order to hunt red deer and reindeer. The question is whether these reindeer were truly wild or the descendants of stock introduced by Norse settlers. The constant traffic which had been going on between Scandinavia and north Britain makes it possible to assume that reindeer were introduced repeatedly. The idea of importing reindeer to Scotland has apparently suggested itself from time to time, for instance to the Duke of Atholl, who imported a few specimens to the

Orkneys in 1816. About 1820 the highlands of Pentland were populated with 200 reindeer which, however, gradually died away. Jacobi suspects that this was not due to lack of attention or unsuitable environment, but to the competition with the large number of red deer already present in the area. Another experiment of this kind was started in 1951 by the Reindeer Council of the United Kingdom.

It is a well-known fact that reindeer are difficult to keep in captivity and one of the reasons is that they have predilections as regards their diet. The food which is generally considered essential is lichen, and here a small measure of success has been achieved. In fact, however, the food requirements, or rather the reindeer's likes and dislikes, are truly extraordinary. They restrict the distribution of the reindeer, they are a contributory cause of migrations and they have helped in hunting and domestication.

The reindeer being a member of the deer tribe, one would expect it to be a grazer or a browser, or perhaps to specialize in de-barking trees. Meadow grass, foliage and bark are the normal food of deer, but although reindeer take all three, they are curiously 'fussy' and there are certain plants for which they show a strong preference. Some grasses are eaten, like *Poa* and *Festuca*, whilst others are not; the heaths (*Erica*) are avoided, but the cranberry is taken. Among the buttercups *Ranunculus glacialis* is eaten, whilst the globe flower (*Trollius*) is avoided. They do not like the needles of conifers, but are fond of horsetails (*Equisetum*). Moss appears to be eaten only when other food is not available, but lichen are eaten regularly and play an important part in their diet.

Reindeer undertake excursions to the coast in order to feed on various kinds of seaweed, and when the fungus season is on they enter forests in order to feed on this delicacy. In their eagerness to obtain it they neglect their normal food and are apt to lose weight. Even poisonous species are eaten, with the result that the deer get drowsy and are then easily captured. Whilst fungi are not now believed to have a high food value, it seems that lichen contain nutrients in concentration. They contain little water, and sugar-forming substances are present.

In addition, reindeer have more carnivorous propensities than any other ruminant. Bogoras (1904–1909) reports that the reindeer of the Chukchi go for the remains of meat and fish thrown away by man, whilst reindeer of the Samoyeds on the Tas River eat the small fish left on the shore by their owners after a fishing expedition. It is not impossible to train domesticated cattle, horse and even camels to eat fish, but the reindeer evidently eat them of their own free will. Moreover, they accept meat and, strangely enough, are active hunters. It is the lemming which is to some extent pursued by them, and Jacobi reports that the Lapps find it difficult to keep their herds together in years when lemmings are abundant, because the deer start hunting them. In the stomachs of killed reindeer the skins of eaten lemmings have been found, and Jacobi learnt from an old and experienced Lapp that the lemming craze was pronounced only in years when the lichen pasture was insufficient. It has also been pointed out that salt-hunger may be at the root of this peculiar habit and Ehrström (1852) suspects that the seized lemming releases urine, which would be the real reason for the reindeer's desire to catch these rodents.

The gnawing of bone and antler by reindeer is not surprising, for all deer do this. Leather is gnawed by hungry reindeer and the droppings of birds like ducks, geese and capercailzies are titbits popular with reindeer. Well known, of course, is the craze for urine. That it should be of human origin is probably due to the circumstances of domestication. The urine of dogs is not despised, whilst that of their own species appears to be rather less popular. When reindeer reach the shore they do not shrink from drinking sea-water, and salt effervescences are greedily licked.

These peculiar fads of the reindeer are almost certainly the result of an attempt to maintain a balanced diet. A species which throughout most of its life depends on snow for its water supply is apt to make use of every possible supply of salts. But this is not likely to be the whole explanation. It has been suggested by Middendorff (1851) and others that nitrogen compounds are the attraction in flesh, urine and so forth, but lichen contains a fair amount of them so that their food is not likely to be particularly deficient in this requirement. The strangest of all the likes and dislikes of the reindeer is perhaps that, though they are eager to lick the human hand for the sake of the sweat, they are not easily induced to eat any food from the hands of man. But whatever the causes of these idiosyncrasies may be, they have had a determining influence both on the distribution of wild reindeer and of their exploitation by man.

The reindeer is the most gregarious of all the Cervidae as, except for the old males, it is most unusual to find single individuals. The herds which form are small in the forests; whilst in the caribou they vary from a few individuals to a few hundred. There may be more occasionally, but really large herds are observed in the tundra. A hundred and seventy years ago Pallas described how, in north-east Siberia, he first saw a few herds of two or three hundred head each, which were followed by thousands and hundreds of thousands, making one moving mass of animals, ten miles and more across. Their antlers appeared like a moving forest. When crossing the Anadir the animals crowded so closely together that they could not avoid being killed by the natives because they could not even step aside, and the fawns were using the backs of the adults as a bridge. There are many other reports of this kind and there is no reason to assume that the numbers congregating on migrations have lessened since (Fig. 5 : 5). The Magdalenian carving from the cave of La Mairie, Dordogne, provides a vivid illustration of some such herd which occurred 20,000 years ago (Fig. 5 : 6).

Jacobi distinguishes the vjell reindeer, the tundra reindeer and the forest reindeer, which all behave differently as regards migration. The vjell reindeer lives on

FIG. 5 : 5. A herd of migrating wild caribou in northern Alaska

mountain ranges surrounded by country unsuitable for reindeer and they show few migratory propensities. They might leave their mountain tundra to descend to the edge of the forest in spring when plenty of luscious food is available there, and in summer they might even penetrate into the forest in quest of fungi, but their movements depend much on local conditions. It has been reported that in Alaska mountain-inhabiting reindeer descend in winter to the lower levels where better food is available.

The tundra reindeer are found in open tundra as far north as the islands of the north coasts of Siberia and Alaska during the summer. This movement has often been attributed to the plague of mosquitoes, from which the deer try to escape to colder, and hence more northerly, places. But it is equally possible that the rise of temperature drives them north, for the dense coat of the reindeer renders temperatures of as little as 50°F. unpleasant for the animal. In winter the deer return to the

FIG. 5 : 6. Engraving on an eagle bone of reindeer following the leader, Magdalenian of the Grotte de la Mairie, Teyjat, Dordogne, France. The length of the scene is *c.* 20 cm. After Breuil

edge of the forest which affords them protection from the gales. It is particularly the stags that go there, whilst it appears that the hinds often stay behind on the tundra. It has also been observed that not all reindeer take part in these migrations and that a number of them stay behind or stop on the way. They do not, however, always return to the same areas and, after having frequented certain summer pastures or hibernation areas for some years, they suddenly abandon them. This unreliability of the movements of the reindeer causes serious risks to the native tribes who depend on them for food, a fact which in no small measure has compelled these tribes to retain their nomadic habits themselves.

Nevertheless, on these migrations certain routes are used regularly, wherever physiographical features tend to restrict the movements of the deer. The same crossings of the rivers are often used year after year and they are, of course, the most prolific hunting grounds for primitive man. The slaughter which is committed among the reindeer does not easily induce them to avoid the crossings in the following year, though regular use of certain parts of the route for hunting purposes appears occasionally to have caused the deer to choose another route (Fig. 5 : 7).

FIG. 5 : 7. Antlers and other bones of caribou washed up on the banks of a river in northern Canada. This illustrates the large losses suffered by reindeer crossing rivers on their annual migrations

The forest reindeer, which live mainly in woods rich in lakes and rivers, migrate far less than the tundra race. In spring and summer they sometimes move up to the top of the mountains or to the sea coast, perhaps in order to get rid of some of the mosquitoes where a fresh wind is blowing. But on the whole the forest reindeer keep to the wooded areas where the long beard-like lichen growing on the conifers provide them with ample food.

On the whole, many variations are observed in the migration habits of reindeer, and a sharp distinction between vjell, tundra and forest types cannot be made. The fact remains, however, that reindeer are very prone to migrate, and sometimes over distances of hundreds of miles. One reason for these movements appears to be the plague of mosquitoes, horse-flies and other blood-sucking Diptera from which reindeer suffer to an extraordinary degree. Their eyes and nose and other soft and thinly haired parts of the body are often clustered with mosquitoes, and the velvet of the growing antlers covered with a black layer of these parasites. It is conceivable, therefore, that the movement to colder, more northerly districts is an attempt to escape this plague. This is regarded as particularly important for the hinds which drop fawns in the spring. The hinds of the tundra reindeer, indeed, are the first to move out into the still snow-covered tundra, where they give birth to the young in places which are still too cold for the mosquitoes and where the tender fawns are relatively safe.

A second reason may be to escape from the comparatively high summer temperatures, as has been mentioned already.

A third reason may be that the food supply afforded by the tundra is actually more wholesome than that of the forest. It is a fact that the reindeer grow very fat during the summer spent in the tundra, whilst they emerge from the forest in a thoroughly starved condition. The density of the snow cover, which is greater in the forest, may be a contributory cause. Finally, it is not impossible that the change of light and darkness inherent in the arctic summer and winter is an inducement to the deer to migrate. It is conceivable at any rate that in autumn, when the days begin to fade, the reindeer move south, so to speak with the light, as far as they conveniently can, and that in spring the reverse movement takes place.

Whatever the cause of these seasonal migrations, they make it easy for hunters to lie in wait and for farmers to control their domesticated stock. As has been mentioned, the masses of reindeer which move about as a single herd are astonishing. Herds of 100,000 to 200,000 are not exceptional; and where several such herds have joined up their numbers rise to millions, as illustrated by the following report taken from the *Ottawa Naturalist* (1917, p. 109):

He stood on a hill in the middle of the passing throng with a clear view ten miles each way and it was one army of caribou. How much further they spread he did not know. Sometimes they were bunched, so that a hundred were on a space of one hundred feet square; but often there would be spaces equally large without any. They counted at least one hundred caribou to the acre; and they passed him at the rate of about three miles an hour. He did not know how long they were in passing this point; but at another place they were four days and travelled day and night. The whole world seemed a moving mass of caribou. He got the impression at last that they were standing still and he was on a rocky hill that was rapidly running through their host.

By halving [these figures] to keep on the safe side, we find that the number of caribou in this army was over 25,000,000. Yet it is possible that there are several such armies.

It can be shown that the late Pleistocene reindeer of Europe also were seasonal migrants, an observation which is of great interest from the point of view of prehistory. Adult male reindeer shed their antlers late in autumn (November-December), and the females and young ones in late winter and early spring. The relative frequencies of broken and shed antlers, and the sex distribution within these groups, can therefore be used to determine the time of the year when reindeer were present in any one area. In Upper Palaeolithic cave sites of the Dordogne, Lacorre (1951) found that adult male antlers were mostly shed, but those of females and fawns were adhering to the skull. He therefore argued that the reindeer were present in winter only, and the same applies to Haute Garonne, Charente and Poitou, according to Breuil.

On the other hand, several sites farther north have yielded the opposite result. At Tornewton Cave in south Devon and Banwell Cave in Somerset, for instance, Sutcliffe (1957) found that the shed antlers were almost exclusively those of females and young. These caves, therefore, must have been occupied by man at the time of the spring migration. Gripp (in Rust, 1937 and 1943) has shown that the Hamburgian sites of Meiendorf and Stellmoor were occupied in the summer (June to September). This and other evidence suggests that towards the end of the Last Glaciation certain European reindeer performed seasonal migrations from south to north in the spring, and back to the south in the autumn. The south and south-west of France would have been obvious winter refuge areas, whence the herds would have gone north into unglaciated western England (much of the Channel then being dry land) and north-east into the periglacial zone of Germany.

Recently, Bouchud has taken up the question of reindeer movements in south-western France from a somewhat different angle. He studied in the main sites of Mousterian age situated near the Pyrenees and paid particular attention to the dentition of young animals, the age of which can be determined approximately up to about twenty-six months on the changes from the milk to the permanent dentition and the state of attrition of the teeth. Knowing that the fawns are born about May, one can calculate the season. This method is much less precise than that relying on the antlers. In Tornewton Cave, Sutcliffe found a single jaw of a fawn about a month old on the evidence of its dentition. It would therefore have been killed about June. For south-west France, i.e. the Pyrenees district, Bouchud (1954) concludes that reindeer were present all the year round. He admits that there were both forest and tundra forms, but holds that migration was insignificant. Since a mixed population of this kind is poor material to establish whether migrations took place, the northern sites with their evidence for summer occupation have to be regarded as decisive. It may well be that along the Pyrenees, where migration farther southward was not possible, woodland and tundra forms mixed, the woodland race being more or less stationary, the tundra form being the migratory type.

Apart from man, the chief enemies of the reindeer are the wolf, glutton and tiger. One must not forget that the tiger extends far into north-eastern Asia where, north of the Amur, he hunts the reindeer regularly. The glutton is a dangerous animal, especially in the forests. By far the most serious enemy, however, is the wolf. This carnivore depends exclusively on the reindeer near the northern limits of its distribution, such as in the arctic archipelago of North America. Reindeer have been almost exterminated by the wolves on certain islands with the result that the latter starve or emigrate. The wolf remains a dangerous animal when reindeer are domesticated, and the Lapps have to fight this pest regularly. It is significant, however, that wolf and man have somewhat similar practices of following the herds of deer and taking their toll. Since in northern Europe the wolf had been taken into domestication by Mesolithic man, it is conceivable that there is a connection between domestication and the adoption of the dog, a view which the writer is inclined to apply not only to the reindeer but to the sheep and goat.

There is a tendency to regard reindeer domestication as a comparatively late event. Laufer (1917) did so, although Hatt (1919) subsequently pointed out that this view was not well founded. Hatt's material, however, does not go back to prehistoric times. That reindeer were hunted by means of decoy deer (as shown in the Eskimo engraving, Fig. 5 : 8) in the ninth century, as reported by Ohthere, and that

FIG. 5 : 8. Eskimo engraving of reindeer-hunting with the use of a decoy bull that induces the bulls of the wild herd to fight. Whilst concentrating their attentions on their adversary, they are killed with bows and arrows

Chinese chronicles relate that reindeer nomadism in Siberia had reached the stage of regular milking in the fifth century, does not take us back very far. The reindeer mask of one of the horses of the Pazaryk kurgans in the Altai Mountains suggests that riding was practised in the first millennium B.C. (see Fig. 5 : 10). Absence of earlier evidence, however, is not surprising in the case of illiterate tribes living thinly spread over an enormous territory in adverse climatic conditions.

There is no intrinsic reason why reindeer should not have been domesticated early in prehistoric times. In fact, it might have occurred prior to the introduction of agriculture, since nomadic tribes should be perfectly capable of organizing the system of mobile control of the reindeer which is practised even today. It is, therefore, not entirely futile to look for indications of incipient domestication of the reindeer in Mesolithic and Upper Palaeolithic times. Then, as today, the reindeer used established routes on their seasonal migrations. Man then was sufficiently intelligent to practise organized hunting, hunting in disguise and to construct animal traps. Was it not an obvious thing for him to try to control the movements of these deer? It may well be that this control remained slight for a very long time and that the animals were allowed to breed without human supervision. In fact, even today the breeding of reindeer is not always controlled by man.

Bouchud has pointed out that in the reindeer remains from certain caves of south-west France young animals are more frequent than in the herds of domesticated deer. This he argues pleads against domestication, and for selective hunting. This is conceivable. In any case, as his material is mainly of Mousterian age, domestication is unlikely. The Magdalenian and epi-Magdalenian sites are those where evidence of reindeer control might one day be found. Indeed, Pohlhausen (1949, 1953, 1954) has recently raised his voice in defence of early reindeer nomadism. He regards it as probable that at Meiendorf and Stellmoor near Hamburg (Rust 1937, 1943) two-thirds of the number of reindeer were herded, and only one-third hunted. Whether his view is correct remains to be seen. It is conceivable, and it would push the beginnings of the domestication of reindeer back to about 12,000 B.C. and into the final Upper Palaeolithic.

Hatt noticed that certain cultural elements are present wherever reindeer nomadism is practised. These are castration by biting, marking of the reindeer's ear, use of the lasso and the use of urine or salt as a means of attracting and dominating the deer. He argues that since these features are found everywhere they must be the earliest elements. This is perhaps not necessarily so. On the other hand, he is right in suspecting that certain other elements of reindeer-keeping, namely riding, driving, milking and certain methods of using the milk, are late introductions taken over from agricultural cattle- and horse-breeding communities of adjacent southern regions. The question of reindeer domestication in the prehistoric past will be difficult to answer from direct evidence, since bones do not offer reliable characters. An exception is perhaps the antlers of castrated males, which the Lapps are able to distinguish from antlers of uncastrated males in shed specimens. This criterion may become useful in recognizing conditions of domestication, since castration would not be practised unless the species had been subdued. So far no male antlers of the castrated type have been found in prehistoric deposits, but few have been examined with this problem in view.

Another indication of reindeer domestication would be the existence or the presence of sledges drawn by deer. Sledges are known from the Mesolithic onwards; indeed Sirelius maintains that the runners found at Saare Jarui in Finland belonged to a reindeer sledge, since they were too large and heavy for dogs and domesticated horses did not exist at that time. The age of the cultural assemblage which belongs to the Finnish Stone Age is not very certain, and recent workers have doubted whether the interpretation of Sirelius (1916) is conclusive.

From the technological point of view, the reindeer has passed its climax. In the Upper Palaeolithic it became temporarily almost the sole supplier of raw material to Magdalenian man, who used its bones, sinews, skins, fat and antlers (Fig. 5 : 9), quite apart from its flesh providing the chief food. But, so far as we know, the reindeer was still hunted only. When its domestication began, its use did not change until after the reindeer nomads came in contact with settled agricultural tribes. They then learned among other things to use the reindeer as a draught animal and for riding.

The frozen horses found in the now well-known kurgans of Pazaryk (Altai) have provided indirect evidence for the riding of reindeer in the first millennium B.C.

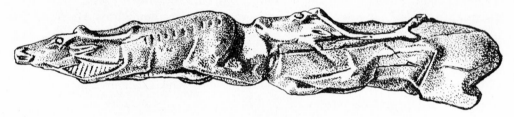

FIG. 5 : 9. Reindeer antler carved to show a pair of reindeer, Magdalenian of Bruniquel (Tarn-et-Garonne), France

One of them wore an elaborate mask which was intended to convert the horse into a reindeer with its antlers. In addition, the saddle was filled with reindeer hair. One gains the impression that this remarkable funeral horse was regarded as a very superior sort of riding reindeer (Fig. 5 : 10). It is the earliest definite archaeological document available for the domestication of the species, and it represents a late stage in the process. Herding must have started very much earlier.

Reindeer-riding is today practised by the Tungus, Yukaghir, Soyot and Karagas in eastern Siberia, and also by the northern Samoyed, Ostyak and Vogul. There are many peoples that do not ride them, for instance the Koryak and Chukchi in the East and the Lapps in the West. Since the saddles used by the Tungus and Soyot resemble horse saddles of Altai, Turk and Mongol pattern, the practice of riding reindeer is evidently based on acquaintance with the horse.

Most riders use the reindeer also as pack animals, including the Tungus and Soyot. The Chukchi and Koryak (who are not riders) do not, nor do the Samoyed. The pack-saddle is of the same Turko-Mongol origin as that used for riding. In the West, the Lapps have a pack-saddle which, according to Hatt, is of quite different construction, so that the practice was here developed independently.

Many tribes that do not ride or pack the reindeer use it to draw the sledge. Among them are the Lapps, Samoyed, Ostyak, Vogul, Koryak and Chukchi. But the driving of reindeer is not a copy of the practices applied to the horse and the cattle as was assumed by Laufer. Hatt has demonstrated that the dog sledge is the prototype of the reindeer sledge. In eastern Siberia the reindeer harness is derived from an ancient type of dog harness.

Fig. 5 : 10. One of the horses from the Scythian mound-burials, Pazaryk, Altai Mountains, fifth century B.C. The horse wears a reindeer mask

The milking of reindeer developed independently in two separate areas, Scandinavia and northern Asia. The sucking of does by herdsmen and children is probably a very ancient custom. But milking and cheese-making are relatively recent. The Lapps almost certainly copied them after they had come into contact with the cattle-breeding Scandinavians, as their words for milk, cheese and implements are of Germanic derivation. The Tungus-Soyot milking industry is of independent origin, and an adaptation from cattle.

These are the chief late developments of reindeer domestication. With increasing facilities for the rapid transportation of food, reindeer-keeping is bound to lose ground.

Nevertheless, its economic importance in northern countries is still great, as shown in a comprehensive monograph by Herre (1955), and in certain circumstances it may even today be regarded as worth while to introduce it to new areas. Some years ago enormous numbers were driven across Canada and fishing Eskimo taught to use them. And the last few years have witnessed the interesting experiment carried out by the Reindeer Council of the United Kingdom to establish reindeer in Scotland.

6

The Goat

SCIENTIFIC NAMES—WILD GOATS—*Capra falconeri* Wagner (markhor; Turkestan, Afghanistan, Baluchistan, Punjab). *C. aegagrus* Erxleben (bezoar; Sind, Persia, Asia Minor, Greek islands including Crete). *C. prisca* Adametz (the supposed wild ancestor of the screw-horn goats with homonymous horns). *C. dorcas* Reichenow (Joura, northern Sporades, possibly feral).

DOMESTICATED GOATS—*Capra hircus* L. (domesticated goat in general, type locality Sweden). *C.h. girgentana* Amschler (screw-horn goat; Sicily). *C.h. mambrica* (mamber goat; Palestine, etc.).

IBEX, NEVER DOMESTICATED—*Capra ibex* L. (Alpine ibex; ranging to Siberia and Himalayas). *C. nubiana* Cuvier (Nubian ibex or beden; Syria, Palestine, Jordan, Sinai, Egypt, eastern Sudan). *C. pyrenaica* Schinz (Spanish ibex). *C. caucasica* Güldenstedt and Pallas (Caucasian tur). *C. primigenia* Fraas (fossil, Palaeolithic caves, Lebanon).

T HE goat was, on the evidence at present available, the earliest ruminant to be domesticated. Much doubt still surrounds its origins, not because the wild ancestors are unknown—for they are known and have survived—but because it is very difficult to distinguish early domesticated from wild goats. Added to this is the lack of distinction between fragments of bones of goats and sheep. In many sites it is impossible to separate these two, with the result that some lists contain the statement that sheep *and* goat are present. Osteologically, skulls and horns are comparatively easily separated. The long bones, however, present great difficulties, at any rate in the domesticated state, and require expert knowledge.

Some time will elapse, therefore, before a distributional picture emerges which shows where the goat and where the sheep was the popular species at the beginning of the domestication of ruminants.

The chief differences between goat and sheep are in their ecological requirements and in the raw materials they supply. The sheep is essentially a grass-feeder, preferring (where available) the protection of open woods. The goat is a browser, preferring foliage of shrubs to grass. In spite of this all goats are well adapted to life beyond the tree-line, both in high mountains and in arid zones, where small shrubs are available in abundance. The goat is probably content with even sparser food than the oriental breeds of sheep, in particular it eats aromatic herbs despised by other ruminants, hence it can penetrate farther into the desert. Apart from the supply of meat which both species provide, the sheep scores in respect of wool and fat, and in the quality of its meat, whilst the goat furnishes more milk. It is possible that the use of milk and its derivatives was first established with the goat, before cattle were domesticated.

Wild goats and fossils

The wild ancestors of domesticated breeds of goat are known to a large extent. By far the most important is the bezoar goat (*Capra aegagrus* Erxleben), which ranges from Sind in the east through Persia and Asia Minor to Crete and the Cyclades in the west. In many parts of this area it has disappeared, and in others it is practically extinct. From Persia it extends into southern Turkmenia (Russian Turkestan) and the Caucasus, and west of Asia Minor a few outposts exist on Greek islands, namely on Crete and Antimilos (Eremomilos) in the Cyclades. The goat from the Isle of Joura (northern Sporades) does not belong here, it requires a separate discussion (see p. 143).

In the late Pleistocene the bezoar extended south into Lebanon, where its remains were found in an Upper Palaeolithic context in Antelias Cave, near Beirut. This goat is a true bezoar.[1] In addition, the bezoar was recorded by Dorothea Bate from the cave called Mugharat-el-Wad on Mount Carmel in Palestine. As the specimen came from a disturbed deposit, its age could not be ascertained; it may have been Palaeolithic or Mesolithic. If Palaeolithic, this find would extend the area of the wild bezoar as far south as the mountains of Palestine. In addition, it was found in the Natufian cave of El Khiam in Israel (Vaufrey, 1951).

This presents us with a problem, for Palestine belongs to the area of the beden, or Nubian ibex, which extends thence to the mountains east of the Nile and south to Ethiopia. Contrary to the view of Schwarz (1935), who associated this animal with the true goat, it is a genuine ibex, for the horn-cores are broad anteriorly.

---

[1] Thanks to the kindness of Père Fleisch, Université Saint-Joseph, Beirut, the writer was able to study the material and to arrive at this conclusion (Zeuner, 1955c). It has been confirmed independently by Hooijer (1961). The *Capra primigenia* Fraas, however, appears to apply to the ibex, which was present also.

Those of wild true goats are keeled instead. The horns themselves repeat, on the whole, the shape of the core, except in the beden which has a more or less distinct keel on the horn, though its core is broad-fronted. The beden thus appears as an isolated branch of the ibex group, separated from its relatives by the bezoar goats of the Greek archipelago, Asia Minor and Persia. There is at present no overlap of goats and ibexes.

The fossil material from the Lebanon caves, however, contains both. In the caves of Antelias and Nahr-el-Djoz they are associated with 'Middle Aurignacian'. Whilst their identification by teeth only is very unsatisfactory, there are a sufficient number of horn-cores proving their presence. More than fifty years ago, v. Fritsch stressed that there were those which are rounded anteriorly, whilst the present writer has convinced himself that three out of four preserved in the collection of the Université Saint-Joseph at Beirut are keeled. Does this imply that the goat and the ibex occurred together in the same localities? From the biological point of view this is very unlikely, for these two species would interbreed. A possible interpretation is that they alternated, perhaps in accordance with climatic fluctuations. It is possible that the ibex indicates more humid conditions than the goat, though today the natural habitats of the two species have everywhere been interfered with by man.

Another possibility, and perhaps the most likely, is that they occupied different altitudinal zones, the beden the higher, and the goat the lower. The beden still survives in fair numbers in Transjordan, mainly on the high mountains in the desert and around the Dead Sea.

One point, however, has emerged, namely that the wild ancestor of the domesticated goat also existed in the late Pleistocene and perhaps the early Postglacial of Syria and Palestine.

Early domestic goats in the East

At the end of the Pleistocene and in early Postglacial times, about 10,000 years ago, Mesolithic hunters and collectors roamed about everywhere. In Syria/Palestine a rich and complex Mesolithic culture appeared, the Natufian. In the cave of El-Khiam, in Palestine, remains of a goat were found by Neuville. In addition, Professor Vaufrey identified a kind of *Bos*, pig, a horse (not *E. caballus*), gazelle and the Nilotic fox. These authors believe that the goat, ox and pig were domesticated, but the evidence is not conclusive. Of the pig, only a single foot bone was found, and of the ox a fragmentary juvenile mandible with milk teeth. These two may well have been wild, especially as they are known as members of the original fauna of Palestine. Of the goat, many bones were found, including three small frontlets with horns showing sharp anterior edges. That they belong to the *aegagrus-hircus* group is thus evident. That they were domesticated is possible, but unproven.

At the moment, the most important evidence for the domestication of the goat comes from Jericho in the kingdom of Jordan. In the Neolithic levels without pottery, dated by radiocarbon at about 6–7000 B.C., scimetar-horned goats are found with cross-sections unlike those of the bezoar. The male horns were gigantic, but much more bilaterally compressed, so that the sub-angular section has disappeared (Fig. 6 : 1). In fact, the cross-section of the core is like that of the Bronze Age goats to be discussed later. The earliest domesticated goat that has been studied thus is a scimetar-horned form (Zeuner, 1955c).

On the other hand, the material obtained in the latest excavations (up to the early months of 1958) contains cores with triangular cross-sections, including one

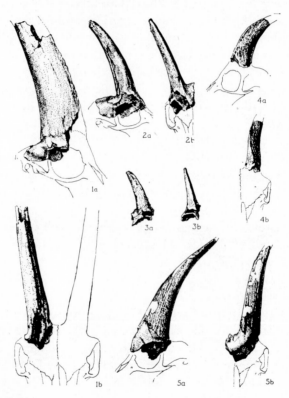

FIG. 6 : 1. Neolithic and Bronze Age goats from Jericho and Cyprus. (1a, b) male right horn-core from pre-pottery Neolithic of Jericho. (2a, b) right horn-core, probably female, from pre-pottery Neolithic of Jericho. (3a, b) right horn-core, probably juvenile female, from pre-pottery Neolithic of Jericho. (4a, b) left horn-core from Early Bronze Age of Jericho. (5a, b) left horn-core, probably male, from Late Bronze Age of Pigadhes, Cyprus.
After Zeuner (1955)

with damage apparently due to keeping the beast in a confined space. The exact archaeological zonation has not yet been completed by Dr K. Kenyon, but on the whole it appears that the 'Neolithic A', i.e. the earlier part of the pre-pottery Neolithic, contains goats very like the wild bezoar. The finds from the Natufian levels of Jericho have not yet been studied. It seems that here, at Jericho, about 7000 B.C. we are very near the earliest known domestication of the goat.

It is possible that the domesticated goat appeared at about the same time or somewhat later at Belt Cave, on the shore of the Caspian Sea. Here, Carleton Coon found bones of goat in late Mesolithic and later levels, and he believes them to be domesticated. Their number, however, is too small to be certain about this, but should further evidence confirm Coon's suggestion domesticated goat would have existed in northern Iran about 6000 B.C.[1] The great distance between the two sites suggests that the domestication of the goat took place rather earlier than this, since it must have had time to spread. In Belt Cave the sheep appears later than the goat, so that a late Mesolithic phase of ruminant domestication may be conceived during which, apart from the dog, the goat was the only animal controlled by man. In Jericho the sheep is not known from the pre-pottery layers at all. That something of this kind is likely to have happened has been pointed out in Chapter 2. The evidence, however, is still unsatisfactory, and there is no obvious reason why the goat should have preceded the sheep, so that one can only state what is known at the present. Thus Jericho remains, for the time being, the earliest site with evidence for domestication of the goat having produced morphological changes.

The earliest domesticated scimetar goat spread over a large part of the Old World during the Neolithic. Except for the Jericho material, however, the cross-sections of the horn-cores have not been described, and it is uncertain whether other Neolithic goats had the flat cross-section of the Jericho type, or the sub-angular one of the wild bezoar, or some intermediate type.[2]

A scimetar goat was identified by Miss King of the British Museum from two Neolithic sites in Cyprus, Khirokitia and Erimi. Whilst she (King, 1953) regarded them as indistinguishable from the wild bezoar, the specimens will have to be re-investigated in the light of the information now available about the cross-sections of the horn-cores. This, in fact, applies to all domestic scimetar goats. If wild, the specimens from Khirokitia and Erimi would demonstrate the former presence of the bezoar in Cyprus, which is conceivable since the species occurs in Asia Minor,

---

[1] This date relies on small samples dated in Chicago, namely early Mesolithic 8004 ± 900, end of Mesolithic 10,560 ± 1200, and Neolithic 8085 ± 1400. The standard deviations are very high, and the chronological sequence is wrong. Evidently some serious error has crept in, though one does not know where. Should the figure of 10,000 years for the end of the Mesolithic be correct, Mesolithic domestication of the goat would have been established.

[2] Except by Reed (1959) who illustrates cross-sections from Jarmo and points out that the domesticated Jericho type with the flat cross-section is present there also. Jarmo, however, though still pre-pottery, is later than Jericho.

Crete and several Greek islands. If domesticated, they would confirm that the Neolithic cultures of the Near East still had the scimetar goat in the fourth millennium, since according to Dr A. Dikaios, the excavator, Khirokitia dates from *c.* 3700 B.C. onwards, whilst Erimi is later, *c.* 3000 B.C.

Turning now to Mesopotamia, the scimetar goat was evidently known there in the fourth millennium, too. The Jamdat Nasr period has provided representations of goats and ibexes in plenty, though most of them are poorly executed brush sketches on pots. It is usually impossible to decide whether goats or ibexes are meant, except where the knots are shown widely separated and at irregular intervals. These may be regarded as bezoar. The pictorial context, however, does not usually suggest domestication. There are many seals showing a tree, with two goats raised on their hind legs in an attempt to get at the foliage. This is exceedingly characteristic of the goat, and it depicts an event common in the south today, where there are trees left for the goats to get at (Fig. 6 : 2). One asks oneself why this scene was regarded as important by the ancient Mesopotamians. Was it because the goat helped them in clearing away scrub and thus in preparing fresh ground for agricultural operations? If so, the goat would be even more responsible for the present desolate conditions of many parts of the Fertile Crescent and of Africa than is generally believed. Moreover, these pictorials would show domesticated goats of the scimetar group, i.e. goats directly descended from the bezoar.

Domesticated goats with scimetar horns appear on vase fragments from Khafaje near Bagdad (3000 B.C.). One of these shows a person feeding two animals with raised tails, one of which has a beard. A similar animal is depicted close by. Though these animals have been interpreted as antelopes, the feeding scene in which even a kid is present suggests that these are domesticated animals. The beard of one, the slightly curved horns of the two animals being fed, and the raised hairy tail, are conclusive evidence that goats are shown.

The discovery of the domesticated bezoar in Mesopotamia in the fourth millennium B.C. was to be expected, for in the adjacent Persian and Turkish mountains the wild bezoar was abundant.

It was found also at Anau in Turkestan, though only in deposits of Period II which occupies the last third of the fourth millennium B.C. and perhaps the beginning of the third. Here the goat is clearly domesticated, and there is no suggestion in the osteological material of its gradual evolution from some wild ancestor. In this locality it appears later than the sheep, as distinct from Jericho and Belt Cave, where the goat is earlier. The Anau goat has a twisted horn of the *prisca*-type to be discussed later. At Tepe Sialk, in northern Persia, the goat is present in Layer 1, which is probably earlier than the Tell Halaf period. But here the remains are regarded as those of wild bezoar.

At Shah Tepé, in northern Persia, Amschler (1931) found that over 15 per cent

Fig. 6 : 2. Goats climbing and feeding on trees in Morocco. It illustrates well the damage that goats do to trees. Photo J. Berlin

of the fauna consisted of goat, and he regards them all as domesticated. The breed, however, cannot be identified. A female frontlet has a short, spike-like, rounded horn-core with no trace of a twist. This does not imply a scimetar goat, though, if the horns of the males were twisted, they were so but moderately. All that can be said about the Shah Tepé goat is that it was smaller than the bezoar or the modern Kashmir goat.

Osteological material has also been studied from Tell-Asmar (Hilzheimer, 1941), at a level of Early Dynastic III age. This is, regrettably enough, the only site in Meso-potamia from which animal remains have at all been collected with care and made available for investigation. This was due to the far-sighted policy of the late Pro-fessor H. Frankfort, and his example deserves to be followed. The fauna comprises in order of frequency the following species: pig, sheep or goat, cattle, onager, dog, gazelle, fish, bird, fallow deer. Regarding the group of 'sheep or goat', a distinction of the species is difficult because most specimens are juvenile. There are three horn-cores of sheep and two of goats, proportions which may well be accidental. The goat cores belong to the twisted type, and apparently one with a fairly close twist, since Hilzheimer refers to it in connection with the 'corkscrew goat' of Ur.

The many pictorial representations from Mesopotamian pots, seals, plaques, reliefs and other objects provide, on the whole, little information. Those of scimetar goats have been mentioned. Those of twisted-horn goats often suffer from the difficulty of distinguishing goat from sheep, for not only are the likenesses poorly executed, but it appears to have been the fashion to breed sheep and goat that looked alike. This fashion is still to be found in the East; in India and in East Africa the two species are often so much alike that they can be distinguished on close inspection only. The head of a goat with horns forming an open spiral is known from Fara near Nippur (c. 2500 B.C.). This, too, appears to be a domesticated specimen, for the

FIG. 6 : 3. Goat's head with screw-horns from Fara, Mesopotamia, c. 2500 B.C. Screw-horned goats appear in the Near East from the Chalcolithic onwards. After Hilzheimer

spiral of the left horn is twisted clockwise (Fig. 6 : 3). The Field Museum expedition to Kish unearthed from the early dynastic levels a specimen which, after reconstruction by Amschler, proved to belong to a 'corkscrew' goat.

On the plaque of Ur-Enlil from Nippur (third millennium B.C.) there appears a goat, recognizable by its little beard and the upturned tail (Fig. 6 : 4). This goat has almost horizontally spreading twisted horns and a long hanging coat of hair. With these characteristics it looks much like a modern Angora goat.

In spite of attempts made by van Buren and others to distinguish ibex and goat in Mesopotamian works of art, it is often impossible to do so. Unlike the Egyptian artists, those of Mesopotamia were bad observers and did not characterize their species and breeds clearly. Occasionally exceptions occur, such as goats with more or less horizontal horns, the tips of which are turned upwards. This is meant to imply the moderately twisted type of horn characteristic of the Angora goat, with its open spiral.

There appears at about the same time a goat with more or less divergent closely twisted 'corkscrew' horns. The best-known example is the 'ram-in-the-thicket' from Ur (2300 B.C.). This type superficially resembles the markhor, a wild goat of Turkestan, Afghanistan and Kashmir, and some authors, like van Buren, consider them as its descendants. An insuperable difficulty of this hypothesis is, however, that the left horn of the markhor is twisted anti-clockwise, and that of the 'corkscrew' goat clockwise. Breeding experiments have shown that the horn-form of the markhor is dominant, so that it is unlikely that the 'corkscrew' of the domesticated form is due either to direct descent from the markhor or to an infusion of markhor blood into a bezoar stock.

In the 'corkscrew' goat of ancient Mesopotamia the horns rise more or less

FIG. 6 : 4. A goat and a sheep shown on plaque of Ur-Enlil, Nippur, Sumerian, c. 2000 B.C. The goat is long-haired and has horizontal, twisted horns somewhat like those of Egyptian Old Kingdom sheep. In this respect it also resembles the goat from the Canary Islands (Fig. 6 : 16)

steeply from the head. This is also the case in some of the Egyptian goats, for instance that depicted on the sepulchral tablet of Sebek-A of the eleventh dynasty (c. 2300 B.C.), but already prior to this date 'corkscrew' goats were known in Egypt, the horns of which usually diverged at a much wider angle. In the tomb of Sahure, of the fifth dynasty (c. 2650 B.C.), such animals are shown, and at Beni Hassan (c. 2000 B.C.) a goat is depicted with twisted horns extending horizontally from the skull. Such variation is to be expected in domesticated species; the angle of insertion of the horns varies quite as much in domestic cattle. That the intensity of the twist varies has been mentioned. It does so to an extent which makes it impossible to use it in the reconstruction of phylogenetic descent. Goats with closely twisted (i.e. 'corkscrew') horns may often constitute a characteristic local breed, but they may well have been developed in several places independently by selective breeding.

The cross-section of the horn-core, however, appears to be a better guide to phylogeny. The writer studied this aspect when investigating the goat remains from the pre-pottery Neolithic levels of the tell of Jericho in Palestine.

The cross-section of male horn-cores of the bezoar, though variable, is characterized by a sharp anterior keel and a sub-quadrangular outline (Fig. 6 : 1). The domesticated scimetar goats tend to have an almond-shaped cross-section. This type first appears in the pre-pottery Neolithic of Jericho, about 6700 B.C. The evidence from Bronze Age deposits in the Near and Middle East suggests that goats with twisted or screw-horns are descended both from the Jericho type and from another closely akin to the original bezoar.

By 3000 B.C. both were present in the Nile Valley. At the 'Neolithic' site of Esh-Shaheinab in the Sudan, excavated by Dr A. J. Arkell and which has been dated at about 3300 B.C. by radiocarbon, the two forms of twisted-horn goats have been found. The abundant one is that with the cross-section of the bezoar type, and the animals were of small size. They were therefore regarded by Miss D. M. A. Bate as closely akin to the modern Nilotic dwarf goat, and the examination of the horn-cores of two such goats has since confirmed her conclusions.

Though on the whole larger, the ancient Egyptian goat belongs to the same group, i.e. its horns have a bezoar-like cross-section. The other type, the horn of which has the almond-shaped cross-section of the Jericho goats (both of the Neolithic and Bronze Age) is represented at Shaheinab by two specimens only, which puzzled Miss Bate, who felt uncertain about their identity. With the large comparative material that has been at my disposal it is now possible to assign them to the Jericho type.

According to Brunton, goat-skins were used in Egypt in the Tasian (Brunton and Morant, 1937) and the Badarian (Brunton and Caton-Thompson, 1928), i.e. in the predynastic period. The majority of these, and those of the proto-historic phase, still had erect ears, whilst later on (as in the sheep) long drooping ears became the fashion. The goat appears to have played a not unimportant part in ancient Egyptian economy. Though the practice of milking has not been proved, the flesh served as food for the poorer classes. As the supplier of water-skins it was then, as today, an important beast. De Garis Davies has described such ancient water-skins. In addition, the skin was used for the wrapping of the dead, a use almost certainly of pre-agricultural origin.

In external appearance the ancient Egyptian goat resembled the sheep in many respects. It was high-legged and short-haired, and it had a long face with a straight nose. Drooping ears became the fashion in the Old Kingdom, but later on erect ears came to the fore once more. Scimetar-horned goats appear to have existed here and there in Old Kingdom times, but by the Hyksos period they had disappeared, although the contrary has occasionally been stated. The shape of the horn was twisted, sometimes approaching the 'corkscrew'. The angle between the horns varied a great deal; and especially in those whose horns were pointing backwards the frontals developed a bulge such as is found in many modern breeds. As a rule, the females were horned, though a few pictorial representations show hornless females and even males.

Perverted horns[1] are not found in goats from Egypt. A pair from Beni Hassan, Tomb No. 201, preserved in the Berlin collection, is not genuine; Boessneck has shown that these horns are mounted on a plaster base.

It is noteworthy that the 'corkscrew' goat has survived to the present day. Amschler identifies it, probably correctly, with *Capra hirca girgentana*, a race of goat discovered by Magliano in Sicily, where the writer has been able to observe it in many places.

It is difficult to say what the occasional presence of scimetar goats means. I have seen no specimens, and pictures of tamed ibex may easily be mistaken for true goats. The twisted-horn goats that reached Egypt with the Chalcolithic, *c.* 3500 B.C., entered the country with other Eastern influences.

What the relation is of the Sudanese dwarf goat to the ancient Egyptian goat is not clear. Most probably it is a variant. The cross-section of the horn-cores is the same in both. Boessneck (1953), however, regards the various statements that dwarf goats existed in Egypt as unconvincing.

FIG. 6 : 5. Humorous papyrus of two foxes or hyaenas leading some goats. Egypt. Brit. Mus. Papyrus No. 10,016. These goats are black, white and piebald, proving that they are fully domesticated

In colour the ancient Egyptian goat varied a great deal. Alongside the single-coloured animals were many piebald ones (Fig. 6 : 5), and this already in the pre-dynastic period.

The modern mamber goat, so common in Egypt and adjacent countries today, with its strongly convex nose, drooping ears and long hair, is not a descendant of the

[1] I.e. specimens in which the left horn is twisted anti-clockwise.

ancient breed. More probably it came from the East, where long-haired goats have always been preferred.[1]

Today the goat is more important than the sheep in Africa, where as a leaf-feeder it finds a livelihood in the most improbable places.

The information available regarding the ancient goats of the Near and Middle East is far from complete. It will not be enough to study specimens stored in the numerous museums, for these do not (with few exceptions) satisfy the modern requirements for stratigraphical details. It will be necessary to collect fresh specimens from carefully excavated sites. What is so far known from the region under consideration appears to suggest that there is only one ancestor, the scimetar-horned bezoar goat. Long before 6700 B.C. this goat had been domesticated, and most of the derived breeds lost the characteristic sub-angular and broad cross-section of the male horn. It may well have been first domesticated in Palestine, though Persia is an alternative. In the fourth millennium goats with twisted horns appear, and gradually become dominant. This change may have coincided with the Chalcolithic stage. By Bronze Age times the twisted horn had become the fashion. The twist itself varies and is not of phylogenetic importance. The twisted-horn goats are descended from two stocks, one being the scimetar-horned Neolithic goat. The other, though twisted, is nearer the bezoar and thus betrays closer kinship with the original stock. The question, therefore, arises whether this group is related to a wild goat with bezoar characters but the horns of which have a twist.

In Western countries the dominant opinion today is that such wild goat did not exist. The Vienna school, founded by Adametz (1914), has, however, maintained that there is fossil evidence for it, and in addition it is possible that the wild goats of the Greek archipelago had horns with more or less distinct twists. This matter, therefore, has to be discussed in some detail, whilst at the same time it provides an introduction to the problem of the domesticated goat of Europe.

Goats in Europe

To understand the history of the goat in Europe it is essential to know whether ancestral wild goats existed anywhere in the late Pleistocene or the early Postglacial. As in the case of the sheep, the answer is not satisfactory and, if the few finds claimed are genuine, the wild goat cannot have been frequent. Moreover, the geographical distribution of true goats and ibexes is not likely to have overlapped much anywhere at any one time. The two species are very closely related and interbreed without hesitation wherever under human influence they have a chance to meet. It may be assumed therefore that the ibex area was nowhere simultaneously inhabited by the true goats under natural conditions unless zones of different altitude made this possible. Ibex are essentially mountain goats that prefer to feed on the vegetation

[1] A primitive mamber with short hair reached the Canary Islands in prehistoric times. (Zeuner, 1959)

of dwarf shrubs above the tree-line. Thence they descend into the forest for protection. Ibex occur (or occurred before they were exterminated by modern fire-
arms) in the mountains of Spain (Sierra de Gredos and Sierra de Guadarrama and
the Pyrenees). Thence they descended to low altitudes during the glacial phases,
presumably simply following their favourite belt of vegetation. In the Last Glaciation
they occurred on the Rock of Gibraltar and were eaten by the inhabitants of Gorham's
Cave which lies at sea-level (Waechter, 1951, and Zeuner, 1953b).

The entire range of the Alps was at one time ibex country; whilst they were all
but extinct some years ago, they are now to be found in several places in Savoy,
the Engadin and elsewhere in Switzerland, Berchtesgaden in Germany and Salzburg
in Austria. Today they live under strict protection. In the cold phases of the Pleistocene, the ibex descended to lower altitudes, either following the belt of alpine dwarf
shrubs that was depressed to only a few hundred metres above sea-level, or even
spreading into the less mountainous country where tundra was flourishing. The
famous Grimaldi caves on the Italo-French Riviera, occupied successively by
Mousterian and Upper Palaeolithic man, contain ibex bones among the food debris,
and so do several prehistoric caves in Switzerland. In France ibex appear to have
occupied the Plateau Central and reached the Dordogne. In Germany an ibex is
known from the Middle Pleistocene of Thuringia. Thus, ibex spread to the lowlands in the glacial phases, but withdrew to the high mountains in interglacial
phases and after the Last Glaciation. They are frequent also in Italian Palaeolithic
caves down to sea-level and as far south as Apulia (Grotta Romanelli). It would be
worth while to study this form in detail with a view to establishing its exact specific
identity.

Other ibex races are found in the Carpathians, the Caucasus, Altai and Himalayas. The ibex is thus an essentially northern form, though it has been mentioned
already that the Nubian ibex, as an offshoot of this group, has penetrated through
Syria, Palestine and Sinai into Egypt and even Abyssinia. Returning to Europe one
finds that it is absent from the Balkan peninsula, Greece (and Asia Minor).

On two occasions it has been claimed that south-east Europe was occupied by
true wild goats in the Pleistocene. This is possible, but neither of the two finds has
been universally accepted. Both are of special interest since they relate to goats
with twisted horns, so that, if genuine, they would suggest a south-east European
origin of at least one group of twisted-horn goats.

The first find was described in 1914 by Adametz and named *Capra prisca*. Schwarz
pointed out, however, that something must be wrong in the interpretation of this
specimen since its type-locality, Zloczar in Galicia, lies in the ibex belt. Several
workers have indeed maintained that *Capra prisca* is a domesticated goat misinter-
preted as of Pleistocene age, especially as it is said to have been associated with what
appeared to be a fragment of horse. The Viennese school, however, adopted *C. prisca*

as both wild and genuine and, at a later date, produced a second find of this kind.

This is a frontlet of a goat with twisted horns described by Sickenberg in 1930. It was found in the loess of Schleinbach in Lower Austria, five metres below the surface. The preservation was loessic, and three metres away from it a molar of a mammoth was recovered. Though the specimen was not collected by the describer himself, one understands why he accepted this fossil as contemporary with the loess.

The morphological characters of the Schleinbach goat, however, are such that it is difficult to accept it as a wild specimen. Evidently, since the question of the existence of a wild twisted-horn goat is at stake, the twist of the horns must not be used as an argument in favour of domestication. But the frontals are pronouncedly bulging, whilst in all goats definitely known as wild their profile is straight or even depressed. Sickenberg stresses this character as one that distinguishes the Schleinbach goat from *Capra prisca* of Adametz. Furthermore, the small degree of divergence of the twisted horns is a domestic feature. Twisting starts with wide, distinctly divergent spirals. In both these characters *Capra prisca* is more primitive than the Schleinbach specimen.

The cross-section of the horn is figured by Sickenberg, unfortunately at the base only. Yet it provides sufficient information to say that the Schleinbach goat did not belong to the group with the almond-shaped cross-section. It is asymmetrical enough to resemble the bezoar, yet it is not sub-angular, thus resembling certain museum specimens of reputedly pure bezoar from western Asia or the Greek islands, the provenance of which, however, is not certain. For what it is worth, the cross-section thus links the Schleinbach goat with those of the Greek islands, about which more will be said later.

What else, then, is known or has been suggested regarding true wild goats in Europe?

Remouchamps is a Mesolithic site in Belgium which has been assigned to the Tardenoisian or the Ahrensburgian culture (Period I of Grahame Clark). From it Rahir reported in 1920 two specimens of goat, without further comment. The associated fauna, comprising reindeer, red deer, horse, *Bos*, arctic fox, red fox, ptarmigan and others, was evidently the food debris (perhaps including the foxes as scavengers) of a hunting community. What these goats were it is impossible to say, but the most obvious interpretation would be ibex.

Nearer to the known distributional area of the bezoar, Bulgaria has yielded remains in the Bacho Kiro Cave and others. These are definitely stated to be wild, and associated with Upper Palaeolithic tools. Details about their morphological characters are not known to the writer.

The existence of a race of bezoar in the southern part of the Balkan peninsula is within the range of possibility.

Fig. 6 : 6. Goat being seized by lion. Scythian-style representation from the Pazaryk tombs, southern Siberia, fifth century B.C.

There remains one other controversial goat to be discussed, that of the island of Joura, north-east of Euboea, in the northern Sporades. This is not the island of Joura in the Cyclades, where the presence of wild goats might be expected because of the closer proximity to Crete and Asia Minor. The Joura goat is well known because of its wild coloration. It is grey, with a dark stripe along the back and with black-and-white fetlocks. At one time it was considered wild, but in 1899 von Lorenz-Liburnau came to the conclusion that it is a feral goat, and thus descended from domesticated stock. This view is now accepted by the writers of textbooks, but its real status may well be more complicated.

Unlike the bezoar group, the Joura goat has horns that are twisted into an open spiral. Its nose is more convex than in the bezoar and the frontals are broader, the latter feature being perhaps a function of the position of the horns. The same characteristics occur in domestic goats, and von Lorenz-Liburnau mentions specifically the Bosnian goat and the saddle goat of the Valais in Switzerland as comparable types. But, apart from their curvature, the horns of the Joura goat have not yet been studied in detail. The only specimen that I have been able to study is a mounted one in the British Museum, the horns of which are securely fixed, so that the cores cannot be examined. The outline of the middle part of the horn itself, however, suggests that an external angle may be present on the core. This is not usually the case in feral goats and would be a primitive character.

That the twist of the horns is so much more pronounced than in any bezoar is not necessarily proof of domestication. The male horns of the goat of Eremomilos, an island near Melos, have their ends distinctly turned outwards, and this may be regarded as the beginning of the Joura twist. The fact that, of all the islands of the Greek archipelago, only Crete and Eremomilos have wild goats suggests that in the past many were inhabited by our species, and it is at least conceivable that these island races displayed a tendency towards twisted horns which increased in the direction of Europe. In other words, the concept of a south-east European wild twisted-horn goat as maintained by Adametz and Sickenberg is not unreasonable, though the material which these authors studied is not conclusive. The Joura goat, therefore, may after all have retained a large proportion of wild blood, in spite of repeated contamination with domesticated stock. The scientific name of the Joura goat is *Capra dorcas* Reichenow, and this name should be used for the primitive south-east European goats, should these prove to represent an original wild race.

The problem presented by these goats is of some importance, since it is conceivable that one or several of the domestic breeds with twisted horns (though not that of Bronze Age Jericho and Cyprus) may be their descendants. In this case, an early centre of goat domestication would have been located somewhere near Greece. This hypothesis is here put forward merely because it deserves attention and in the hope that excavators in the area will in the future pay more attention to the collection of osteological material.

Archaeological evidence from Greece and the islands suggests that both scimetar and twisted-horn goats were domesticated. All records from ancient Greece suffer from lack of scientific information. Clearly, statements like 'sheep or goat', or goat only, convey nothing in an area where the beast occurred in the wild state. From Crete, goat is reported from the Neolithic, but sheep not until the Late Minoan period (*c.* 1600 B.C. onwards). No mention is made of the breed of goat (Fig. 6 : 7).

FIG. 6 : 7. Seal impression from Late Minoan period of Lyttus, Crete, showing a chariot drawn by goats. The animals appear to be of bezoar-type, and it is interesting to note that goats were actually used as draught animals. Photo, Ashmolean Museum, Oxford

Similarly, 'sheep or goat' were used together with cattle and pig by the barley cultivators of the Neolithic A of Greece, and goat is stated to be present in the Neolithic B at Sesklo, and Dimini, *c.* 2500 B.C. Troy I (*c.* 2400 B.C.) had it, like the approximately contemporary Körös culture of Hungary.

On Greek coins a scimetar goat appears at Paros, in *c.* 700–480 B.C. (Fig. 6 : 8), and one with twisted horns is depicted on a coin of Archelaus I, of 413–399 B.C.

(Fig. 6 : 9), as well as on many others (Fig. 6 : 10). The most remarkable likeness of a goat that the classical world has produced is undoubtedly the gold rhyton from Pamagurishte in Bulgaria. It shows the anterior portion of a male goat of the Joura type.

FIG. 6 : 8. Kneeling goat on silver coin from Paros, Greek islands, 700–480 B.C. Scimetar goat looking backwards. Diam. 12 mm. After Head (1959)

FIG. 6 : 9. Silver coin of Archelaus I, 413–399 B.C. Fore-part of a hairy goat with twisted horns of the *dorcas* type. Diam. 10 mm. After Head (1959)

FIG. 6 : 10. Bronze coin from Paros, one of the Aegean islands, fourth century B.C., showing a high-legged goat with shortened, somewhat twisted horns and a long beard. This type is close to the average domesticated type. Diam. 15 mm. After Head (1959)

The spread of the domestic goat into northern Europe

Let us now consider what archaeological evidence tells us about the appearance of the goat in northern Europe. The breed that arrived in the Neolithic was of the scimetar type. It appears to have been imported from the south-east by the Danubian invaders, for horn-cores resembling the bezoar were found in two *Bandkeramik* settlements in Württemberg, south-west Germany. At the Viesenhäuser Hof, Markung Stuttgart, a skull and a scimetar horn-core were found in 1931 and recognized as what they were by O. Paret. The other specimen was found as long ago as 1887 in Bad Cannstatt near Stuttgart, but recognized only in 1933 by Professor Vogel. Both finds probably antedate the Neolithic of the Swiss lake-dwellings.

In the earlier Neolithic lake-dwellings the goat is relatively frequent. Later on, the sheep increases in number at the expense of the goat. This succession has been observed elsewhere. The date of the Swiss lake-dwellings is too late to indicate the actual order of domestication, the cause is more likely to be ecological: the goat as a destroyer of woods being useful in the early stages of colonization, the sheep as a grass-feeder being more valuable once open wastelands had been created by the impoverishment of the soil through primitive agricultural practice.

About the affinities of the early Swiss goats opinions differ. At the sites of Egolzwil 2 and Seematte-Gelfingen scimetar-horned goats are found, at the former they are found exclusively. That these are descendants of the bezoar is evident, and modern investigators like Hescheler and Rueger (1942) subscribe to this view. The Egolzwil goat continued to the late Neolithic and the Bronze Age and has perhaps survived to the present day in some of the Alpine breeds. Links in the chain are provided by the Late Bronze Age site of Zürich-Alpenquai and by the smaller race that occurs in deposits of the Roman period. This group of breeds, therefore, presents no particular problem. It is likely to be descended from the bezoar-like imports of the Danubians, and it came from the south-east. Herre (1943) holds that the modern dwarf goat of Lapland is a direct descendant of the turbary goat.

On the other hand, goats with twisted horns, too, appear in Europe relatively early. The twist is not so strong as to suggest an animal with 'corkscrew' horns, and it is on the significance of this twist that authors disagree. Hilzheimer said that the oldest lake-dwellings have yielded a small goat with twisted horns. But this very statement is disputed. According to Hescheler and Rueger, Hilzheimer has misunderstood the text of Studer's description, and the twist is in their opinion non-existent.

A large goat with twisted horns, however, appears in the middle period of the Swiss lake-dwellings, the so-called 'copper-goat'. This was apparently a true 'corkscrew' goat. After the late Neolithic and the transition to the Metal Ages this type is not found until the Roman period, during which it was perhaps imported anew. It is believed to survive in the saddle goat of the Valais.

The evidence from Switzerland and south Germany thus establishes that the scimetar-horned goat was the first-comer in the Neolithic of central Europe. A goat with twisted horns, however, was present here and there, though rare. In the Bronze Age they became the dominant breed in Austria and Germany, and the scimetar-goat became a relict surviving in some areas, such as valleys in the Alps, and some parts of Scandinavia.

In Hungary, also, it survived at least into the second phase of the Bronze Age. At Tószeg, the scimetar goat occurs in levels v and p, representing the Nagyrév culture of the Early Bronze Age, and in level o, the base of the Hatvan culture. There is no trace of a goat with twisted horns here, and one wonders by what route the latter entered northern Europe, if not via Hungary. It is, however, conceivable that the Tószeg people lost interest in the goat, for not only do sheep gain the upper hand in the course of the Bronze Age, as elsewhere, but goats disappear completely above level o.

In the late Neolithic (*Schnurkeramik*) grave of Föllik, Burgenland, Austria, remains of at least two female goats and a kid were found. One had a horn-core large for a female, with a width of 26 mm. at the base and an antero-posterior diameter of 37 mm. According to Amschler it resembles the modern 'Black-neck' goat of Switzerland with its distinctly, but not tightly, twisted horns. This form, therefore,

FIG. 6 : 11. British domesticated goat from Upper Sandaig, Inverness, resembling the Hebrides breed. Similar types common in Scandinavia. Horns twisted *dorcas*-fashion, hair long. Photo Ronald W. Clark, July 1955

belongs to the *prisca* type, of which it is one of the earliest European representatives. The large size of the female horns distinguishes it from those of the Swiss lake-dwellings, and it may represent a new breed that was slowly spreading into Europe from the East. Similar horns of the *prisca* type were described by Professor Amschler from the Urnfield and later Bronze Age cultures, the Hallstatt and Roman period of Austria. From Olivala some cut and sawn horns are known which must have been used as scrapers. The La Tène oppidum of Manching in Bavaria (Pölloth, 1959) had goats with *prisca* horns. They varied little and were larger than Neolithic though smaller than modern goats in Bavaria. Their number is small compared with the sheep, and Pölloth considers that they were mainly kept by poor people as cheap producers of milk.

As in southern countries such as the Canary Islands (Zeuner, 1959), the goat has become feral in sparsely populated parts of temperate countries. In some areas it has reverted to the wild type in coloration, but the domesticated horn-form remains. In others little change occurred, and it is a mistake to call such goats 'wild' (see, for instance, Baker, 1954, on Wales).

Little would be gained by expanding this survey. Both types of goat have been bred in Europe to the present day, though the moderately twisted horns predominate (Fig. 6 : 11). This is perhaps due to interbreeding, and possibly also to the appearance of a twist in a scimetar breed. Horn-shape is notoriously variable.

FIG. 6 : 12. Small bronze goat of the Imperial Roman period, Rhineland, of the type illustrated and figured in Fig. 6 : 11. Whether this long-haired goat was as short-legged as shown is uncertain. Rheinisches Landesmuseum, Bonn. Reg. No. U1258. Natural size.

Markhor and Circassian goat

There is one group of wild goats with perverted horns, the markhor of Turkestan, Afghanistan, Baluchistan, Kashmir and the Punjab. The horns of the male are large, and the intensity of the twist varies from an open spiral to a closely wound 'corkscrew'.

Fig. 6 : 13. Kneeling goat on silver stater from Celenderis, Cilicia, 450–400 B.C. It is not clear whether it is intended to show a wild or domesticated type, although horns are twisted *dorcas*-fashion. Twice natural size. Author's collection

Fig. 6 : 14. Silver coin of Emperor Philippus II, A.D. 244–249, showing a high-legged goat with short hair and a very long beard. The horns are upright and appear to be of the Circassian type. Twice natural size. Author's collection

This group plays practically no part in the domesticated stock of the West. From the Caucasus through Turkestan into central Asia, however, a domestic goat with perverted horns is found which the Turks brought to Asia Minor and thence to Egypt. This is the Circassian goat (Fig. 6 : 15). Antonius and others have suggested that it is the descendant of the markhor, and it is certainly one of the very few domestic breeds that could have come from that stock. The horns of the Circassian goat are almost vertical and twisted around their long axis tightly, but curiously enough with a very small angle of torsion. Another peculiarity is that the cross-section of the horn-core differs from that of all bezoar descendants in being blunt in front and keeled posteriorly. That this goat is not derived from the bezoar is thus evident. There is as yet no archaeological evidence concerning its history.

Summary

The goat was probably the earliest ruminant to be reduced to the state of domestication. Both the Belt Cave in Persia and the pre-pottery goats of Jericho suggest it. The Natufians of Palestine may have owned goat herds. It remains to be seen whether the goat was followed by the sheep, or *vice versa*, or whether they were domesticated

Fig. 6 : 15. A domesticated goat of the *falconeri* type from Altai Mountains, Kosh Agach steppe on the Mongolian border. Note perverted horns. After Amschler

Fig. 6 : 16. Feral goat from the island of La Palma, Canary Islands. This goat has reverted in most respects to the wild type except that the horns are closely twisted, but very similar goats still occur among the domesticated stock of the Canary Islands. Specimen exhibited in the Museo Canario, Las Palmas de Gran Canaria

simultaneously. It would be premature to be dogmatic on this point, though in several Neolithic localities the goat appears first.

In the course of time, however, the sheep got the upper hand, especially in temperate countries, presumably because its meat is tastier and less tough and because it produces both fat and wool. Moreover, where cattle are kept without difficulty the need of keeping goats as milch animals does not arise. Yet, where pasture is scarce, where thorny scrub dominates over grass, where it is difficult on account of lack of good food and water to keep cattle, the goat becomes an important economic factor (Figs. 6 : 16, 17, 18a, b); for it is able to live under conditions which

FIG. 6 : 17. Digging-hook made from a goat's horn, prehistoric, Gran Canaria, Canary Islands. The use of these remarkable hooks for the tilling of the land was described in the early Spanish records. An unusual example of the goat as a supplier of raw material. Length 20 cm. Museo Canario, Las Palmas de Gran Canaria

do not suit sheep, and it provides milk in quantities which are large compared with the size of the animal. Hence the goat has been kept for preference in the mountainous districts and the dry steppes all over the world.

As a producer of raw materials for technical processes, the goat is less important than the sheep. Its skin has been used since time immemorial for water containers, but it does not supply fat and its hair is usually coarse, wool in the strict sense of the word being rare. Therefore, though goat's hair is used, and no doubt has always been used where available, the sheep became the most important producer of spinning material. One wonders why the goat has not been completely replaced by the sheep. The reason appears to be that as a browser it prefers environments different from those liked by the sheep. It can thrive on desert scrub, and it yields more milk than its relative and rival.

Finally, another possibility has to be considered. Was the goat so important to begin with because it was the original milk-producer, and did its usefulness decline when cattle were domesticated?

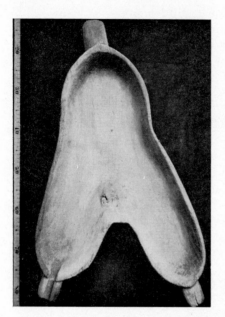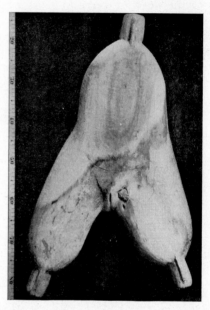

FIG. 6: 18(a). Upper side of a shallow wooden tray having the shape of a goat's udder, possibly used for separating the whey from the cheese. Note the overflow in the left teat

FIG. 6 : 18(b). Underside of the same bowl, carved in the shape of a female human body with an incision suggesting the genitalia. This important discovery was first interpreted by Don Simón Benítez Padilla who considers the wood to be *Euphorbia* sp., which, if confirmed, would further emphasize the connection with 'milk', the arborescent spurges of the Canaries being very rich in milky juice. This utensil displays a most interesting symbolism combining human fertility with goat's milk. That the goat played a part in the fertility cult of the ancient Canarians is described by Bernaldez. According to this authority there existed in the fourteenth century a temple where sculptures of a woman and goat in the sexual act were worshipped by means of libations of milk. Specimen in the Museo Canario, Las Palmas de Gran Canaria

7

The Sheep

SCIENTIFIC NAMES—This list is inevitably elaborate in view of the confusion that exists concerning names of sheep. The system of the wild forms here adopted after careful consideration is closely akin to that of Russian writers like Bobrinskoy and Gromova, and of Ellerman and Morrison-Scott in this country. Subspecies have been enumerated only in so far as necessary, the lists being incomplete. Vernacular names are commonly used for the major groups, but care should be taken to distinguish the arkal or arkar from the urial and from the argali. The Recent sheep have been treated as separate species, but they are very closely related to one another and form what taxonomists call a species-group.

VILLAFRANCHIAN SHEEP—*Ovis antiqua* Pommerol (Auvergne), *O. shantungensis* Mats. (Nihowan, China).

LOWER PLEISTOCENE—*Ovis savinii* Newton (Cromer Forest Bed, England), *O.* cf. *vignei* Blyth (Frankenbach and Lauffen, Württemberg).

UPPER PLEISTOCENE—*Ovis argaloides* Nehring (Čertova Cave, Moravia), *O. ammon fossilis* Pavlov (Transbaikalia).

PROBABLY POST-PLEISTOCENE—*O. mannhardi* Toula (Lower Austria), *O. africana* Pom. (Algeria).

RECENT SHEEP, MOUFFLON GROUP—*Ovis musimon* Schreber 1782. *O.m. musimon* Schreber (Sardinia), *O.m. occidentalis* Brandt and Ratzeburg (Corsica), *O.m. ophion* Blyth (Cyprus), *O.m. anatolica* Val. (Asia Minor), *O.m. armeniana* Nasonov (Armenia, western Transcaucasia), *O. laristanica* Nasonov (Laristan, southern Persia).

URIAL GROUP—*Ovis orientalis* Gmelin 1774 (*nec* Lydekker). *O.o. orientalis* Gmelin (eastern part of Elburz Mountains, Persia; Kopet Dagh Mountains, extreme south-west of Russian Turkestan), *O.o. arkal* Eversmann (arkar or arkal, Ust-Urt urial; lowland steppes between

153

Caspian Sea north of Kara Bugas and Lake Aral, separated from other races by a strip of desert, the Karakum), *O.o. cycloceros* Hutton (Afghanistan, Baluchistan, Waziristan), *O.o. urmiana* Günther (Lake Urmia in western and Isfahan in central Persia), *O.o. erskinei* Lydekker (western Elburz), *O.o. vignei* Blyth (urial; Kashmir and western Tibet), *O.o. punjabensis* Lydekker (Salt Range, Punjab), *O.o. bochariensis* Nasonov (Baljuan, eastern Bokhara).

ARGALI GROUP—*Ovis ammon* L. 1757 (argali; headwaters of Irtish and Amu Darya, eastern Pamir to Tian-Shan and Altai, Tibet, northern Himalayas from Ladak to Sikkim, Mongolia, northern China). *O.a. ammon* L. (Altai), *O.a. polii* Blyth (Pamir). Many other subspecies.

BIGHORN GROUP—*Ovis canadensis* Shaw 1804 (bighorn of the Americans; from the Stanovoi Mountains in Transbaikalia and the mouth of the Yenisei River to Kamtchatka and the Tchukchen peninsula in the Old World, the mountains of western North America, northern Canada, Mexico).

DOMESTICATED SHEEP—*Ovis aries* L. 1758. The names of this group cannot be correlated or synonymized with those for the wild races in accordance with the International Rules for Zoological Nomenclature. Whilst many later writers have refrained from introducing new and invalid names, some are much used in publications on domesticated animals and archaeology, as for instance the following: *Ovis aries palustris* Ruetim. (turbary sheep; Neolithic Switzerland), *O.a. studeri* Duerst (copper sheep; Switzerland), *O. longipes palaeo-egyptius* Gaillard and Duerst (ancient Egypt), *O. jubata* Fitzinger syn. *O. aries africana* L. (Fezzan to West Africa), *O.a. platura* (fat-tail sheep; Levant, North Africa), *O.a. dolichura* (long-tail sheep; Africa, Asia Minor, Arabia, India), *O.a. steatopyga* (fat-rump sheep, Asia) and many others.

NEXT to the goat, the sheep was the earliest ruminant to be controlled by man. That the goat was domesticated earlier is suggested by the evidence at present available, but it is conceivable that the sheep came first in some areas. That the sheep would have been domesticated with the help of the dog, much like the goat, has been pointed out on p. 61. On the whole, evidence favours a western Asiatic origin for the domesticated sheep, though certain breeds are un-doubtedly descended from wild races other than the western Asiatic.

The sheep of the Villafranchian period prove the existence of an ancestral stock which extended from western Europe (*Ovis antiqua* Pommerol) to China (*Ovis* cf. *shantungensis* Mats.). Pleistocene remains are scanty, though interesting. *Ovis savinii* (Newton) comes from the Cromer Forest Bed of East Anglia, an interglacial deposit. Lydekker has already pointed out that this sheep resembled a large moufflon. To the same group appear to belong undescribed remains labelled as *Ovis* cf. *vignei*, from Frankenbach and Lauffen in Württemberg, preserved in the Naturaliensammlung, Stuttgart.

Upper Pleistocene sheep are more numerous, though rarely properly described. It may be regarded as certain that wild sheep occurred in Europe north of the Alps, apparently during one or more phases of the Last Glaciation. They are known from several localities in France, including Chatelperron; from the Magdalenian site of Kesslerloch, Switzerland; from Danzig; and, most important, from the Čertova Dira in Moravia. From this cave, Nehring described a large sheep, which he called *Ovis argaloides*. This comparison with the argali has often been taken to mean that this sheep was an argali. In fact, only its limb bones are known, which are large and point either to a small argali or one of the urial group. It is therefore conceivable that Asiatic steppe sheep penetrated as far west as central Europe along the belt of loess steppe which existed at the time. The moufflon, which prefers the protection afforded by trees, is less likely to have inhabited such an environment.

Late Glacial or early Postglacial wild sheep have occasionally been reported. The most remarkable are those mentioned by Tscherski from the Yana Delta in northern Siberia where they appear to have existed, together with horse, bison and tiger, in the Alleröd oscillation. They are attributed to the bighorn group which still lives in northern Siberia. The Pleistocene of China has yielded *Ovis shantungensis*, the type originally described by Matsomuto (not to be confused with the Nihowan form). *Ovis mannhardi* Toula from Eggenburg (Lower Austria) and an '*Ovis africana*' reported by Pomel from the Grotte du Grand Rocher at Guyotville (Algeria) are probably domesticated specimens erroneously regarded as of Pleistocene Age.

There are four main types of wild sheep still living: the moufflon of Europe, Asia Minor and western Persia; the urial of western Asia and Afghanistan; the argali of central Asia; and the bighorn of northern Asia and North America. No true wild sheep occurs in North Africa or elsewhere in that continent. North African rock engravings, of course, show many sheep and of these the majority are undoubtedly domesticated. The remainder carry no weight since their wild status cannot be proved. It must be pointed out, however, that there occurs in the North African mountains an animal which is locally called the *mouflon à manchettes*, a member of the family Ovidae. It is, however, not at all closely related to the sheep. More properly, it is called Barbary sheep (*Ammotragus lervia* Pallas), and many engravings are known as well as bones, indicating that this species was a common game in prehistoric North Africa. Contrary to many statements in the earlier literature, this species was never domesticated.

The moufflon group

Two areas of moufflon exist today, one in western Europe, the other in western Asia, mainly Asia Minor. The European moufflon (*O.m. musimon* Schreber) has today a curiously restricted distribution, being confined to Corsica (Fig. 7 : 1) and Sardinia. It was at one time believed to have occurred in Sicily, but this statement appears to be due to the mistaking of a Sardinian locality for a Sicilian one. Fitzinger (1860) reported about 100 years ago that wild sheep occurred in quantity on the mountains of south-eastern Spain. This record is less easily dismissed, since Blyth, in 1841, also refers to moufflon-like sheep on the Iberian peninsula, with the following words: 'It is sometimes stated, but I do not know upon what authority, that a few of these animals are still found upon the mountains of Murcia.' But there appear to be no other records, whilst in those particular mountains the Spanish ibex is abundant which, with its comparatively short horns, may have been mistaken for a wild sheep.

FIG. 7 : 1. Moufflon ewe from Monte Cinto, Corsica. This specimen carries small horns, but other ewes are hornless. Photo Lutz Heck

The complete absence of wild sheep from the Continent of Europe is a curious matter. It has greatly contributed to the exclusiveness with which the urial-origin of all European domesticated sheep has been claimed. Yet there are north-west European and African breeds showing unmistakable moufflon characters. This point will be discussed later on. With a shoulder height of about 65–70 cm. the European moufflon is the smallest wild sheep. The back and the sides are dark reddish-brown, with a blackish median line from the neck along the back, gradually fading out. In winter the older rams have a conspicuous white patch on each side. This is commonly called the saddle-patch, though the two areas never unite across the back. This patch occurs on other moufflon, but in no other sheep. In front of it a vertical dark line is commonly present. The underparts are of a lighter colour, and become whitish in winter; they are often marked off by a black line. The tail is short, with twelve vertebrae, and the necks of the rams carry a dark ruff on the underside (Fig. 7 : 2).

FIG. 7 : 2. Moufflon herd in London Zoo. Though they are shedding their coats the colour pattern is already visible, including the black line along the side of the belly. The general colour varies from a light brown to almost black. All have black horns. Note that moulting occurs in patches which may have suggested the use of wool to early man (see text). Photo F.E.Z.

The horns of the European moufflon are curved in a circular fashion (ammon's horn). The tips are either turned outwards in the normal way (this appears to be the rule in Corsica) but in other specimens the tip turns inwards towards the neck. This twist of the horn is called 'perverted', it is comparatively frequent in Sardinia. About 50 per cent of the Corsican ewes have horns up to 20 cm. long, whilst the remainder are hornless. The horns of the ewes and of the young rams have a sharp inner frontal edge, a condition which German writers call *Ziegenhörnigkeit* ('goat-hornedness').

In Sardinia hornless ewes appear to dominate. I owe this important information to Dr Lutz Heck; it will be seen later on that the frequent occurrence of horns in moufflon ewes weakens the argument that all European domesticated breeds must be descended from the urial.

It is interesting to note that the moufflon have established themselves well in many forests of central Europe. About 1840 the first specimens were transplanted from Sardinia to the deer park of Lainz in Austria by Prince Eugen. This original colony was used to start a similar one in Hungary, and most of the German moufflon are derived from the Hungarian, i.e. originally Sardinian stock.

In recent years, however, numbers of Corsican specimens have been added. Lutz Heck estimated the number of German moufflon at between 10,000 and 15,000 in 1945; with this one should compare the 300-odd wild specimens of Corsica, and the Sardinian stock which is hardly larger. There are other introduced herds in Holland, Luxemburg, Switzerland, Italy, Poland, the Carpathians, Yugoslavia, Rumania and Crimea.

The moufflon have taken to the European forests as if they were their natural habitat. Heck points out that although they feed on grass, moufflon are fond of the protection of open forests. This is a condition which is found in most central European forests, in which the pine is an important tree. Moreover, grazing is usually available in such forests. It is a misconception to regard sheep in general as steppe animals. The Cypriot moufflon live, like the European, in open woods, and Bobrinskoy pictures the Afghan urial in the same environment. The Ust-Urt urial (or arkar), however, and many races of the argali live in the steppe and semi-desert.

In Cyprus, Asia Minor, Transcaucasia and parts of Persia the oriental moufflon is found (*O.m. ophion*, etc.). On Cyprus it is very nearly as small as the European form (Fig. 7 : 3), but on the Asiatic continent it attains to a height of over 80 cm. In coloration it resembles the European form. The saddle-patch is present in winter and the male animal with its dark, reddish-brown coat, the black lines, the saddle-patch and the white feet presents a beautiful picture. The females are of a lighter brown, and the saddle-patch is very indistinct or absent. In summer both sexes are much paler, and the coat becomes sleek.

The horns form open circular spirals and are pronouncedly perverted, so much so that large horns injure the neck. The females are hornless, at least in Cyprus where I have ascertained it. There are still about 300 Cypriot moufflon in the Stavros Forest of Cyprus. They are usually seen in small groups. The maximum size of a flock observed by Mr Kamitsis, the forest officer, is seventeen. But on one occasion they did not hesitate to join a large herd of goat, so that they appear not to be averse to larger congregations. The Cypriot moufflon feed mainly on grass, though they spend most of their lives in forests (with little undergrowth).

The oriental moufflon is not generally believed to have produced domesticated sheep, though there is reason to suspect that some breeds are descended from it. It

Fig. 7 : 3. Male of Cypriot moufflon in the Stavros
Mountains, Cyprus. Photo F.E.Z.

is as short-tailed as the European form. Its distribution covers a considerable portion of the western Asiatic mountains adjacent to the Fertile Crescent. Almost the whole of Asia Minor once had it, and it extended both into Transcaucasia and into central Persia (Isfahan) and southern Persia (Laristan). The last-named locality, however, harbours a form which may be regarded as a distinct species (*Ovis laristanica* Nasonov). Thus, sheep of the moufflon group at one time occurred all along the northern mountain fringe of Mesopotamia.

The Urial group
The ancestor of the largest number of domesticated breeds is probably the urial (*Ovis orientalis*, Gmelin). It occurs from Transcaspia through Turkestan, northern Persia and Afghanistan to western Tibet and the Punjab. Like most other wild sheep it is partial to mountains, but on the Ust-Urt plateau, between the Caspian

159

Sea and Lake Aral, its subspecies *Ovis orientalis arkal*, the 'arkar' (*sic*) or Ust-Urt urial (Fig. 7 : 4) occurs in the steppe. The present restriction of sheep to mountainous areas is perhaps to some extent the result either of persecution or of absorption of lowland races into domesticated breeds. The lowland urial of Ust-Urt undoubtedly represents a likely ancestor of some domesticated sheep, in so far as environment, manner of life and even certain characteristics of the body are concerned.

FIG. 7 : 4. Male urial from Ust-Urt region. Note the flattened anterior face of the horns and absence of moufflon saddle-patch. Photo Lutz Heck

These sheep stand from 80–90 cm. high. Their horns are large, strongly wrinkled and curling forwards by the sides of the face, ammon-fashion. They usually do not form much more than one complete turn, and the tips are turned slightly inwards or outwards. In the Ust-Urt urial the two front angles of the horns are very pronounced, giving them a flat surface. The females have short upright horns.

Urial are greyish brown in winter, and reddish or fawn in summer with whitish underparts. A ruff of black stiff hairs often adorns the throats of the rams. Their horns are whitish and thus quite distinct from the black moufflon horns.

The urial is the only sheep which according to Lydekker (1912) had a slight tendency to have a longer tail, though in the descriptions of the wild races it appears as short. Hilzheimer (1941), too, in discussing the sheep from the Mesopotamian site of Tell Asmar, holds that the tail of the urial is comparatively long (10 cm.), compared with the oriental moufflon, for which he gives a length of at most 3–4 cm.

Both values appear too short, but since much depends on the method of measuring, the proportional difference may be accepted.

In northern Persia and adjacent Turkestan the area of the distribution of the urial comprises well-known early Neolithic settlements. As a game animal it occurred at Anau and Shah-Tepé, and presumably at Belt Cave also.

The Argali

The argali (*Ovis ammon* L.) must not be confused with the arkal, a race of the urial. It is a very large sheep with a shoulder height of up to 120 cm. and occurs farther east and north-east than the urial, ranging from Bokhara through the Altai Mountains and Tibet to northern China. It has certainly contributed to the domesticated stock of India and the Far East, but in connection with the origins of sheep-breeding it is of subordinate importance. The horns of the argali are very large and strongly wrinkled, turning forwards by the side of the face in a spiral which often forms more than one complete circle, their tips pointing outwards. The horns are particularly thick at the base, where they touch in the rams, and the ewes are normally horned also. Argali are pale-coloured and tend to show much white on the hind quarters. The tail is very short.

The Bighorn

The bighorn (*Ovis canadensis* Shaw) is the only wild sheep which can safely be excluded from the ancestry of domesticated stock. It stands about one metre at the shoulder. The skull is relatively short, and the orbits are very prominent. The horns are comparatively smooth, apart from lines of growth, and the front outer angle is strongly developed. They form about one complete circle and the tips point outwards.

These sheep range from Mexico to Alaska, and in northern Siberia westwards to the mouth of the Yenisei.

Characters of domestication

The literature on the domestication of the sheep is voluminous. Much speculation has entered into the discussion, usually certain tenets being adopted and believed to be correct. Among the supposed domestication characters are the presence or absence of horns in the females, length of the tail, quality of the coat and hair colour.

Instead of discussing the numerous views that have been held concerning the origin of domesticated breeds, it is here preferred to start from the wild species and thus to look for those domesticated breeds that can, with some degree of probability, be derived from one or the other of the wild forms, considering the remainder of the domesticated stock as of uncertain origin. Gradually this category will be reduced as research continues.

All domesticated sheep are descended either from the moufflon, the urial or the argali. Though these are usually treated as species for the sake of convenience, they are not only extremely closely related to each other, but connected by intermediate forms.

What, then, distinguishes domesticated from wild sheep?

Wool. To the European observer the most striking characteristic of the domesticated sheep is its thick coat of wool. This is largely due to the almost universal adoption of the Merino or some other wool sheep. There are, however, many non-European domesticated races with a normal coat of hair concealing the short wool, whilst the winter coats of wild sheep have quite normally dense wool which is long enough on the body to make the hair inconspicuous. Since sheep-breeding appears to have originated in parts of western Asia, where the winters are very cold, the selection of individuals with unusually long wool and the breeding from them of a wool sheep would have been a comparatively easy matter. Hair has by no means disappeared even in European breeds, primitive ones like the Soay having retained long hair on the neck, whilst many tropical breeds have sleek coats of hair. A few breeds are entirely naked (Fig. 3 : 1).

The presence of wool, therefore, is a matter of degree. It is best developed in the wild sheep of snowy winter climates. In these, however, it is present in abundance, and there is no need to assume that the discovery of the use of wool was due to a special act of human intelligence. The winter coat is shed in patches, sometimes of large size. The writer has himself plucked such patches. They consist mainly of matted wool, with a small amount of hair. No early sheep-breeder could have failed to notice the useful qualities of this material.

If he was already familiar with the art of twisting vegetable fibres into threads, he would have quite naturally proceeded to spinning wool, obtaining his crop in the first instance from the moult of his animals. On the other hand, if he was not acquainted with that art, the making of felt would have suggested itself. The fact that there is a large area of central Asia in which felting is extensively practised appears to indicate that in these parts of the world spinning and weaving were preceded by felting. Neither felting nor spinning is tied to agriculture; both may well have begun in pre-Neolithic times and even initially have been based on crops obtained from game animals.

Evidently, once the stage of purposeful domestication had been reached, selection would have been applied in order to develop prolific wool producers. In hot countries, however, and in those where vegetable fibres were preferred (Old Kingdom Egypt, for instance), sheep with little wool were kept.

Long tail. A very curious feature present in many domesticated sheep is the long tail.

All wild sheep have extremely short tails with not more than thirteen[1] vertebrae. There are domesticated breeds with a normal short tail, such as the Soay and Faroes breeds, whilst others have up to thirty-five vertebrae, the tail being long enough to trail on the ground. Our modern wool-sheep belong to an intermediate group, though docking is practised to a large extent in order to avoid excessive soiling of

FIG. 7 : 5. The vertebrae of the tail of a Soay sheep. After Ewart

the tail. In dry countries, however, sheep can be seen with long thin tails dangling down almost to the ground like a limp piece of rope. Some of the long-legged African group belong here.

Fat tail. Great length is not the only remarkable feature observed in the tails of some domesticated breeds. Often an astonishing amount of fat develops on the tail or near it. The long tail can at the same time be fat (*O.a. dolichura*), as in the sheep described

[1] The number is variously given as twelve or thirteen. This depends on the presence or absence of the vestigial terminal vertebra (Fig. 7 : 5).

by Herodotus (III, 113) from Arabia which carried their tails behind them on little carts (Fig. 7 : 6). This contraption for the conveyance of a delicacy much coveted by the breeder has continued to the present day. It was depicted by Rudolf the Elder in his *New History of Ethiopia* in 1682 and it is still used today in some parts of India and Asia Minor.

FIG. 7 : 6. Long-tailed Eastern sheep carrying its tail on a small cart. First illustrated in Rudolf the Elder's *New History of Ethiopia*, A.D. 1682

Another group of sheep very popular in North Africa and the Levant is the broad fat-tailed sheep (*O.a. platura*). Its tail is actually of medium length, but the tip curls upwards, whilst two large lumps of fat grow on the sides of the basal portion. In Tunisia and again in Palestine these sheep are bred almost to the exclusion of others. Tails can attain a weight of ten pounds, whilst the carcass of the same animal may weigh no more than fifty or sixty pounds. To this group belongs the dumba sheep of India and central Asia, and it too was known to Herodotus from 'Arabia'.

From certain fat-tailed sheep appear to be derived the fat-rumped breeds of Asia, in which the tail bones are much reduced, whilst the deposition of fat is concentrated on the buttocks (*O.a. steatopyga*). These variations in the condition of the tail are unique among domesticated animals. They are particularly surprising in view of the fact that there is no variation in the tail of wild sheep, which is always short. Antonius remarks that only the tail of the Ust-Urt urial group has a slight tendency to be longer. Should this be correct it would provide additional evidence for the derivation of the long-tailed domesticated breeds (including the fat-tailed) from the urial group. My attempts to verify this statement, however, by counting the tail vertebrae on museum material have been unsuccessful, since the tails are almost never completely preserved on skeletons of wild specimens.

One would expect the deposition of fat to be a specialized character that appeared late in the history of the domestication of the species. Yet they are depicted already on the famous Peace Panel of the Standard of Ur of about 2400 B.C. (Fig. 14 : 5).

Lop-ear. A character of domestication which sheep share with some goats, pigs and rabbits is the lop-ear. In wild sheep the ear is very small and stiff. With African domesticated breeds in particular the lop-ear is the fashion (Fig. 7 : 7). It appears to have been popular in ancient Egypt from Old Kingdom times onwards, though the ears were in those days still smaller than in many lop-ear breeds of modern tropical Africa.

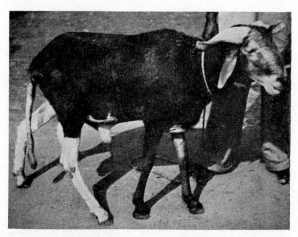

FIG. 7 : 7. Hair-sheep from the Sudan, intermediate between Haussa and lop-eared types. A long-legged breed with horizontally twisted horns of primitive shape and a dewlap. Photo Lutz Heck

Convex nose. A strongly convex nose, the ram's or Roman nose, is often associated with the lop-ear. Sheep of this type spread over northern Africa in late prehistoric times, apparently from Egypt. But the convex nose is not entirely confined to domesticated breeds, moufflon rams have it occasionally. It is possibly connected with a shortening of the jaws. If so, its further development would be the result of the process of face-shortening that has occurred in nearly all domesticated animals.

Shape of horns. In wild sheep the shape of the horn is relatively constant in each race, and it is for this reason much used in scientific diagnoses. Even so, however, the best-known races show enough variation to suggest that a great many varieties would arise as soon as natural selection is impeded by the breeder.

One would therefore expect the perverted horn of certain moufflon to re-appear frequently among domesticated sheep. In fact, they are extremely rare, and if present almost prove descent from a moufflon (p. 157). It is, on the other hand, conceivable that man selected intentionally animals with everted tips, because perverted horns are apt to injure the back and are thus undesirable.

The horns of domesticated breeds are often much smaller than those of wild sheep and sometimes absent even in the rams. But there are many breeds, among them some of the most popular modern ones, of which the rams are equipped with respectable pairs of horns. A fairly general difference between large domesticated and wild horns is that the latter rise much more steeply. One might say that domestication has caused a weakening of the horn base so that it tends to drop away to the side, instead of rising steeply.

Horns describing more than one complete circle are, among the wild sheep, found only in some races of the argali, especially in Poli's sheep. In domesticated breeds such horns are frequently met with.

The shape of the horn may be interpreted as the result of the interaction of two growth rates; one being the rate of curvature, the other the longitudinal rate of growing away from the skull. If the latter is great, a long open spiral will be formed as in *O.a. polii*, and if it becomes very fast the horn assumes the shape of a twisted stick (screw-horn), as in the zackelschaf of the Balkan countries (Fig. 7 : 8).

FIG. 7 : 8. Zackelschaf, a south-east European breed with very long screw-horns, still found in Hungary, Rumania, etc.

The ewes are either hornless or horned. When horns are present they are invariably much smaller than in the males. Since it is a universal rule in the males that very strong horns develop an outer frontal angle in addition to the inner which is always present, weakening of the horns implies a flattening of the curvature corresponding to the outer frontal angle. In other words, weak horns tend to resemble those of goats, in which the inner frontal angle only is developed. This condition is occasionally called *Ziegenhörnigkeit* (goat-hornedness) by German writers. Unfortunately, others use the same term for open spiral horns, which grow horizontally away from the head. It is therefore advisable to avoid the use of this term altogether.

It is regarded as unlikely that wild races whose females are hornless would have domesticated descendants, the ewes of which have horns. This argument was used to prove that the Neolithic sheep of the Swiss lake-dwellings could not be descended from the moufflon. Although it may be correct to derive this sheep from the urial group, the females of which have horns, the argument must be used with great caution. Many ewes of the European moufflon are horned (see p. 157). Those of the Cypriot moufflon appear to be hornless, but it is extremely unlikely that the moufflon races of the Asiatic mainland, which approach the urial in their characters, should all be entirely hornless. Unfortunately, museum collections are singularly deficient in female specimens whilst they abound in capital rams—the result of big-game hunting.

A curious feature is the appearance of supernumerary horns. Four-horned sheep are frequent among the short-tailed breeds of western Europe, especially the loaghtans of the Isle of Man and also the hunia of Tibet.[1] When four horns are present, the lower pair is usually bent downwards semi-circular fashion, whilst the upper pair is more or less straight and rises steeply. But such horns must almost be regarded as pathological, for they are nearly always irregular, varying in size, direction and shape on the two sides of the head. Occasionally, additional horns are present. Up to seven have been observed.

The one-horned sheep known as the unicorn barwal of northern India, on the other hand, is the product of a surgical operation. It is fully described in Lydekker's *The Sheep and its Cousins*, so that it suffices to say that a red-hot iron is applied to the horn-sheaths. After treatment of the wounds the horns continue to grow in a fused condition arising from the middle of the frontal as if they were one.

Colour of hair and wool. The European observer is so used to seeing white sheep that even professional archaeologists have in recent years reconstructed Neolithic sheep in a garb of white wool. It is more likely that those sheep were more or less of a uniform brown.

In the domestic sheep (as in most other domesticated mammals) two types of colour distribution are observed. One is evidently derived from the wild coat, usually by simplification, one or more of the pigments present in the wild coat having dropped out. The extreme of this development is monochrome coloration, but it rarely goes so far as to extinguish the shading in the face, particularly round the muzzle, and on the feet.

The other type of colour pattern is characteristically confined to domesticated

[1] The earliest appear in the Bronze Age of Europe, according to Ewart.

animals (except for a few, like the Cape hunting-dog). It is the piebald or skewbald pattern of irregular patches of brown or black and white. The extremes of this group are monochrome white, brown or black animals.

Evidently the first group should contain the more primitive breeds. There are indeed domesticated breeds of sheep still exhibiting a colour pattern closely resembling that of wild moufflon. Strangely enough, they are confined to Africa south of the Sahara (Guinea and Abyssinia).[1] No instance has come my way of the preservation of the colour scheme of the urial or the argali. It might be argued that the plain brown or whitish breeds with dark heads are a case in point, but the distinctive features of the urial pattern, the black stripe or patch behind the foreleg, and the white belly, appear to be unknown in domesticated breeds.

A uniform brown, with a darker head and neck, however, must be regarded as a primitive type, as it is found in the Soay and other sheep that have primitive characters besides this, and it is at least indicated in some urial races, though their basic colour is much paler.

The colour scheme of the *heidschnucke*—black and brown face and legs, with whitish wool—is characteristic of short-tailed breeds of the primitive type, but black legs do not occur in any wild sheep. Usually, they are pale or striped. As to whitish wool, this is not to be surprised at. In many mammals the undercoat of wool is naturally whitish, so that if it grows excessively at the expense of the hair a whitish coat of wool will emerge. Since the wool of wild species is often provided with dark tips, the rather rarer dark wool of sheep is also easily explained. The dark legs, however, remain a problem. I have consulted many workers on sheep, including several Russian ones, without finding any indication that dark legs are characteristic of a wild race. The white belly, however, appears to be absent in a few Eastern forms. The feet of the urial and the argali, however, lack the distinctive black-and-white pattern of the moufflon group. For what it is worth, this may be taken as an indication that broadly speaking the moufflon has contributed little to the breeds of domesticated sheep.

It appears, therefore, that wild coloration was one of the first characters to disappear when sheep began to be domesticated, and that fashion, and possibly superstitious views about the inherent qualities of certain colours, determined the breeders' selection.

Whilst wool sheep of the medium-tailed group are mainly white, dark faces and legs are relatively common. Light-brown colours are frequent in tropical breeds, and they may be a reminder of the fawn or reddish summer coat of many races of Asiatic moufflon and the urial, especially where they are associated with sleek hair.

Otherwise, black, white and skewbald or piebald are the most popular colours, and often the local requirements are very rigid. It appears that special colour types

---

[1] Apart from some Soay sheep, see p. 189.

and patterns were regarded, at an early stage, as an essential expression of the high qualities of a breed.

On the whole, moufflon have horns of a blackish colour, whilst in the urial and argali groups they are usually pale-coloured. Since many of the commoner breeds, particularly European ones, have pale-coloured horns, this may be taken to indicate affinity with the urial group rather than the moufflon, whilst black-horned sheep may be suspected of having moufflon blood.

Size and proportions. Broadly speaking, high-legged sheep are common in arid countries where the animals have to be continually on the move in search of food. This character is probably easy to select, and so has arisen repeatedly, though it is paralleled by the corresponding difference between the more short-legged moufflon and the longer-legged urial.

Similarly, body size is extremely variable. Dwarf sheep are the old Shetland breed, which is only about 45 cm. high, and the Cameroons sheep which are hardly taller. Such small sheep are suitable to be kept in confined spaces; they might almost be called house-sheep.

On the other hand, very large sheep are too strong to be easily handled in the shearing process, hence the medium-sizes are everywhere the most popular. It is certainly impossible to use size or proportions of the body as an argument in tracing the ancestry of domesticated breeds, except in so far as in the early stages sheep which were smaller than their wild ancestors are likely to have been the rule, once penning was introduced.

The hypothetical prototype of domesticated sheep

From what has been said about the races of wild sheep and what is suggested by surviving domesticated breeds, it appears likely that two prototypes of domesticated sheep have to be assumed, one belonging to the moufflon group, the other to the urial.

In both, the hair coat would have been sleek, reddish in summer, and with dense wool underneath the hair in winter. The moufflon type would have been the more colourful: reddish brown with a white saddle-patch in winter, a horizontal black line separating the white belly from the brown flanks, and with vividly coloured white legs marked with black, and with blackish horns. The urial type would have been paler, but equipped with a black vertical streak or patch behind the shoulder, and with pale horns. Both types of ancestors had a ruff on the neck, but in the urial it was much more conspicuous.

It appears that most wool-sheep are derived from urial stock, whilst a number of hair-sheep, both archaeological and surviving, suggest affinity with the moufflon group. The geographical distribution of these two types is important. The moufflon type originally occupied parts of western Europe, Cyprus and Asia Minor and the mountain ranges bordering on Mesopotamia and the Persian Gulf. The urial group, on the other hand, occurred to the north of the moufflon zone, from the Caspian Sea to Baluchistan and Bokhara. The early Mesopotamian sheep of the urial type, therefore, must have come from beyond the moufflon belt. This suggests, and is in part borne out by archaeological evidence, that a very early centre of sheep domestication lay in the north, possibly as far north as Bokhara or the Aralo-Caspian steppe. There indeed, where the winter is intensely cold, the use of wool would have been discovered at an early date.

On the other hand, the moufflon stock appears to have continued to be used mainly for meat supply and milking. They are bound to have been crossed with urial descendants on many occasions, though part of this stock reached Africa, beyond the Sahara, where it has managed to survive to the present day.

At a very early date modification, and mostly simplification, of the colour pattern took place. Either the horns retained the shape they had in the wild ancestors, or increased outward growth produced screw-horned types. The ear was at first small and stiff, as in predynastic and early dynastic Egypt, but lop-ears subsequently became common. The increased growth rate of wool on the body (not at first on the neck and head) profoundly changed the external appearance of the wool breeds. Finally, the length and shape of the tail were strongly affected in many descendants of the urial to which, in all probability, all medium and long-tailed breeds belong, unless this character was passed on to the moufflon stock by crossing.

It has been said before that the first control of wild sheep may have been effected with the aid of the dog well back in the pre-agricultural stage of economic evolution. The first uses would have been meat, skin and possibly milking. The idea of using wool may well have occurred to such primitive sheep-breeders when they noticed the wool coming off in large wads during the moult, in a naturally felted condition. The manufacture of felt, which is still popular in central Asia, would thus have been initiated by the observation of the moulting process.

As I have pointed out before, however, the spinning of wool is likely to have been practised first by peoples who were already familiar with the spinning and weaving of plant fibres. Plant fibres are long and straight, which primitive wool is not, and there is a continuous line of evolution conceivable from the making of mats of sedges or grasses to the weaving of cloth from prepared and spun vegetable fibre.

It is in the light of this knowledge of the wild ancestors that the archaeological evidence for the domestication of the sheep has to be viewed.

Archaeological evidence

The archaeological evidence for the domestication of the sheep is purely osteological for the earliest period. For the later periods, pictorial evidence is plentiful and on the whole critically studied. One cannot say this, however, regarding the bones; very few sites indeed have been studied by palaeontologists. Where this has been done, both the investigator and the excavator have reaped ample reward. The earliest sites for domesticated sheep lie in western Asia, which, therefore, is here considered first.

Western Asia

Apart from Jericho, in the Jordan Valley, the animal remains of which are being investigated, the Belt Cave in northern Iran, near the coast of the Caspian Sea, is the earliest site that has produced domesticated sheep. Carleton Coon (1951) distinguished in this cave three major periods of occupation, as follows:

Date B.C.	Period	Layers	Number of sheep bones	Percentage of total bones
	ceramic Neolithic	1—7	15	21.1
5000				
	pre-pottery Neolithic	8—10	12	36.4
6000				
	late Mesolithic	11—17	25	2.7
	earlier Mesolithic	18—28	0	0

The first evidence for the presence of sheep appears during the late Mesolithic. The people were still hunters, their chief game being gazelle and ox. Wild sheep and wild goat were hunted also, and there is no evidence that lambs were slaughtered. It is, however, in this period that, according to Coon, the herding of goat may have begun (see p. 133). In the pre-pottery Neolithic period, which on the somewhat unsatisfactory evidence of a few radiocarbon dates appears to have lasted from 6000–5000 B.C. in the Belt Cave, the number of sheep bones rises sharply to over a third of the total. Coon thinks that sheep were herded and kept largely for the sake of meat and skins, whilst lambs were slaughtered only in restricted numbers. He estimates that about an eighth of the lambs were killed, whilst the rest were allowed to grow up, but it must be noted that the evidence is slender, there being only twelve specimens of sheep from the layers in question.

In the pottery Neolithic, immature sheep predominate. This is taken to mean that young animals were killed for food, whilst mature females were kept for breeding and possibly milking.

The position of Belt Cave, close to the urial area, is suggestive. Until fresh evidence from other sites becomes available it may be assumed that sheep-herding and breeding had begun in northern Persia by 6000 B.C., at a time when agriculture was still non-existent or in its initial stage. The control of sheep by man may have begun earlier than this, in the lowlands of Turkestan where sheep occur in the plains and where man and his dog might well have been tempted to control their movements.

The only other pre-pottery Neolithic site from which domesticated sheep have been reported is Jarmo (Braidwood, 1951) in northern Iraq, excavated by Dr Braidwood of the Oriental Institute, Chicago.[1] Here, agriculture was practised just before pottery was introduced. The bones are being studied at this moment. Sheep (or goat), oxen, pig and dog make up 95 per cent of the total of bones. Domesticated animals were thus already supplying most of the meat. This period has been dated at about 4970 B.C. by means of radiocarbon.

The early pottery sites of Iran, Turkestan and Iraq all have sheep. In the early Hassuna phases, which lie somewhere between 5000 and 4500 B.C., sheep occur associated with cattle, and by the time of Hassuna Phase VI (contemporary with Tell Halaf, c. 4500 B.C.) northern Mesopotamia had, according to Mallowan's excavations (Mallowan and Rose, 1935) at Tell Aswad and Arpachiyah, pigs in addition to sheep, goats and cattle, though hunting was still practised on a large scale.

The site of Tepé Sialk (Vaufrey, 1939) in Iran has yielded sheep from Layer I onwards. This is approximately contemporary with Hassuna (5000–4500 B.C.), and it is noteworthy that the majority are very like urial.

In the oldest deposits of Anau in southern Turkestan the wild urial is found as a game animal, whilst from Period Ib onwards (c. 3500 B.C.) domestication is evidenced in the reduction of the horns, which eventually disappear altogether in many specimens. At the same time, the number of remains of sheep increases enormously over that of cattle.

A similar set of conditions is observed in Shah Tepé in northern Iran. In Layer III (the oldest, c. 3000 B.C. or a little earlier) Amschler (1940a) identified three remains of a wild sheep besides over a hundred remains of a domesticated form. Needless to say, the domesticated sheep occur in the later levels also. Shah Tepé III is approximately contemporary with the Uruk and Jamdat Nasr periods of Mesopotamia. At Uruk (Nöldeke et al., 1937) (c. 4000–3500 B.C.), two kinds of sheep were kept besides oxen and goats. But specialization had gone further than this, for the Uruk period can boast no fewer than thirty-one varieties of the ideogram for 'sheep', presumably indicating, besides sexes and ages, a much larger number of breeds than are actually known to us. The Jamdat Nasr period (c. 3000 B.C.) has again yielded pictorial representations of two breeds of domesticated sheep. One is a hairy animal with a conspicuous throat ruff, reminding one of the urial, but its tail is already lengthened, its horns are of the straight 'corkscrew' type which does not occur in any wild sheep, and its ears may be either erect or drooping. This screw-horned hair-sheep is found at the same time in Egypt, where it was named *Ovis longipes palaeo-aegyptius* by Duerst and Gaillard (1902).

---

[1] Dr C. Reed (1960) has not been able to confirm the presence of sheep at Jarmo.

Besides this hairy screw-horn sheep, at least one other occurred in the Jamdat Nasr period, which had a fleece of wool. It is evident, therefore, that by 3000 B.C. the development of special breeds was well on its way in Mesopotamia.

In fact, a third breed is shown at Jamdat Nasr, with spirally curved horns reminiscent of *Ovis orientalis cycloceros* Hutton, the Afghanistan race of the urial. This sheep exhibits abundant evidence of domestication: it has a fleece, its ears are usually drooping and its nose is convex. According to Hilzheimer, it had a very short and lean tail. It appears to have been present at Kish, and is illustrated in Langdon's report on that site (1924–1934). Hilzheimer believes that all sheep represented as being milked belong to this breed, which we may call the ammon's horn wool-sheep. Varieties of this type occur and it is probable that interbreeding of the three major breeds was practised on a large scale.

A fourth breed of sheep appears at about the same time in Ur. This is the fat-tailed sheep, shown on a bowl of Uruk III age (*c.* 3000 B.C., Fig. 7 : 9). It is also depicted on the famous Peace Panel of the Standard of Ur (*c.* 2400 B.C.). This fat-tailed sheep displays many primitive characters, for its head profile is still straight, its ears are pricked and it is fleeceless. In the course of time this sheep acquires more signs of domestication, such as a fleece, drooping ears and hornless ewes. It appears on the wall reliefs of the palace of Tiglathpileser III (Late Assyrian period, *c.* 745–727 B.C.), and seems altogether to have been popular in 'Babylonian and Assyrian' times, according to Hilzheimer.

Fig. 7 : 9. Fragment of stone bowl showing a fat-tailed sheep being attacked by an eagle. Uruk III, *c.* 3000 B.C. Metropolitan Museum, New York, No. L.3042.9. After van Buren

Of a fifth breed, evidence is scanty, though it is of some interest. This is a wool sheep with long stick-like horns. It is known from Ur (Legrain, 1936, pls. 195, 200, 203, 211). This type is remarkably like the modern zackelschaf of the Balkan countries, and it is almost certainly derived from the screw-horned sheep.

For the early dynastic period of southern Mesopotamia, a careful analysis of the bone material is available from Tell Asmar, thanks to Professor H. Frankfort's careful collecting and to Dr Hilzheimer's identification. This site dates from Early Dynastic III to Gutian (*c.* 2500–2100 B.C.). Hilzheimer holds that most of the Tell Asmar sheep belong to the screw-horned sheep, of which horn-cores were found. Whether it was the hairy or the wool-bearing variety, however, cannot be decided.

It may therefore be said that by 2000 B.C. Mesopotamia had at least five main breeds of sheep, namely the screw-horned hair-sheep, the screw-horned wool-sheep, a 'zackelschaf', the ammon's horn wool-sheep and the ammon's horn fat-tailed wool-sheep. These breeds all show a tendency for the ewes to become hornless, for the ears to become pendant and for the tail to become longer. The screw-horned hair-sheep had retained the wild coat, but its horns and tail had changed. The ammon's horn wool-sheep, on the other hand, had kept more or less the primitive type of horn, and the short tail of the wild sheep, whilst its coat changed. Neither can be regarded as more primitive than the other. The other breeds were derived from these two basic ones and may therefore be left out of the discussion.

If one raises the question of what the wild ancestor of the Mesopotamian domesticated sheep is likely to have been, the answer is simple regarding the hair-sheep. Its long hair fringe on the neck, the tendency of its tail to become long, and the screw spirals of the horns point to the urial group, that is to north-eastern Iran and Turkestan, and probably to Baluchistan. This sheep, therefore, was not domesticated locally, and not in the mountains bordering Mesopotamia to the north and east, for these are, or were, inhabited by moufflons.[1] It has been suggested more than once that the ammon's horn sheep is descended from the moufflon group which, with *Ovis laristanica*, reaches as far south-east as Laristan. In the ranges bordering Mesopotamia to the north it would have occurred in plenty and thus been easily obtainable by the ancient inhabitants of Mesopotamia. On morphological grounds, however, this claim is less secure, since the 'short tail' depicted on archaeological specimens is, even in Hilzheimer's opinion, only a few centimetres shorter than that of the primitive urial group. Furthermore, the horns of the moufflon group tend to be perverted, whilst the ammon's horn spiral is normal, that is it turns outwards. Whilst admixture of moufflon blood must inevitably have taken place, there is reason

[1] The curious patchy distribution of urials and moufflons quoted by Hilzheimer (1941, p. 33) on the authority of Cheesman has yielded to a more natural arrangement of races. *O.o. cycloceros*, in particular, is an Afghanistan form not found in western Persia. Even if an urial occurs in Shiraz, this is still much to the east of ancient Mesopotamia.

to believe that the ammon's horn wool-sheep, too, is descended from the urial group.[1]

Passing to the Levant, interest is naturally focused on those sites which have yielded an early Neolithic devoid of pottery, especially the Tahunian group of Palestine with its distinctive flint industry including sickle-blades. Childe comes to the conclusion that they were semi-nomadic groups practising shifting cultivation and stock-breeding combined with hunting, fishing and collecting. To what extent these different activities contributed to the economy of these people is, however, a question which is likely to be settled by the excavations at Jericho under the direction of Dr Kathleen Kenyon, the animal finds from which are being studied under the direction of the writer.

In the fifth millennium B.C. there follows the pottery-making Neolithic of Jericho, Umm Qatafa, Yarmuq River and other sites. On the Yarmuq, Stekelis found, and Miss Dorothea Bate determined, the bones of wild boar, gazelle, camel and birds, as well as of calves, goats, sheep and dogs. Of these, the dog and the sheep must have been domesticated. Archaeologically, the site can be correlated with Hassuna in Iraq and with Merimde in Egypt, on the evidence of its herring-bone ornamented pots. The range of the domesticated sheep therefore included Palestine from about 5000 B.C. onwards.

Cyprus

Cyprus is an outpost of the oriental moufflon, and one wonders whether this was ever taken into domestication. Its remains are known from the Neolithic site of Khirokitia (c. 3700–3000 B.C.) where several horn-cores, found by Dr Dikaios and studied by Miss J. E. King (1953), were indistinguishable from the wild males. A few horns of a goat of the bezoar type were identified also. In addition, there were numerous limb bones of sheep or goats, which showed that these animals were eaten in quantity, and also many remains of the Persian fallow deer, *Dama mesopotamica*, and of a pig. Finally, a small cat was found. All these species may have been wild, and (except for the cat) hunted. It is impossible to find proof of domestication though the large numbers of bones of sheep or goat render it conceivable. But if there was domestication, one could apply the same argument to the pig and the fallow deer, and it is not inconceivable that the latter were herded or kept in enclosures. Cattle are absent altogether. The fauna of Khirokitia is strange indeed, the more so as it is comparatively late. It is to be hoped that other sites, particularly

[1] One might expect Sialk I to afford proof of this view, since it has from time to time been said that two breeds of domesticated sheep occurred there, in the earliest pottery-making Neolithic (5000–4500 B.C.). Vaufrey, however, found only one small upper jaw that was very probably derived from a domesticated animal. The remainder of the specimens were males and females of urial. Whether these were domesticated or not is impossible to say. In size, they are on the small side, though within the variation of the wild. Females and immature specimens predominate, which may be interpreted as meaning that the herds contained few adult males, males being mostly slaughtered when young. On the other hand, selective hunting would have the same effect.

Sotira, which is at present being excavated, will yield more conclusive material. If domestication was practised in Cyprus at that time, it was of the pastoral type, and cattle (well known at that time elsewhere) were absent. The impression is gained that the Khirokitians practised a sheep-cum-goat pastoralism of the kind found at the same time in the Sudan, though there the goat was dominant. Cyprus at that time appears to have been a backwater.

In the Bronze Age of Cyprus cattle can be added to the list, and domesticated sheep is in evidence. In addition, the excavation of the Late Bronze Age site of Myrtou (thirteenth century B.C.) by Miss J. du Plat Taylor, the fauna of which I was able to study (Zeuner, 1957), revealed the well-preserved frontlet of a Cypriot moufflon. It was found lying on top of a heap of bones on the floor of a courtyard close to an altar; they represented the remains of offerings. That the Cyprus moufflon should have been among them is interesting though hardly surprising, for it is a noble game. Most of the offerings, however, were Persian fallow deer, and the possibility that this species was domesticated in Cyprus deserves to be taken seriously. If so, there is no reason to regard the domestication of the Cyprus moufflon as unlikely. The evidence available for domestication in Cyprus is indeed exceptional in some respects. It is even conceivable that the first Neolithic immigrants arrived without domesticated animals (except the dog) and that they drew on the wild stock available, of which the Persian fallow deer was the most easily obtained as it lived in the lowland woods. This suggestion of a special history of domestication in Cyprus may fall to the ground when more faunal remains are studied. At the present, it is an interesting possibility.

Was the Cypriot moufflon, or one of the races of the Asiatic mainland, ever taken to areas where it does not occur naturally? This would provide the soundest evidence for occasional domestication.

The only instance that has come to the writer's knowledge is an ivory carving from a tomb at Menidi near Athens, of the Mycenaean period (Fig. 7 : 10). In his *Fauna of the Antique*, Keller compared these sheep with the Bündner sheep of the Alps, but Lydekker subsequently noticed that the peculiar curvature of the horns is meant to indicate perversion, a feature of the Asiatic moufflon which distinguishes it from the urial. The animals shown look much like Cypriot moufflon in

FIG. 7 : 10. Mycenaean sheep resembling Cypriot moufflon, but certainly domesticated as indicated by lengthened tail. Mycenaean period, from Menidi. After Hilzheimer (1926)

summer coat. It is going too far to regard this as proof that some race of the Asiatic moufflon was domesticated and taken to Greece, though it should be regarded as possible. The alternative is to regard the ivory carving as imported from Cyprus or Asia Minor, and depicting wild sheep. Yet, no matter how this particular issue will be settled, at some time or other, and somewhere in the borderlands of the Mediterranean, or perhaps the Persian mountains, moufflon must have been domesticated. There are several breeds of sheep, especially in Africa and north-west Europe, which cannot be descended from the urial.

Africa

Since no wild sheep are known to have existed in Africa towards the close of the Pleistocene, all domesticated sheep encountered in Africa must be derived either from Asia or from Europe.

The earliest and most plentiful evidence comes from the Nile Valley. No site is known, however, of domestic animals occurring in a pre-pottery context. The Tasian culture (*c*. 5000–4500 B.C.) had sheep or goat and the Fayum people of 4500–4000 B.C. had cattle and pig in addition. The Badarians, apparently cultural descendants of the Tasians, had sheep besides cattle, but had no pig. This information paints a picture much like that of Mesopotamia in the fifth millennium, namely that wherever pottery makes its appearance the sheep is present also.

That the domestication of the sheep took place before pottery was invented is, however, suggested by Belt Cave. Near Khartoum in the Sudan two important prehistoric sites were excavated by Dr A. J. Arkell. The older, called Early Khartoum, was a pure food-collectors' and hunters' culture with a microlithic industry and bone harpoons, thus reminiscent of the Mesolithic of Europe. Indeed, these people did not practise agriculture, nor had they any domesticated animals. And yet they made excellent pottery which, with its wavy-line decoration, appears to be related to the Badarian. Arkell regards it as ancestral to this culture. An alternative view would be that it is a provincial variant or even a descendant of it, adopted by hunting and collecting tribes populating the Sudan, which with its wealth of game at that time did perhaps not make it worth while to take to settled life and practise agriculture.

That such interpretation is possible is more clearly suggested by the later site of the Khartoum area, Shaheinab. Arkell has clearly shown that its 'gouge culture' developed from the 'wavy-line culture', and it is closely related to the Neolithic of the Fayum. The Shaheinab people had permanent settlements, though they were still mainly hunters and fishers. Ninety-eight per cent of the animal remains were those of wild animals. The domesticated were represented by small goat, whilst a single horn-core is almost certainly that of a sheep, as suggested by its slightly concave inner surface. At Shaheinab, therefore, goats were normally kept, but sheep were not unknown.

In view of the affinities of this site to the Fayum, its date is of considerable interest. Two radiocarbon dates were obtained, one from charcoal (material mainly collected by Mr Sadik Nur), the other of molluscan shells, and these were 3108 B.C. and 3494 B.C. respectively.[1] Since both samples came from a dry climate, and since the two counts were made on different materials, the dates are unlikely to be grossly inaccurate. Their mean points to something like 3300 B.C. for Shaheinab. This is only just a predynastic age by Egyptian standards and some 800 years later than the Fayum Neolithic A (radiocarbon date 4145 B.C. $\pm$ 250). It is thus likely that the goat-keeping settlement of Khartoum was a belated outpost of the civilization of the Fayum which had already adopted stock-breeding on a much larger scale. It thus appears that the sheep first came to lower Egypt, which it had reached approximately by 5000 B.C., and that it spread slowly up the Nile, some having reached Khartoum by 3300 B.C.[2]

What type of sheep was it that reached Egypt?

The earliest pictorial evidence comes from the predynastic period. The Nagada palette, for instance, depicts sheep in a manner which, though coarse, does not neglect any of the diagnostic features. They are sleek-haired, with a conspicuous ruff down the throat; have long, straight, loosely spiral horns; and a long tail extending beyond the hocks. The ears are small and erect. In other words, this is in every detail the primitive variant of the screw-horned hair-sheep with which we are familiar from Mesopotamia. It is the *Ovis longipes palaeoaegyptius* of Gaillard and Duerst. Though first named from Egypt, and perhaps slightly earlier there than in Mesopotamia, this sheep is so plainly the descendant of an urial that it must have come from Turkestan or Persia, presumably via northern Mesopotamia. It is therefore one of the best pieces of evidence for the influx of Asiatic elements into Egypt, probably in Gerzean times.

Assuming that the screw-horned hair-sheep reached Egypt not earlier than the beginning of the Gerzean (early fourth millennium B.C.), a time for which V. Gordon Childe has brought forth much evidence of Asiatic trade contacts, we are left with the possibility of earlier types of sheep having reached Egypt and the Fayum in the fifth millennium or even before that. For these, evidence is admittedly scanty owing to the lack of osteological distinction between sheep and goat. It may be that all 'sheep' bones from the Tasian, Badarian and Amratian eventually prove to be those of goat. Duerst and Gaillard (1902) are supposed to have osteological proof for screw-horned hair-sheep in the Egyptian Neolithic. But if we give them the benefit

---

[1] Chicago No. 753, charcoal 5060 B.P.$\pm$450; No. 754, shell 5446 B.P.$\pm$380.

[2] The interpretation given by Arkell (1953) to the radiocarbon dates suffers from his mistaking the standard deviation for the extreme limits of the date. This common misunderstanding is discussed in Zeuner, 1951a.

FIG. 7 : 11. The corkscrew-horned hair-sheep of early Egypt. Relief on tomb of Urarna (Werirni), fifth dynasty, *c.*2500 B.C. Sheep treading in seed. Note the comparatively long tail and horizontally twisted horns characteristic of the Old Kingdom breed. After Davies (1901)

FIG. 7 : 12. Ancient Egyptian hair-sheep represented with certain goat characteristics (beard). Beni Hassan, *c.* 2000 B.C. After Griffith (1896)

of the doubt, it may become necessary either to postulate the introduction into Egypt of an earlier type of sheep (for which there is some indirect evidence) or to assume that the screw-horned hair-sheep arrived in the Tasian.

The later history of the hair-sheep in Egypt is easily related. The early types, single-coloured and stiff-eared, give way to piebald and lop-eared forms later on. The style of the horns, however, never varied and was perhaps considered a matter of some importance. The breed disappears from the Egyptian scene with the Middle Kingdom, when it is replaced by a wool-sheep (p. 183).

Fig. 7 : 13. Frieze of sheep from Uruk-Warka, Mesopotamia, c. 3500 B.C., showing a horizontally horned hair-sheep resembling that of Old Kingdom Egypt. After Heinrich (1937)

The Egyptian screw-horned hair-sheep, however, is not completely extinct. It has continued to exist in outlying districts, the breeds of the Niger and Benue districts being particularly close to it. In addition, this ancient stock gave rise to several modern breeds of Africa which are characterized by high legs and hair. Wool[1] nowhere occurs in this group, unless crossing with wool-sheep has taken place. In general, large lop-ears are the rule, and not only are the females hornless (this is the case in the late hair-sheep of the Old Kingdom also), but in some breeds the males have lost their horns.

One breed of sheep descended from the Egyptian hair-sheep is the long-legged sheep of Guinea. (It is noteworthy that several primitive breeds survived on the periphery of the area covered by domestic sheep.) In these animals the profile is convex and the eyes are placed high in the skull and close to the drooping ears. The rams carry thick horns and a long ruff on the throat. The tail is of medium length, reaching the hocks, the hair is smooth and short as in the summer coat of the wild sheep. Its colour varies more than usual, there being uniformly brown, black and white specimens, though more commonly patches of white occur in a brown or black coat. This form had reached south-west Africa before the arrival of the Europeans.

Another long-legged sheep is the hornless lop-ear. It is easily recognized by its very long drooping ears which reach below the sides of the head, the absence of

[1] In the sense of a product.

horns in both sexes, very convex profile and a tail which reaches almost to the ground, though it is not fat. A curious feature is that these animals stand higher at the croup than at the withers. The hair is often long and woolly. Its colour is frequently dark reddish-brown, or it is lighter, like that of Jersey cows. Others are white.

The Bishari of Upper Egypt keep large flocks of lop-eared sheep in the neighbourhood of Assuan. Such sheep are common elsewhere in Upper Egypt, Nubia and the Sudan (Fig. 7 : 14) and have spread across North Africa to Morocco. Similarly, they have spread eastwards as far as India.

FIG. 7 : 14. Hair-sheep from Sudan resembling type shown on North African rock engravings. Photo Lutz Heck

A related type is the Nigerian long-legged or Hausa sheep. It has the same long drooping ears, a convex profile and the eyes close to the base of the ears. The tail reaches well beyond the hocks. The hair is shaggy, especially in the rams, which have a long mane and ruff. The rams are equipped with horns that curve outwards and downwards in an open spiral. The main colour is white, with patches of black and brown, especially round the eyes.

These specialized descendants of the Egyptian hair-sheep were never bred in Egypt itself. The most important breed, the lop-ear, appears to have developed in the Sudan whence at some time it reached southern Algeria by way of the Sahara oases. For, curiously enough, the pictorial evidence from Libya lacks the sheep almost completely or entirely so, whilst long-legged hair-sheep with convex profile of the face are faithfully depicted on many rocks in southern Algeria. Some are shown carrying a disc on their head, which is suggestive of a sheep cult derived from Egypt. Whilst some Algerian rock engravings show hornless ewes, others, like the rams, are portrayed with small horns. Their curvature is difficult to interpret. It may have been as in the modern Hausa sheep, a short open spiral growing away from the head,

FIG. 7 : 15. Same type of sheep as shown in Fig. 7 : 7, from Kawa, Sudan. Egyptian style. A granite ram protecting the statue of the Nubian Pharaoh Taharqa, *c.* 680 B.C. After Hilzheimer (1936)

or more of an ammon's spiral placed close to the head as in the later Egyptian wool-sheep. Whether this is the expression of an admixture of wool-sheep blood remains to be established. In any case, the horns were small.

The breeds so far mentioned all appear to be derived from the screw-horned, long-legged hair-sheep of ancient Egypt. There is a second group which shows certain moufflon characters and which was called *Ovis aries africana* by Linnaeus, though it is better known under Fitzinger's name, *Ovis jubata*. These animals have manes on the back of the neck of old rams, short to medium tails, horns of the ammon's type and are, in their brown varieties, occasionally equipped with the whitish saddle-patch of the moufflon. These sheep are considerably smaller than the long-legged group. They occur from the Fezzan and the Sudan to West Africa and include the Dinka sheep of which Schweinfurth relates that the mantle of hair round the neck sometimes gives it the appearance of a miniature buffalo. The Baluba sheep of Tanganyika belongs to the same group. Lydekker points out that its black horns curve forward by the side of the face in moufflon fashion. Both blackness and curvature thus reveal its descent from the moufflon. The most remarkable breed of this group, however, is the pygmy sheep of the Cameroons which stands only 45 cm. high at the withers. The blackish horns are a mere 5 cm. long and the tail is short. The colour of the coarse hair is reddish brown, except for the short and erect ears, portions of the face and the underparts which are black; a whitish saddlepatch is occasionally present.

Finally, a short-tailed and lop-eared maned sheep from Abyssinia must be mentioned, which is brown with a saddle-patch (Fig. 7 : 16). With its short tail and saddle-patch it should belong to the moufflon group, though its horns are of the

182

FIG. 7 : 16. Short-tailed hair-sheep with moufflon patch, horizontal screw-horns and lop-ears, from Abyssinia. It suggests the penetration of moufflon breeds into Africa. Specimen in British Museum (Nat. Hist.)

screw-type, characteristic of the ancient Egyptian breed. Lydekker thought it was a hybrid between a maned sheep and a long-legged sheep.

The presence of moufflon descendants in Africa, south of the Sahara, is thus probable. There is no archaeological evidence for their passage through Egypt in proto-dynastic times or later. Perhaps these were the very first sheep to reach Africa in the Neolithic. This is no more than a guess, which would make it possible to derive these sheep from the Asiatic moufflon. The alternative would be to regard them as descendants of the European moufflon, assuming that they passed through Morocco to West Africa and thence eastwards to the Dinka and Abyssinia. Though evidence is lacking for either way, the first suggestion appears to be the more acceptable.

In Middle Kingdom times the Egyptian hair-sheep was replaced by a breed with ammon's horns and wool. This sheep had a but slightly convex nose, and the hair on the head was short. In appearance it may have resembled the modern Scottish Blackface. The colour of the fleece was whitish, brown or black. As to the tail, Gaillard found it on twelfth-dynasty mummies to be of the fat-tail type, though the pictorial evidence does not portray this character. It may be that it does not show in the usual lateral aspect, or normal medium-tails were kept beside fat-tails, or else the fat-tails proved unpopular. In any case, the Egyptian wool-sheep must have come from Asia, where the Mesopotamian ammon's horned wool-sheep is a conceivable ancestor.

In spite of the fact that in Egypt proper this new breed replaced the older hair-sheep completely, its predecessor continued to receive worshipful attention. This is revealed by several pictures of wool-sheep rams (Fig. 7 : 17) which, in addition to their normal ammon's horns, carry a pair of screw-horns on the head. These sheep were for some time interpreted as natural four-horned specimens. It is out of the question that they were such, for the horns are not bent in the manner characteristic of four-horned breeds, but represent two pairs belonging to two quite different

FIG. 7 : 17. Sacred Egyptian ram of New Kingdom age wearing a crown composed of horns of Old kingdom sheep, snakes and other attributes. The domesticated Egyptian sheep of that time had the curled horns of the Ammon type, hence this animal appears four-horned. The small beard is taken from the goat. It, too, is intended to indicate superior status

breeds. Moreover, it should have aroused suspicion that many of these rams are shown equipped with small goat's beards. Evidently they were intended to represent the divine essence of the ovine-caprine group of domesticated animals.

That this combination is artificial has been proved by the discovery of Roman-period mummies of wool-sheep which carried a mask with the horns of the hair-sheep. This interesting find was discussed by Professor Keimer. The head-dress, including the supplementary horns, was made of stucco and wool.

One thus comes to the conclusion that Africa received four main waves of domesticated sheep. The first is conjectural, it would have consisted of a primitive breed of the moufflon group. The second was the screw-horned hair-sheep of urial stock, which arrived from Mesopotamia in the Gerzean phase. The third was the ammon-horned wool-sheep which arrived in the Middle Kingdom and by New Kingdom times had replaced the older breed completely in Egypt, though not elsewhere. Finally, the fourth wave would have brought the fat-tailed sheep which is still popular in North Africa, possibly from the Roman period onwards, except for occasional introductions from the Middle Kingdom onwards.

Everything points to an Asiatic origin of all four waves, though it is not inconceivable that the moufflon descendants reached Africa from Europe. It is also noteworthy that primitive races have survived to the present in many remote districts, such as the moufflon group in Fezzan and the Cameroons, and the hair-sheep in West and south-west Africa. Needless to say, there is no evidence of African sheep ever having been crossed with the wild Barbary sheep (*Ammotragus lervia*) which belongs to a different genus. Unfortunately, the French of North Africa call it moufflon, which is short for '*mouflon à manchettes*'.

Europe

Among the European sheep of about a century ago, which were monographed with so much care by the Austrian mammalogist Dr Fitzinger (1860), there were many short-tailed breeds apart from medium- or long-tailed ones.[1] Today little is left of those interesting local breeds, the Merino and other improved breeds having swept them off the map. In considering the origin of European domesticated sheep it is essential, therefore, to consult Fitzinger's great work which was published about 1860, at a time when the Theory of Evolution had not yet been accepted. Lydekker, writing in 1914, refers to several of Fitzinger's breeds and points out that they have either become extinct or nearly so.

The urial descendants in Europe. The most widely known of the prehistoric sheep of Europe is the turbary sheep (*Ovis aries palustris*), the form found in the Neolithic lake-dwellings of Switzerland. It was investigated by Rütimeyer in 1861 and later by Duerst, Keller and others. Though the views concerning it have varied, it is still essentially agreed that Rütimeyer's theory of descent from the urial is correct. The two main arguments in favour of urial descent, however, namely that the horns are present in the female and that the tail was relatively long, rest on slender foundations. All earlier authors, including such a careful investigator as Cossar Ewart, believed that the ewes of moufflon are hornless. That this is a mistake has

---

[1] No distinction is here maintained between medium- and long-tailed breeds. Once the number of tail vertebrae has begun to increase, further distinction becomes arbitrary.

been pointed out on p. 157. That the tail of the turbary sheep was longer than that of the moufflon is a view not based on skeletal evidence, for no complete tail has ever been found. If Duerst, Keller and Lydekker describe it as long, they rely on modern breeds such as the Bündner sheep, which are believed to be related. There is no reason to think that they are mistaken in this respect. The urial descent of this sheep is thus mainly confirmed by some characters of the skull only, namely by the horns of the few rams known, and by the *size* of the horns of the ewes which is superior to that of the largest moufflon ewes.

According to Rütimeyer, the turbary sheep was of small size; had slender and graceful legs; and small, erect, two-edged and goat-like horns. Such sheep still exist in Grisons where they are known as *Bündner Oberländer Schaf* (Fig. 7 : 18). Curiously enough, Rütimeyer never mentioned the rams, but Duerst, the investigator of the fauna of Anau, described from the Swiss lake-dwellings rams with large curled horns

Fig. 7 : 18. Ewe from Vrin, Grisons, Switzerland, showing rounded, long, 'goat-like' horns, evidence of urial descent. After Adametz

as the so-called Copper sheep (*O. aries studeri*) and this was subsequently almost universally accepted as the ram of the turbary sheep. It will be shown presently that this view cannot be maintained. In due course, other large-horned specimens were found to occur together with the 'goat-horned' ewes. Hescheler and Kuhn, for instance, mention that at the Neolithic site of Egolzwil 2 besides many small flattened horns three large ones were found, which were strongly curved and twisted round the axis.

In addition, Adametz (1937) and others have stressed that the reputed descendants of the turbary sheep, which survive in various parts of the Alps, have rams with horns very much of the type found associated with the 'goat-horned' females. They were strong, flattened anteriorly, and twisted in an open spiral round an axis extending laterally away from the head.

If one looks for related primitive breeds one is led to some known in the eastern Alps as *Steinschaf*. Both these and the *Bündner Oberländer Schaf* are, according to Adametz, closely related to the *Zackelschaf*, a remarkable breed which was at one time common in Lower Austria and is still bred in large numbers in Hungary. Thence it extends to the south of the Balkan peninsula, including parts of Yugoslavia and Bulgaria, Albania, Greece and Macedonia, the Greek islands (particularly Crete, from where it was described by Fitzinger) and western and north-western Asia Minor.

The zackelschaf is characterized by straight, stick-like horns which are twisted 'corkscrew' fashion and grow away from the body. Their type represents the extreme to which the development of screw-horns can go. The twist is the result of an excessively fast, outward growth rate, which overwhelms completely the circular growth rate dominant in moufflons.

The zackelschaf was not unknown in ancient Mesopotamia (p. 174). It was present in the fourth millennium B.C. and it had a coat of wool then, as it has today, combined with a relatively long body and thin legs. Its descent from the urial group has been argued repeatedly. It thus appears that sheep of this type drifted with the spreading Neolithic culture from western Asia by way of the Balkan peninsula into Europe.

The turbary sheep, however, was not a zackelschaf in the strict sense, the horns of its rams forming a loose spiral much like that of the ancient Egyptian hair-sheep. Wool-sheep with such horns were known in the Jamdat Nasr period of Mesopotamia, the 'woolly screw-horn sheep' mentioned on p. 173. The zackelschaf is distinguished from it mainly by its extremely straight horns. If these two breeds were taken into Europe by the Neolithic invaders from the East, the evidence is satisfactorily accounted for.

The further progress of the turbary sheep in Europe, however, was not unimpeded. Though it reached Switzerland, north-western Europe was for some time the domain of another primitive sheep, as will be explained later on. The fact that the European territory of the zackel-cum-turbary sheep coincides approximately with that of the Danubian culture may or may not be significant. In any case, the breeds that came this way were variable in the intensity of the twist of their horns.

The moufflonoid sheep of Europe. When the search for the rams of the turbary sheep began, it was pointed out that the Swiss lake-dwellings had yielded a sheep with heavy spiral horns described by Duerst as the Copper sheep (*Ovis aries studeri*). As is evident from its name, Duerst regarded it as a separate breed, but it has in recent years become the fashion to deny its racial status and to regard it simply as the male of the turbary sheep. In agreement with Adametz's observations, however, the present writer considers this view as untenable. The heavily horned Copper sheep is, as Duerst quite correctly said, not identical with the turbary sheep.[1] Two alternatives exist for its derivation, namely either from one of the ammon-horned urial descendants of the East or from the moufflon.

On the whole the moufflon is not regarded as an important ancestor of the domesticated sheep, especially not in Europe. Yet there is sound evidence in favour of it, which emerges when one studies the remainder of the Swiss material and then proceeds to compare it with that from other parts of Europe.

Very occasionally, hornless skulls occur in the Swiss Neolithic. They become frequent in the Bronze Age. The ewes of the turbary sheep, therefore, appear to have lost their horns in the course of time. Such hornless females were at one time regarded as a third distinct breed, the so-called Bronze sheep, but Reitsma and others have shown that this is an insignificant variation.

The importers of the first sheep preferred the goat to a great extent. Sheep became gradually more popular, particularly during the Metal Ages. The same is observed elsewhere in the earlier phases of domestication, be it the Neolithic of Windmill Hill in Britain or of Cyprus. The reason cannot simply be that the goat was domesticated before the sheep, for the process occurred at very different times in several countries. It is almost certainly connected with the different ecological requirements of the two species. Goats prefer leafy food and are therefore useful in forested countries where the newly arrived farmer wants to keep down the growth of trees and shrubs. Sheep, on the other hand, feed mainly on grass and therefore can only be bred extensively where large areas have already been cleared of forest. The order of goat followed by sheep is thus ecological and need not indicate that the goat was domesticated before the sheep. In steppe countries the sheep is the most obvious animal to be domesticated.

In Switzerland the horned and hornless varieties of the turbary sheep were still abundantly kept in Roman times. The Romans, however, imported from the south a much heavier sheep with larger horns, a type known from representations in Italy, such as on the Situla of Bologna.

At that time the geographical distribution of breeds was still comparatively simple, and it may have remained so well into the Middle Ages in northern and north-west Europe, where hardy and ecologically well-adapted breeds were kept for preference. Even a hundred years ago the basic pattern was still in existence as becomes evident when one studies Dr Fitzinger's papers.

The most remarkable result is that at that time short-tailed sheep with certain moufflon characters occurred all along the northern and western borderlands of Europe, whilst to the south, and indeed often interspersed, medium-tailed sheep existed. To be more precise, the moufflonoid short-tailed sheep were found in north

---

[1] It should be remembered that not every large-horned Neolithic sheep from Switzerland is an *O.a. studeri*, there are among them the true males of the turbary sheep. The ewes of the two races have not yet been distinguished, and this may even be impossible.

Russia and Finland; in Norway, Sweden and Denmark (where they were much crossed with medium-tailed breeds even in Fitzinger's day); in north-west Germany; in Western France, the Auvergne and Provence; and in Andalusia and Castile in Spain (where they had become extinct by the beginning of the twentieth century).

In the British Isles breeds belonging to this group were confined to the Shetlands, to some impure strains in the Orkneys, the Isle of Man (Loaghtan sheep), certain of the Outer Hebrides and the St Kilda group (whence the well-known Soay sheep comes).

These sheep have the following characters in common: They are small with small and upright ears. The rams have well-developed horns with the slightly everted spiral of the Western moufflon; the ewes are either hornless or have very small horns. The fleece is coarse, shaggy and partly hairy, the head and often part of the neck being hairy. Occasionally a throat ruff is present in the rams. The tail has only twelve to thirteen vertebrae, as in the moufflon.

The colour varies a great deal, there being many white, brown, black and part-coloured specimens. Brown, however, is a popular colour, and in some of the races primitive coloration occurs.

Of the northern breeds, Fitzinger relates that one pattern was reddish brown with neck and chest blackish below, with a yellow-brown face and a whitish snout. The tail was black. The lower legs were brown and black except above the hoofs and on the fetters, where they were grey. Horns and hoofs were blackish brown, as in the moufflon. This type of sheep occurred from north Russia through Scandinavia, whence it had been taken to the Faroes and to Ireland.

The Soay sheep (Figs. 7 : 19 and 7 : 20) is the most primitive surviving member of this group. Not only does it resemble the moufflon in the shape and the black colour of the horns of the rams, but also in the frequent occurrence of goat-horned females. It is still more significant that the most pure-bred Soay sheep available have preserved moufflon characters of coloration which are truly remarkable.

As in the moufflon, the basic colour is brown.[1] In the face, the snout and areas round the eyes are more or less mixed with white hair whilst the bridge of the nose tends to be blackish. The neck is more or less covered with long hair. The belly is whitish or light-brownish, and the black flank-stripe is present behind the elbow, though extending less far posteriorly than in the moufflon. A light-coloured patch surrounds the tail. It has also been reported that the whitish saddle-patch of the moufflon occurs occasionally in Soay sheep, though I have not seen it. The forelegs are characteristically moufflon-coloured. This pattern, be it noted, is very pronounced in the moufflon as distinct from the urial and argali.

[1] The Soay sheep are no longer pure. As first recognized by Ewart, there is an admixture of urial blood. The following description is based on a small flock kept in the gardens of the Zoological Society of London in 1954 which is comparatively pure. Another flock of relatively pure stock exists in the zoological gardens of Amsterdam.

FIG. 7 : 19. Soay sheep in London Zoo. Note black horns
keeled anteriorly and moufflon pattern on legs, especially
of the male, indicating derivation from this wild species.
Photo F.E.Z.

FIG. 7 : 20. Same herd of Soay sheep in London Zoo. The ewe
in the foreground showing clearly the black line along the side
of the belly. Photo F.E.Z.

The short-tailed sheep of north-west Germany and formerly Normandy, the Auvergne and Provence are less characteristically coloured, though a dark brown much like the main colour of the Soay is very common, especially in the north German Heidschnucke. But in this breed grey specimens occur also in which the grey underwool has penetrated the dark coat on the back and the flanks, so that the animal is light-coloured. It must be kept in mind, however, that the Heidschnucke group of breeds is no longer homogeneous, and that it contains an important admixture of urial blood (Fig. 7 : 21).

Fig. 7 : 21. Ram of 'Heidschnucke' from Niesuticze, near Novo Grodek, Poland, age eighteen months. Note light-coloured, anteriorly flattened horns characteristic of urial. After Adametz

That the northern short-tailed sheep are descended from the moufflon is difficult to refute. With their short tails they are more primitive than the turbary sheep, and their horns as well as their colour relate them to the moufflon. To whom then is the domestication of this group of sheep to be credited? It might be argued that the idea of sheep domestication spread from the lands occupied by the Danubians to outlying districts, but there were at that time no wild sheep to be found between north Russia and Spain, unless one accepts as correct Fitzinger's statement that moufflon occurred in the mountains of Murcia in Spain.[1] Local imitation of an example set by the Danubians is thus out of the question.

A more feasible suggestion is that the western Neolithic immigrants, the people of the leather vessels, brought with them sheep of moufflon descent. On their way they may well have passed through moufflon territory, in Sardinia or Corsica, or perhaps Sicily or southern Spain. If they introduced the short-tailed sheep into

[1] This record is probably based on the Spanish ibex, but the former existence of wild sheep in Spain cannot be ruled out.

western Europe, whence they would have reached the British Isles, one is still left wondering how these sheep managed to get to Scandinavia and even northern Russia, countries that lay open to the urial descendants, and why the moufflonoid sheep did not at once become evident in the Swiss lake-dwellings, where the Cortaillod Culture should have introduced it. In fact, it did appear with the 'Copper Age'.

That the Swiss Copper sheep belongs to the moufflon group has been discussed already (see p. 187). Moufflonoid sheep also appear at Castellachio near Bologna,[1] associated with the turbary sheep. The Terremare people thus appear to have been acquainted with the domesticated moufflon, which is hardly surprising in view of the proximity of Corsica and Sardinia.

If one considers the possibility that the moufflonoid sheep was introduced by one of the late Neolithic immigration waves from the West, one is struck by the close agreement of its distribution with that of the megaliths. The chief difference is in the density of distribution, for these sheep are sparse in the Iberian peninsula where there are many megaliths but extend north-east into the Baltic provinces where evidence for megalithic penetration is scanty. It would be easy to explain this

[1] Determination by Strobel *teste* Ewart.

FIG. 7 : 22. Moufflon rams in a pine forest, north Germany. Derived from Sardinian stock and influenced by selective hunting. Photo Lutz Heck

condition as due to the replacement of those sheep in the south by later breeds brought by later immigrants, and their extension north-east by their suitability to heathland and pine forests.[1] It is thus conceivable that the moufflonoid sheep came into Europe with the megalithic migration.

A third alternative, however, exists. It is the assumption of a pre-Danubian stratum of pastoral sheep-breeding which had reached Europe from the West before the arrival of the leather-vessel people, who were mainly cattle-breeders.

Teeth and leg bones of sheep have been found in several Mesolithic sites in western Europe. To be precise, they ought to be called 'goat or sheep', for in no case could it be ascertained with certainty which of the species was present. On the other hand, the teeth are small and would agree with those of a sheep of Soay size. In either case the presence of a small ruminant in a Mesolithic context is of great interest. It must, however, be realized that all sites in question are later than the pre-pottery Neolithic of the eastern Mediterranean, and it is possible therefore that the knowledge of sheep-breeding had spread to the West prior to the arrival of the west European Neolithic in the proper sense. The four sites in question are Téviec (Tardenoisian, one molar), Cuzoul de Gramat (Tardenoisian, several teeth and one astragulus) and Sauveterre (Tardenoisian III, several molars, but pottery also). Apart from these French sites there is one 'Sauveterrian' site in Britain, Three Holes Cave near Torbryan in south Devon. Here three cheek teeth, two fragments of vertebrae and a fragment of a phalanx were found in layers V and VI which contained the Mesolithic industry. It is possible that the Sauveterrian of England is later than that of France and possibly contemporary with the French Tardenoisian. Attention may be drawn to a 'moufflon' skull described by Herre from Jutland, which however was not found in a prehistoric context. These finds have caused me to take the alternative of pre-agricultural sheep (or goat) keeping in Europe seriously.

Which of these alternatives is right will have to be decided on osteological evidence. It will be more than ever necessary to collect bones from well-investigated sites and to re-identify the material that is resting in museums. Only skulls, however, are likely to be useful in this respect for the time being.

It appears that Cossar Ewart is right in suggesting that an original moufflon stock became in the course of time mixed with urial (i.e. turbary) blood in many places. This explains perhaps why Reitsma was unable to distinguish the sheep of the Dutch terpen from the turbary group. Ewart also recognizes a strain of urial in the Soay sheep. I am not convinced that he is right here, for his view was largely based on the presence of small horns in some ewes and the occasional eversion of the horn-tip in the rams. Both these features occur, as is now known, in the wild moufflon also.

---

[1] The moufflon, released in the pine woods of central and eastern Europe, is thriving today under such conditions (Fig: 7 : 22).

The curious four-horned (or multi-horned) sheep are regarded by Ewart as crosses of moufflon and urial breeds. Indeed, they have retained certain primitive characters. Some are, for instance, short-tailed. But the usually irregular horns are pathological. The four-horned sheep first appeared in the Bronze Age according to Ewart, though I have been unable to trace the locality. In the broch at Jarlshof, Shetland, it occurs together with normal-horned sheep in an Iron Age context.

There is no doubt that many of the post-Beaker invasions brought urial sheep to Britain. Many of the older breeds belong to this group, some being remarkably hardy. The Scottish Blackface is one of them. These breeds, and later ones locally developed, replaced the moufflonoid stock everywhere except in the most outlying districts of the north, the Hebrides and the Orkneys (where in the first half of the nineteenth century a moufflonoid sheep was still in existence[1]). Similarly, they succeeded in surviving into the nineteenth century on the Continent, where they are, however, much restricted today.

Better feeding and greater attention to quality of carcass and wool have worked against the survival of primitive breeds in Europe, and favoured the spread of others unknown in antiquity.

The Merino

The most important of these today is the merino, an originally Spanish breed with an unprecedented yield of wool. It is an ammon's horn wool-sheep and therefore quite possibly one of the descendants of the Mesopotamian wool-sheep of this type. Other breeds belonging to the same group, such as the Southdown, are also medium-tailed and equipped with a fleece of close, curly wool.

More than a hundred years ago Low thought that the merino group had originated in North Africa. Even if he was right, however, this cannot have been more than an intermediate station. During the period of the Roman Empire, and probably long before it, ammon's horn wool-sheep were imported from western Asia and Egypt into Mediterranean countries. The Bologna Situla appears to represent one of these. With the Roman civilization this wool-sheep reached North Africa and Spain.

The reason for the late discovery of the value of the Spanish merino is to be sought in its poor mutton qualities. For a peasant population in the Middle Ages meat supply and resistance of the breed to environmental conditions were the most essential requirements, so that it was not until the great expansion of the wool industry that the merino came to the fore. The French King Louis XVI established a merino farm in his park at Rambouillet where they developed a very large body and excellent wool. King George III, encouraged by this success, tried to get a flock

---

[1] Not identical with those of north Ronaldshay that live all the year round outside the wall surrounding the cultivated ground.

FIG. 7 : 23. An early Mesopotamian wool-
sheep on a terracotta box in early Assyrian
style. Exact provenance unknown. British
Museum No. 92/989

in 1787 at a time when their exportation from Spain was prohibited. A flock of poor quality reached this country, having been driven secretly into Portugal. In 1791 a first-class flock was obtained officially by permission of the King of Spain, and they were subsequently kept at Kew, where they were crossed with British breeds. On the whole, however, the merino was not a success in Britain, since they are slow in reaching maturity and cannot easily be fattened. As they are content with poor and dry pasture (thus betraying their Mediterranean origin) they spread rapidly to dry countries and are today most important in South Africa, Australia and South America.

The merino is here mentioned as an example of a descendant of the ammon's horn wool-sheep, which appeared first in Mesopotamia. There are many other representatives of this group, often crossed with each other as well as with other types of sheep, so that it is no longer possible to elucidate their history. From the archaeological point of view it is important to remember that the great spread of this group over the Mediterranean and western Europe coincides with the Iron Age and later periods.

India

Very little work has been done on the history of the sheep in India and, so far as I am aware, Lydekker's summary of 1912 is still the best. In the mountain ranges of the Himalayas and in Tibet breeds occur which betray urial descent, such as the Hunia, which is tall and strong enough to be used to carry salt over the passes. Four-horned rams are not rare among them and there appears to be little objection

195

FIG. 7 : 24. Greek helmet, sixth century B.C., showing a slightly 'ram's-nosed' sheep with normal horns with everted tips, small stiff ears and no ruff. This type should be related to the early Mesopotamian wool-sheep rather than to the moufflon of Cyprus

to regarding the Hunia as allied to the four-horned sheep of Europe. Merchants could be seen driving flocks of sheep carrying loads of thirty-five to forty pounds each. These were placed on their backs without cords. This observation is mentioned by Major Skinner in *Jardine's Natural History*. This writer mentions incidentally that in 1830 or thereabouts children in South America used sheep to ride to school on.

Another Himalayan breed is the barwal. The rams with their massive horns, the bases of which almost touch each other, suggest the presence of argali blood. They are used as fighting sheep. The so-called unicorn sheep of Nepal belong to this breed. Searing of the horn-buds with a hot iron causes the horns to grow upwards in a fused condition.

In the hotter parts of India breeds of sheep are kept which are closely related to those of western Asia and Africa. The dumba, which occurs from Turkestan to western India, is a fat-tailed breed. Others belong to the long-legged and lop-eared groups. There is no archaeological evidence for their history.

FIG. 7 : 25. Gold mohur of Mughal Emperor Jahangir, A.D. 1605–1627, showing fat-tailed sheep. This breed was brought to India by the Moslem conquerors. On this coin it figures as a zodiacal symbol for Ares. Jahangir was an unconventional Moslem ruler, who, under Hindu influence, placed animal and human figures on his coinage. Author's collection. Photo by Frank Purvey of B. A. Seaby Ltd. Natural size

Summary and conclusion

The complex picture presented by the history of domesticated sheep may be summarized as follows:

1. The sheep was domesticated with the aid of the dog before agriculture was fully developed. The sheepdog played a vital part in the domestication of ruminants.

2. The original centre of domestication is the Aralo-Caspian steppe and Turkestan. Thence sheep-keeping spread early into Persia, and later into Mesopotamia.

3. The domesticated race of wild sheep was in the first instance the arkal, which belongs to the species of the urial. For the sake of convenience this group is here called the urial group.

4. The five main breeds which had reached Mesopotamia by about 2000 B.C. were: (1) the screw-horned hair-sheep (also in Egypt); (2) the screw-horned wool-sheep; (3) the zackelschaf; (4) the ammon's horn wool-sheep and (5) the ammon's horn fat-tailed wool-sheep. All these were of urial stock, so far as is known.

5. The Asiatic moufflon appears to have been domesticated occasionally. Moufflon descendants exist as an early stratum in tropical Africa. Unless they are derived from the European subspecies, they must have reached their present habitats by way of Egypt before Gerzean times, when the Mesopotamian breed (1) was established.

6. The ammon's horn wool-sheep (Mesopotamian breed (4)) reached Egypt from the East in Middle Kingdom times and subsequently replaced the earlier breed.

7. Europe experienced three major waves of introduction. Domestic sheep of urial stock (Mesopotamian breeds (2) and (3)) were brought to the Balkan peninsula and thence breed (2) was taken as far west as Switzerland by the Danubian immigration (turbary sheep). Another domesticated sheep was present to the north and west of the great forest belt, probably also in the Neolithic, certainly from the Calcolithic onwards, which was of moufflon stock (Soay type). Subsequently the two intermingled, the turbary sheep penetrating into the area of the Soay type. The third

197

wave of domestic sheep to reach Europe was one of the Mesopotamian type (4) which had been established in Egypt from the New Kingdom onwards and thence spread to many Mediterranean lands, including Greece, Italy and Spain. It followed the Roman conquest to the north. The merino belongs to this group which proved superior to all others in the quality of its wool.

8. In so far as sheep are kept in India, Tibet and other countries of east and south Asia, they are of western derivation, and basically of urial stock. Argali blood has, however, been introduced repeatedly, and a few breeds are claimed to be of almost pure argali stock.

Technological aspects

Fat is a substance with many industrial uses. Before domestication began, it had to be obtained from game animals. With the domestication of the sheep it became available in practically any quantity required. Sheep fat was in due course replaced by vegetable oils in the Neolithic, though for culinary purposes it continued in esteem among Eastern peoples. Nevertheless, the numerous technological uses of fats almost certainly were greatly developed as the result of the domestication of the sheep.

The use of wool was probably discovered when the peculiar mode of moulting in large coherent patches was observed by the first domesticators. It would have been easy to make sheets of felt from such material, and felt-making has remained an important industry in many parts of central Asia, where it is even today associated with nomadic culture. Spinning and weaving were probably first practised with vegetable materials.

Woven cloth made of wool was not readily accepted in areas where good plant fibre, mainly flax, was available and where the climate was sufficiently mild. It therefore developed mainly in climates with a cold winter, and its subsequent spread to warmer zones was probably due to the development of finer qualities of wool.

It thus appears that the domestication of the sheep, apart from ensuring a permanent meat supply, also improved greatly the supply of raw materials, of skins, hair, fat and bone. All these became in due course available from other sources, namely the other domesticated ruminants. But the production of wool has almost entirely remained a monopoly of the sheep.

This chapter may be concluded with a report on the use of sheep as fuel, incredible as it may seem. J. Holland (1835, pp. 15–16) writes as follows:

Wood was formerly so scarce at Buenos Ayres, and cattle so plentiful, that sheep were actually driven into the furnaces of lime-kilns, in order to answer the purposes of fuel. This fact could hardly have been mentioned as credible, however undoubted, if a decree of the King of Spain, prohibiting this barbarous custom, were not still preserved in the archives of Buenos Ayres.

Mammals Domesticated in the Early Agricultural Phase:
The Crop-robbers

THE first step towards food production as distinct from food-gathering was made when goat and sheep were brought under the control of nomadic man and his dog. The second step was the invention of agriculture, which settled man by tying him to the land.

Agriculture, especially in the countries of the river-civilizations, has a by-product which made it possible to domesticate other species of animals, namely the waste vegetation of fallow land and the offals of food plants, such as straw and coarse leaves. It also led to the growing of fodder plants. Domesticated animals could now be penned or stabled and fodder could be brought to them as needed. When this stage had been reached in the early Neolithic, the large ruminants began to interfere with the new artificially created environment. They came as crop-robbers but ended up as domesticated beasts in the pens and stables of the Neolithic farmer.

The large ruminants which were thus taken over by man are cattle (ox), Indian buffalo (arnee), yak, banteng and one or two others. Only the prehistory of cattle is reasonably well known. Moreover, it deserves particular consideration in view of the influence it has exerted on early farming and technology. Another beast that belongs to the group of crop-robbers is the pig.

8

Cattle

SCIENTIFIC NAMES—*Bos primigenius* Bojanus (aurochs or wild cattle; Europe, North Africa, Egypt, Palestine, Mesopotamia, Persia, remainder of temperate Asia north of central Asiatic mountains. Extinct since seventeenth century).
Bos namadicus Falconer (Pleistocene of India).
Bos (*Novibos*) *sauveli* (Urbain) (kouprey; Recent, Cambodia).

DOMESTICATED BREEDS—*Bos taurus* L. (general name) (*B. longifrons* Owen syn. *B. brachyceros* Owen *in litt.*), *B. indicus* L. (zebu or humped cattle; India and Africa).

Two large-sized species of hollow-horned ruminants have existed in Europe since the early Pleistocene. One of them, the bison, survives in a few specimens. The other, the aurochs, is extinct as a wild animal, though its blood survives in the domesticated breeds of cattle.

Before proceeding further, it is necessary to settle a problem of nomenclature which has arisen in connection with the gradual extermination of these two wild species. Originally, the aurochs, i.e. the ancestor of our domesticated cattle, was known in Germany as the Auer (Latin *urus*, Polish *thur*). The other species, which is now called 'bison' from its Latin name, was known in Germany as the Wisent (Polish *żubr*). When, in the course of the seventeenth century, the aurochs became extinct and a legendary animal, its name came to be applied indiscriminately to the extinct species as well as the bison. By that time the latter also had been exterminated in west and central Europe, and was surviving only in the remote parts of Poland, Lithuania and Prussia, and farther east. Hence 'aurochs' came to mean simply a large wild bovine and, eventually, the only surviving species, the bison.

This was the state of things when the scientific study of animals began, and the

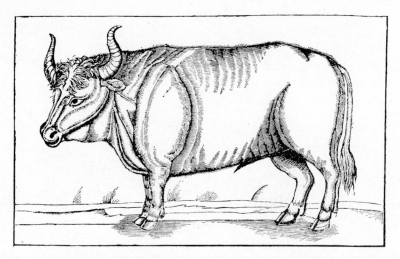

FIG. 8 : 1. Aurochs as depicted by Heberstain, 1549

word 'aurochs' quite naturally was accepted as the proper one for the bison, even in some scientific writings. By now, however, this mistake has been corrected and all serious publications use 'aurochs' properly to denote wild cattle, the ancestor of the domesticated breeds.

Domesticated cattle (in the strict sense of the word) are the descendants of a group of races of *Bos primigenius*, the urus or aurochs. Its economic significance increased as civilization advanced and today it is the most important of all domesticated animals as a producer of meat, milk and hides. It is certain that its domestication was undertaken before 4000 B.C., but nothing is known of its actual beginnings. There are many theories to explain the differences of present-day breeds by deriving them from various types of wild cattle. In addition, it is possible that inter-specific crossing has played a part in the development of some of the Eastern breeds.

Distribution of the wild species
Wild cattle are regarded as a genus, *Bos*, different from the bison (*Bison*), the yak (*Poëphagus*), the gaur group (*Bibos*), the Indian buffalo (*Bubalus*), the Anoa (*Anoa*) of the Sunda archipelago and the African buffalo (*Syncerus*). But these so-called genera are so closely related that they can interbreed and produce fertile progeny. Some authorities give recognition to this by uniting all the bovine cattle in one large genus, *Bos*. It is important to realize this in view of the fact that crosses between the species may have influenced the development of domesticated breeds.

A form, the status of which is still doubtful but which is of great potential interest, is the kouprey of Cambodia (Urbain, 1937; Coolidge, 1940; Bohlken, 1958; Braestrup, 1960). In several respects intermediate between *Bos* and *Bibos* it has been interpreted as a primitive wild bovine or as a cross between the two subgenera. More evidence is required to settle this matter.

The true cattle (*Bos* in the strict sense) are most closely related to the south Asiatic gaur and banteng, from which they appear to have become separated in the course of the Upper Pliocene. In the Siwaliks of India a *Bos acutifrons* occurs, which Pilgrim regards as the possible ancestor of the Pleistocene wild cattle, i.e. of both *Bos namadicus* of India and of *Bos primigenius* of Europe. An Asiatic origin of the group is altogether likely, since the aurochs is either very rare or altogether absent in the Lower Pleistocene of Europe. It became fairly frequent in the Great Interglacial, but not abundant until after the end of the Ice Age. With no ancestral forms known from anywhere in Europe (for the *Leptobos* of the Italian Villafranchian are not ancestral to *Bos*, according to Merla), this increase in the frequency of wild cattle looks very much like an invasion from elsewhere, attempted repeatedly and succeeding finally in the Holocene. By this time the species had spread as far west as Spain and Morocco and eastwards to China and Siberia. It did not, however, reach North America. This almost universal distribution of the wild species in the temperate zones of the Old World makes it even more difficult to discover the original centre of domestication.

The external appearance of wild cattle is well known. The last survivor died in a Polish park in 1627, and there are several good descriptions available, including illustrations. The bulls were large, up to six and a half feet at the shoulder, and often equipped with very long horns. The best surviving picture was discovered by the British zoologist Hamilton Smith in an Augsburg shop early in the last century. The picture itself is lost, but a good reproduction exists (Fig. 8 : 2). It must be

FIG. 8 : 2. The aurochs based on a picture of the last surviving specimen found by Hamilton Smith in an Augsburg shop and published in 1827

noted, however, that it does not represent the large type of bull which was so common in the late Pleistocene and the early Holocene. This type had horns which turn first outwards and then forwards, with the tips slightly turned upwards. In Europe it is safe to say that rising horns, as shown in the Augsburg picture, are characteristic of weak individuals and possibly of cows.

The colour of the hair coat of the bull was black with a white stripe along the back and white curly hair between the horns; the muzzle was white or greyish. The summer coat was more sleek, especially in the southern races, whilst the winter coat was thick and somewhat curly. This appears to have been the normal coloration in central Europe. Towards the south and west, the line on the back tended to be yellowish or reddish. Other variants show a large diffused saddle of lighter colour, brown or fawn, and it is conceivable that some races normally retained such relatively light colours even in old bulls. It appears that the cows were mostly brownish red, occasionally diffused with black, but some had the male colour though with a pronounced brown or fawn saddle that would spread over the sides of the belly. There are still cattle showing the wild colours in Corsica, parts of south-west Europe and in North Africa, especially Morocco. The calves of both sexes appear to have been red until about six months old.

The various characteristics of the aurochs, such as size and shape of horn, stature and coloration, are still to be found in certain domesticated breeds, but they are not all combined in a single breed; were it so the aurochs would still be alive. In 1921 the idea occurred to Lutz and Heinz Heck that it might be possible to 'reconstitute' the aurochs by crossing breeds of cattle that exhibit certain characteristics of the wild ancestor. Genetically it seems that many domesticated breeds are mutations with recessive genes, and that several of the features, such as single colour, are due to the absence of certain genes which are present in other breeds. If, therefore, one should mix all the available domesticated breeds, there is a chance that eventually a breed would be obtained in which many or most of the genes of the aurochs would be combined. This, though obviously not exactly identical with the ancestral aurochs, would at least resemble it fairly closely and might breed true. The attempt has been remarkably successful. Heinz Heck, Director of the Munich Zoo, crossed Hungarian and Podolian steppe cattle, Scottish Highland cattle, grey and brown Alpine breeds, piebald Friesians and Corsicans. After some years of breeding the first two specimens turned up, one male and one female, which had the desired characteristics of the aurochs. These 'reconstituted aurochsen' continued to breed fairly true to type. No throw-backs are said to have occurred, and the only variation is in the intensity of coloration and the degree of development of the horns, characters known as variable in the wild ancestor. By 1951 there were forty of these reconstituted aurochsen living (Heck, 1951).

Another breeding experiment was carried out by Professor Lutz Heck (1952) in the Zoological Gardens, Berlin (Fig. 8 : 3). He started from material of south-west European origin, namely Spanish fighting cattle, the Camargue breed of the Lower Rhône, and Corsican cattle. In addition, he used English park cattle. Since these are more like aurochsen than the breeds used in Munich, a satisfactory result was obtained within a very short time. Unfortunately, the Berlin stock was lost during the war, but some specimens are surviving in the zoological gardens of Augsburg, Cologne and the Neanderthal. Others which had been placed in the famous forest of Białowieża in eastern Poland are known to have survived.

FIG. 8 : 3. 'Reconstituted' aurochs in Berlin Zoo. Result of breeding experiments carried out by Professor Lutz Heck. Photo Lutz Heck

It is interesting to note that, together with the physical, the mental characteristics of the aurochs reappeared. The 'reconstituted' animals are fierce, temperamental and extremely agile if they are allowed to run wild; and in Białowieża (Poland), Rominten (east Prussia) and the Schorfheide, near Berlin, they became extremely shy. The justification of these experiments undoubtedly lies in the advantage of having live animals which represent the ancestral type with reasonable accuracy and thus provide a more convincing picture than any reconstruction ever can.

It may be noted that there are certain differences between the Berlin and Munich breeds. The former, very naturally, appear to resemble the south-west European race and some specimens can be matched almost exactly with French and Spanish cave paintings. The Munich breed is perhaps more characteristic of the aurochs of central Europe; it is more heavily built and has a tendency to develop a dewlap. The horns of the Berlin breed are almost exactly like those of the fossil aurochs, though smaller. Those of the Munich stock betray their origin from Hungarian steppe and Scottish Highland cattle in the lateral expansion of the horns. In view of the variability of the wild ancestor, however, this matters little.

The horn form, in particular, seems to have been variable even within small geographical areas. In the Dordogne, during the Last Glaciation, aurochsen with drooping horns were frequent, as indicated by cave art (Fig. 8 : 4). In the British

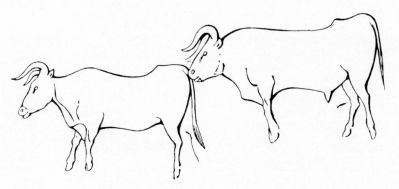

FIG. 8 : 4. Wild aurochs bull following a cow. Magdalenian engraving on a stalagmite in the Grotte de la Mairie, Teyjat, near Combarelles, Dordogne, France. Length of engraving about 1.22 metres. Note attempt made by artist to show characteristic curvature of the horns. After Breuil

Isles during the Great Interglacial large down-curved horns were comparatively common, but they occur together with others of normal type, in which the tips of the horns lie at the level of the crest between the horns or even higher (Fig. 8 : 5). Horns exhibiting an upward trend appear to have been rare in the European wild population, though they were not absent, and in some areas they were considerably more frequent than in others. It is possible that Egypt was one of these areas. Duerst described as *Bos taurus macrocerus* a breed which perhaps survives in some central African breeds of today. Upturned horns occur again in the Indian *Bos namadicus*, a wild race resembling the Egyptian form in some ways. The wild cattle of Anau in Turkestan, found in the lowermost layers (Ia), were regarded as *Bos namadicus* by Duerst (1908), and he believed that during Period Ib there originated from it a domesticated breed that was like that of ancient Egypt. From Period II onwards small short-horn cattle began to replace this older breed. At Shah Tepé, northern Persia, Amschler (1940a) found a large skull with stout down-curved horns, which he believes to belong to a wild specimen. If he is right in his assumption there would have existed not far from Anau a wild race possibly ancestral to the well-known *longifrons* group of domesticated breeds. Amschler's specimen comes from Level III,

which is approximately contemporary with Anau II, the age of which has been given as 2500 to 3000 B.C. Domesticated *longifrons* cattle, however, were found both above and below the level of the supposedly wild specimen.

To sum up, the aurochs varied a great deal in horn shape and size, both individually and geographically. Unfortunately, only a few finds have been properly described, and there are great gaps in our knowledge. Where a detailed regional investigation of the available materials has been carried out, as by Leithner (1927) and Lehmann (1949) in central Europe, La Baume (1947b) in the Val di Chiana (Tuscany), and Portis (1907) near Rome, the great variability around a standard type is very obvious. A male from which any one of the domesticated breeds may have been derived is therefore likely to have been available almost anywhere. Nevertheless, one is inclined to believe that a domesticated breed has descended from that wild geographical race which exhibits its characters most frequently.

The wild cattle on the friezes in the Aurignacian cave of Lascaux in south-west France are so well drawn that they deserve close study. They are the best prehistoric pictures available of the wild ancestors of domesticated cattle, and all belong to *Bos primigenius*. In his monograph on this cave Windels (1948) attributes certain specimens to *Bos longifrons*, thus implying that a separate wild species existed at that time. This is not so (Zeuner, 1953b). The identification by Windels appears to have relied mainly on the slender head shown (Fig. 8 : 6), in fact they are cows of *Bos primigenius.*

Fig. 8 : 6. A red cow from the cave of Lascaux with a black head and a white stripe along the back. In all probability the head was merely much darker than the body, a type of coloration which still occurs in certain domesticated breeds. After Windels

The coloration of *Bos primigenius* is well known, as has been explained above. The black or reddish-black bulls with their light-coloured line extending along the back, and some similar hair between the horns, are shown in Lascaux, and so are the usually reddish-brown cows with their darker heads and legs. The black bull, No. 26, shows the coloration particularly well (Fig. 8 : 7). It has been suggested that attempts were made to re-draw the profile of the back, but I am inclined to regard the double line as a way of showing the white line on the back. The cow, No. 21, also shows the light stripe on the back, and, in addition, the dark head (Fig. 8 : 6).

Apart from these normal-coloured bulls and cows of Lascaux, there are some unusual ones shown in outline only, or filled in with white and a certain amount of black stippling. Since the characteristics of normal coloration are shown so accurately, these individuals have to be taken seriously. I have always held the view that they were intended to represent rare pale-coloured or albinotic specimens, such as occur occasionally in wild herds of other animals. The white stag, for instance, has haunted the imagination of hunters for centuries, although few indeed have ever been killed.

The white cattle of Lascaux appear to have been either practically white, with small blackish spots on the head and the foreportion of the body (Fig. 8 : 8), or in

FIG. 8 : 7. Bull of *Bos primigenius* of the Late Pleistocene as depicted in the cave of Lascaux, south-west France. Note the white stripe along the back. Upper Palaeolithic. After Windels

FIG. 8 : 8. Another bull from the cave of Lascaux, with long horns. Although only the forepart is shown, this specimen appears to have been pale-coloured and dappled. After Windels

addition with a black nose and chin (Fig 8 : 9). The legs appear always to have been dark. Similar coloration occurs in English park cattle, a resemblance which Heck (1952) regards as evidence for the primitive character of this group of domesticated breeds (e.g. Chillingham, Cadzow). McKenny Hughes and Hedger Wallace, however, maintain that our white cattle are the descendants of cattle imported during

FIG. 8 : 9. Another bull from the cave of Lascaux, with exceptionally long horns. This appears to have been a pale-coloured specimen with black dots on head and a dark muzzle. After Windels

the Romano-British period, and there are indeed plenty of similar white cattle to be seen in parts of Italy. Whitehead (1953) is also inclined to hold this view. Whilst one cannot therefore agree that the white cattle are the modern survivors of *Bos primigenius*, Heck's idea that white specimens had a magical value remains acceptable.

The only problem is whether such white specimens really existed in nature. In the case of *Bos primigenius*, a species extinct in the wild state, this can no longer be verified, but there is suggestive evidence available concerning the American bison. Colour aberrations of this normally brown species were described by Garretson (1938). Among the herds that thronged the prairies in the nineteenth century, pied, spotted, light-grey and creamy individuals occurred, though rarely. This author illustrates a white bison skin with a dark head and some irregular black cloudiness mainly on the forepart of the body. This pattern is very reminiscent of the white

Lascaux aurochsen. It may therefore be said that, in a species so closely related to *Bos primigenius* as is the American bison, individuals not unlike those shown in Lascaux Cave do occur. Their conspicuousness on the Lascaux friezes suggests that they attracted the attention of the Upper Palaeolithic hunters. Since most of the cave art of that period was nothing but hunting magic, it is reasonable to attribute a magical significance to these specimens shown in the cave.

Domestication

Archaeological evidence at present available shows that by about 2500 B.C. there were already several well-characterized breeds of domesticated cattle in existence; the beginnings of cattle domestication, therefore, are far earlier than this date. In India, and indeed Mesopotamia, humped cattle were in existence in the fourth millennium B.C. besides other mostly large breeds that appear to be derived from local races of *Bos primigenius*. In Egypt several breeds were known, certain of which were piebald and others hornless.

The evidence from Europe

In Europe, however, a breed appears in the early Neolithic which is generally called *Bos longifrons* (correctly *Bos brachyceros* Owen; Zeuner, 1962b). The view is held, among both zoologists and archaeologists, that it was a very small beast. McKenny Hughes in 1896 described it as 'a very small animal; probably not larger than a Kerry cow'. Measurements carried out by M. Maitland Howard have shown, however, that the Neolithic cattle were often not inferior in size to many of the modern breeds, and the belief in their small size is probably in part due to the large number of immature specimens found in prehistoric sites. But much work remains to be done about their osteology in spite of an enormous volume of literature already in existence. Hescheler and Kuhn (1949) have rightly pointed out that in most sites the number of measured specimens available is small.

Longifrons cattle were first made known to science by Owen in 1846 under the name of *Bos brachyceros*. A few years later the large material excavated from the Swiss lake-dwellings was monographed by Rütimeyer (1862). He distinguished three breeds: *brachyceros*, *primigenius* and *trochoceros*. Of these, the *primigenius* breed is believed to be descended from the wild *Bos primigenius*. The *trochoceros* breed was withdrawn by Rütimeyer himself as an individual variant of the *primigenius* breed in 1867. Its characters are most noted in the modern *frontosus* cattle, such as the Bernese cattle of Switzerland and similar piebald breeds. The distinction of *brachyceros* and *primigenius* breeds, however, has been maintained for a century. What does it imply?

Longifrons cows are characterized by the height of the forehead above the orbits (hence the name *longifrons*), small horns curved forwards and inwards, a pronounced eminence on the frontal ridge between the horns and a high parieto-occipital region.

These features are striking when compared with *Bos primigenius* (Figs. 8 : 10, 8 : 11 and 8 : 12), though there is a tendency even among wild European urus to show one or two of them occasionally. In the early Neolithic of Switzerland, however, the 'peat cow', as the *longifrons* cattle were termed, is readily distinguishable even from domesticated *primigenius* breeds.

In the lowermost stratum of the Neolithic site of Saint-Aubin, on Lake Bienne, Switzerland, Dottrens (1946, 1947) found exclusively *longifrons* cattle, and other sites had given the same results to Rütimeyer and other investigators. In other early sites, such as Egolzwil 2 and Seematte-Gelfingen on Lake Zürich, however, which also belong to the earliest lake-dwellings of Switzerland, Hescheler and Rüeger found three categories of size, the largest of which comprises the wild *Bos primigenius*. The authors stress the absence of diminutive specimens. With a minimum height of 1·15 m. at the withers, the smallest group exceeds many of the modern breeds. Their horn-cores differ from those of the *longifrons* breed and are reminiscent of the aurochs, though small. The middle group may comprise a mixture of the two others. This evidence suggests that in the local early Neolithic some Swiss lake-dwellers bred cattle derived from *Bos primigenius* or at least contaminated with the local wild blood.

It thus appears that the lake-dwellers, who are known to have arrived as immigrants, brought the domesticated *longifrons* breed with them. In due course they would have allowed their stock to interbreed with the local aurochsen, and in any case it would have been difficult to prevent this under primitive conditions.

The fact that *longifrons* cattle can be distinguished from *primigenius*-derived cattle has aroused controversy. Some believe firmly that two wild ancestors must have existed, whilst others consider *longifrons* as a descendant of the wild *Bos primigenius*. In practice it is difficult to prove either alternative, but the second is more probable. The vast majority of fossil skulls of aurochsen are of males which are harder and, therefore, more resistant to destruction than those of females, while the vast majority of *longifrons* skulls come from cows, as is to be expected in domesticated herds. The differences are thus accentuated by comparing the bulls of one form with the cows of another. Some authors have pointed out that the characters of *longifrons* are not altogether absent in *primigenius*, especially in the smaller and immature specimens and in the female sex. Leithner comes to the conclusion that there is no reason not to derive *longifrons* cattle from the European aurochs. From the morphological point of view, he is undoubtedly right.

The archaeological evidence for the sudden appearance of a well-characterized, small, domesticated breed is, however, strongly against local domestication, and the centre of origin of the *longifrons* breed was probably outside Europe. Since no such cattle are believed to occur anywhere in the Mediterranean region or the northeast at so early a period, investigators have again and again attempted to find the origins of the *longifrons* cattle in the more northerly parts of western Asia. It is

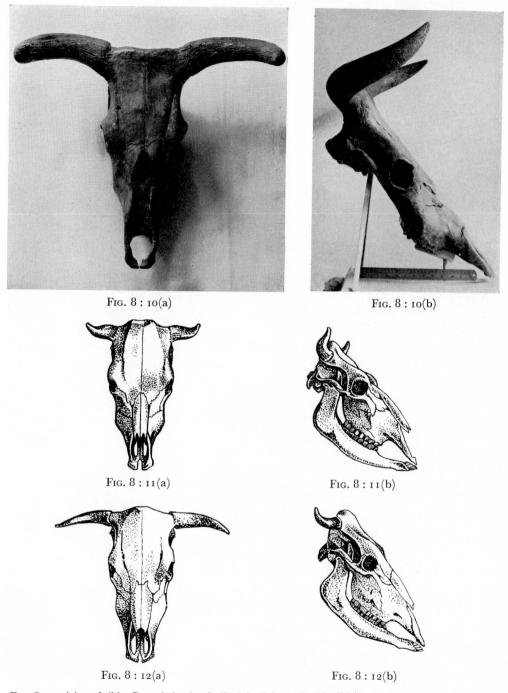

Fig. 8 : 10(a)

Fig. 8 : 10(b)

Fig. 8 : 11(a)

Fig. 8 : 11(b)

Fig. 8 : 12(a)

Fig. 8 : 12(b)

Fig. 8 : 10 (a) and (b). *Bos primigenius* skull. A bull from the Neolithic—earliest Bronze Age site of Dorchester, Oxon. Excavation by Prof. R. C. Atkinson. Specimen in Dept. Environmental Archaeology collection

Fig. 8 : 11 (a) and (b). Skull of the *brachyceros* breed, Switzerland. After Hescheler and Kuhn

Fig. 8 : 12 (a) and (b). Skull of the so-called *frontosus* breed. After Hescheler and Kuhn

possible that the breed is indeed derived from there. If Amschler is right in regarding his large *brachyceros* skull from Shah Tepé as a wild '*longifrons*', some substance would be given to this hypothesis. But even without it the view remains tenable. An important characteristic of the primitive *longifrons* breed appears to be its small size.[1] Small size is usually regarded as an almost unavoidable result of the first stage of domestication. But the early breeds of the Near and Middle East were by no means small, certainly not so small as some Neolithic *longifrons* of Europe. It appears that these animals may have been bred specifically for small size, or that small size was obtained unintentionally as the result of keeping stock on a starvation diet and in unhealthy conditions. This was regarded as an advantage. It is evident that large cattle are not easily moved from place to place, and that a population which lives in temporary settlements and practises shifting agriculture might prefer large numbers of small-size cattle of a peaceful mentality to small numbers of large-size cattle.

The first indications of the presence of domesticated cattle in northern Europe are at Dyrholmen in Denmark, a site of the Ertebølle period, the fauna of which was investigated by Degerbøl (1942). If domesticated cattle were present there, however, it would not have been the *longifrons* breed but a type more closely resembling *Bos primigenius*. Moreover, the stratigraphy of this site is not clear, and it is possible that these bones are so late as to be contemporary with Neolithic and Bronze Age sites. There is, however, nothing improbable in the occasional occurrence of domesticated descendants of aurochsen in Europe prior to the beginning of the Neolithic proper. An early Neolithic skull from Satrupholm (Schleswig-Holstein; Herre, 1948) is the oldest certain domesticated specimen found in the north. It resembles the aurochs closely, but is smaller.

At Manching, in Bavaria, the La Tène people had cattle of very small size and, as in other domesticated species, a progressive reduction from the Neolithic to the Iron Age is characteristic. Nevertheless, the few large bones present suggest that already in pre-Roman days trade brought cattle from the Roman southern lands into the Celtic areas. In the Roman period large breeds of cattle are present, but with the disintegration of Roman power they disappear again, leaving a stock as small as that of the La Tène period to continue into the Middle Ages (Schneider, 1958).

In the Viking town of Haithabu in Schleswig (Siewing, 1960; A.D. 800–1050), the size of the cattle varies a great deal, covering about the lower half to two-thirds of the total variation of domesticated European cattle. It is very interesting that castration was practised (13 per cent bulls, 32 per cent castrates, 55 per cent cows). Siewing attributes this to the need for draught animals in a place where ships had to be dragged overland from the North Sea rivers to the fjord of the Schlei, which is part of the Baltic.

[1] This was not invariably so (see p. 211).

In some cases the *primigenius* and the *longifrons* stocks have been kept comparatively pure. The Alpine cattle and the Jersey breed, as well as the Shorthorn, are *longifrons* stock. On the other hand, the Hungarian and Podolian steppe cattle, the large-horned cattle of the Romagna in Italy, the Scottish Highland race and the fighting cattle of Spain all represent the *primigenius* stock. But crossing has been practised to such an extent that the vast majority of modern breeds must be regarded as intermediates. In Friesian cattle, for instance, it is possible to find skulls ranging from the *primigenius* type to characteristic *longifrons* specimens. It is probably no longer possible to distinguish modern cattle according to their ancestral stock except in cases such as those quoted in this paragraph.

Evidence from western Asia

At Anau, in western Asia, Duerst found a domesticated *Bos* of large size in Period IB. This long-horned form had nothing to do with *longifrons*. But in the course of Period II the size of the animals diminished to some extent, possibly because a smaller breed had reached the locality together with other domesticated animals which are known to have appeared at that time. This possibility receives support from the evidence of Shah Tepé in northern Persia where Amschler found a *longifrons* breed.

In Mesopotamia many of the illustrations of domesticated cattle are evidently of beasts derived from *Bos primigenius* and not related to the *longifrons* breed (Fig. 8 : 13). In Arpachiyah, near Mosul, a site that dates from the Tell Halaf period, about 4500 B.C., thus antedating the finds from Shah Tepé and Anau considerably, there are many of these representations. Unfortunately, the skeletal remains of the animals both wild and domesticated which were contemporary with the earliest inhabitants of the site were not recorded, and so we are thrown back on artistic evidence only. Here, although there are numerous representations of cattle, sheep,

FIG. 8 : 13. Copper head of a bull (height *c.*11.7 cm.) from Temple of Sin at Khafajeh, Mesopotamia, Early Dynastic II, *c.* 2500 B.C. After Frankfort

goat and pig both in the round, in the form of clay or terracotta figurines and amulets, and painted on the pottery of that 'Halafian' era, not one of these figures shows any of these animals in a domesticated context such as becomes common with the invention of the cylinder seal at a slightly later date.

In spite of this, however, the very number of these figurines, the occasional excellence of the amulets, the fact that the *bucranium* motif was extremely popular on the beautiful painted pottery of this period (Fig. 8 : 14) suggests the possibility of

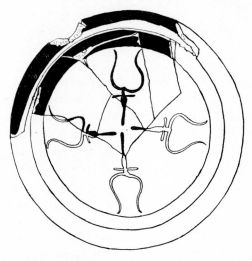

Fig. 8 : 14. Bucranium design on pottery of the Tell Halaf period found at Arpachiyah, *c.* 4500 B.C. After Mallowan and Rose

domestication. Moreover, the economy of Arpachiyah was prosperous enough to afford the manufacture in quantity of luxury articles, such as the finest painted pottery of the time and of exquisite amulets, so that it is very likely to have relied on a fully developed agricultural and stock-producing background. The domestication of cattle can therefore be assumed to have taken place.

Should further evidence be needed, it is provided by the humped cattle ('zebu') of the Indian type. This domesticated form had moved even into northern Mesopotamia by about 4500 B.C. One rather rough and somewhat doubtful figurine of a humped bull was found in the earlier Halafian period at Arpachiyah (Mallowan and Rose, 1935, Fig. 48, No. 14), and thereafter figurines and jar-sealings showing this animal were by no means infrequent through all the predynastic and early dynastic periods in Mesopotamia, and later. Perhaps the best illustration of a humped bull known from Mesopotamia is carved on a fragment of a stone vase that was found by Frankfort (1936) at Tell Agrab (Fig. 8 : 15) in a temple dating from the early dynastic period, although Frankfort himself dates the vase slightly earlier, attributing it to the predynastic period known as the Jamdat Nasr. It would thus date from

FIG. 8 : 15. Zebu depicted on a green steatite vase from Tell Agrab, Mesopotamia. Pre-Sargonic Sumerian, Early Dynastic II–III, *c.* 2700–2800 B.C., or earlier. From same site hornless cattle and domesticated pig are known. After Frankfort

about 3200 B.C., and one fragment depicts a humped bull standing in a stall facing a manger, while another shows a man, probably a priest, whose hands are held in the Sumerian attitude of prayer, sitting outside. The work is typically Sumerian, though the idea depicted, a sacred bull in its stall, is foreign to Sumer but typical of India.

On cylinder seals from the predynastic and early dynastic periods there are carved scenes which indicate that two different types of cattle were favoured, one with short horns and the other with horns that were conspicuously long. The two types derived directly, or indirectly (via a *longifrons* stock), from *Bos primigenius*.

These cylinder seals, together with various sculptured works, are invaluable. Not only do they show the different breeds of cattle, but also scenes with cattle in different domestic contexts, such as a herdsman feeding cattle, or a man driving a bull, or the herding of cows and calves (Fig. 8 : 16). That cattle were used for traction is shown by the figure of a bull drawing the sacred sledge of a goddess. There is also a

FIG. 8 : 16. Domesticated cattle from early Jamdat Nasr period gathered round a shed or hut, *c.* 3000 B.C. Impression of a cylinder seal. After Frankfort

bull shown standing in a sacred boat supporting a shrine on his back (Fig. 8 : 17). In the Temple Oval at Khafajeh, of the Early Dynastic III period, a limestone plaque was found depicting harnessed bulls probably drawing a sacred vehicle

FIG. 8 : 17. Cattle being used for transport. Bull carrying a shrine on its back. Uruk period, Mesopotamia. After Frankfort

(Frankfort, 1939). From the early dynastic temple of A-Anni-Pad-Da at Ur came a mosaic frieze with a milking scene (Fig. 8 : 18). It demonstrates that the domesticated cattle of that period were milked from the back instead of from the side, a position that perhaps originated in the fact that sheep and goats were milked from behind. This, incidentally, may be regarded as evidence for the priority of the domestication of these species over that of the cattle. A stone vase from Tell Agrab (Fig. 8 : 19) of about the same date, or slightly earlier, *c.* 3200 B.C., appears to show that cattle were used for work in the fields, as they are in the Near East today, either for drawing the plough or for treading out the corn on the threshing floors. This vase

Fig. 8 : 18. Mosaic frieze from the façade of A-Anni-Pad-Da's temple of Nin-Kharsaf, Ur, Mesopotamia, *c*. 2900 B.C., showing cows being milked from behind—goat-fashion. After Woolley

Fig. 8 : 19. Small bowl from Tell Agrab, Mesopotamia, Jamdat Nasr period, *c*. 3000 B.C., showing a cow or calf polled on the right side. After Frankfort

shows a man coming in from the fields carrying his flail and accompanied by a cow; a calf runs out to meet the cow, who licks it in greeting.

It should here be mentioned that on this vase, and on a cylinder seal of the same period, the Jamdat Nasr, which shows three cows moving in procession to the right, all the grown animals are shown with one horn only. This horn is the left one in each case, in other words the horn on the side farthest away. Therefore it is not, as might be expected, a conventional way of showing the side-view of one horn hiding the other, in which case only the nearest and therefore concealing horn would be expected to be shown. It seems possible that this curious presentation may indicate 'polling', the mutilation or cutting-off of one of the horns, practised at this period perhaps in connection with some agricultural technique or some religious conception.

219

The idea is further supported by the indication of a scar where the right horn was cut off (Fig. 8 : 20).

During the Akkadian dynasty, about 2200 B.C., one cylinder seal from Ur shows a water buffalo, the treatment of the animal's horns allowing for no doubt

FIG. 8 : 20. Single-horned cattle from the Jamdat Nasr period, c. 3000 B.C., Mesopotamia. This seal impression shows clearly that cattle were polled on the right side, the middle one has a knob on the tip of the horn, perhaps for protection. After Frankfort

FIG. 8 : 21. Bronze statuette of bull having horn tips artificially blunted by knobs (see Fig. 8 : 20). Late Bronze Age or early Iron Age (Nuraghian culture), c. 800 B.C., from Sassari, Sardinia

as to the identification. It is, however, probable that the water buffalo was known in Mesopotamia before this (p. 249).

In ancient Mesopotamia as in other early civilizations the bull played an important part in religion. It will suffice to say that from the renderings of the anthropomorphic bull-men on cylinder seals and statuettes of the early periods the bull was a constant motif in the art and architecture of the country (Fig. 8 : 22). From earliest times, down past the great figures of winged bulls with human heads which guarded the entrances to the palaces of the Assyrian kings, to those which did the same for the palaces of the Achaemenid Persians, in the monumental style, and

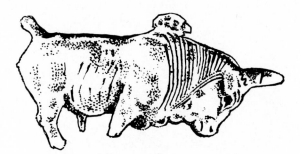

FIG. 8 : 22. One of five ivory carvings of charging bulls from the Palace of Sargon II at Nimrud, Mesopotamia, *c.* 715 B.C. After Mallowan

in the delicate ivories which adorned the furniture, bulls, cows and calves were favourite subjects for artists through the millennia.

Although our record of domesticated cattle in the Near East is fairly complete, it is in Egypt, where the mural art imposed by the religion depicts every form of occupation, that the documentation becomes particularly full.

Before discussing the domestication of cattle in Egypt the slight skeletal evidence for cattle in Mesopotamia must be mentioned. Apart from the mention of cattle from Nineveh (Thompson and Mallowan, 1933), at Tell Asmar (Hilzheimer, 1941) a few specimens were found, and these were inadequate to determine the breed. The specimens were confined to the Early Dynastic III period and the immediately subsequent period which ended at about 2300 B.C. A medium-sized bovine appears to have been kept, which, on the evidence of a pair of horn-cores, seems to have belonged to the group of *primigenius* breeds. That such breeds existed in Mesopotamia in Sumerian times is well established on pictorial evidence, as has been shown earlier.

Evidence in Egypt

In Egypt the evidence for the early domestication of cattle is not very clear. In the Fayum, in the Neolithic A level at Kom W, Miss Bate identified *Bos* in nine cases, but she does not state if there is any evidence for domestication. It appears that the bones from this site come from several periods, and because of their mixed condition must be discounted. The Neolithic A of the Fayum has been dated by the radio-carbon method to about 4540–4100 B.C.

The Sebilian cattle found at Kom Ombo were wild. Gaillard (1934, p. 29)

recognizes a large *Bos* which he identifies with *Bos primigenius*. In addition there is a
'*Bos brachyceros*', of which one frontal has been found. Its crest has the slightly wavy
outline observed in many female skulls of *Bos primigenius*, though the same outline is
characteristic of the *longifrons* breeds. Especially in view of the supposed age of Kom
Ombo ('Paléolithique supérieur'), there is no evidence that cattle were domesticated
in that locality.

At Nagada (Toukh: Gaillard, 1934, p. 73) a small type of cattle is evidenced by a
number of bones, including small metapodials. Horns have not been found, but
the outline of the frontal crest resembles *longifrons* types, as one would expect it to do
in a breed much reduced in size. The Nagada cattle, therefore, may be regarded as
domesticated, but there again the dating evidence for the remains is not clear.

Other predynastic Egyptian sites which have domesticated cattle attributed to
them include Merimde Benisalâme in the delta, and Omari near Cairo, but
further evidence is needed. We are on firmer ground in the Nagada I, or Amratian,
period, the earlier of two consecutive predynastic periods which preceded the rise
of the dynasties in about 3200 B.C. A radiocarbon determination within the
Nagada I period gives about 3700 B.C., a date which is slightly later than the roughly
dated Arpachiyah site in Mesopotamia. At El Amrah (Randall-MacIver and
Mace, 1902) clay models of cattle were found in graves. One consisted of cattle
standing in a row (Fig. 8 : 23). Their horns have the characteristic shape of *Bos*

FIG. 8 : 23. Proto-dynastic (*c.* 3200 B.C.) clay
models of cattle from a grave at El Amrah, Egypt.
After Randall-MacIver and Mace

primigenius, and we must therefore regard them as a primitive breed probably
derived from the local wild cattle of the Nile Valley. The tomb that contained them
is of Sequence Date 36 (near the end of the Nagada I period). A bull, cow and calf
of the same type came from a tomb of Sequence Date 31 (the earliest period of
Nagada I). In addition, a model with long horns rising obliquely upwards dates
from the middle of the Nagada I period. These models suggest that the long-horned

cattle that later on became so popular in Egypt were not only known but also domesticated, at least from the beginning of the predynastic Nagada I period.

Wild cattle of a race apparently closely related to the European abounded in the swamps of the Nile Valley. They are frequently depicted from predynastic times onwards. On the proto-dynastic slate palettes of about 3200 B.C. this wild bull, probably representing the victorious king, is depicted trampling his enemy, a bearded Asiatic (Fig. 8 : 24) as on the 'Bull Palette', or razing the walls of a city

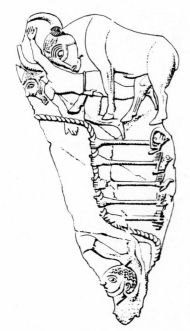

FIG. 8 : 24. Fragment of an Egyptian proto-dynastic (*c.* 3200 B.C.) palette showing a wild bull. After Legge

with his horns as on the Narmer Palette. On yet another palette of this period, representing tribute brought from Libya, a line of bulls is shown. The style in which these wild bulls are shown is somewhat reminiscent of Mesopotamian representations of the species, and the bucranium is once more in evidence.

That wild cattle were indigenous in Egypt explains the appearance of a pure and primitive *primigenius* breed there, from which the later long- and short-horned breeds are both descended.

From the sculptures and hieroglyphs of Egypt four different breeds of domesticated cattle can be deduced. These are a *primigenius* breed with small horns, a *primigenius* breed with lyre horns, a *primigenius* breed with double-lyre horns and hornless cattle (Figs. 8 : 25 and 8 : 26). From the colourings of the painted reliefs, and from the small coloured models which were placed in tombs, the colours of these cattle can be seen. They had plain black, brown, brown and white, black and white, possibly pure white, and white spotted with black like the Lascaux cattle.

The tomb reliefs give a vivid idea of the different activities in which domestic cattle were used, and two of the Old Kingdom tombs give particularly attractive

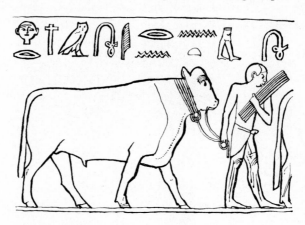

FIG. 8 : 25. An early example of hornless cattle in Egypt, from the tomb of Achti-Hotep, late fifth dynasty, c. 2500 B.C. After Boessneck (1953)

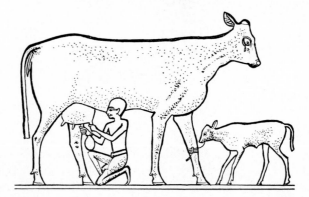

FIG. 8 : 26. Hornless cow, with calf tied to foot, being milked from the side. From coffin of Kawit. Eleventh dynasty, c. 2050 B.C. After Boessneck (1953)

renderings of these scenes (Ti and Mereruka). Here one sees cows drawing ploughs, and bulls being driven on the threshing floors to trample out the corn with their feet. In one scene a cow is shown calving, with the herdsman helping by pulling the calf, and next to her another cow is being milked. Here the milkman works from her side, but the animal's back legs are tied together; she appears to be the mother of twins, as while the milking is in progress one calf is being held away from her and another is tethered by her head to soothe her. The cows in this scene are both of the 'double-lyre' horned type.

The Egyptians also appear to have fattened their cattle by forcible feeding. In the Mereruka tomb (Duell, 1938, Plate 153), three bulls are shown lying down being fed by their herdsmen, whose hands are in the bulls' mouths. A fourth animal is kneeling on one knee, drinking water from a bowl. In the accompanying registers of reliefs the Egyptians are shown forcibly feeding reluctant hyaenas and antelopes; presumably all these animals were being fattened for the table.

The art of roping and throwing a bull, a necessary preliminary to its slaughter, is depicted in the same tomb. Here one sees several men wrestling with the animal to get a rope round its horns and legs, and finally it is brought to its knees. The actual killing of the beast is shown in nearly every tomb. Its legs are tied tightly together, the head is upward and backward, and its throat is then cut. The animal is then carved up in a most scientific way, beginning with the forelegs.

Other reliefs show cattle grazing and moving about the country, always in charge of their herdsmen. As the cultivated area of Egypt is today a network of canals, so it was from the time of the early dynasties, with the additional difficulty of the presence of papyrus and reed swamps which no longer exist. The movement of cattle, therefore, necessitated constant wading, in places where it was shallow enough the herdsmen waded too, carrying the younger calves on their backs; but where the swamps were too deep the herdsmen used reed canoes to which the younger animals were secured by rope and towed, while the grown ones swam. That the herdsmen slept out with their charges is shown by the blankets they carry over their shoulders.

The tomb of Huy, who was the Viceroy of Nubia, northern Sudan, in the reign of Tutankhamun, about 1300 B.C., contains interesting scenes showing the arrival of tribute at the Egyptian Court. These show the long procession of cattle, both long-horned and hornless, and the arrival of the Nubian princes. One of these princes stands in a chariot, driven by a charioteer and drawn by two piebald, hornless bulls. These animals have rich trappings, and decorated caps on their heads, and appear to be properly bitted and not driven on a headstall only. In front, and facing them, stands a groom who is apparently not only laying a soothing hand on their foreheads but is also encouraging them by holding some foodstuff under their noses.

Another interesting scene shows the cattle being transported down the Nile to the Court by boat. Here open boats, propelled by oars, have large cages of open woodwork built upon their decks. In these cages the animals are confined. One shows four bulls, all long-horned, two skewbald and two piebald, and another fragmentary scene shows a hornless animal. The spartan quarters that were provided for cattle being transported by boat contrast strongly with the splendour of the accommodation provided for the Viceroy's chariot horses in the viceregal ship of state.

One group of large, long-horned piebald bulls that are being presented as tribute have most interesting decorations which seem to provide a link with the distant past and the present Sudan. The tips of their horns have been decorated with model open hands, while on their heads between the horns are model negroid heads wearing necklaces, ostrich plumes and earrings. Here there may be a link between a familiar motif on predynastic Nagada I vases, where a female figure is depicted with up-raised arms, probably executing a ritual dance. Today, in the Sudan, the women of the Dinkas perform a dance with their arms held in a similar position which they call the cow dance. They appear to perform this dance because cows are pleasant, useful creatures. The origin of this custom is lost in antiquity, but may well be connected with the African component, which, linked to the Near Eastern, formed the characteristics of the ancient Egyptian civilization. Dinkas also sometimes mutilate one horn of a cow, this gives a 'crumpled' effect which they say makes the horns look more like arms. This 'crumpled' horn can also be seen occasionally among cattle on the Egyptian reliefs. It also reminds one of the single-horned cattle of the Jamdat Nasr period in Mesopotamia already mentioned (Fig. 8 : 20).

The hunting of wild cattle is shown as a favourite sport throughout the dynasties. In an Old Kingdom hunting scene dating to about 2300 B.C. the chase takes place inside a fenced enclosure (Duell, 1938, Plate 24), and here hounds are shown attacking antelopes, while a lion attacks a bull by seizing it by the nose. The same scene appears in the Middle Kingdom, about 1800 B.C. At this period bulls are also shown being hunted in the desert and shot with bows and arrows. Apparently, when brought nearly to a halt they were lassoed and finished by a blow from an axe (Beni Hassan). The most famous scene of wild-bull hunting is that carved on the mortuary temple of Rameses III at Medinet Habu. Here the Pharaoh is shown hunting in reed marshes; he is standing in a chariot drawn by two galloping horses and shooting with bow and arrow. One bull is shown transfixed by arrows, lying on its back dying, and another is brought to its knees wounded, while a third lies on its back dead. These animals appear to have been genuine wild aurochsen, but there were possibly exceptions in later times, when herded domesticated bulls may have been released for hunting.

The humped Indian bull (zebu) is also shown in the reliefs. They were popular only from the eighteenth dynasty onwards (c. 1570 B.C.), and are shown being presented to the temples for sacrifice, for instance at Amarna (Fig. 8 : 27).

The bull and cow were of great importance also in the religion of ancient Egypt. The Apis bull was famous throughout ancient times, and his origin must be looked for in prehistoric days. The earliest written reference to Apis comes in the reign of a second-dynasty king called Khasekemui, and is to be found on the Palermo Stone.

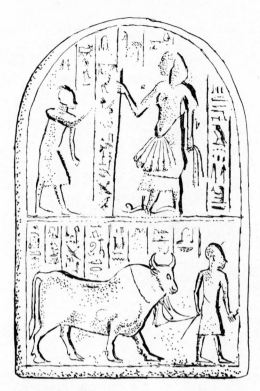

Fig. 8 : 27. Stele of Bebwawi, Amarna, showing what appears to be a zebu bull. Eighteenth
dynasty. After Davies (1908)

This stone contains the annals of the first two Egyptian dynasties, together with
hints of the earlier times before the country was united under one king. Dating to
about 2800 B.C. it is one of the earliest truly historical documents extant. The Apis
bull had to fulfil certain requirements: he had to have a saddle-mark of different-
coloured hair,[1] and a coloured spot on his tongue. A complicated ritual developed
round the animal which is well documented in the religious writings of ancient
Egypt. In the later dynasties, about 700 B.C., and probably much earlier as well (but
archaeological evidence is still lacking), the dead Apis was mummified, buried in a
vast sarcophagus and placed in a great rock-cut vault under the desert at Saqqarah.
From pictorial evidence it seems that Apis was of the long lyre-horned breed of
cattle, but with the special markings, and that there was no distinct Apis breed as
such.

There were at least four other sacred bulls in the earliest days of dynastic Egypt
which probably became assimilated by Apis. Hathor, the sacred cow, was also of

[1] This is evidently the pale saddle-patch so common in wild cattle.

227

very ancient and probably foreign origin. When depicted she is usually shown full-face, a human head with cow's horns, a convention utterly foreign to Egyptian art. Two Hathor-like heads crown the Narmer Palette which dates to about 3200 B.C. (Fig. 8 : 28). Various bucrania are also shown on the standards of ships painted on

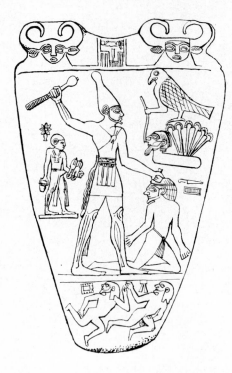

FIG. 8 : 28. Proto-dynastic Egyptian palette of Narmer (*c.* 3200 B.C.) with two bulls' heads. Also shows hawk which played an important part in the religion of Egypt. After Flinders Petrie

the pottery of the Nagada II period, and on ivory plaques from the royal tombs of the first dynasty. It is possible that these bucrania indicate a cultural contact with Mesopotamia.

That the early economy of Egypt was based on agriculture and livestock is evident, but it is interesting to note that one of the best aids to our knowledge of the early chronology is by the records of the cattle census that was made all over the country every two years. The earliest records of this census are to be found on the above-mentioned Palermo Stone. This census was taken so that the wealth of the country and the amount of tax payable in kind could be determined. Its existence confirms that by the time of the first dynasties cattle as well as other livestock had been long established in Egypt.

In ancient Jericho no skeletal evidence has so far been found proving that cattle were domesticated in the pre-pottery and pottery Neolithic phases. The bones suggest the presence of both bulls and cows which, however, are likely to have been hunted. The horns of the males are indistinguishable from these of *Bos primigenius*. In the pottery Neolithic it is more likely that domestication of cattle had begun. There is a crude and poorly preserved clay figurine (Kenyon, 1953, pl. XXXVII) which appears to have represented an ox-like animal.

The Cretan bull cult

The cult of the bull reached the height of complexity in Minoan Crete. The bull-leaping sport described by Sir Arthur Evans from mural paintings found in the palace at Knossos (Fig. 8 : 29) is so well known that it has even been found worthy to decorate one of the postage stamps of modern Greece.

FIG. 8 : 29. Minoan bull sports as shown in Palace of Minos, Knossos, Crete. Piebald coat shows that these bulls belonged to a domesticated breed. After Evans

There has been much controversy over the question of whether these bulls were domesticated or wild. Most workers rather like the idea of regarding the fierce animals shown as wild aurochsen, although Spanish fighting cattle of the present day are a domesticated breed. There is no argument for or against the domesticated condition in fierceness alone. On the other hand, many Minoan bulls are shown with a very clear piebald or skewbald pattern on the skin, which is not normal in the wild state. Others are spotted with starlike marks, a pattern also known in certain breeds of cattle. Van Lengerken (1955) defends the truly wild nature of the Cretan cattle by pointing out a white chalcedony engraving of Late Minoan age, which shows a calf hit by an arrow. On the other hand, steer-throwing experts maintain that the feats performed by the acrobats seizing the bull by the horns were possible only with beasts specially bred or trained. In my opinion the frequent occurrence of piebald, skewbald or spotted specimens settles the matter in favour of domesticated stock (Fig. 8 : 30i). Moreover, it is very unlikely that the isolated island of Crete, surrounded by deep sea, was ever reached by *Bos primigenius*. The same applies to

FIG. 8 : 30. Sketches illustrating the apparent Mesopotamian connections of the Minoan bull cult. Bull and lion are of equal strength, but the lion attacks the bull (a–c); gods and man subdue the bull, the lion contesting it (d–e), bulls symbolized as humans with animals' heads, having become gods or demons; they can be subdued by man (f–g). Bull sports developing in connection with the capture of feral (but domesticated!) beasts, demonstrating the supremacy of man over the animal (h–i). Bull-sacrifices have developed in which the double-axe, of Mesopotamian origin, plays a part (j–k). The god, triumphantly standing on the bull, holds up his double-axe (l–m). This series clearly shows Eastern origin and gradual penetration to Crete, Greece and even Hungary. The bull sports of Crete may have been inspired by Egypt, but the double-axe and the humped bull point to Mesopotamia.

(a) Lion attacking bull. Relief on stone cup, Sumerian, c. 2500 B.C.

(b) Lion attacking bull, Ras Shamra, Syria, c. 1400 B.C.

(c) Lion attacking bull, Minoan gold seal, Crete

(d) God subduing bull, lion contesting the act. Neo-Babylonian seal. Note that the bull is humped

(e) Bull being forced down by a man. Jasper seal from Mycenae, probably under Minoan influence. After Evans

(f) Syro-Hittite bull-men, from a cylinder seal

(g) Theseus killing the Minotaur, Cretan seal. Minotaur shown as bull-headed man

(h) Capturing a bull, Egyptian, eighteenth dynasty, c. 1450 B.C.

(i) Bull sports in Mycenaean Greece. Palace at Tiryns, Pelopenesos. The bull is white and red, hence definitely domesticated. After Lengerken

(j) Double-axe amulet from Arpachiyah, Iraq, c. 4500 B.C. See also Fig. 8 : 33. After Mallowan

(k) Bull's head and double-axe symbol at Knossos, Crete

(l) Hittite god standing on humped bull and holding double-axe, c. 900 B.C. Humped bull suggests Eastern provenance, see (d)

(m) The same god, now called Jupiter Dolichenos, on a Roman bronze relief from Hungary. Note the double-axe. The bull is European

(n) Milking from behind, a rare survival of the ancient practice (see Fig. 8 : 18). Late Minoan seal from Knossos, Crete

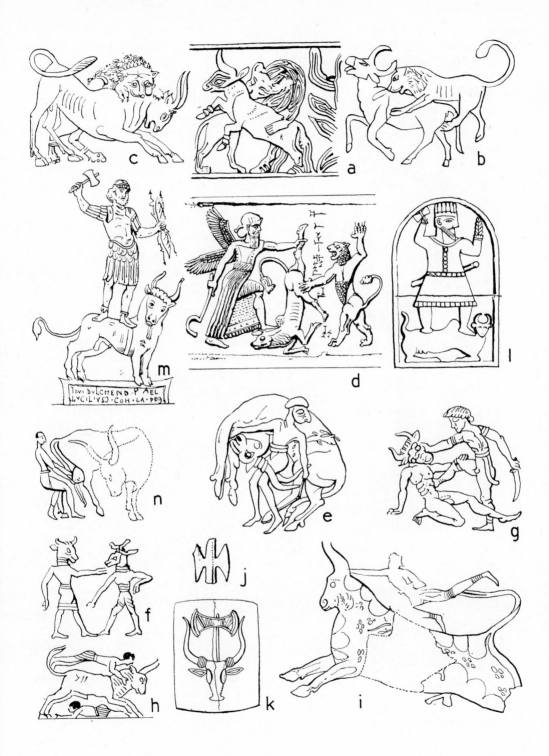

c a b

m d l

n e g

f j i

h k

Cyprus, which is much nearer the Asiatic mainland. It is likely therefore that Neolithic cattle-breeders arrived in Crete at some remote time, conceivably at the

(a)

beginning of the pre-Early Minoan Neolithic, about 3500 B.C. About the same time Khirokitia in Cyprus did not yet own cattle. It is conceivable that once cattle had reached the island of Crete with the aid of man some became feral and roamed the countryside, and that this was the stock from which the beasts for bull-leaping sports and sacrifices were obtained.

(b)

There is no doubt that these bulls had to be caught without injury. Several scenes of capture are known, the most elaborate being depicted on the two cups from Vapheio near Sparta, which are considered to be of Minoan origin[1] (Figs. 8 : 31 and 8 : 32) and date from about 1500 B.C. One of the cups shows the animals being captured by means of a net and the ensuing difficulties, whilst the other depicts the ensnaring of a bull by a decoy cow and his eventual capture by a man who ties a rope to one of the hind legs. Even today

(c)

decoy cows are used in Spain in order to lure from the ring bulls that have proved unsuitable for a fight. In another hunting scene shown on

[1] One of them shows date palms, which grow in Crete.

FIG. 8 : 31

FIG. 8 : 31 (a) to (c). Scenes of catching bulls for the sports from the 'decoy cup' of Vapheio, Greece. Minoan art. This and the following gold cup, Fig. 8 : 32, are in the Athens Museum; *c.* 1500 B.C.

(a) Bull following the scent of a cow

(b) Bull and cow in friendly conversation

(c) Meanwhile a rope is attached to hind leg of the bull by a man

FIG. 8 : 32

FIG. 8 : 32. 'Netting cup' from Vapheio, showing bulls caught in a net

a small Late Minoan crystal plaque a skewbald bull is running into a rope extended between two trees, whilst a man is jumping on his back. This, therefore, can only represent the capture of a feral beast (Zeuner, 1962a).

It is very likely that the Cretan cult of the bull had its origin in western Asia. Mallowan is emphatic about it, citing the bucranium motif as evidence. This occurred at Arpachiyah (northern Iraq) already in the Halaf period, *c.* 4500 B.C. (Fig. 8 : 14). A double-axe amulet (Figs. 8 : 30j and 8 : 33) provides further evidence, and also a stone tool of the same shape, for the double-axe is pre-eminently the symbol of divinity in ancient Crete and specimens are often found associated with bulls' heads (Fig. 8 : 30k). In the Dictean cave on Crete, where Zeus was supposed to have been born, masses of double-axes were found which had evidently been used as sacrifices. The connection between the double-axe and the bull survived into much later times. From the late Hittite period, about 900 B.C., a god holding a double-axe is known standing on a humped bull (Fig. 8 : 30l). The figure of Jupiter Dolichenos standing on a bull and holding the double-axe in one hand and a bundle of flashes of lightning in the other is evidently descended from it (Fig. 8 : 30m). This Roman deity was venerated from Mesopotamia across Anatolia into the Balkan peninsula, up the Danube and down the Rhine into Britain.

FIG. 8 : 33. Two double-axe pendants from a burnt house at Arpachiyah, Iraq. Tel Halaf period, *c.* 4500 B.C. After Mallowan and Rose

Professor Mallowan attaches particular importance to the architectural parallels found in the circular buildings at Arpachiyah in Iraq and at Khirokitia in Cyprus. He thus finds it hard to avoid the conclusion that none of these things could have appeared in Crete in particular and elsewhere in the Mediterranean 2000 years later had they not ultimately descended from the energetic villagers of prehistoric Assyria (Mallowan, 1956).

There are other parallels between ancient Mesopotamia and Crete and these refer specifically to cattle. On many cylinder seals of Babylonia, demigods are shown manhandling bulls (Fig. 8 : 30d). There is a green jasper seal found at Mycenae (Fig. 8 : 30e) and published by Evans in 1930 which shows a similar scene of Minoan-Mycenaean origin. The motif of the lion jumping on the back of a bull (Figs. 8 : 30a and 8 : 30b), so frequent in Babylonia, occurs both in the Minoan (Fig. 8 : 30c) and the Mycenaean civilizations, for instance on a stone carving from a tomb at Vapheio (van Lengerken, 1955, Figs. 194, 195). Another parallel is afforded by the milking of cows from behind, between the hind legs. A Late Minoan seal from Knossos (1500–1400 B.C.) (Fig. 8 : 30n) shows this practice with which we are already acquainted from the early dynastic temple of Al Ubaid (p. 218). And, finally, the Minotaur himself must be mentioned, as he is represented as a human being with a bull's head (Fig. 8 : 30g). This hybrid type of being is very familiar from Babylonian mythology. It thus is indeed probable that the bull cult of Crete is of Asiatic, if not of Mesopotamian, origin.

The Minotaur is well known to everybody from the Greek legend of Theseus and Ariadne. This and other stories appear to have some foundation in historical facts, particularly in relation to the significance of the bull cult in Crete.

The Minotaur was believed to be the hybrid progeny of Pasiphae, the wife of Minos, and a bull. This lady was a nymphomaniac who required a bull for her satisfaction. Daedalus, her husband's chief engineer, built her a dummy cow in which she used to hide. As a result of this the Minotaur was born. The Minotaur was placed in the centre of the labyrinth from which nobody could find his way out. Into this were sent the twelve Athenian youths and maidens who had at that time to be supplied annually to Crete. The Minotaur would devour them in due course. But on the occasion of Theseus's party things took an unexpected turn. Ariadne fell in love with Theseus, and she persuaded her father Daedalus to help. He provided a ball of string, with the aid of which Theseus, having slain the Minotaur, was able to find his way out of the labyrinth. That Daedalus got into trouble with Minos goes without saying. There is no room in this context to relate the rest of the story of Daedalus, his son Ikarus, and of Theseus and Ariadne. Evidently this legend is based on an annual human sacrifice to a bull coupled with a contest of skill. Is this perhaps the garbled version of memories of human tribute that had to be paid by Athens to Crete, when Crete was the dominating naval power in the eastern Mediterranean? If so, it is perhaps not out of place to suggest that this happened when Crete was still utterly foreign to Greece and speaking a non-Greek language. For the existence of a Greek language on Crete in the time when the 'Linear B' script was used, and which Ventris has deciphered so ingeniously, rather suggests cultural and commercial influences emanating from the Greek mainland. The time of the Linear B script, which was used in Mycenaean Greece also, at Mycenae and Pylos, is the Late Minoan period, about 1550–1100 B.C. The Theseus episode thus would have happened before the sixteenth-century B.C.

The Cretan legend places it even earlier, namely near the beginning of the Minoan civilization, unless the Minotaur contrived to live on for centuries, which is possible. Is the Minotaur the symbol of the sacred bull sports of the Minoans? These so-called games or sports were certainly extremely dangerous, and it is conceivable that the leapers who were exposed to the bulls, possibly after some training, were indeed supplied by subject or tributary nations rather than by the Cretans themselves.

The technical origins of the bull sports are most probably to be found in the rural art of bull-catching. Cattle living in semi-wild conditions are difficult to get hold of, especially when they are required unharmed. The practice of catching them by hand has in many places been, and still is, a test of bravery. The Toda, a primitive aboriginal tribe of southern India, still catch buffalo for sacrifices with their bare hands,[1] two men each seizing the two horns, one the tail and others trying to get on the back. These are the usual feral buffalo of India. The Cretans appear to have used similar techniques with their cattle, according to their mural paintings, and the Vapheio cups show methods of capturing that are rather less sporting, namely decoying and netting.

The games were performed in front of large audiences as depicted in the Palace of Knossos. An enclosed space was reserved where the bulls were confronted with a team of unarmed men and women whose task it was to seize the bull by the horns and to allow themselves to be thrown up into the air in such a way that they somersaulted over the back of the bull (Fig. 8 : 29). Some modern authorities on steer-throwing maintain that this feat is not possible because bulls attack sideways, trying to gore their adversary with one horn. Whilst this is often enough true, a visit to Spanish bull-fighting performances convinces one that bulls are quite capable of attacking with the head down and straight forward. It must, however, be admitted that the acrobatic feat is not likely to have been performed exactly in the way shown in the Minoan pictures. Also, there were many variants. Finally, it has been claimed that both the bulls and the leapers were trained for the purpose, and this is quite probable since even the simplest of the acts shown was a performance of no mean order. It is conceivable that there were both professionals and slaves, captives and human tribute involved. The professionals would have corresponded to the trained gladiators of the Roman arena, whilst the other classes provided the expected flow of blood, much as criminals and Christians did in the Roman circus.

These games were closely connected with the veneration of the bull in Minoan Crete, although they hardly formed part of a religious service. Evans found skulls of very large bulls mounted in the palace and bulls' heads are often shown associated with the double-axe symbol. In the House of the Sacrificed Oxen was a tripod altar and with it the horns of a large bull. In some houses there are pillar crypts equipped with a pillar to which the sacrifice may have been tied and beside which a pyramidal block provided the support for a double-axe. The association of the bull with the double-axe is clear enough. The sacrificial chamber being a crypt dug into the ground, it occurred to Evans that the purpose of these offerings was to propitiate a deity of the earth. As Knossos had been destroyed many times over by earthquakes, it must have been an important function of daily life to appease the subterranean powers. Evans was deeply impressed with the resemblance of the rumbling of an earthquake to the roaring of a bull, and he recalled the line from Homer, 'In bulls does the earth shaker delight.'

[1] According to M. de Golish, fourteen buffaloes were recently sacrificed upon the death of a woman.

The unique bull cult of Crete thus appears to have originated in the following way: The first agriculturalists came in contact with *Bos primigenius*, and though they subsequently domesticated this species their respect for the overpowering strength of wild bulls remained. Hence the bull was worshipped as a symbol of strength or at least regarded as such. There is ample evidence in Mesopotamia, and from that country the practice spread west. A people emigrating from western Asia brought with them into Crete both domesticated cattle and bull worship. Here in Crete they discovered what they regarded as evidence for the existence of a subterranean bull who with his horns shook the earth. Moreover, he roared in a most convincing manner. Since the activities of the subterranean bull were dangerous to man, propitiation ceremonies were developed. These appear to have taken two forms: the sacrifice of ordinary cattle, and the sacrifice of humans to fighting bulls. Since it was in Crete in the Cave of Dicte that Zeus was born, he became inevitably associated not only with the double-axe symbol the immigrants had brought with them from Asia, but also with the bull. It is therefore not in the least surprising that Zeus, when desiring to abduct the young lady Europa from the Greek mainland to Crete, assumed the shape of a bull.

Cattle in China

The available evidence clearly suggests that domesticated cattle reached China from the West. According to Wagner four types occur: the large *primigenius* cattle, a smaller *longifrons* breed which retained he coloration of the wild forerunner to a great extent, a small completely black *longifrons* breed in the northern provinces, and the zebu in the south. There is, however, plenty of evidence that in southern China much zebu blood has been mixed with northern cattle, and there are many variants of the zebu that lack the fat hump. Like the buffalo, cattle are largely kept for labour. They are important as draught animals (Fig. 8 : 34) and there is, or rather was until recently, no systematic breeding. Milk production is practically non-existent. Since the Chinese themselves state that cattle came to China from the West, they cannot have derived it from the northern cattle-breeding communities where dairy products play an important part. It is more likely therefore that cattle reached China originally from the south-west, before the Aryan invasion of India introduced the use of milk into that country.

Humped cattle

There remains to be discussed a peculiar type of tropical cattle, the distribution of which is centred in India. This is the humped cattle, or zebu. It is without a shadow of doubt a very early breed, for at Mohenjo-Daro both *primigenius* cattle and zebu appear on the seals (Figs. 8 : 35 and 8 : 36).

The zebu is characterized externally by a prominent hump on the shoulder, a

Fig. 8 : 34. Farming and reaping. The domestication of cattle provided man for the first time with animal energy which he learned to exploit for transport and labour. From the Turi-Huang Temple Cave No. 61 in China, tenth to eleventh centuries A.D. (Sung Dynasty)

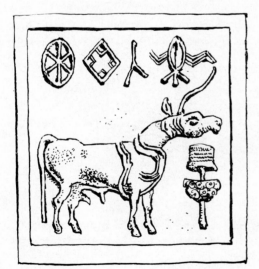

Fig. 8 : 35. Seal from Mohenjo-Daro, West Pakistan, showing a bull of the *primigenius* breed, *c.* 2500 B.C. The rope or lead round its neck and chest implies that the beast was at least tamed if not domesticated

Fig. 8 : 36. Seal from Mohenjo-Daro, West Pakistan, showing a zebu bull, *c.* 2500 B.C.

long face, usually steeply upright horns, drooping ears, small brow-ridges which give it a peculiar expression, a dewlap and slender legs. Its colour varies, but is commonly of the grey type varying to white or black. Many crosses have occurred between zebu and *primigenius* breeds, especially in Africa, and these should be left out of consideration.

FIG. 8 : 37. Silver coin of a Hindu king of Ohind, India, *c.* A.D. 875–900, showing a highly bred zebu with hump falling over. Twice natural size. Author's collection

With its hump, the zebu superfically resembles members of the *Bibos* group of wild cattle, which occur in India, Burma and the Sunda archipelago. Gans (1915), however, has pointed out that the structure of the skull is so different in *Bibos* that the zebu cannot be regarded as a domesticated descendant of this genus. An alternative would be to assume that the *primigenius* breed of cattle was crossed with a species of *Bibos*. Such crossings are regularly practised in Assam, where the resulting animals are called mithan (p. 253). These, however, do not resemble the zebu. Moreover, Slijper holds that the hump of the zebu is not just a store of fat, nor is it supported by the dorsal spines of the vertebrae (as it is in the gaur and other *Bibos* species),

FIG. 8 : 38. Modern African zebu depicted on a postage stamp, Cameroons

but is a much enlarged muscle. In spite of these results of recent studies, it remains to be explained why the humped cattle are restricted to hot climates with a dry season. The hump is a genetically fixed character already well developed in the calf at birth.

The zebu with its long face, steep horns and hump is so distinct an animal that its origin has been discussed frequently. In view of the fact that zebu and *primigenius* cattle were sharply distinguished by the Mohenjo-Daro people, a separate origin of the two is likely. That the *primigenius* breeds came from temperate or western Asia is evident from the distribution of their wild ancestor in these parts. In India, however, a closely related wild cattle is found throughout the Pleistocene, *Bos namadicus*, and it is conceivable that the zebu is its direct descendant. Osteological characteristics are not distinct enough to prove such derivation conclusively, but the slenderness of the face, especially of the muzzle, and the comparatively small supraorbitals favour it. To accept it would make it possible to understand why there is a specifically tropical breed of cattle present from the earliest times onwards, and now distributed from China to Africa, with India as the focus.

This view, however, is not accepted by everybody, though it was shared by the Swiss palaeontologist Stehlin. Some authors have held the remarkable opinion that the zebu was introduced into India from the west, i.e. from Africa. There is no prehistoric evidence to support this, nor is there any palaeontological evidence, for no wild race of *Bos* is known from tropical Africa in the Pleistocene. One might think of southern Arabia as a possible country where zebu could have originated, but there is absolutely no evidence available for or against such a view. Its presence in very early prehistoric sites in India makes its Indian origin virtually a certainty.

The archaeological record of the zebu begins with a rough figurine from the earlier Halafian period at Arpachiyah in northern Mesopotamia, which has been mentioned already. This takes us back to about 4500 B.C. That the oldest find should be Mesopotamian may be regarded as an archaeological accident, for subsequent ones point to India, and indeed have been regarded as evidence for Indian contacts with the Mesopotamian civilization.

A bitumen vessel from the second period of Susa, about 3000 B.C. or slightly earlier, takes us into Iran. At Nineveh humped bulls appear on stamped seals in the Jamdat Nasr period. At Rana Ghundai in northern Baluchistan, a Chalcolithic site, humped bulls are depicted on pottery which can be correlated with Sialk III or Hissar I, and thus with the Al Ubaid period of Mesopotamia, pushing them well back into the fourth millennium. The Indus Valley civilization has provided abundant representations of humped cattle, especially from Mohenjo-Daro.

The zebu became popular in Egypt in New Kingdom times. There are many illustrations dating from the eighteenth dynasty (Figs. 8 : 39 a and b). Two kinds appear to have been bred, a short-horned one (Fig. 8 : 39a) and another with horns

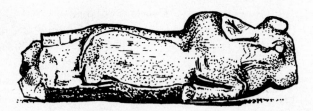

FIG. 8 : 39 (a). Ivory knife-handle (length *c.* 7.8 cm.) showing a zebu from ancient Egypt, probably eighteenth dynasty, site unknown. After Hornblower

FIG. 8 : 39 (b). Short-horned breed of zebu, eighteenth dynasty of Egypt, 1570–1345 B.C. Bronze weight of 1 *deben* (93 gm.), height 4 cm. Museum Berlin, No. 13804

of normal size. Lengerken mentions that the sacred bull Mnevis was a black zebu, but this remains to be proved.

The earliest record from Palestine comes from Gerar (Fig. 8 : 40), in the sixth century B.C., this early post-Exilic record may be the result of Persian influence. After this time zebus become well known all over the eastern part of the Mediter-ranean. They appear on many Seleucid coins from the fourth century onwards. They never succeeded, however, in ousting *primigenius* and *longifrons* breeds in the rest of the Mediterranean, presumably because humped cattle were climatically un-suited to non-tropical countries. A small-horned zebu is shown on a Greek bronze figurine from Smyrna of the second century B.C. (Fig. 8 : 42). Needless to say the Romans were familiar with this kind of cattle, i.e. following the opening-up of eastern trade by Alexander.

Conclusion

It is no exaggeration to say that the domestication of cattle was the most important step ever taken by man in the direction of exploitation of the animal world, after the

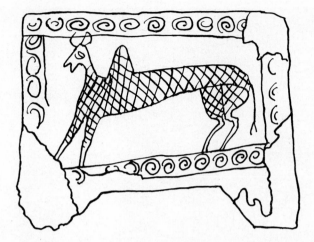

FIG. 8 : 40. Drawing of a humped bovid from Gerar,
Palestine, sixth century B.C.

initial step of the domestication of the dog (Zeuner, 1962 *a, b*). Unlike the group of smaller ruminants, cattle require considerable attention and organization of the community. Their large size must have presented difficulty at the beginning and food supplies required careful consideration wherever man lived in permanent settlements. It is, therefore, very probable that the first domestication of cattle was preceded by the establishment of agricultural practices which would, as has been pointed out, have provided the meeting ground for man and cattle in the first instance. That secondary nomadism with cattle has developed in certain areas, especially in Africa, does not affect the picture prevalent at the time when domestication began.

One might ask oneself why man went to the trouble of domesticating a beast more difficult to look after than the small ruminants. It is here for the first time that I believe that an economic outlook may be assumed. As so often with early communities, the supply of meat was almost certainly a subsidiary consideration. There is plenty of evidence from prehistoric cattle-breeders that the number of cattle kept was comparatively small. Though some of the stock may have been killed in the autumn to reduce fodder requirements in winter, many of these communities relied to a great extent on hunting for their supply of meat. The advantages that cattle brought to man may have lain in another field from the beginning. Since milking of goats appears to have been practised from early times, it is conceivable that cow's milk (possibly supplemented by blood, as is done by the Masai today) was the foremost consideration. In addition, cattle supplied hides of a strength that made it possible to supplant wood in the manufacture of shields. There are many other applications of hides which need not be enumerated.

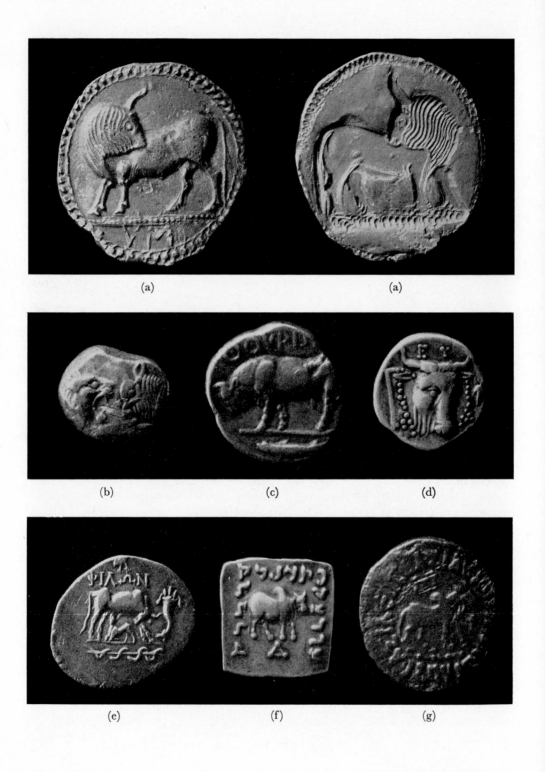

(a) (a)

(b) (c) (d)

(e) (f) (g)

FIG. 8 : 41. (opposite page) Cattle on coins.

(a) Obverse and incuse reverse of silver stater from Sybaris, Lucania, Italy, 550–510 B.C. Appears to represent an aurochs

(b) Silver siglos of Croesus, Lydia, 561–456 B.C., showing head of lion facing head of wild bull

(c) Silver stater from Thurium, Lucania, Italy, 440–420 B.C., showing domesticated bull of *primigenius* breed

(d) Silver drachm from Eretria, Euboea, 369–366 B.C., showing head of domesticated bull of *primigenius* breed

(e) Silver drachm from Dyrrhachium, Illyricum, 229–100 B.C., showing cow and calf

(f) Zebu on Indo-Greek square silver drachm of Apollodotus I, 185–162 B.C.

(g) Indo-Scythian bronze coin of Azes I, 90–40 B.C., with zebu

All author's collection, and twice natural size

FIG. 8 : 42. Greek bronze statuette of a zebu from Smyrna, Asia Minor, second century B.C. After Lengerken

FIG. 8 : 43. Bronze statuette of a Roman bull of *primigenius* breed from Trier, West Germany. Imperial period. Original in Rheinisches Landesmuseum, Bonn. No. U.1254

Fig. 8 : 44. Zebu being milked from side in presence of the calf. Full-size stone relief carved into the rock at Mahabalipuram, south-east India, seventh to eighth centuries A.D.

One of the secondary uses of cattle products is the dung which this animal produces in sufficient quantities to become a valuable fuel in areas where wood is scarce (Zeuner, 1960). It is also well known that it is used for building purposes, as well as many others; as a combustible paste it was invaluable. The concentration of cattle in or near human settlements may in addition have caused man to discover the utilization of manure to fertilize his crops.

The most important role of cattle from the technological point of view, however, was that at an early stage it became a beast of burden and later of traction. This it still is in many parts of the world, though in others it has been replaced by the horse. It is indeed probable that the development of wheeled transport is closely connected with the domestication of cattle.

This species has thus played an exceptionally important part in the history of domestication. The use of animal energy had been realized in addition to their use as sources of raw material and food. From this time onward, therefore, animals were exploited in much the same way throughout the millennia until, quite recently, mechanical transport has begun to relieve the beasts of their onerous duties.

9

Buffalo, Yak and Banteng

SCIENTIFIC NAMES—*Bubalus bubalis* L. (Indian or water buffalo, arnee; India, Ceylon, Burma to Sunda Isles. Imported westwards as far as Italy, eastwards to China and Japan.)

Bubalus depressicornis H. Smith (Anoa, dwarf buffalo; Celebes, not domesticated).

Bos (*Bison*) *bonasus* L. (European bison; formerly northern Europe, never domesticated).

B. grunniens L. (yak; Tibet, thence to other parts of central Asia).

B. (*Bibos*) *banteng* Wagner (banteng; Burma to Java and Borneo).

B. (*Bibos*) *gaurus* H. Smith (gaur or 'Indian bison'; India to Burma, with the domesticated gayal).

Syncerus caffer Sparrman (African buffalo, never domesticated).

Buffaloes

THERE are two quite distinct groups of buffaloes, of which the African has never been domesticated. The latter are distributed over the whole of the non-arid parts of Africa and occurred in north-west Africa well into the Neolithic, if not later. The only African area from which they appear to have been absent is Egypt. In Algeria in particular they were frequent in the Neolithic when hunters engraved them in numbers on rocks (Fig. 9 : 1). These North African buffaloes were at one time regarded as a form of the Indian buffalo (Pomel's *Bubalus antiquus*, 1893, Fig. 9 : 2), because of their very large and evenly curved horns. It has since been established by Miss Bate that this was the result of a convergence of the two species in horn form, and that the resemblance was purely superficial. In the Asiatic and European forms the vomer is extended to divide the internal nasal opening.

FIG. 9 : 1. Rock engraving of a buffalo, Neolithic or later, Ksar el Ahmar, Oran, North Africa. Miss Bate has shown that this type of buffalo belonged to the African species. It was not domesticated. After Frobenius and Obermaier (1925)

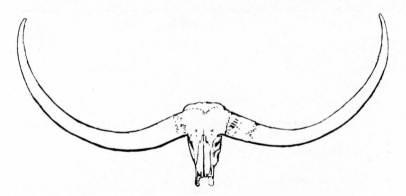

FIG. 9 : 2. Skull of *Syncerus antiquus*, the extinct North African buffalo, from the Pleistocene deposits of Djelfa, Algeria. After Pomel (1893)

Contrary to widely held belief, therefore, north-west Africa never had indigenous Indian buffaloes. Europe, on the other hand, possessed one in the Great and possibly the Last Interglacials, one specimen (Fig. 9 : 3) having been found at Steinheim, near Stuttgart, the locality of Steinheim man (*Bubalus murrensis* Berckhemer). A second European specimen came from central Germany (*Bubalus wanckeli* Schertz) and there are a few others. Another suspected buffalo (*Bubalus iselini*) has, however, been shown to be an aberrant bison. The true Indian buffalo or arnee was originally confined to India and Ceylon, so far as is known. There this large beast lives in grass jungles near the water in which it likes to wallow. The domesticated buffaloes have

246

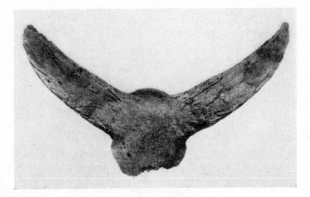

FIG. 9 : 3. *Bubalus murrensis* Berckhemer. Skull from the gravels of Steinheim, Württemberg, where the famous human skull was found. Great Interglacial, *c.* 250,000 years old. Length between horn-core tips *c.* 115 cm.

retained this habit (Fig. 9 : 4). They have altogether changed very little, compared with their wild ancestor, and interbreeding with wild specimens is probably as frequent where such still exist, as domesticated specimens become feral. The Indian buffalo has a thin coat of hair which it loses with age. The hair is black or reddish, but very rarely white specimens are known to occur in nature. Its horns are flat above and strongly ribbed, a character that makes them unmistakable. They do not voluntarily interbreed with domestic cattle, with which they are less closely

FIG. 9 : 4. Indian buffaloes in a water-hole in northern Gujarat, north-west India. Photo F.E.Z.

related than yak, bison, gaur and banteng. According to an oral communication from Mr Prater, however, such crosses have now and then occurred. The main variation is in size, from gigantic (India) to minute (China), and hornless breeds are favoured occasionally.

The buffalo cannot exist without water (Fig. 9 : 4). This requirement restricts its distribution, though it often survives better under tropical conditions than most cattle. It is used as a draught animal in agriculture, where its strength is of great value, for the ploughing of rice-fields (Fig. 9 : 5) and the treading-in of seed. Here and there it is used for riding, but its great breadth makes this sort of exercise somewhat uncomfortable. Buffalo milk is richer than ordinary cow's milk. Some fifty years ago it was thought that the buffalo might become important in Europe for this reason, but meanwhile the Jersey and Guernsey cattle have outdone the buffalo. Buffalo butter is more solid than cow butter, and does not easily turn rancid. It is

FIG. 9 : 5. Water buffalo working in the rice-fields in China. From an ancient print

therefore to be preferred in the tropics. Its greenish-white colour, however, does not appeal to everybody.

The domesticated buffalo—known in Indonesia as kerabou—spread over the Indies at an early date. It started its career as a crop-robber, as is borne out by the many instances of crop destruction by wild buffalo today. But archaeological evidence for their history as domestic beasts is curiously scanty. Whether the Indus Valley civilization had them in the domesticated state is not certain, though they were known as is shown by the seals (Fig. 9 : 6) and they were used somehow, as bones

FIG. 9 : 6. Seal impression from the Harappan culture of West Pakistan, Mohenjo-Daro, *c.* 2500 B.C., showing that the water buffalo was already domesticated in north-west India at that date. Natural size

were recovered at Mohenjo-Daro. They were known also in Mesopotamia at a very early date.

A seal impression was found below the level of the royal cemetery at Ur, which means the buffalo was known prior to 2500 B.C. In the Akkadian period it was comparatively frequently depicted, and the curved horns are usually shown from the top. Frankfort illustrates a cylinder seal of the Akkadian dynasty, the 'seal of the servant of Sargon', with two buffaloes (Fig. 9 : 7). A seal of the time of Shar-kali-

FIG. 9 : 7. Two Indian buffaloes near the river being watered by two men-gods. Mesopotamian cylinder seal of the 'Servant of Sargon', Akkadian dynasty, *c.* 2500–2100 B.C. Based on Frankfort (1939)

sharri, the successor of Naram-sin (*c.* 2150 B.C.) shows two buffaloes being fed by two men, a scene which suggests at least tame, if not domesticated, beasts. Two alternative explanations may be offered. It is conceivable that the Indian buffalo existed wild in Mesopotamia. Though there is no positive evidence to this effect, some workers such as Hilzheimer and Slijper take this for granted, and the former goes so far as to say that the buffalo was the first wild bovine to become extinct in Mesopotamia. On the other hand, it is equally conceivable that domestic buffaloes had been introduced from India, and one might quote the resemblance of some of the scenes depicted on seals to similar ones from the Indus Valley complex. This question, therefore, remains to be settled.

It is a fact, however, that the buffalo's westward spread was slow, late and discontinuous. This is puzzling in several respects. The beast was undoubtedly known in ancient Mesopotamia but it did not reach Egypt until the Middle Ages, although it would have been eminently useful there. The discontinuity of its distribution is probably due to the fact that it thrives only where there is water and preferably swamp. One would expect it to be adopted in such areas all over the Mediterranean.

Perhaps there has always been some antagonism against the buffalo, which is much less docile than cattle and occasionally dangerous. Where cattle supplied all the needs, there was no reason to experiment with buffaloes. But this does not explain why Indian buffaloes did not appear in the Roman circus. Considering the close trade connections that existed with India (as established at Arikamedu by Sir Mortimer Wheeler), one wonders why buffaloes should not have reached Rome.

The Indian rhinoceros was known to the Hellenistic world and is mentioned by Aristotle. The Romans, though they procured the two-horned species from Africa, are unlikely to have left the Indian species unmentioned had it reached the capital. It must be pointed out that the well-known relief of an Indian rhinoceros from Pompeii, preserved in the Naples Museum, is a fake and patently a copy of Albrecht Dürer's rhinoceros engraving of A.D. 1515. Thus it may be regarded as certain that the Indian rhinoceros never reached Rome. Moreover, it is doubtful whether other Indian animals were successfully shipped to the Mediterranean. The exceptions are of course the Indian elephant and the zebu which arrived by the overland route, the former being directed by mahouts. One thus comes to the conclusion that the sea traffic between India and Rome via Egypt was not equipped for the transport of large animals, and this might explain the absence of the Indian buffalo also.

Pliny speaks of a *bubalis* (*H.N.* VII, 15), but this word originally denoted an antelope, the hartebeest. In his time, however, popular usage began to transfer this appellation to the European bison, and it has ever since remained as a name for large bovines, for the Indian and African buffaloes and for the American bison.

For the European bison, however, it was abandoned in favour of *bison*, the latinized form of the Germanic *Wisent*.

It was in A.D. 723 that a visitor to Palestine, St Willibald, saw Indian buffaloes in the ghor of the Jordan Valley, where they are in use at the present day. He related how surprised he was at these strange animals. As Keller points out, St Willibald had travelled through Italy and Sicily, where buffaloes are to be seen today, so they cannot have been known there then. His date is about a century after the spread of the Moslem religion to Mesopotamia. It thus looks as if Indian buffaloes were at that time used in Mesopotamia whence they had reached the Jordan Valley. From there they may have reached Egypt in the Middle Ages where, early in the nineteenth century, they successfully survived a *Rinderpest* which killed nearly all the cattle in the country. But they did not spread farther west in North Africa, nor did the Moslems take them to Spain.

Another route, however, established itself along the Balkan peninsula, and this in advance of the Moslem conquest. It appears that the southern Slavs knew the buffalo, which may have reached south Russia by way of Persia. About A.D. 1200 Bulgaria and Macedonia had buffaloes in plenty. Thence they spread to Hungary, which marks their northernmost outpost.

A few attempts were made to establish buffaloes in other countries. Those in Sicily and Italy (especially the Naples region) were permanently successful. The story that the Lombards introduced them from Hungary is regarded as incorrect by Keller. Napoleon made an attempt to establish them in the Landes; it proved a failure. Other experiments in Germany and Spain were even more short-lived.

Whilst the buffalo's westward progress has thus been slow and restricted, the beast proved an outstanding success in the Far East. From India its use spread to Indo-China and the Sunda archipelago. It also reached China itself and thence Japan. In all these countries it is of real importance in connection with rice-growing. The muddy rice-fields are the very environment in which buffaloes thrive (Fig. 9 : 5). This close association may be regarded as evidence that the original domestication of the buffalo was located in the rice-growing area, and it is conceivable that it lay in Indo-China or south China rather than in India. But up to the present there is no archaeological material to support this view.

There is, however, some osteological evidence for the presence of wild buffaloes in the Pleistocene of China. In the Lower Pleistocene *Bubalus brevicornis* Young and *B. teilhardi* Young are found, whilst the Upper Pleistocene has yielded *B. wansjocki* Boule and Teilhard. Whether these are ancestral to the domesticated races of China is not known and may never be established with certainty.

At the present day the domesticated buffalo is found in south and west China. It is prominent wherever in the swampy lowlands rice is cultivated. In such places the buffalo is considerably more resistant to diseases than cattle. In northern China it is gradually replaced by cattle of various types. It is conceivable that the arnee was indigenous in southern China. Many different breeds have been produced and it has been known in the domesticated state since the very earliest times. The breeds are distinguished by body size, length and shape of the horns, the degree of hairiness, and colour. It varies in height from 110 to 150 cm. at the withers, and the horns may be as much as one metre long, whilst hornless breeds exist also. The cross-section of the horn often retains the triangular shape characteristic of the wild species, but in some breeds it becomes more or less round. Whilst black and dark-brown colours predominate, light colours occur occasionally, and albinos are known.

The Chinese buffalo is fully adult when six to seven years old, and reaches an age of twenty to twenty-five years. For breeding they must be at least three years old, and the gestation period is over ten months. It is therefore a slower breeder than domestic cattle. Its food is coarser than that of cattle and it is content to browse on reeds and other swamp vegetation not eaten by other domesticated ruminants.

The buffalo is first and foremost a beast of labour, employed in the preparation of rice-fields, for the pulling of carts and the working of mills and wells. It is stronger than domestic cattle.

It is used for milking only under European influence, since the Chinese never adopted dairy economy as known in northern and western countries. As to meat production, this is important only in parts of China where the population is predominantly Moslem. The quality of the meat is said to be much the same as that of cattle. The skin is an important product and the leather made from it is exceptionally heavy and strong. It goes without saying that the horns are used also and worked into a variety of articles.

Yak

Very little can be said about the Yak, the long-haired bovine of central Asia. Its centre is evidently Tibet, where it occurs wild as well as domesticated. Colour types have been bred, and there are varieties which lack the horns. Yaks can be crossed with cattle, including zebu, and the hybrids are very popular since they are quieter and more peaceful beasts. But hybrids are infertile in the male sex. The area of distribution of the yak extends from Tibet and Ladak north round the Tarim Basin to Mongolia. In the northern parts it is probably introduced, and in the Sayan Mountains it meets the reindeer and the camel.

The first mention of at least part of the yak is found in Martial (XIII, 71). He describes the *Muscarium bubalum*, a very precious sort of fly-whisk made of the tail of a kind of ox. The yak's tail, which is hairy from the base, has been used for this purpose in Eastern countries ever since. That Roman ladies owned such contraptions in the time of Domitian shows that the overland trade route from the East was then fully in use.

Marco Polo saw yaks in the thirteenth century. He described them from Tamgut, believed to be the country around the lake called Koko Nor. Apart from exaggerating their size (comparing them with elephants), he describes them correctly and praises the quality of their fine, long and glossy hair. Their main function was, and still is, to be a beast of burden and labour, and occasionally for riding. Their milk and wool are important products.

The yak, being an animal of the mountains above 2000 m., has penetrated into China only in the border provinces of Yunnan, Sze-chuan and Kansu, where it is important as a beast of burden enabling commercial relations with Tibet. The yak can carry loads of 150 kg. with ease over the most dangerous mountain paths. In addition, the animal is used for riding in Tibet, as shown, for instance, by Colonel Bailey (1948).

Yak's milk is used in Tibet, where it is an important ingredient of *tsamba*, mixed with tea and barley meal. An alcoholic beverage, *airan*, is made of yak's milk by the Kirgise. In the treeless highlands yak-dung is the most important fuel available.

Banteng, Gayal and Mithan

There remains to be discussed the representatives of the subgenus *Bibos*, characterized by long spinal processes of the thoracic vertebrae which give the animal a sort of hump. There are further osteological differences in the skull between *Bibos* and true cattle. Nevertheless, all *Bibos* freely interbreed with cattle,[1] especially the local zebu, but the latter do not owe their hump to the infusion of *Bibos* blood as has been explained on p. 238.

There are two wild species: the gaur of India and Further India, mainly a mountain species; and the wild banteng of Further India, Borneo and Java. In peninsular India there are no domesticated *Bibos*, but in Assam and the rest of the area of distribution there are. The *Bibos* have a shoulder-hump due to extension of the spinous processes of the third to eleventh dorsal vertebrae, sharply defined white feet and a dewlap divided into two parts, which leaves the throat free.

In Assam the domesticated form is called gayal. The term mithan is probably synonymous with it, though this is not quite certain. Domestication has continued for long enough to produce parti-coloured, black and also white specimens. It is probably descended from the gaur, with which it freely interbreeds. This process is encouraged by their Naga owners, as it is regarded as an improvement of the race (Fig. 9 : 8). The gayal also interbreeds with zebu cattle, and these crosses are regarded with favour in certain districts, and it is possible that the term mithan is applied to such crosses or to crosses between gaur and zebu. According to others mithan is merely another name for the gayal.

[1] Slijper (1951) states that only female progeny is fertile. In a hybrid series of three generations bred in the London Zoo and published by Lydekker (1898) only females were produced.

FIG. 9 : 8. Mithan bull from Naga village, showing many characteristics
of wild gaur. Photo C. R. Stonor

The importance attached to interbreeding is remarkable. In order to induce the animals to do so, salt-licks are supplied in the forests. They attract the wild beasts, and once they are frequented domestic females are driven there. This practice may shed light on the development of some of the *primigenius* breeds of domestic cattle in prehistoric Europe. It altogether represents a system of animal husbandry in which something is done to prevent degeneration.

Curiously enough, the practical uses of the gayal are few. The Naga are not likely to use much milk, and the animals do not appear to be employed a great deal for agricultural work, though this is the case in some areas. Their flesh is eaten, and gayal or mithan sacrifices play an important part in the lives of these tribes.

Regarding the mithan, Mr C. R. Stonor of Sarisbury Green, Hampshire, has kindly supplied me with first-hand information which differs in some respects from current views. I am therefore reproducing it here almost *verbatim*. At the same time, I wish to draw attention to his papers dealing with the natural uses of the animal and listed in the bibliography (Stonor, 1950, 1957).

The main feature that taxonomists have used in differentiating the mithan from the wild gaur is the great bony forehead. This can be explained by the circumstances of domestication. The horns of the gaur turn inwards to face each other over the forehead. The horns of the mithan are characteristically outward facing. Now, the main importance of the mithan is as a sacrificial animal, and among the tribes that keep them the most prized beast for a sacrifice is the one with the finest head, which is estimated both from the size of the horns and the length of the span from tip to tip. Selective breeding for these qualities could very easily produce, as an accompaniment to the large and outward growing horns, the great bony forehead. This would be needed to support the weight of the heavier, straighter horns.

In the hills along the Burma frontier, it is the tribal custom to breed for colour as near to the wild gaur as possible. In the Himalayan tracts of Assam this is not so; and the tribes there will sacrifice mithan of any colour; so that under domestication any pied or white sports that appear can flourish.

In most areas there is a limited amount of deliberate interbreeding with cattle: either for trading out, or for producing a beast that will give a good milk supply. I know that most zoologists assert sweepingly that the mithan originated by crossing of cattle with the wild gaur. I would say this is far from being proved. One of the most intriguing characteristics of the mithan is that it has all the browsing, forest-living habits of the gaur, and comes far nearer to gaur in its habits and appearance except that while the gaur is one of the fiercest and most intractable beasts of the jungle, the mithan is by absolute contrast one of the tamest and most docile of domestic animals to be found anywhere. Now and again, in some areas a wild gaur bull will run with a herd of tame mithan and it is interesting that the progeny usually or always have the more slender, inward facing horns of the wild father, and also inherit the savage, unmanageable disposition.

To my mind the mystery of the original domestication of the mithan is how such a savage beast could completely change its temperament in the earlier phase of its domestication so as to become manageable by the peoples concerned, and make it worth their while to go on with the process. It is noteworthy that wild gaur seem never to be captured and tamed anywhere in the region concerned.

It is often said that the mithan originated on the Assam-Burma border. It is, however, kept by the tribal peoples north of the Brahmaputra River, in the great Himalayan tracts between the borders of Burma and Bhutan, in great numbers, and is as well established there as in the other area. The fact is that the Assam-Burma border was known about before the Himalayan tracts concerned were explored. Mithan were first studied in the Naga Hills, and it was idly assumed that this is where they originated. We can safely say the process of domestication may have begun anywhere in the total range of distribution.[1]

The banteng has been more extensively domesticated than the gaur. Large herds are kept in Java and Bali, and they are often crossed with zebu.

No archaeological evidence is available for the time when gaur and banteng were first domesticated. But their geographical distribution suggests that it was the feat of the Indo-Chinese or Malays. The zebu, on the other hand, is characteristic of peninsular India; there is no primary connection between its domestication and that of *Bibos*, as was at one time regarded as probable.

---

[1] The story related to me in India is that the mithan is a cross of gaur and zebu, produced at the salt-licks described earlier. From the F_1 generation, F_2 and F_3 are produced by crossing with zebu, whereafter recourse is had to the wild gaur once more. I am mentioning this without further comment.

10

The Pig

SCIENTIFIC NAMES—*Sus strozzii* Meneghini (Pliocene; Europe and Asia). Probable ancestor.

S. scrofa scrofa L. (wild boar; Germany, France and other parts of Europe north of the Alps). *S.s. meridionalis* Major (Mediterranean wild pig; Mediterranean lands). Includes *S.s. barbarus* Sclater (North Africa).
S.s. attila Thomas (Eastern wild boar; from Transylvania through northern Asia to Amur).

S. cristatus Wagner (Indian wild pig; India, Ceylon, Further India, but not Malay peninsula). *S. vittatus* Müller and Schlegel (Sunda pig; Malay peninsula, Sunda Isles to Timor. Its range has been expanded, probably by man, to New Guinea.)

The European domesticated pigs are essentially descendants of *Sus scrofa*, and the Chinese ones of *Sus vittatus*.
S.s. palustris Rütimeyer (turbary pig; Swiss lake-dwellings, etc.; not a species).

IT IS certain that the domesticated pigs are the descendants of a species-group of wild pigs ranging from Europe to eastern Asia. The European representative is the wild pig, *Sus scrofa*; the eastern Asiatic is *Sus vittatus* M. and S., the banded pig. Kelm (1939) has shown that these two extremes are connected by transitional races found in the geographically intermediate areas. The Mediterranean races (Figs. 10 : 1 and 10 : 2) have been separated as *Sus meridionalis* Major. They are intermediate between the European and eastern Asiatic groups in several respects, particularly in the formation of the lacrymal bone of the skull. This is long in *Sus scrofa*, but short in *Sus vittatus*. Much has been written about the significance of the shape of this bone in the pig. An excellent summary of the geographical races of

256

the wild pig was published by Kelm (1939). It incorporates Russian research on the pigs of Siberia.

Nearly a hundred years ago Rütimeyer noticed that there occurred in the Neolithic lake-dwellings of Switzerland a small and gracefully built pig which in its skull showed certain characteristics of the banded pig. Since that time the view has been widely held that the European domesticated pig was first introduced from farther east, and perhaps in part derived from eastern Asiatic races. On the other hand, investigations carried out by Reitsma (1935) in Holland, Pira (1909) in Sweden and Amschler (1940a) in Persia (Shah Tepé) suggest that domesticated pigs were derived from local wild pigs, and long before their time Nehring had shown that even the turbary pig could well be a descendant of the European *Sus scrofa*. Most authors today, therefore, hold the alternative view that the domesticated pig is nearly everywhere derived from local wild forms (Fig. 10 : 7). The chief trouble in this matter has always been that authors speak (and think) of 'the domestic pig', whilst in fact two different types have been required and bred; one being a large herded pig, the other a sty-pig, or even a house-pig (as it is today in China). It is the latter that has puzzled investigators and, oddly enough, it is quite true that most modern sty-pigs have Chinese blood in their veins. This does not, however, apply to the prehistoric groups where, nevertheless, two types are often encountered together.

That two types of domestic pig occurred simultaneously in the past is easily demonstrated by evidence from Switzerland. In the earlier group of Neolithic lake-dwellings the small turbary pig (*Sus palustris* Rütimeyer) occurs beside the ordinary European wild pig. There is no doubt that this turbary pig was introduced into

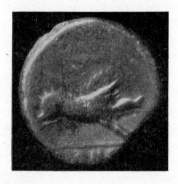

FIG. 10 : 1   FIG. 10 : 2

FIG. 10 : 1. Obverse of bronze coin from Arpi, Apulia, third century B.C., showing slender Mediterranean wild boar with erect mane and long snout. Diameter 20 mm. Author's collection

FIG. 10 : 2. Obverse of silver hemidrachm of the Aetolian League, Greece, 279–168 B.C., showing the same type of wild pig as Fig. 10 : 1, but even more high-legged. Diameter 18 mm. Author's collection

Switzerland by Neolithic man from the East, though from where precisely is not known. Towards the end of the Neolithic the local wild pig also was subjected to domestication. The remains of this race occur, for instance, at Lattrigen, Lüscherz

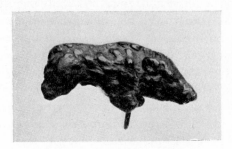

FIG. 10 : 3. Roman bronze figurine of wild boar, Rhineland, Length *c.* 4 cm. Rheinisches Landesmuseum, Bonn

and Sutz on Lake Bienne. In the first two sites it is accompanied by a small number of turbary pigs, whilst at the third site the turbary pig is the more frequent. From this time onwards the two breeds of pigs run parallel, up to the Iron Age.

The turbary pig of the late Neolithic is a particularly small breed with shortened jaws. Since the ordinary turbary pig does not disappear completely, three breeds co-existed by the end of the Neolithic, namely the turbary pig, its small form and the domesticated *Sus scrofa*. The first two, and especially the second, may well have been house-pigs suitable to be kept in the lake-dwellings themselves.

In the Bronze Age site of Möringen (Lake Bienne) the same three races are to be found, although pig-keeping was much reduced in view of the great development of sheep-raising. The domesticated *Sus scrofa*, however, was the most popular type. The important station of Alpenquai-Zürich of the Late Bronze Age shows that its popularity decreased in the course of this period, the turbary pig coming once more to the fore. It remained the dominant race in the Hallstatt and La Tène periods. The pig was again becoming popular, but at the same time it decreased in size, so that it resembled the 'small form' of the Bronze Age as shown for instance by the settlement of Bat Panadisch near Bonaduz described by E. Kuhn (1946). In Roman times the small breed of the turbary pig continued to flourish. It was not until the Middle Ages that the *scrofa* breeds became important again. According to Kuhn, the turbary pig has survived to the present day in some of the Alpine valleys.

What, then, is the origin of this turbary pig? The history of the Swiss breeds shows clearly enough that the European wild pig was domesticated and that the outcome was not a turbary pig. Those authors who claim that European pigs are derived from the local wild form are, therefore, right in so far as certain breeds are concerned. But the sudden appearance of the ready-made turbary pig in the Neo-lithic proves importation from elsewhere, though perhaps not from eastern Asia. The importation hypothesis is not disproved by the observation that there are

FIG. 10 : 4. Killing a medieval domesticated pig (high-legged breed with bristles). From an early-fourteenth-century manuscript ('Queen Mary's Psalter', Occupations of the Months, December) in the British Museum

numerous transitions between the turbary pig and the *scrofa* group. In part they are the crosses between the two breeds, whilst in part they are due to a fact which was first pointed out by Forsyth Major and later by Antonius, but has since been almost invariably overlooked. It is that the wild pigs of south-east and south Europe tend to resemble *Sus vittatus* in the shape of their lacrymal bones. It is no longer necessary, therefore, to derive the turbary pig from eastern Asia. South-east Europe might well be its original home, as exemplified by Ulmansky's pigs from the peat bog of Ljubljana in northern Yugoslavia (Ulmansky, 1913). The Danubians may be responsible for this importation. The pig was owned by the Körös people of Hungary about 2400–2500 B.C. About the same time it was present in Troy I and the Neolithic B of Sesklo in Greece. It is also known from the Neolithic A of Greece, which is probably earlier than 2500 B.C., and the Neolithic villages of Crete had it also.

It is, nevertheless, noteworthy that the domesticated pig has nowhere been found at sites which are earlier than the Neolithic agricultural revolution. In this respect it agrees with cattle, but differs from sheep, goat and dog which appear prior to this date.

Even in Asia the domesticated pig is associated with permanent settlements only. At Shah Tepé it occurs in a small form alongside a large wild pig which was hunted, in Level III (the lowermost), which is contemporary with Anau II and Uruk. At Anau it appears earlier, in the lower part of Period I B (contemporary with Al Ubaid). As to the origin of this small pig, Amschler came to the conclusion that it was derived from the local wild pig, whilst Duerst followed the hypothesis of Rütimeyer of the *vittatus* origin of the breed, largely because remains of wild pig are

259

absent from the lower strata of Anau. He admits, however, the possibility that the domestication may have taken place in 'some other oasis of Turkestan'. In Belt Cave, Coon found that the pig was not domesticated until the Neolithic with pottery, weaving and cereal culture had begun, and the few remains of pig found in the pre-pottery Neolithic levels at Jericho belong to the wild race of the Jordan Valley.

In Mesopotamia the domesticated pig is represented by figurines (Fig. 10 : 5) and paintings of all the early periods, including painted Al Ubaid ware from Lagash and the Tell Halaf level of Arpachiyah. The last-mentioned locality, which is the earliest of the known occurrences of the domesticated pig, yielded clay figurines that were described by Mallowan and Rose (1935).

FIG. 10 : 5. Small ivory pendant of domesticated pig from Tell Agrab, Sumer, 2800–2700 B.C. (pre-Sargonic). A fat, apparently naked, breed with drooping ears, but still with slender snout. A highly bred type, surprisingly early. After Frankfort

It is altogether unlikely that the pig was domesticated before the establishment of permanent settlements. It is indeed difficult to imagine how a nomadic community, and even tribes that changed their habitations twice annually according to the season, could cope with the art of pig-driving, since the animal is notoriously unaccommodating in this respect. Hence, the pig was valuable to the settled farmer only. Antonius continues this line of thought further, pointing out that the pig is not bred by modern nomads who, on the whole, despise it or have religious prohibitions against the consumption of its meat. This he regards as the result of the sense of superiority of the nomad over the settled farmer, whose supply of pig's meat, as coming from an animal not worthy of the nomad's consideration, would come to be regarded as taboo.

Duerst's view that nomads who practised domestication brought the pig to the settled peasants of the West can thus no longer be maintained. The evidence rather corroborates the alternative that the domesticated pig was not moved over great distances, that it was slowly passed on from village to village, and that in many places it was independently and repeatedly raised from wild stock (Figs. 10 : 6 and 10 : 7). The European turbary pig is no exception to this rule, since it is in all probability the descendant of a Mediterranean wild race and not of east Asiatic origin. So is the pig that was kept by the prehistoric inhabitants of the Canary Islands (Zeuner, 1959).

The chief purpose of pig-breeding is undoubtedly that it is the most prolific and

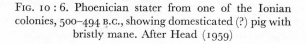

Fig. 10 : 6. Phoenician stater from one of the Ionian colonies, 500–494 B.C., showing domesticated (?) pig with bristly mane. After Head (1959)

Fig. 10 : 7. Silver stater from Lycia, 480–400 B.C., showing high-legged pig with bristly crest, like the preceding, reminiscent of wild pig. Reverse: incuse square with triskeles of cocks' heads. After Head (1959)

abundant supplier of meat and fat for the kitchen. The possibility of either herding it, allowing it to find its food in the woods, or of keeping it in a confined space, in a sty or even in the house, has made it extremely useful to the farmer.

It is all the more surprising that there are parts of the world where the pig is not only despised but even taboo. That it is regarded as unclean by Jews and Moslems is well known, and it was so at least for certain social strata in ancient Egypt.

Many reasons have been suggested for this curious attitude. It is quite different from that towards dog and horse, which are not normally eaten because man feels an aversion to eating his comrades and companions. It has often been said that the fat of the pig is unhealthy in hot climates, yet it is eaten in the tropical Sunda Isles, New Guinea and the South Sea Isles. Also, mutton fat is extremely popular in the area where the pig is 'untouchable' today.

Nor is obesity more injurious to human health in hot countries than in temperate ones, as is borne out by the figures of many inhabitants of Africa and western Asia.

Tacitus maintains that the Israelites did not eat pork because it carried a kind of leprosy. Perhaps some other illness was meant. It is true that some people are allergic to pork in hot weather. Also, the pig carries tapeworms and other worms, and of course trichinosis, the latter being a dangerous disease which frequently causes blindness or death. But none of these can be called 'kinds of leprosy' by any stretch of imagination.

The best explanation so far put forward is that of Antonius. As the pig is valuable to the settled farmer only, the nomads, who have always felt superior to the farmer, came to despise the pig as well as the farmer who bred it. In due course, they developed religious prohibitions against the animal they themselves could neither breed nor keep.

The ancient Egyptians kept pigs from the Neolithic at least into early dynastic times in quantity, but after the third dynasty they became much less important (Fig. 10 : 8).

From the first half of the eighteenth dynasty, mural paintings are known showing pigs treading the seed and Herodotus also relates that they were used for threshing. Their employment as agricultural helpmates is thus evident, although they were unclean. It appears that not all Egyptians ate pork, that eating it was permitted

FIG. 10 : 8. Egyptian illustration of domesticated pig guarded by monkeys on a boat, from a granite sarcophagus of Taho, twenty-sixth dynasty, 600 B.C. (Louvre Museum No. D.8). Fat but bristly pig with slender snout, resembling medieval European pig. After Keller

on certain days only, and that even the touch of the animal was regarded as pollution. The souls of the wicked were believed to migrate into pigs.

It is conceivable that the Mosaic taboos against the pig were directly derived from Egypt.

Later on in New Kingdom times the pig was sacred to Seth, an evil deity.

No matter what the orientals thought about the pig, it was held in universal esteem in the countries of the classical world, as well as by the Germanic and Celtic tribes. In the pastoral areas of ancient Greece (Figs. 10 : 9a and b) and Italy the herded pig was indeed an important and useful animal. To begin with, its grubbing habits have a profound effect on forest soil and gradually destroy undergrowth, where the

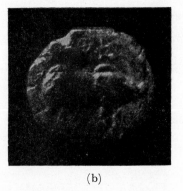

FIG. 10 : 9 (a). Bronze coin from Eleusis, Attica, 350–300 B.C., showing fat, maneless, short-legged pig, a highly domesticated breed. Diameter 14 mm. Author's collection

FIG. 10 : 9 (b). Bronze coin from Athens, Attica, 220–83 B.C., showing same type of pig as Fig. 10 : 9 (a). Diameter 19 mm. Author's collection

(a)   (b)

pigs are frequent (as they would be near settlements). They eat the seeds of oak, beech and hazel, reduce vegetation and uproot seedlings. In a short time grass tends to replace the thickets beneath the high trees. In this manner pigs prepare the way for man, both in regard to pasturing—for the pig can be followed up by the sheep as happened in the Bronze Age of northern Europe—and in regard to agriculture. Moreover, all kinds of wasteland produce food for herded pigs, not only acorns and beech nuts, which are well known, but wild apples, berries, chestnuts, slugs, insects and worms, as well as fungi. They were also efficient in the digging-out of the nests of mice, voles and other rodents. The swineherd was, therefore, an important person in ancient times, and it was worth while to herd pigs with the aid of dogs, in spite of the somewhat self-willed nature of the animals which are not easily driven in a definite direction.

Imperial Rome developed pork into a dish of great complexity.

Whole pigs were roasted and placed on the table. Sometimes one half was roasted while the other was boiled. The back provided the best meat, but the greatest delicacies were the udders and the vulva, the latter especially after an abortion.

Hams were salted and smoked from Asia Minor to Gaul, and the art of making sausages by filling intestines with chopped meat is also first mentioned as a Graeco-Roman practice.

Fattening of pigs was an important matter, and many special kinds of food were known. Should the poor pig have died from over-eating, or drinking too much of the fattening fluid, it was considered as superior. It was also believed by some that the taste was much improved if the pig was killed by piercing with a red-hot spit.

It is all the more curious that the consumption of piglets was not at first popular. Perhaps the Germanic and Celtic subjects cultivated this type of food. At any rate, it was considered fare for the rich in the third century A.D.

Gandert (1954) describes the finds made in Germanic tombs at Leuna near Halle (central Germany). They are of the third century and contained both fowl (see p. 452) and pig. Hams were found in two of the graves, and a large pork chop in another. Two contained in addition roast piglets. Such piglets are shown also on a Roman bronze lid from Mundelsheim (near Marbach on the Neckar). But the bones of young pigs are conspicuously absent from the refuse-heaps of Roman *castella*. It may not have been considered as a food fit for fighting men—as Gandert thinks—though on the other hand there may have been sound economic reasons not to waste immature beasts.

In post-Roman times piglets are no longer found in tombs but hams continue, as for instance in the Wendel tombs of Uppland (Sweden).

Apart from its culinary importance the pig succeeded in making its way into some of the religious cults of the classical world. There is the myth of Adonis, with whom Aphrodite was enamoured, who was killed while out hunting, by a boar who was Ares in disguise. This curious story is of considerable age and according to Hahn (1896) of Babylonian origin. It was still popular among the lower classes in classical times and may to some extent have contributed to the very divergent views regarding the pig.

Swine were sacrificed to Aphrodite, though only when she was associated with Adonis.

In Argos, Thessaly, Cyprus and in parts of Asia Minor, too, pigs were sacrificed to Venus.

In other places, however, the sacrifice of pigs was expressly forbidden. Oddly enough, in this respect also we encounter the strange contradiction that runs through the history of the pig. Whilst the pig was completely excluded from the Temple of Hermithea in the Chersonesos, and nobody was allowed to wear sandals of pig-skin in the precincts of the Temple of Alectrona in Rhodes—evidence that the pig was considered unclean—pork was not eaten on Crete out of gratitude to the pig whose squealing drowned the cries of the baby Zeus when Cronos was seeking to devour him.

The pig was also used for the purposes of purification, for instance in Greece, where the blood of piglets was regarded as particularly effective. At Delphi, Apollo thus cleansed Orestes who had killed his mother.

The sacrifice of the pig was common practice in connection with oaths and treaties. In the *Iliad*, Agamemnon sacrifices a boar to Zeus and Helius. When Rome and Alba Longa made a treaty a boar was killed by smashing its head with a stone. The use of a stone suggests that the custom goes back to the Neolithic. In later Roman times treaties and promises were commonly sworn over a pig, as is illustrated on coins (Fig. 10 : 11).

One is so much used to the pig as a supplier of pork that one is apt to overlook its other uses. There have indeed been many. In Egypt as well as in Greece it was used (in the muzzled condition) to tread in the seed after floods or rain; with its somewhat pointed feet it made holes of the right depth suitable for germination.

Rather more remarkable is the practice of searching for truffles. Pigs are natural grubbers equipped with efficient noses, and they will eat truffles with delight. In Périgord, south-west France, this propensity is exploited, and the animals are trained to help man in finding the coveted subterranean fungi (Fig. 10 : 12).

Still more remarkable is the use of the pig as a retriever. About this strange practice, Mr Walter Shepherd has very kindly supplied me with information from which it emerges that it must have been the practice perhaps for centuries in the New Forest, especially from the eleventh to the fifteenth centuries, when the inhabitants were forbidden to have dogs of a size large enough for illicit hunting. Mr Shepherd quotes Kenchington's *The Commoners' New Forest* regarding the sizes of dogs:

If small enough to creep through a large antique iron stirrup, now kept at the Verderers' Hall in Lyndhurst as an interesting relic, dogs were considered too small to hunt. The dimensions of the opening of this stirrup are ten and a half inches by seven and a half. If you wished, for personal protection or other reason, to keep a larger dog, you could do so only if he were expedited. This meant that its fore feet were maimed by cutting off certain toes so that the deer stood in no danger from its sorties.

FIG. 10 : 10. Silver didrachm of Lyttus, Crete, fifth to fourth century B.C. Shows a boar's head with exaggerated features. The steep forehead and the crinkled nose suggest a highly domesticated animal. Twice natural size. Author's collection

FIG. 10 : 11. Roman Republican silver denarius gens Veturia; (moneyer Ti. Veturius, 110–108 B.C.). Shows the curious custom of taking an oath on a pig or piglet, then current among the armies of Italian states. The kneeling soldier holds the pig, the two standing ones touching it with their swords. Diameter 20 mm. Author's collection

FIG. 10 : 12. Searching for truffles with the aid of pigs in Périgord, southwest France. The sow is presumably muzzled, the piglets follow the mother and are 'learning'. The man is ready to pick up the truffles when found. A high-legged country-pig resembling the Spanish (Fig. 10 : 17) is being used. Illustration based on a postcard

This iron stirrup is now known as 'King Rufus's Stirrup', and some antiquarians date it as late as Tudor times. Evidently the pigs were trained as substitutes for hunting or retrieving dogs, to be used in an area where the game was not to be killed by the commoner.

It is thus natural that very little information is available about hunting-pigs. The only detailed report refers to a sow named Slut (Fig. 10 : 13), an oil painting of which is in the possession of Mrs Dorey in Brockenhurst and which is here reproduced with her kind permission.

FIG. 10 : 13. 'Slut', the retrieving pig of the New Forest, Hampshire. Photo W. Shepherd

Slut belonged to Sir Henry Mildmay. She started her retrieving activities at the age of eighteen months. *Rural Sports* (vol. 3, 1807) relates:

Of this most extraordinary Animal will be here stated a short History, to the Veracity of which there are hundreds of living Witnesses. Slut was bred in the New Forest and trained by Mr Richard Toomer and Mr Edward Toomer, to find, point and retrieve, Game as well as the best Pointer; her Nose was superior to any Pointer they ever possessed, and no two men in England had better. Slut has stood Partridges, Black-game, Pheasants, Snipe and Rabbits in the same day, but was never known to point a Hare. When called to go out Shooting, she would come home off the Forest at full Stretch, and be as elevated as a Dog upon being shown the Gun

These examples of pigs being used for unusual purposes illustrate that only in exceptional circumstances would man have employed them thus. The truffle-finding pig is a specialization, and it was perhaps more common in the Middle Ages when pigs were regularly driven into the woods and when truffles were still plentiful. The retriever pig was evidently a kind of substitute developed in the case of an emergency.

Other emergencies may have resulted in the use of pigs as draught animals. Few domesticated animals have not at one time or another been tried that way. Pig-carts are reported from the New Forest, and they have been used from time to time on the Continent.

The pig is the principal supplier of meat to the Chinese, and there is no doubt that pig-breeding is of considerable antiquity in China. It would however be going too far to say that it started earlier in that country than elsewhere.

In densely populated areas the pig that is easily kept in stys, and can even be reared in houses, scores over all other domestic animals whose flesh is normally eaten. In addition, it is more prolific than any other large mammal, it is comparatively long-lived, mature within a year and capable of producing two litters annually. Any casualties among the litters would have been eaten, as indeed roast sucking-pigs have been regarded as a delicacy for at least 2000 years.

The European domesticated pig was the descendant of local wild forms almost everywhere. This is not surprising since in spite of its physical strength it is easily tamed, as Lutz Heck has pointed out. With its omnivorous habits there was no difficulty in getting it accustomed to food available in a settlement. Wild pig today feed on acorns, beechnuts, potatoes, beet and even corn and fern roots. In addition, they feed on any carcasses they find; on mice and voles they happen to dig up; leverets and fawns, eggs, reptiles and insect larvae are taken, as well as earth-worms.

In addition, wild pig have social tendencies which make them suitable for domestication. Their social unit is essentially the family (Fig. 10 : 14). In the autumn they form packs of ten to thirty individuals. Several females join to form such groups while the males tend to remain solitary.

The medieval pig was a high-legged, long-snouted form which still survives in

Fig. 10 : 14. High-legged naked sow with lop-ears, and three piglets. Imperial Roman coin of Titus, A.D. 79–81.
After Keller

many outlying country districts in Europe (Fig. 10 : 4). This is the herded pig encountered, for instance, in Spain (Fig. 10 : 17), and it may be regarded as representative of the external appearance of most early European pigs. Generally speaking, the body size (and some structural features) of pigs are very dependent on feeding conditions (see, for instance, Fig. 10 in Herre, 1938), and it is not surprising that Boessneck (1958) found considerable size fluctuations in the course of time. Though smaller than wild pigs, those of the Neolithic and Bronze Age of central Europe were relatively large. They decreased in size until the beginning of the Roman period, but within the area of Roman occupation pig bones became distinctly broader, which Boessneck attributes to improved living conditions. Overall increase in size is observed in the Middle Ages in Bavaria, whilst in the north they continue to decrease during this period.

The La Tène *oppidum* of Manching in Bavaria (Opitz, 1958), with its very small pigs, confirms Boessneck's views, and so do the medieval pigs of Haithabu in Schleswig (*c.* A.D. 1000, Siewing, 1960).

About 150 years ago the European country pig began to undergo a great change. It was due to the importation of Chinese pigs which are true derivatives of the *vittatus* group. They were first introduced into England, and the Berkshire pig,[1] for instance, changed quickly into the thick-set beast we know today. In addition, a few

[1] The Berkshire has undergone numerous changes since; it has been studied by Herre (1938).

FIG. 10 : 15. Wild boar in snow. Mecklenburg, north
Germany. Photo Lutz Heck

FIG. 10 : 16. Wild sow. Near Lainz, Wiener Wald, Austria.
Photo Lutz Heck

FIG. 10 : 17. The domesticated Mediterranean high-legged pig
with lop-ears. Near Granada, Spain. This breed, which is driven
on 'pastures', is slender and agile. Photo F.E.Z.

Indian breeds were imported also and crossed with the European. These crosses brought into the European strains some properties which were regarded as desirable, such as early maturation and high fertility. In addition, the Chinese pig fattens much more quickly. Low, who wrote his book on the *Domesticated Animals of the British Islands* over 100 years ago, also maintains that the smaller size of the Chinese pig was in his time regarded as an advantage, as indeed at the present day the best prices are paid for pigs that are not too heavy.

In China the pig is a most important domestic animal, not only because it is a prolific breeder but because it can be kept in a confined space. There are possibly other reasons, such as the aversion to eating beasts of burden like the larger ruminants. There are two groups of Chinese pig. The southern form is according to the structure of its skull related to the Indian wild species, *Sus cristatus*; it usually has upright ears and the nose is short and robust. The pig of northern China is derived by Wagner from a local wild form intermediate between *Sus cristatus* and *Sus scrofa*, which still occurs in the less densely populated parts of northern China and Manchuria. The breeds derived from it have been intensely domesticated, they are lop-eared and there are many varieties, among them the well-known masked pig.

Modern European pigs display enormous variety in their growth forms which find expression in their skeletons (Wiarda, 1954). The mixture of European and Chinese blood, coupled with the natural plasticity of pigs under conditions of domestication appears to have resulted in a variability of the stock which makes Recent domesticated material almost useless in work on prehistoric breeds.

Very little attention used to be paid to feeding the pig, which had to be content with offals, human faeces and leaves. In order to fatten the pig, castration is practised on a large scale. It is applied not only to the male but to females also, and this in a manner which throws some light on primitive methods which may well go back to the Neolithic, and which show what can be done without modern veterinary knowledge. The female piglet is castrated by means of two cuts only about 2 cm. long, through which the ovaries are extracted with a small hooked tool and then pinched off with the fingers. Without any further ado the piglet is allowed to run away, and the number of casualties is reported to be negligible.

From the technological point of view the pig is, on the whole, less important than other species. At all times it was a convenient source of high-grade food (Figs. 10 : 4 and 10 : 18). Its bones are useless, since they remain in the state of incomplete fusion of the parts long into the age of sexual maturity. The epiphyses (ends) of the long bones are not solidly attached to the shaft (diaphysis), and their texture is soft. The tusks were occasionally used for ornaments, but in that case they were probably taken from hunted wild boars rather than domesticated specimens. The fat had of course many uses, in cosmetics, medicine and crafts, and the skin provided a special

FIG. 10 : 18. Hunting wild boar. Mesolithic or Neolithic, eastern Spanish art. Rock shelter of Val del Charco del Agua Amara, Teruel, Spain. After Obermaier

type of leather. The bristles, too, must have been used much as they are at the present day. But in all these respects the pig never had an exclusive position. There were always other supplies available.

The use of the pig for traction, truffle-grubbing and retrieving is purely incidental. It was in ancient Egypt only that the pig was employed for a specialized job, the treading-in of the seed. Its indirect effect on the forest soils in connection with the Neolithic conquest of the wooded parts of Europe far exceeded in significance all its other technological applications.

FIG. 10 : 19. Wild British boar on bronze coin of London mint. On obverse head of Carausius, A.D. 287–293. A coin of the Second Legion (Parthica), from the hoard of Little Orme's Head. Diameter 20 mm. Author's collection

GROUP III

Mammals Subsequently Domesticated Primarily for Transport and Labour

THE first steps in the use of animals as sources of energy were taken with cattle, as has been pointed out already. It appears that this idea contributed much to the popularity of the large bovines, especially when the increasing wealth of the settled communities made the problem of transport more acute. Man was compelled to take quantities of raw materials to the settlement, whilst in nomadic times these were often worked on the spot. The amount of goods produced also was increasing.

The necessity of transport and the evident advantages of large beasts, coupled with the difficulties of life in tropical forests, appear to have resulted in the domestication of the Indian elephant at an early date.

The need for desert transport became acute when desiccation of areas adjacent to the desert belt made previously cultivated areas uninhabitable. The secondary nomadism developed under those conditions took advantage of two highly mobile beasts, the horse in the steppes of central Asia and the camel in the desert steppes of central and western Asia.

In the civilizations of the large river valleys, however, the swift animals were not accepted until comparatively late. An exception is the training of the onager to draw carts in Sumer, almost certainly a copy of the example provided by the horse of the more northern countries. In the Nile Valley the ass was domesticated early and, as is well known, became the chief means of small transport in semi-arid countries.

The domestication of this group of animals used for transport and labour is a fascinating problem. Whilst contacts between man and animal species were, as usual, provided by overlaps of social media, the domesticators must from the first have been aware of the advantages that were likely to accrue to them. This use of power not derived from the human body was one of the greatest steps in the evolution of technology.

Those first organizers of transport, however, did not lack feelings of gratitude towards the beasts they were harnessing. It is truly remarkable that none of the animals of this group is an ordinary kind of food.[1] Man regarded them as helpmates and as members of his own social group.

[1] Exceptions usually indicate a late or secondary adoption of the animal.

11

The Elephants

SCIENTIFIC NAMES—INDIAN ELEPHANT—*Elephas maximus* L., with three races: *E. maximus maximus* L. (Ceylon), *E. maximus ceylanicus* Blainville (Ceylon), and *E. maximus indicus* Cuvier (India and Further India, Sumatra, Borneo).

AFRICAN ELEPHANT—*Loxodonta africana* Blumenbach, at least two races: *L. africana africana*, the large East African, never domesticated, and *L. africana cyclotis* Matschie, the small Sudanese, North and north-east African. The small West African elephant from Gabon etc. is known as *L. africana pumilio* Noack. *L. africana* and *L. cyclotis* are by several authors regarded as distinct species.

IT IS commonly believed that only the Indian elephant is tamable. Whilst it is true that this species is the more docile, the African elephant was at one time an important beast employed by the armies of North African rulers. In order to appreciate the reasons for the adoption of the African species, and indeed the history of the domestication of elephants in general, let us briefly consider first the distribution of the wild species.

Distribution of the wild Indian elephant
The Indian elephant (Fig. 11 : 1) is in all probability a descendant of the group of *E. hysudricus* of the Indian Villafranchian, and related to the group of *E. meridionalis*, from which the mammoth (*E. primigenius*) and the straight-tusked elephant (*E. antiquus*) of the European Pleistocene are descended. The Indian elephant appears originally to have been indigenous in the entire Indian peninsula, including Ceylon, though perhaps not west of the Rajputana Desert.

FIG. 11 : 1. Indian elephant. Note humps on the forehead, rounded
back and small ears

There is no evidence that it ever occurred north of the Himalayas, but it extends today through Further India to Sumatra and Borneo. A thousand or fifteen hundred years ago it was found also in southern China. According to information kindly supplied by Professor Eve Edwards, two references to this effect are incorporated in T'ang works (A.D. 618–909), namely one by Tuan Kung-lu in his work *Pei Hu Lu*, stating that a small black variety of elephant was found both in Hsün-chou, near Canton, and in Lei-Chou, not far from Pak-hoi. Its tusks were small and red, and it was captured and killed for the sake of its trunk, which was regarded as a great delicacy.

The other reference is by Lu Hsün, in *Ling Piao Lu I*, the oldest topography of the Annam, Kuang-tung and Kuang-si region in existence. Wild elephants are said to have occurred in these regions, and that author saw them himself frequently in use as beasts of burden.

This Chinese area of distribution of Indian elephants was contiguous with the present one in Further India.

In the West, however, an isolated colony of Indian elephants existed in Syria until the eighth century B.C. It suggests that late in Pleistocene times Indian elephants extended through Persia and northern Mesopotamia to the borders of Asia Minor, but in prehistoric and early historic times they were already extinct everywhere between India and Syria. The evidence for the Syrian elephants is as follows:

On the Middle Euphrates and on the Chabur River there existed in ancient times an area where wild elephants were to be found. That they belonged to the Indian species is suggested by a picture in the grave of Rekhmere (Egypt), of the

276

fifteenth century B.C. The elephant on the Black Obelisk of Shalmaneser III also could be cited in support of the former existence of a west Asiatic race of Indian elephants, if indeed this specimen came from Armenia. The original area of distribution of the Western elephants may thus have been wider than is suggested by the records of hunting expeditions of Egyptian and Assyrian kings.

Of fossil remains, only two lower jaws are known. They were excavated by Woolley in Levels II (c. 1575 B.C.) and IV (c. 1475 B.C.) of Atchana-Alalakh in Syria.

It has been suggested that the Syrian elephants (as they are commonly called) were originally imported from India by Assyrian kings for hunting purposes. This is not likely, for there are records of a hunting expedition of Thothmes III (1501–1447 B.C.), the Egyptian conqueror of Syria. His encounter with elephants in 1464 B.C. is related on the Barkal Stele, and again in the biography of Amen-en-heb who says:

Again I saw another successful deed which the Lord of the Two Lands accomplished in Ni. He hunted 120 elephants at their mud hole. Then the biggest elephant began to fight before his Majesty. I was the one who cut off his hand while he was still alive, in the presence of his Majesty, while I was standing in the water between two rocks. Then my Lord rewarded me. . . .

This event took place in the fifteenth century B.C., when Assur was still insignificant. When the Assyrians were establishing their empire under Tiglathpileser I (c. 1125 B.C.), this king reached the hunting grounds of Thothmes III. But he killed only ten males and caught four alive. It appears that their number had diminished. As Barnett has demonstrated, the flourishing ivory industry of Syria and Phoenicia in the second millennium relied on supplies from this source.

There is a report which suggests that these elephants extended south into Aramaea. It is related by Meissner in his book, *Könige Babyloniens und Assyriens*; he states that the Aramaeans of Bit-Amukkani and of Bit-Jakini, the old land by the sea . . . sent silver, gold, lead, copper, ivory and elephant-skins. This raises the question of the former presence of the Syrian elephant in Palestine. It should be noted, however, that the elephants found at Bethlehem in 1933, and mentioned by Miss Bate, are of Pliocene or early Pleistocene age and are too early to have any bearing on this question. In Acheulian deposits also elephant remains were found, but they were not specifically identifiable.

At Beth-Shan, the modern Beisân in the Valley of Jezreel, a Hittite hematite seal was found. According to Rowe (1930), it shows two deities with an elephant and dates from the fourteenth century B.C. Whilst it would confirm the existence of the Syrian elephant somewhere in the region, its Hittite style might indicate a more northerly source. This seal, therefore, is not likely to prove the existence of the Syrian elephant in Palestine at that time.

When Ashurnasirpal II (859–833 B.C.) arrived on the Syrian scene, he killed thirty elephants and obtained some alive for his zoological garden. But, soon after, the elephants must have become extinct, as there are no further records.

Other references to elephants and to ivory are numerous in the Assyrian period. But though it is to be suspected that these refer mainly to the Syrian race, commerce with India was sufficiently developed to allow for importation from that country. Similarly, mention of elephants kept in zoological gardens, as for instance at Kalhu in Assyria at the time of Ashurnasirpal, are of no value in this context.

The hunting propensities of the Assyrian kings are likely to have been an important cause contributing to the extinction of the Syrian elephant. On the other hand, the recent excavations at Nimrud by Professor Mallowan have shown that there was a very considerable trade in carved ivory flowing from Syria into Assyria in the ninth and eighth centuries B.C. Oddly enough, the subjects were more often than not imitation Egyptian, which goes to prove that the trade was indeed from west to east. Where did the Syrian makers of these ivories obtain their raw material? It is more than probable that it was not carried from India to Syria and that the Syrian elephant was the source. If so, its rapid extermination is easily explained by the ivory craze of the ninth and eighth centuries B.C. This was, incidentally, also the time of King Omri of Samaria (886–874 B.C.), famous for the wealth of ivory used in his palace.

The history of the Syrian elephant throws much light on the history of the city of Byblos, once famous for its ivory trade. Originally this trade depended on ivory supplies from the hinterland. As the elephants came to be exterminated, partly by the spread of deforestation but mainly by ruthless hunting, a new ivory supply had to be looked for. By 800 B.C. the art of ivory-carving was still going strong, so that there must have been a new source of raw material. It is unlikely that this was far-away India, the overland trade route being blocked by rising Assyria. I suggest that this ivory came from Africa *via* Egypt, and that Byblos and neighbouring Levantine cities bartered it for timber from the Lebanon. This trade must have created close connections with Eygpt, and this country was consulted for artistic inspiration. Egyptian temples were erected in Byblos. The ivory carvings of the seventh century recently found by Mallowan in the palace at Nimrud show strong Egyptian influence and thus bear out this idea. The Assyrians, however, coveted the Mediterranean seaboard with its flourishing trade. When they succeeded in occupying it, trade with Egypt, a hostile state, became impossible. In all probability the timber was now diverted to the Assyrian Empire, and the art of ivory-carving died out for lack of raw material. The town as a whole lost its former significance.

There remains the problem of the strange gap between India and the western area of distribution in Syria, which extended perhaps south into Aramaea and north to Armenia. The explanation may be ecological. The Indian elephant is a tree-forest species which needs a mild climate. Such environment in all probability existed along the foothills of Persia and in the lower valleys late in the Pleistocene and early in Postglacial times. But the gap corresponds in part to the Fertile Crescent and it is conceivable that the suitable biotopes were destroyed by the spread of agriculture in prehistoric times. The only evidence that elephants may have been living in Persia is found in the Indian treatise called *Gaja Shastri*, which describes them as bluish with whitish hair. But it is uncertain whether these were wild or domesticated.

The remarkable isolated colony of the Syrian elephant was never a source of domesticated or trained stock. When elephants became popular in warfare outside India it was because contacts with that country had become intimate, and there is no reason to assume that the Persians had local wild elephants at their disposal.

The wild African elephant

The African elephant differs from the Indian species profoundly in several respects (Fig. 11 : 2). The ears are larger, the forehead lacks the frontal bulges of the Indian, the outline of the back culminates near the pelvis, and the molars consist of few lamellae which are rhomboidal in shape. For these and other reasons the African species have been placed in a separate genus, *Loxodonta*.

In most treatises only one species is recognized, *Loxodonta africana*, but Morrison-Scott (1947) and other authors are inclined to regard the small elephants of the northern territory of the formerly Belgian Congo and the Sudan as a distinct species,

FIG. 11 : 2. African elephant. Note absence of humps on forehead, very large ears and the eminence of the lumbar vertebrae. Photo A. Sutcliffe

L. cyclotis. It differs from the larger in the shape of the ears and in other characters. The recognition of this form has an important bearing on the question of domestication.

The African elephant best known to European workers is that of East Africa, especially Kenya. This is indeed a large beast, attaining an average height of ten feet at the shoulder. It is thus noticeably larger than the Indian species.

Large races occur, or occurred, also in South Africa and in West Africa, for instance in the forests of Ivory Coast.

The smaller races appear to be characteristic of the Sudan and the adjacent woodlands. They average a little over seven feet at the shoulder. In the Congo these elephants have been systematically and successfully trained for work in the forests during the last sixty years. It is important to note this fact, for a similar small African race was once indigenous in North Africa and used by the Carthaginians. Small elephants occur also in French Equatorial Africa (Gabon). Farther west, Bigourdan and Prunier recognized three races: the large one in the forests of Ivory Coast already mentioned, a smaller one with reddish skin from the north of Ivory Coast and a dwarf race, not more than seven feet high, from Nioro on the Upper Colombine River east of Bakal ($15\frac{1}{2}°$ N.). The northernmost occurrences are at Kiffa (Senegal, north of Bakal, $17°$ N.). A small race occurs also Sierra Leone.

Thence it is not far along the coastal belt to Rio de Oro, where the last remnants of the North African forest fauna are still surviving (red deer, for instance). It is conceivable that this was the geographical link between the Sudanese elephants and the small race of North Africa which became extinct in the Roman imperial period and which Hanno saw about 500 B.C.

In Egypt and the eastern Sudan elephants were known from prehistoric times onwards. How far north they ventured in the Nile Valley is not known. But representations like that on the Caernarvon Ivory (Fig. 11 : 3), a flint-knife handle, and the Davis ivory comb (Fig. 11 : 4) testify to the fact that Egyptians of the late Gerzean period were familiar with the beast. The elephant vase in pink limestone, described by Glanville from the British Museum collection, is either late predynastic or early dynastic. Thereafter, evidence for elephants ceases, the next record being that of Thothmes hunting the Indian species in Syria. From this it may be inferred that the African species had become extinct in Egypt proper in early dynastic times. In the eastern Sudan however the species survived into the last century. It was from this stock that the Ptolemies derived their war elephants, whilst the same area had been a centre of ivory production for a long time, the traffic having been organized mainly by way of the Red Sea. The last haunts of this race appear to have been in Eritrea where, according to Sir William Gowers, they were seen near the headwaters of the Baraka River in 1868. Of five specimens shot the cow measured 7 ft. 8 in. at the shoulder, and the larger of the two bulls 7 ft. 4 in.; the other two were young males. These are the measurements of the forest elephant, and Gowers is therefore right in

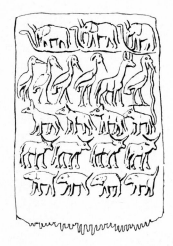

FIG. 11 : 3. So-called Caernarvon ivory; a flint-knife handle of Late Gerzean period of pre-dynastic Egypt, showing a wild African elephant. After Petrie

FIG. 11 : 4. Davis ivory comb; another Late Gerzean Egyptian work of art depicting African elephants. After Petrie

maintaining that the small race of the African elephant extended across the Nile to the coast of the Red Sea.

In Libya and north-west Africa wild elephants survived into the Roman period. They were the stock on which the Carthaginians relied for the equipment of the army as will be shown later on. Evidence for the presence of the wild species is abundant in the form of rock engravings of early as well as of late periods. Some particularly vivid representations have been found in Libya (Figs. 11 : 5 and 11 : 6) which belong to the naturalistic style of Graziosi's pre-Neolithic period. Fig. 11 : 7

FIG. 11 : 6

FIG. 11 : 5

FIGS. 11 : 5 to 11 : 7. Engravings of wild elephants from Libya. All based on Graziosi. (5) shows an exceptionally naturalistic specimen from Arréchin. (6) comes from the region of Bergiug and shows an elephant putting his trunk in his mouth and behind him a buffalo. These two engravings belong to the Early Naturalistic group of Graziosi. The third (Fig. 7) comes from Wadi Massauda and belongs to the Stylized group, which may well be Neolithic or even considerably later. Two camels and a man are also shown

FIG. 11 : 7

281

shows how elephants were depicted in the last phase of Libyan rock engravings, which is perhaps already contemporary with the foundation of the Phoenician colonies of Carthage etc. on the North African coast. As these elephants occurred in the forests of the Atlas ranges right to the Atlantic coast, Hanno, the Carthaginian seafarer, was able to observe them on the sea-shore about 500 B.C.

Sir William Gowers has proved conclusively that the North African elephant was a race of small size. Polybius and other Roman writers, who must have been familiar with the north-west African elephant, described it as being smaller than the Indian species, and it appears that these animals were not strong enough to carry howdahs holding several warriors. Philostratus (*c.* A.D. 200) said that the Indian elephant is as much taller than the African as the African is taller than the Mycenaean horse. From this information Gowers calculated that the north-west African elephant would have been 7 ft. 9 in. high. This suggestion finds further support in a Barcid coin showing an African elephant with a mahout directing the beast with an ancus (hook) (Fig. 11 : 15i). Assuming that there is no distortion in the design, the proportional sizes of elephant and rider being correct, Gowers calculated that the elephant would not have been more than eight feet tall at the shoulder. It thus appears that seven to eight feet would have been the average height of the north-west African animal.

The available evidence, therefore, suggests that there was a circum-Saharan species of African elephant which is perhaps identical with *Loxodonta cyclotis* of northern Congo or the small race of Senegal which survives at Kiffa, 17°N. It extends from the coasts of the Red Sea along both sides of the Sahara to the coasts of the Atlantic. This vast reservoir was tapped for the purposes of domestication from the third century B.C. onwards, after having been reduced by hunting for ivory and skins in earlier times. It should be noted that the African elephant is less restricted to tree-forest than the Indian elephant and that it is often found in scrubs and open country. These habits made the species more accessible to man. At the same time they may have brought the elephants into contact with the farming communities which have always been averse to them because of the damage caused to crops. The

Fig. 11 : 8. Elephant as depicted on a mosaic in the Roman city of Djemila, northern Algeria. It shows clearly that the artist had no living specimens at his disposal and that he drew the elephant from hearsay. By the fourth century A.D., therefore, the species had been exterminated in that region. Based on photo by F.E.Z.

small African races living in more open country, therefore, were in many places exterminated or pushed back into uninhabited country more easily than the larger Indian species and the large races of tropical and South Africa. When, therefore, the domestication of this species became an economic proposition, its extermination in the whole of North and north-east Africa was completed within a few centuries.

Domestication of elephants

The domestication of elephants has presented man with problems which are absent in the case of other species. They are mainly due to the large size of the beast. On the one hand this quality implies superior strength, but owing to its body mass an elephant is unable to do hard work for more than a few hours at a time. Their economic use thus is inevitably restricted, and it was only when their usefulness in war was discovered that the practice of elephant domestication spread over the whole civilized world of the time. Elephants cannot normally be penned, though fortunately they are docile animals and therefore relatively easy to lead and to keep under control.

Contrary to widely held views, elephants breed in captivity. There is, however, a serious drawback in the loss of work in the female, the pregnancy period being long, varying from eighteen to twenty-four months. The babies suckle for at least a year and follow the mother until they are five years old. Moreover, the youngster cannot be used for work until he is fourteen years old. Indian elephants are adult at about sixteen years according to Gee (1950) and a calf is produced every three or four years. The best age for working elephants is between thirty and forty years. The average age reached is seventy years, though some may live to more than 100 under good conditions.

No wonder that man on the whole preferred not to control elephants too severely. It was more economical to allow them to lead a free life and to capture and tame the individuals required for work. The exceptions to this rule are rare. Elephants have been bred in captivity from time to time where supplies of captured specimens could not be obtained, and where it was desired to have special types of beasts, such as white ones.

One would expect the physical strength of the elephant to reduce the number of methods by which it can be captured. In fact this is not the case, though great strength of materials used is an obvious prerequisite. The small Congolese elephants are pursued on foot or horseback until a youngster is detached from the herd and captured with nooses. Deraniyagala (1951) relates that in Ceylon selected bulls are occasionally stalked and noosed by hand, but with the large elephants this method is the exception. In Assam two koonkies approach a three-quarters-grown elephant and noose it. Occasionally drugged food is used, the drug usually being opium.

All other methods make use of traps of some kind or other. Nooses may be suspended from trees and worked by men, or they are set on the ground on an elephants'
track. The end of the noose rope may be attached to a tree, or else a deer antler is
tied to it which catches in the vegetation. The most successful methods of capturing
elephants enlist the help of tame individuals. Female decoys may entice a wild bull
into a pen. On a large scale elephants are caught by the stockade method, widely
used today in India and Assam. A large funnel-shaped stockade is built which ends
up in a small enclosure. A wild herd is slowly driven into it. This may take many
days, since the animals must not become suspicious until the last moment, when it
is too late to turn back. They are extracted from the enclosure with the aid of tame

FIG. 11 : 9. Capture of Indian elephants by the stockade method.
Based on photo by E. P. Gee

elephants. Since in this manner entire herds can be captured, the erection of an
expensive stockade and the driving are well worth while (Fig. 11 : 9). But much
manpower, tame beasts and a good deal of organization are required.

A very interesting method is still used in Madras Province. It is the pitfall
method described by Wilson. The elephants fall into carefully prepared pits, which
are just large enough to take the animal but too small to allow it to move about.
They are extracted from the pits by roping to tame animals and raising the floor
of the pit by means of logs thrown in until the captured animal can climb out
(Fig. 11 : 10).

It will be noticed that all these methods of capturing elephants were well within
the capabilities of primitive man, and even of Palaeolithic man. The size of the
animal, therefore, did not present an obstacle to domestication.

FIG. 11 : 10. Capture of elephants by the pit-fall method, using tame females as decoys. Based on photo by C. C. Wilson

It is not surprising that already in the Indus Valley civilization domesticated elephants make their appearance. On the other hand, such large animals could not have been domesticated in the nomadic stage. At the earliest, they belong to the same phase of domestication as the cattle. The practice remained restricted to the Indian region until the Alexandrine conquest, in consequence of which it was extended within a century to the confines of the Western world.

The first records of capturing African elephants appear to be those of Ptolemy's map of 151 B.C. showing the areas where they could be obtained. In Ceylon, too, they were caught before the Christian era. The first European account is by Aristotle (IX). Pliny (A.D. 44) related the tale of ambassadors from Ceylon. Curiously enough, he does not mention the domestication of the African species, though he reviews its distribution in North Africa. Since the breeding of elephants is more or less uncontrolled, domesticated breeds, as we find them in other beasts that have been drawn into the orbit of man, have not made their appearance, except that individuals with white patches on the skin and wholly white ones are much prized and encouraged to breed in Further India.

Domestication of the Indian elephant

The earliest evidence for the use of elephants is to be found on fifteen seals from Mohenjo-Daro (c. 2500–1500 B.C.). The elephants shown clearly belong to the Indian species. It is curious however that some have at the end of the trunk a double tip. This is a character of the African elephant, and it has resulted in some speculation. One should remember however that these seals are not accurate representations of the animals and that the trunk of the elephant has often been called his hand (Amen-en-heb, p. 277), so that the movable tip would be compared with the fingers. Whether there were one or two would have been a matter of little importance to the designer of the seal.

Six out of the fifteen Mohenjo-Daro elephants more or less distinctly show a line extending down from the back behind the foreleg (Fig. 11 : 11). Attempts have been made to explain it as part of the natural system of skin folds. If a living Indian elephant is examined, it will be found that there are no large skin folds that could conceivably be represented by the lines shown on the seals. The alternative theory that the line indicates a covering cloth or wrapping on the back is therefore much the more acceptable. It is thus probable that the Indian elephant was domesticated by the time of the Indus Valley civilization (2500–1500 B.C.).

FIG. 11 : 11. Seal impression from Mohenjo-Daro of an Indian elephant distinctly showing the outline of a rug covering the back. It must, therefore, be regarded as domesticated. About 2500 B.C. Natural size

With the evidence from Mohenjo-Daro at hand, it is not surprising to find that elephants were familiar beasts of burden in the Mauryan period, from the fifth century onwards, and later. At Taxila in the Punjab a fifth-century punch-marked coin was found showing an elephant on the obverse (from Level IV, Bhir Mound). Other coins of this type come from Singavaram and Paila. In addition, terra cotta toy elephants with or without riders appear in Taxila from the fourth century onwards. It appears that after the Greek conquest of north-west India the elephant became the symbol of the rulers of Taxila. Philostratus relates that in the first century A.D. a sacred elephant lived in the Sun Temple of that city. But elsewhere, too, the elephant appears on coins of the Graeco-Indian period (Fig. 11 : 12); it was perhaps used as a symbol of royal authority. Evidence for the domestication of elephants is so abundant from that period onwards that examples need not be quoted. One point is perhaps noteworthy, that it was used as far to the north-west as the area of Peshawar, where it appears on the coins of the city of Puskalavati.

FIG. 11 : 12. Square coin of the Indo-Greek period of north Pakistan, silver drachm of Apollodotus I, 185–162 B.C. Inscription in Greek. Note the typical bulges on the head of the Indian elephant. The reverse shows a zebu and the inscription is in a local Indian script. Twice natural size. Author's collection

Elephants in Mesopotamia

There is but little evidence that the Indian elephant was known in Mesopotamia proper. From the early part of the Jamdat Nasr period comes a seal showing an animal with the body of a horse, legs of cattle, horns and with a long trunk (Fig. 11 : 13). Professor Frankfort (1939) cautiously called it a monster, though it was he who kindly drew my attention to it. It indeed suggests knowledge of the elephant from hearsay rather than direct observation. Thus it points to contacts with the Indus Valley civilization, the obvious source of elephants at the time.

FIG. 11 : 13. Elephant-like monster from a seal of the Jamdat Nasr period of Mesopotamia. After Frankfort

Another seal was found at Tell Asmar in Iraq (Fig. 11 : 14) showing an Indian elephant together with an Indian rhinoceros and a crocodile. According to Frankfort, the seal resembles in style those from the Indus Valley civilization, so that either the subject or the entire seal may have been imported from India.

The elephant was better known to the Assyrians in Shalmaneser III's time. It was hunted by this king in Syria, and, according to the Black Stele (841 B.C.),

287

Fig. 11 : 14. Mesopotamian seal impression from Tell Asmar, Iraq, resembling in style those from the Indus Valley civilization. A particular indication of Indian connections or origins is the excellent picture of a single-horned rhinoceros and of a crocodile of the gharial type. After Frankfort

received as tribute from the land of Musri. This country is believed to have been situated to the north, but the Indian elephant (which can be specifically identified on the stele) and the monkeys that came with it rather suggest an Indian origin of this tribute. On the other hand, Bactrian camels, a northern species, were sent also, and in view of the one-time existence of this elephant in Syria it is not inconceivable that elephants once existed in Armenia. The monkeys would, of course, remain difficult to explain. In any case, however, the Black Stele elephant was not a native nor a domestic animal of Mesopotamia.

It is only during the Seleucid and even the Parthian periods that trained elephants appear in Mesopotamia, undoubtedly as a sequel to the contacts with India established by Alexander the Great. Clay figurines from this period are known from Nippur (Legrain, 1930, p. 35, pl. LXI, No. 326). As a matter of fact, elephants had been domesticated at least in north-west India by about 2500 B.C. as indicated by the seals of the Indus Valley civilization (Fig. 11 : 11).

The Alexandrine Period

The conquest of the Punjab however not only brought direct contact with Indian elephants to men of the Western world, it also became the starting point of a new strategy in Western wars, based on the elephant taking over the function of a heavy tank, whilst at the same time the dromedary became the equivalent of the light tank or armoured car.

The introduction of the Indian elephant into the Hellenistic kingdoms is well illustrated by evidence from coins.

The very beginning of this story is shown on a coin probably minted in Babylon

288

(Fig. 11 : 15b, c). On the obverse of this decadrachm there appears Alexander the Great on horseback, attacking with a spear King Porus of the Punjab who is seated on an elephant. On the reverse Alexander stands holding his spear and wearing a helmet with a large plume, whilst Nike is crowning him. This remarkable coin commemorates the Battle of the Hydaspes in 326 B.C.

The premature death of Alexander in 323 B.C. did not retard the adoption of the new weapon. When, only two years later, Perdiccas the Regent attacked Ptolemy of Egypt he already had Indian elephants at his disposal. The impact of this event on Africa will be discussed later.

In any case, the Seleucids of Syria continued to have Indian elephants. The beasts appear on coins like Fig. 11 : 15d, c. 306 B.C., and that of Seleucus the son of Antiochus I who was executed as a rebel in 266 B.C. In 302 B.C. Seleucus I exchanged several provinces for five hundred elephants from King Chandragupta of the Indus. These animals proved decisive in the Battle of Ipsus (302 B.C.).

A curious contraption makes its appearance immediately after the death of Alexander—the elephant quadriga (Fig. 11 : 15e, f). A gold coin of Ptolemy I minted in Cyrene shows the king's portrait on the obverse, and a chariot drawn by four elephants on the reverse. Their small ears and convex backs prove that Sir William Gowers is right in regarding them as Indian. They may have been some taken from either Perdiccas or Demetrius.

But if four elephants were actually used to draw a two-wheeled chariot, such performance was surely confined to processions (Fig. 11 : 16). Elephants are difficult to direct unless they are led or mahouts sit on them, and they are very apt to walk backwards unexpectedly. From this time onwards the elephant quadriga, or occasionally the biga, became a symbol of power. It appears on many coins from the mints of Alexandria (Fig. 11 : 15u) and Cyrene.

Yet, partly perhaps because of the policy of the Seleucids to prevent the Ptolemies from obtaining Indian elephants, and partly because of the difficulty of transporting the large beast quickly and in quantity overseas, it never obtained a foothold west of a line from the Balkan peninsula to Palestine. As will be shown later, Hannibal may have owned one specimen.

The Macedonians, however, were supplied with them. This stock provided the opportunity for the first encounter of Romans with elephants, in the war against Tarant. This proud city called in the help of King Pyrrhus of Epirus, when in 282 B.C. trouble arose over a Roman fleet entering the harbour of the town without permission. Pyrrhus arrived with twenty elephants which helped him to defeat the Romans in the Battle of Herakleia, 280 B.C. This was the only occasion when Indian elephants were employed in quantity on Italian soil. Those which came with the Carthaginians eighteen years later belonged to the African species.

The Romans did not meet the Indian species again until the Battle of Magnesia.

a

b

c

d

e

f

g

h

i

k

j

l

m

n

o

p

q

r

u

s

t

Fig. 11 : 15. Coin evidence for the history of the elephant. (a) Pre-Mauryan cast bronze coin from India, possibly Taxila. Uninscribed. *c.* 350 B.C. or earlier. Author's collection. (b), (c) Reverse and obverse of the famous silver dekadrachm of Alexander the Great, showing the king on horseback fighting King Porus of the Punjab seated on his elephant. Obverse: Alexander being crowned by Nike. Mint of Babylon, *c.* 326 B.C. This coin marks the beginning of the westward progress of the domesticated elephants. After Head (1959)

(d) Silver tetradrachm of Seleucus I, Alexander's successor in Syria. Shortly before 306 B.C. Indian elephant now established as far as the Mediterranean. After Head (1959)

(e)–(f) Silver coin of Seleucus I, probably from 293–281 B.C., showing on reverse an elephant quadriga, four elephants drawing a two-wheeled chariot on which Athene is standing. The elephant quadriga subsequently became a popular symbol of kingship. After Head (1959)

(g) Bactrian silver coin of 250 B.C. with King Demetrius wearing elephant scalp on his head (hardly feasible in practice). Celebrating independence of Bactria from the Seleucids

(h)–(i) and (j)–(k). Two Barcid silver coins showing the Carthaginian god Melkarth on the obverse and *African* elephants on the reverse. Illustrates the training of the African species by the Carthaginians in preparation for the second Punic war, issued in Spain, before 218 B.C. The elephant on the first coin has a rider with an ancus. After Head (1959)

(l) Bronze coin of Antiochus III of Syria, with Indian elephant, 222–187 B.C. Shows that use of the Indian species continues in the eastern Mediterranean. Author's collection

(m) Bronze coin of Antiochus VI of Syria, still commemorating the use of the Indian elephant, 145–142 B.C. Author's collection

(n) In the same manner, the Indian elephant continues in use in the East: Indo-Greek square bronze coin of Lysias, *c.* 150 B.C. Author's collection

(o) In spite of the disasters that befell Hannibal's elephants, the Carthaginians continue to remember their use: elephant on Spanish bronze coin, second or first century B.C. But the picture is poor; perhaps there were no live models available. Author's collection

(p) Similarly, and with more justification, King Jugurtha of Numidia (118–106 B.C.) shows an African elephant on his silver coin. The obverse shows a head almost identical with (j). The parallel is obvious: Jugurtha considered himself as the successor of the Carthaginians. After Head (1959)

(q) Silver coin of Quintus Caecilus Metellus Pius, *c.* 77–76 B.C., of gens Caecilia, Italy, commemorating the victorious Battle of Attilio Regolo in 250 B.C., when African elephants were first defeated. This good portrait of the African species remained a stock dye for many years. Author's collection

(r) Another silver denarius commemorating Attilio Regolo, of the family of Q. Metellus Scipio, and issued in 46 B.C. It shows a poor likeness of the elephant; apparently the beasts were less frequently seen. Author's collection. About the same time, Caesar issued elephant coins (See Fig. 11 : 17)

(s) Silver denarius of Septimius Severus, A.D. 193–211. This emperor of Berber extraction was fond of African elephants, but the coin pattern is clearly based on the Metellus series. Author's collection

(t) In India, the Indian species continued in use: Indo-Scythian bronze coin of Azes I, 90–40 B.C. On reverse: zebu. Author's collection

(u) One of the large cast bronze coins of the Alexandrian mint of *c.* A.D. 95, reign of Domitian, with elephant quadriga. Here the beasts have become simple symbols of kingship. Obverse with head of emperor. Author's collection. All coins shown natural size

Fig. 11 : 16. Roman medal showing Nero and Agrippina in triumph on an elephant chariot. This and a similar medal of Augustus clearly show that the cart was fairly solid and not a two-wheeled chariot. From the *Menageries*, vol. II, 1831, p. 294. The Augustus medal is illustrated in Richard Carrington's book on elephants (p. 196)

When, in 217 B.C. at Raphia, Antiochus III lost all his Indian elephants to Ptolemy IV, he hurriedly sent to India for a fresh supply. These he kept until he met Scipio in 190 B.C., at Magnesia not far from Smyrna, where he was completely defeated. In spite of the heavy reparations he had to pay, and in spite of the loss of Asia Minor, the Seleucids once more procured elephants from India under Antiochus IV Epiphanes. This king was careful not to use them against the Romans, but they made their appearance in the fights against the Jews who had risen under the Maccabeans (167 B.C.).

From this time onwards the Indian elephant was known and used all over the ancient East. It remained a symbol of power as shown in its continued use on coins for instance (Figs. 11 : 15l, 11 : 15m and 11 : 15n). As a weapon in war, however, its value decreased as the Pax Romana was spreading across the countries that had made most use of it.

Domestication of the African elephant

There is no evidence that theAfrican elephant was domesticated before the Ptolemaic period, though, in the days of Augustus, King Juba II of north-western Africa believed that elephants were branded in Carthage 400 years before his time. He himself captured one with such a mark. Since elephants do not attain an age of four centuries, this story cannot be accepted as proof of pre-Ptolemaic domestication.

The Ptolemies were enthusiastic elephant-keepers. It had been known in Egypt since predynastic times that elephants existed in the south (see p. 280). They were abundant until recently in eastern Sudan, and this stock became the source of the trained animals used by the Ptolemies.

That Ptolemy I was familiar with the use of Indian elephants in war is certain, for they were a normal weapon in the army of Alexander the Great. But it appears that at the death of Alexander in 323 B.C. the satrap of Egypt was left without any.

When two years later, Perdiccas attacked Ptolemy, his forces included Indian elephants. With them he tried to cross the Nile, using the animals as a breakwater, but he was defeated. It is possible that Ptolemy obtained Indian elephants on that occasion. It is certain, however, that in 312, when he defeated Demetrius at Gaza in Palestine, he obtained a fair number, perhaps all the forty-three that his opponent had put in the field. On a gold coin minted in Cyrene Ptolemy's portrait appears on the obverse, and a chariot drawn by four elephants on the reverse. Their small ears and convex backs suggest their Indian origin.

It would have been bad policy on the part of the Ptolemies to rely on captured elephants alone. Some may have reached Egypt now and then by way of exchange, but their Syrian neighbours would hardly have supplied them with sufficient numbers to be of military importance. The obvious thing to do was to establish an independent source of supply.

Since Egyptian trading stations existed all along the Red Sea coast of East Africa the main task was to organize capture and transport. Ptolemy II selected two ports, Ptolemias Theron, near the present-day town of Aqiq, and Adulis, near Massawa. The elephants were caught in pits and taken to Egypt in specially constructed boats. Ptolemy III Euergetes was particularly fond of using elephants. Many detachments of soldiers were despatched to catch them. For the training of these elephants Indian trainers were hired at first, and were in due course replaced by local successors who had learned the art from them. Gsell (1913) is convinced that the term Indoi thus came to denote the profession of elephant-trainers all over North Africa. Ptolemy III used his elephants successfully against Asiatic opponents, especially in the third Syrian war, which took him as far as Asia Minor. His contacts with Asiatic armies enabled him also to secure Indian elephants. This is expressly stated in an inscription at Adulis set up by an officer in charge of elephants.

It is conceivable that one of these elephants was presented by Ptolemy Euergetes to Carthage. Gowers and Scullard hold, on numismatic evidence, that Hannibal had at least one Indian elephant (their Pl. XVI). Coins from Etruria and from Campania or south Italy depict what appear to be Indian elephants. 'It may well be that the Indians survived the rigours of the Alps better than the main bulk of the Africans and that the sole surviving beast on which Hannibal himself rode through Etruria was an Indian.' The name of this elephant appears to have been Surus, interpreted as 'the Syrian'.

Ptolemy IV Philopater (221–205 B.C.) fought with seventy-three mostly African elephants against Antiochus III in the Battle of Raphia. The Syrian king had 102 Indian elephants. Most of Ptolemy's elephants refused to fight, however, and the historian Polybius attributes this to the inferior size of the Africans. Sixteen of Ptolemy's elephants were killed, whilst Antiochus lost only five. Later in the battle fortunes changed and Ptolemy eventually succeeded in capturing all the remaining Indian elephants of Antiochus. This was in 217 B.C. After this, Egypt is unlikely to have been short of Indian elephants.

The fact that one or more Indian elephants actually reached Carthage, and the example set by Egypt in capturing and training the African species, must have inspired the Carthaginians. They were not slow in adopting the new weapon, the heavy tank consisting of an elephant with warriors mounted on his back with or without a turret, especially as the forests of the Atlas ranges were full of wild specimens. In the first Punic war Carthage entered Sicily and used sixty elephants in the Battle of Annone in 262 B.C. This was only sixty years after the death of Alexander the Great. Seven years later they put a hundred elephants into the field in the Battle of Attilio Regolo (Figs. 11 : 15q, r). In 250 B.C. the Roman general Metellus took 104 elephants (more according to some sources) from the Carthaginians in the Battle of Palermo. This is ample evidence that elephants were tamed in north-west Africa.

There is no doubt that this elephant was the African species. It has been pointed out in an earlier paragraph that the North African race occurred wild in many places in Algeria and Morocco, and apparently in Libya also. Elephants were therefore available locally, and the Carthaginians are known to have sent out expeditions to catch them. The training is regarded by Sir William Gowers as the achievement of Indian mahouts, who were engaged via Egypt. This is conceivable regarding the first few generations. But later on North Africa surely had its own elephant-trainers.

The Carthaginians continued to use elephants with considerable success, although the Romans gradually became familiar with them. Those obtained by Metellus in 250 B.C. were taken to Rome, where some were made to run about in the circus, being chased with blunt spears, in order to demonstrate that they were not so fierce as was generally believed. The Roman soldiers nevertheless continued to take care. But means were designed to confuse the elephants so that they turned and destroyed their own lines. The most efficient was fire. Flares were used against them. It was also believed that elephants disliked the squeaking of pigs, as reported by Aelian, Pliny and Seneca. The most remarkable counter-attack was made by the Megareans when they were besieged by Antipater (a little before 300 B.C., the elephants being Indian). They covered live pigs with pitch. This was set on fire and the animals were driven into the lines of the elephants.

The second Punic war brought the Romans into contact with African elephants on the European mainland. In 218 B.C. Hannibal crossed the Pyrenees with thirty-seven of them. But most died on the way to Italy. The war was settled in favour of Rome, when Scipio went to Africa. When it became known in Carthage that he was preparing to cross the sea, Carthage quickly sent out an expedition to catch elephants. It is evident therefore that their training did not require a very long time. Perhaps it was in part due to insufficient training that in the Battle of Zama (202 B.C.) the eighty Carthaginian elephants turned round and caused great confusion in their own lines.

After this war the Romans had enough African elephants to use them occasionally themselves, as for instance against Philip of Macedonia and Antiochus. These elephants were obtained either as war-spoil or as presents made by friendly North African rulers. Micipsa, king of Numidia, for instance, furnished elephants to the Romans over a period of thirty years (148–118 B.C.). The emperors of Rome however no longer used elephants in warfare, perhaps because they were found too difficult to manage, to be kept well fed, to be transported overseas and, above all, it was much too difficult to replace losses. Polyaenus however reports that Caesar used an elephant when he crossed the Thames in 54 B.C.

This was evidently a show-piece, and it is unlikely that large numbers were shipped to Britain, considering the somewhat improvised nature of that brief expedition. Again, it is stated by Dio that the Emperor Claudius in A.D. 43 included elephants in his equipment for the conquest of Britain. He visited Colchester on this occasion and, curiously enough, two fragments of very large bones were found during the excavation of that site. Whilst Miss Dorothea Bate seriously considered the possibility that these might indeed be remains of Claudian elephants, she submitted them to Dr F. C. Fraser of the British Museum, in order to test the alternative that they came from whales. Dr Fraser considered this the more likely interpretation, but the bones are too poorly preserved for definite identification.

In his African war against the Pompeians and King Juba I, Caesar obtained sixty-four elephants. Subsequently, it became the fashion to point out that in the Moorish language *caesai* meant elephant, implying a connection with Caesar's name. This idea is even shown on coins (Fig. 11 : 17).

Elephants were in all probability used for peaceful purposes in North Africa until advancing agriculture and increasing desiccation destroyed the remainder of

FIG. 11 : 17. Silver denarius of Julius Caesar (48–44 B.C.) showing an Indian elephant trampling down a snake, symbolizing Caesar's victories in Gaul. The use of the elephant as a symbol for the imperator is believed to be due to the resemblance of his name to the Numidian word for elephant. Twice natural size. Author's collection

the wild stock. In the Roman town of Leptis Magna an elephant statue (Fig. 11 : 18), three feet high, was erected in the main street in the first or second century A.D.

Elephants were popular in Rome for show purposes. Julius Caesar used forty of them when celebrating his victory over Gaul. Elephants were trained to do all sorts of tricks which can be seen in circuses at the present day. Germanicus (*c.* A.D. 15) bred elephants in Latium, twelve calves being mentioned. These animals were trained to dance, to wear clothes like humans and to sit down and have meals from plates and drink from precious cups like men. Evidently these were not warlike creatures. Altogether, the idea of the fighting elephant did not appeal to the Roman. Pompey made himself unpopular when he used elephants for fights in the circus.

FIG. 11 : 18. The elephant in the forum of Leptis Magna, one of the great cities of Roman Libya, possibly first century A.D. It is a poor effigy of the beast; either the species had already become locally extinct, or the Indian elephant with its smaller ears and convex back was known. Based on Aurigemma (1940)

Pliny relates that the animals were killed with spears although their behaviour suggested that they were asking for mercy. The public was outraged and people were shedding tears. With the extinction of the North African race the elephant vanished from Rome. Specimens that reached Europe in later centuries came invariably from India (Fig. 11 : 19).

Conclusion

The history of the domestication of two of the three species of elephants is thus of peculiar interest. For well over 2000 years the practice remained confined to India, the homeland of one of the species. Its spread westwards was in no small measure helped by the improving systems of roads, initiated under the Persians and developed by Alexander. The use of the large beasts to terrorize the enemy made them popular with the Seleucids in particular, and the Ptolemies copied the art, employing the

Fig. 11 : 19. An elephant as illustrated in a Latin
zoological treatise published in England early in the
thirteenth century. An Indian elephant is clearly
intended, the only species that may occasionally have
been available at that time. Its war-like functions had
by then completely disappeared; it had become a
subject of curiosity. British Museum MSS 57

small North African species. This in turn inspired the Carthaginians, the spread from
India to north-west Africa having been effected in the short span of sixty-six years.

But there were drawbacks in the use of this 'heavy tank' of the ancient world.
Much fodder was required and the beasts became easily tired. They were much
more difficult to guide than horses and often played havoc with their own lines.

Whilst the North African elephant was captured on so large a scale that it
became extinct, the source of supply for the Indian species was too remote. Losses

in battle, therefore, were difficult to replace. Moreover, the Pax Romana made them redundant after the first century A.D.

As a beast of burden, and for lumbering, elephants were hardly a paying proposition in the ancient world, when human slaves were in good supply. The elephant is not an efficient worker except in the jungle where man and the ordinary beasts of burden do not succeed. In the cultivated and deforested regions of the Roman world there was thus no permanent place for this animal, except as a curiosity which the rulers were proud to show to the population from time to time.

12

The Horse

SCIENTIFIC NAMES—VILLAFRANCHIAN HORSES—*Equus stenonis* Cocchi, *E. robustus* Pomel.

PLEISTOCENE HORSES—*E. suessenbornensis* Wüst, *E. mosbachensis* v. Reichenau, *E. germanicus* Nehring, *E. abeli* Antonius.

POST-PLEISTOCENE WILD HORSES—*E. caballus ferus* Pallas (syn. *E.c. przewalski* Poliakoff) (Przewalski's horse, Mongolian wild horse). *E. c. gmelini* Antonius (tarpan; south-east Russia and northern Europe, extinct). *E.c. silvestris* v. Brincken (forest horse; ? central and west Europe). Tundra horse, (extinct).

DOMESTICATED HORSE—*E. caballus* L.

NEXT to the dog the horse is, for many reasons, the animal most intimately associated with man. Unlike others, both the dog and the horse have been looked upon as companions of man, although as far as the horse is concerned this applies mainly to conditions outside the town civilizations. The association of man and horse has, with many peoples, developed into a biological symbiosis, and the taboo against eating horseflesh is the result of it. If one compares man's attitude to the horse with that to the cow, one sees the difference. Except in India, where the cow takes the place of the horse, the former is largely regarded as a subject of exploitation.

The history of the horse is most often considered from the angle of modern domestication, and the investigators have, as a rule, become shipwrecked in the sea of real, hypothetical and unknown wild races from which our domesticated breeds

299

may have sprung. Another common approach is by way of the wild horses of the
Upper Pleistocene of western Europe, using the evidence provided by cave art and,
to a minor extent, osteology. But this results in a too narrow, north-west European
outlook and induces investigators to recognize the races and species of far-distant
lands in a restricted area.

Pleistocene and Postglacial wild horses

The very complex and highly problematical palaeontology of the recent horses
(i.e. caballine horses, hemiones or half-asses, asses, zebras) is perhaps best viewed
as a case of species evolution and progressive differentiation into geographical races
or subspecies.[1]

A chart of the distribution of equines in late Pleistocene times prior to the
beginnings of domestication (Fig. 12 : 1) may serve as the basis for discussion. It
reveals the remarkable, but little-noted fact that the horse-like animals of the Old
World are distributed over the more open lands like geographical races of a species.
The true (caballine) horses occupy the lowlands north of the great mountain ranges;
the half-asses (hemiones) the dry zone of Asia from the Gobi to Persia, with exten-
sions into north-west India, Syria and Arabia; the true ass North and north-east

---

[1] The preceding evolution of the horses to the *Equus* stage is well known and not considered here. Those
interested should consult Simpson's book (1951).

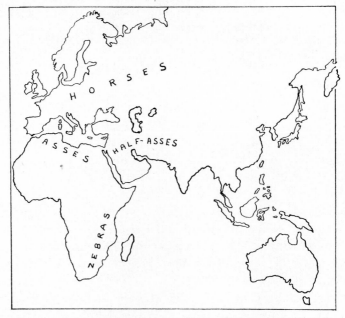

FIG. 12 : 1. Late Pleistocene distribution of the members of the
genus *Equus* (horse) showing that there are practically no overlaps

Africa; and the zebras East and South Africa. This distribution suggests that late in the Tertiary an ancestral type of horse spread over the regions just outlined[1] and subsequently developed geographical subspecies which have since become distinct species. Even at the present day the species of horse, half-ass, ass and the zebras are capable of producing mules. Lydekker (1912) has collated the evidence on this point.

While these species continued to evolve their characteristics, they also began to differentiate into geographical races (or subspecies) which are now more or less distinct. These are easily recognized in the half-asses, because domestication has not interfered with their distribution. In the zebras the differentiation has gone further, and three good species can be distinguished, namely the mountain zebra in the south, the quagga in the middle of East Africa and Grevy's zebra in the north. Antonius (1937) has pointed out that the southward and northward spreads of the quagga or common zebra must be of comparatively recent date. The ass species was composed of three races in the wild condition, and the true horse of at least two, more probably three. With these, however, domestication has interfered, and their original boundaries of distribution are difficult to reconstruct.

It is perhaps worth while to point out that this type of distribution is well known to the zoogeographer. The red deer may be mentioned as another example. There is the red deer of Europe, the maral of Persia and the wapiti of Siberia and North America. These have frequently been treated as closely related species, and each of them can in turn be subdivided into minor geographical races. But the modern systematist regards them as an 'artenkreis' or species-group if specific differences have made their appearance, and as a 'rassenkreis' or subspecies-group if the differences are but slight.

Now it is true that horses other than the true caballine horse have been described from the Pleistocene of Europe. Apart from the group of *Equus stenonis*, which continued from the Villafranchian into the Lower Pleistocene and which may be ancestral to some surviving species, there have been found in the Upper Pleistocene horse-like bones which are not *E. caballus*. Thanks to the efforts of Stehlin of Basle and Graziosi of Florence, who have studied these remains (1935), their specific identity is now considerably clearer than it used to be.

In particular, the presence of hemiones or half-asses in central Europe had been claimed mainly on the basis of gracefully built leg bones. In countries which are in open connection with central Asia via the steppes of south Russia and Siberia (where the kulan, one of the half-asses, used to occur around the Ural River), it is understandable that such bones were assigned to half-asses. Stehlin and Graziosi, however, have shown that many of these specimens are not well enough preserved to be

[1] Also into the Indian peninsula (*E. namadicus*) and China (*E. sanmenensis*) where the horse died out in the Pleistocene.

determinable and that others belong to a wild true ass, *Equus hydruntinus*. This species was very common in Italy in the Upper Pleistocene, and it was a game of the Upper Palaeolithic hunter. From there it managed to penetrate into France and western Germany, where it occurred together with the horse. This is one of the few overlaps which have occurred among horse species. Another may have been due to the temporary penetration of the horse into Palestine in the Upper Pleistocene (Bate, 1937a) which properly belongs to the area of the half-asses.[1] There may be an overlap between the half-asses and the Przewalski horse in Mongolia, and others (unimportant in the present context) exist between Grevy's zebra and the common zebra in north-east Africa. From the point of view of domestication, it is essential to be aware of the fact that these overlaps are very slight, and normally each horse species is confined to a well-defined area in which no other occurs. In other words, if two species of the horse genus are found in an archaeological deposit, it is more likely than not that at least one of them was domesticated and brought to the locality by man.

Let us now consider the races of the true horses prior to the beginnings of domestication. Instead of trying to analyse the cave paintings, engravings and sculptures, let us first survey the zoological and palaeontological evidence for races of the wild horse.

Two races of wild horse survived into the twentieth and nineteenth centuries respectively. One is Przewalski's horse (Fig. 12 : 2), which roamed about in Mon-

[1] The identification of the Palestine horse has, however, been contested by Vaufrey (1951, p. 208).

Fig. 12 : 2. The herd of Przewalski horses in the Animal Park of Hellabrunn, near Munich. Altogether about sixty of these animals are being kept in captivity in zoological gardens, whilst about forty are still believed to be living wild in Mongolia. The colour is yellow-dun with lighter body, but the legs are dark. Photo F.E.Z.

golia until modern fire-arms put an end to most of them after the First World War and the Russian Revolution. It has been established, however, that about forty individuals of this wild horse still survive in the Tachin Shara Nuru Mountains (Latitude 44°N., Longitude 94°E.), in Mongolia. Specimens were caught alive between 1942 and 1945 and one of these was still living in captivity in 1959 (Mohr, 1960).[1] The other is the tarpan (Figs. 12 : 3 and 12 : 4), the horse of south Russia which became extinct in 1851 in the Ukraine. Originally, both were widely distributed in the temperate zone, and Hilzheimer (1935) regards the fortieth degree of longitude as the approximate boundary line between the two races.[2] This is probably too rigid a view, as will be shown presently. In addition, there may have been other geographical races, of which an eastern Siberian and a north-west European one are

[1] Specimens bred from stock captured earlier in this century are to be seen in many of the larger zoos.
[2] Those who read Lydekker's books (1912) on the horse should note that he applies the name 'tarpan' mistakenly to the Przewalski horse.

FIG. 12 : 3. A reconstruction of the tarpan, the extinct European wild horse. It was mouse-grey with a lighter belly and had a dark stripe over the back. It became extinct only about a century ago. Painting by Miss M. Maitland Howard, carried out under the direction of the writer

better substantiated than others. The tarpan was a small mouse-grey horse with upright mane and a 'dark stripe from the neck to the tail'. As Lundholm (1949) has shown, it differs from the Mongolian wild horse in the flatness of the forehead, the wavy profile of the cranium and two depressions, the first of which lies between the eyes and the second between the middle and anterior thirds of the nasal. In addition, the supra-orbitals are vaulted above the level of the forehead. The nose is low and short, especially compared with the Przewalski horse.

FIG. 12 : 4. Re-bred tarpans in the Animal Park of
Hellabrunn, near Munich. Photo F.E.Z.

Of this tarpan only two skulls have been preserved, which were described in detail by Tscherski (1892) long ago, and of which the recent comparison with Swedish fossil and prehistoric horses by Lundholm has produced valuable results. The steppe tarpan lived in south-east Europe, where it was observed in 1769 by Gmelin whose fascinating and little-known report is to be found on page 311. The extinction of the last survivors in the Ukraine in the middle of the last century has been related by the Russian zoologist Falzfein. That this wild horse should have been hunted prior to domestication is obvious enough, and that hunting continued until destruction was complete is related by several observers. The persecution was due not merely to a desire to obtain the game, but because the wild horses interfered with agriculture and the wild stallions had the habit of abducting the domesticated mares. By the end of the eighteenth century truly wild horses of the tarpan group survived only in the Forest of Białowieża in eastern Poland, where the last few were captured in 1812, and in the Ukraine, where the last survivors were killed in 1851.[1]

With regard to the other two subspecies, the eastern Siberian one has almost certainly not contributed to the domesticated stock of horses, if it existed at all. But it may have been a close relative of the tundra horse of Europe (rather than the oft-quoted Przewalski horse). Unfortunately it is not well attested. That there was a horse contemporary with the mammoth in eastern Siberia is certain, since at least two carcasses of white horses and many bones have been found thawing out from the ground ice. A horse with complicated enamel folds on the molar teeth has been described from Lyakhov Island in northern Siberia by Brauner (1933). In addition, Pfizenmayer (1926), who recovered the famous Beresovka mammoth now exhibited in Leningrad, heard reports from hunters who had visited the extreme north-east of Siberia, a country remote even for the Siberians, that white horses were living there. They told him a story approximately as follows:

Of course we did not fail to ask our guests what game they were hunting in their far distant hunting grounds on the Omolon. Then it was that old Taitchin mentioned 'wild horses'. Since living wild horses are known to science only from the steppes of central Asia, we were naturally reluctant to trust this old Lamut, though his story was confirmed by young Amuksan's excellent imitation of neighing. And it is not likely that these honest people were telling lies. They described in detail the horse which lives on the tundra near the forest border. It is about the size of the Yakut horse, covered with long, whitish-grey hair, and the flesh is pleasant to eat and very fat. Should these horses be derived from escaped domesticated stock, it is difficult to understand how they ever reached the remote and uninhabited region between the Omolon and the Anjuj, the two largest north-eastern tributaries of the Kolyma.

Lundholm comments that if there is much substance in this story, the Russians are likely to have taken it up. But no confirmation has reached the Western countries.

The extreme western race of the horse is equally poorly founded. More than anywhere else it has bred in the minds of those who thought that the large and heavy 'cold-blooded' horses of north and west Europe required an ancestor different from that of the slender Arab. The protagonists of this hypothesis were able to point to

---

[1] There are two doubtful records of survival of tarpans: by Heptner (1934) to 1918, and by another source who reports that they survived in the southern Ural Mountains until 1924. Unfortunately we are now unable to trace the latter. The end of the Polish horses was described by Janikowski (1942). It should be noted that Nobis (1955) denies the one-time existence of the tarpan altogether by merging it with the domestic horse. This simplifies his approach considerably, but does not do justice to the many records of tarpan survival.

the large Pleistocene horses (like *E. germanicus*, *E. abeli* (Fig. 12 : 5), etc.), whilst its adversaries emphasized that there is a chronological gap between these Pleistocene horses and their supposed descendants, the Clydesdales, Shires (Fig. 12 : 6), Belgians, Frisians, etc., for these do not appear before the Hallstatt period and are almost certainly connected with the introduction of heavy armour in the Iron Age and later. That breeding for size is possible in other domesticated animals is too well known, and it is unwise to introduce size into the hypothetical phylogeny of the domestic horse.

As long ago as 1888, however, Wilckens described the enamel pattern of the molars of the cold-blooded horses, which is more complicated than that of the tarpan, the Przewalski horse and their descendants. V. Reichenau (1915) found a similarly complicated pattern in the large Pleistocene horses like *E. germanicus*. Some later workers regard this complication of the enamel folds simply as a function of the absolute size of the tooth, and therefore of no phylogenetic significance. But Lundholm's work on wild and prehistoric horses from Sweden has shed new and unexpected light on this problem, for the Postglacial wild horses of Sweden proved to have an enamel pattern of the *germanicus* type.

It is not surprising, therefore, that the view of Antonius that there was a wild ancestor of the heavy horse in western Europe is still held at the present day, even by some weighty authorities, though of course not without variations. The foremost are at present Staffe in Germany, Lundholm in Sweden, Hančar in Austria and Gromova in Russia. Naturally, all these authors derive the heavy domestic horse from this supposed ancestor (see p. 330).

Should a Western wild heavy horse prove to have really existed, it would have to carry the name of *Equus caballus silvestris* v. Brincken.

The horses of the Upper Pleistocene of western Europe have attracted the attention of prehistorians, not only because they were a regular game often hunted in large numbers (as at Solutré), but because many paintings, engravings and sculptures have survived, portraying them. On the whole, these cave representations of horses have suggested to their investigators an affinity to Przewalski's horse. One reason for this is that the cave artists succeeded in expressing those characters which distinguish a wild horse from a domesticated one (such as relatively heavy head, thick neck, upright mane, short body, graceful but relatively short legs), which today can be studied in Przewalski's horse only. Identity, however, does not necessarily follow from such resemblance.

Some workers consider that other races of horses are shown in the caves in addition to Przewalski's horse. Capitan, Breuil and Peyrony (1924), for instance, believed they could distinguish four types of horse in the Combarelles Cave (Fig. 12 : 7) at Les Eyzies, namely the Libyan, the Celtic, a Nordic type and the tarpan, whilst the true Przewalski horse would not have been present. As long ago as 1905

FIG. 12 : 5. Reconstruction drawing of *Equus abeli*, a heavy Pleistocene horse for which osteological evidence is available. After Antonius (1922)

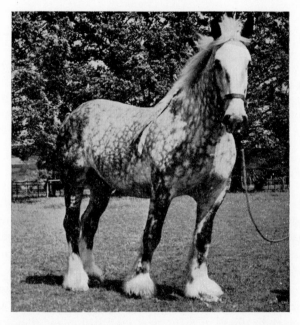

FIG. 12 : 6. Modern shire horse bred by Fremlins, Ltd.

Osborn had recognized similar types, but including Przewalski's horse instead of the tarpan.

On the other hand, if allowance is made for inaccuracy of drawing and psychological and stylistic factors, one is driven to assume a cautious attitude. This is

307

Fig. 12 : 7. Magdalenian drawing of a heavy horse from the cave of Combarelles, Dordogne. Regarded as the possible ancestor of the shire horse and other heavy breeds of Europe. After Breuil

well expressed by M. Windels and Mlle Laming in their recent work on the Grotte de Lascaux (Fig. 12 : 8), as follows:

Un examen plus attentif des fresques montre que plusieurs caractères comme la forme de la tête, la position de la crinière, l'attache de la queue, sont indifféremment appliqués aux deux types considérés. Et on peut se demander s'il s'agit bien de types distincts et non plutôt d'imprécision ou de fantaisie de l'artiste. La question s'est déjà posée à propos des Combarelles et d'autres grottes ornées. On a cherché à y distinguer plusieurs variétés d'équidés et à les rattacher aux types fossiles ou actuels connus. Aucune solution n'a paru définitivement s'imposer.

It is necessary to consider the issue from a biological point of view, admitting the possibility that several distinct races are shown and at the same time making allowance for seasonal appearance, style and inaccuracy. Above all, allowance has to be made for the very different appearance of horses in summer and winter. Many Palaeolithic horses are depicted in their winter coat (Fig. 12 : 9).

Races of the same species cannot normally occur together in the same area and yet keep separate without interbreeding and thus mixing their racial characters. If they do preserve their characters in these circumstances, they must be given the status of species. Since it is known that all domesticated horses, even those supposedly derived from different wild ancestors, are capable of producing fertile crosses, and since the Przewalski horse and the tarpan both have interbred freely with domesticated types, they are clearly members of one and the same species. If, therefore, one accepts the cave pictures as evidence of different geographical races of the horse species having occurred in the same area, they cannot have been there simultaneously.

FIG. 12 : 8. Small horses depicted in the Palaeolithic cave of Lascaux, Dordogne, France. The fauna of Lascaux represents a temperate phase, probably the First Interstadial of the Last Glaciation, and these should, therefore, be the earliest known pictures of wild horses. Almost certainly tarpans, not Przewalski horses. After Windels

FIG. 12 : 9. Engraved and painted horse in shaggy winter coat from the Magdalenian cave of Niaux, near Tarascon, south France. As long ago as 1921 this was identified by Othenio Abel as a tarpan, thus destroying the myth that all European wild horses were Przewalski horses. After Cartailhac and Breuil

The pictures would then belong to different periods. If, on the other hand, one accepts them as contemporaneous, it appears that the differences shown in the pictures would have to be discarded as irrelevant. There is, however, a third alternative—the assumption that several 'ecotypes' of a single species are represented.

Ecotypes are varieties of animals adapted to certain kinds of environment and which have acquired some distinctive morphological characters. They are frequently found in species capable of varying their habits in accordance with the environment. An example is provided by the reindeer. In North America it occurs as a forest form (the caribou) and a tundra form, and the two corresponding ecotypes were, in all probability, present in Europe, though only the tundra reindeer has survived in this continent (see p. 114). Similarly, the European roedeer occurs as a forest form and as a field form. These two ecotypes are hardly distinguishable morphologically, but they are described as remarkably constant in their habits.

As to the horse, it is certain that Przewalski's horse is a denizen of the dry continental steppe. On the other hand, the last survivors of the wild horse of central Europe (which became extinct in Poland in the eighteenth century) inhabited forests. The last surviving tarpans of south Russia lived in the fertile steppe of the black-earth country, and thus formed a link between the 'forest' horse of western Europe and the Przewalski horse of the central Asiatic desert steppe. In addition, the suspected existence of a tundra horse in north-east Siberia may be recalled.

If then these 'races' of horse are regarded as ecotypes rather than as geographical subspecies, it becomes possible for any one of them to evolve wherever the suitable environment happens to exist. One need only recall that during the Last Glaciation central and west Europe were covered with varied environmental belts, ranging from the tundra belt to the loess steppe on the one side, and to taiga and deciduous forest on the other. The environments which the races of the horse inhabited in Postglacial times prior to their extinction, therefore, were all available in glacial Europe, and the cave representations of Upper Palaeolithic horses may after all show various ecotypes. It is perhaps unnecessary to add that ecotypes become geographical races wherever a type of environment reigns exclusively over a large area. But the concept of the ecotype makes it possible for apparently racial types to co-exist in close proximity and to evolve independently in discontinuous areas. It is no longer necessary to assume vast migrations of the Przewalski horse and its pure-blooded survival among other, closely related, horses.

The difficulties involved in the assumption of co-existence of several geographical horse races in the same environment have led a number of authors to simplified interpretations of the cave pictures. Abel (1922), for instance, followed Osborn in assuming the presence of Przewalski's horse in French cave art, but he also believed that he could recognize the tarpan in a carved head from Mas d'Azil and other Palaeolithic works of art. Boule (1899), however, as well as Duerst (1908) and

Lydekker (1912), went a long way towards an ecological interpretation, but they still regarded the Przewalski horse as the probable ancestor of all other French races, and more recently Bourdelle (1938) has followed them, reducing the number of types into which his 'Przewalski' horse evolved to three.

The following ecotypes may be tentatively assumed to have existed in Upper Palaeolithic times in western Europe:

Equus caballus L.
> Tundra ecotype
> Grassland ecotype
> Loess-steppe ecotype
> Forest ecotype.

The scientific names to be applied to Postglacial survivor races are as follows:

Przewalski horse: *Equus caballus ferus* Pallas (=*E.c. przewalski* Poljakoff)
Tarpan: *Equus caballus gmelini* Antonius
Forest horse: *Equus caballus silvestris* v. Brincken.

Should the horse from Białowieża forest be indistinguishable from the tarpan, as is considered possible by Antonius, v. Brincken's name would have priority over Antonius's, as it is the older. On the other hand, this name may be claimed for the hypothetical, Western, heavy, forest horse.

The stock which contributed most to the domesticated horse is in all probability the tarpan. This race, the existence of which has quite recently been doubted by Nobis (1955), was a very real one, as is evident from the descriptions of eighteenth- and nineteenth-century authors, which unfortunately are rarely consulted. The most important are those of Baron Falzfein (1919) who relates details of the extinction of the pure breed. On the other hand, the traveller Gmelin met them in 1769 and left us a vivid description which I have translated in view of the scarcity of his book:

In the spring of 1769 I made an observation which will be welcome to friends of natural history.

Here, in the neighbourhood of Voronesh, there were plenty of wild horses a few years ago, but they were driven farther and farther into the steppe, and often dissipated, because of the damage they caused and which will be discussed presently.

The desire to get acquainted with these animals, the existence of which is doubted by contemporary naturalists such as M. de Buffon, and also the desire to find out how they are captured, induced me to travel to Bobrovsk. This small town lies 100 werst from here. On arrival I asked the inhabitants the whereabouts of the wild horses, but they said that they had not been seen either during the last hay-making or in the winter. It was to be suspected, however, that they had moved on into the steppe, where there had been plenty in the past and also in the preceding winter. I therefore continued my journey to Syelo Tchichonko, 45 werst from Bobrovsk. Here I learnt with pleasure that I had to travel a few more werst only to meet them.

As I had previously engaged a sufficient number of peasants experienced in this kind of hunting, I continued and found the reports of the inhabitants confirmed. After another 6 werst we saw about 2 werst away six horses which were running together. As soon as they saw us, however, they fled with the utmost speed.

It is unnecessary to describe our further efforts to catch them: on that day we got nothing.

On the following day we set out with a larger number of peasants, in order to be able to occupy all strategic points in the vast steppe, and especially on the left of the Don River, and on the right a wood. We continued the hunt in vain during the morning, but in the afternoon we saw many of them led by a stallion, the others following. The peasants said that as soon as the stallion was killed it would be easy to obtain several others. They therefore made every effort to lasso him, and at 5 o'clock in the evening he eventually fell into the hands of the picket posted at the wood. He killed the stallion with a spear.

The third day, a yearling foal was caught alive with ropes, and two wild mares were killed, together with a Russian horse. A hybrid was obtained with ropes. This is the way of catching this kind of horse. I will now describe them briefly according to their natural characteristics, and in so doing their habits will be clarified.

The largest wild horses are hardly as large as the smallest Russian. Compared with other parts, their head is extraordinarily thick. Their ears are very pointed, either of the size of those of tame horses (so it was with my specimens) or long, almost like asses' ears, and drooping (such the Governor has obtained). Their eyes are fiery. Their mane is short and frizzly.

Their tail is more or less covered with hair, but always somewhat shorter than in tame horses.

They are mouse-coloured, and this is a feature observed in all wild horses of this district, whilst writers have elsewhere spoken of white and ash-grey ones only. But in my horses the belly is of the latter colour, and the feet are black below the middle and down to the hoofs. Their hair is very long and so thick that one imagines that one is feeling a pelt rather than a horse's skin.

They run with the utmost speed, and at least twice as fast as a good tame horse. They are afraid of the slightest noise and run away. It is quite true that a herd chooses a stallion to be its leader, who always goes first, the others following. Thus it happens that as soon as the leader is killed the others go astray, not knowing where to go, and become the prey of the hunters. Even so, however, some are able to escape.

They like to stay near the hay-stacks that the peasants have erected in the steppes, without preparing any bed whatever on the ground. They stick to them so industriously that two of them are able to finish a hay-stack in a night, which explains their fatness, giving them a well-rounded appearance.

This, however, is not the only damage they do. The stallion is very much after the Russian mares, and if he can get hold of one he will not let her go, but take her with him. Thus I mentioned a Russian horse that was among the wild ones. But the matter can be clarified further as follows.

A wild stallion once saw a tame stallion with tame mares. He was interested only in these, but the tame stallion would not put up with it and they got into a violent fight. The tame stallion defended himself with his feet; the wild one, however, bit his adversary with his teeth and in spite of all resistance he succeeded in biting the tame one until he was dead, so that he could abduct his coveted mares.

It is therefore not surprising that the peasants use every possible means to defend themselves and to chase the wild horses away. When a wild stallion mates with a tame mare, a hybrid is produced which has some features of the tame and some of the wild horses. It appears that the Russian mare we had killed was the mother of the hybrid we obtained alive; for firstly she was already rather old, and moreover black; the hybrid was mouse-brown mixed with black. His tail was more hairy, but not yet entirely so. The head was thick, the mane short and frizzly, the body shape more oblong, whilst the hair was as in tame horses, both in length and density. . . .

Wild horses caught alive (which is always done with ropes) are very difficult to tame and to get used to doing work. I do not know whether their natural obstinacy or the peasants' lack of familiarity with the methods is to be blamed for it. I am, of course, speaking only of the wild horses of this district. All information agrees in that they are no use for riding, that they dislike walking alongside another horse, and that they mostly die a year later.

The modern Polish konik is much like a tarpan and is known to contain the blood of the tarpan of Białowieża forest. The Ukrainian horse is known to have absorbed the last remnants of the grassland tarpan in the middle of the last century. This story has been recorded by the Russian zoologist Falzfein. Hilzheimer regards it as probable that the modern Arab also is ultimately derived from this stock.

Przewalski's horse supplied some of the domesticated breeds of central Asia and China. This view is widely held and based on plastic representations of early Chinese horses. But, regarding the Mongolian pony, Rumjancev has shown that affinities are much closer with the tarpan than with the Przewalski horse. It appears, therefore, that Mongolia received it domesticated from the West at a relatively late date. Subsequently, interbreeding must, of course, have occurred. The Chinese domestic horses have shed some light on this matter; they will be discussed below.

Domestication

In spite of occasional assertions to the contrary that are to be found in the earlier literature, the horse was not domesticated by Palaeolithic or Mesolithic man. Nor does it figure among the earliest groups of domesticated animals. From 2000 B.C. onwards the horse-drawn chariot swept across the Western world, a contraption which requires elaborate domestication and special training. The chariot itself, of course, is older. It is therefore reasonable to assume that the horse was domesticated considerably before 2000 B.C.

Who were its domesticators and where did it happen? The horse is a large and swift animal which could not have been herded like sheep. It is thus very unlikely that it belongs to the pre-agricultural phase of domestication. It is also inconceivable

that wheeled vehicles, carts and chariots were developed *pari passu* with the domestication of the horse, for this animal is too impatient to allow itself to be used in such
experiments. Animal power was first used for transport purposes in the early agricultural phase, when strong and slow-moving beasts, mainly bovine, became available.

The fact that the domesticated horse is almost exclusively of tarpan stock limits
the possible area of origin to west and central Europe north of the Alps, eastern
Europe and western Asia north of the mountains as far east as Russian Turkestan.
That horse domestication did not originate in western or central Europe is a point
on which all workers on the subject agree, partly for chronological reasons and partly
because the horse was rare there, most of the country being too densely forested.
This restricts the probable area of domestication to the Ukrainian and east Russian
steppes, Kazakhstan and the steppes of western Asia mainly around Lake Aral
and including the plains of Turkestan, Ust-Urt Plateau and Turan. The western part
of this zone was still a centre of horse domestication in Scythian times (Fig. 12 : 10).

FIG. 12 : 10. Scythian horse wearing a mask
of unknown significance from mound-burials
at Pazaryk, Altai Mountains, fifth century
B.C. See also Fig. 5 : 9

Since archaeological evidence early enough to shed light on the first stages of
horse domestication is completely lacking, one can only try to make reasonable
suggestions. It is probable that agriculture spread at an early date into the plains of
Turkestan, as far as they receive water from the mountains, for these steppe countries
had in places excellent soil which lent itself to primitive crop-raising as much as any
part of the Fertile Crescent. It must, however, be realized that the agriculturally
valuable soil is patchily distributed and the localities are separated from one another

by unproductive lands, mainly salt steppes and deserts. Whilst this would have fostered a tendency for independent cultural and political units to develop, the problem of transport must have presented itself at an early date. It is not intended to maintain that animal traction was invented there, merely that it was important. The first beasts to be used would have been cattle.

Most agricultural areas on the edge of the desert succumbed to desiccation after a millennium or two of crop-raising because, on the one hand, natural water stored in the ground was used up and, on the other, because primitive agriculture destroys the soil and thus invites the desert in.

Under such conditions transport by means of oxen becomes something of a problem, both for lack of water and fodder. That man should have cast an eye on the horse is natural and it is thus that its domestication may have begun.

The horse gave man greater mobility than he had ever had before, and it made possible a *secondary* nomadism, combined with temporary crop-raising. Once this system had been developed, it swept the Western world, except the densely forested areas where its progress was slow. The movement started about 2000 B.C. or some-what earlier. The reason why this wave of migrations could pass through many countries without upsetting the then existing economic structures is perhaps that the secondary nomads were well adapted to the cultivation of the poorer soils and waste-lands for which the established civilizations of the river valleys did not care. More-over, the number of the invaders may have been small. A comparison with the gipsy migration is perhaps not out of place, though not really satisfactory. But if one imagined Europe without the horse at the time of the arrival of the gipsies, the com-parison might convey some idea of what happened. That the invaders with their horses made themselves rulers of the country here and there is another matter.

The people who brought the horse across the mountains to the Near and Middle East appear to have spoken Indo-Germanic languages. Thus the original centre of the domestication of the horse might briefly be circumscribed as Turkestan. This view is, however, not based on archaeological evidence, but on biological con-siderations.

Evidence from the Middle East and the eastern Mediterranean

Remains of 'horse' have been found in some of the early prehistoric sites of the East and often been quoted as evidence for domestication. Unfortunately, not one of them bears the test of critical examination. The important ones are Anau, Sialk and Shah Tepé.

The earliest supposed evidence for the domestication of the horse comes from Anau, a place on the edge of the plains of Turkestan, near Ashkhabad at the foot of the mountains of northern Persia. This position is significant, since the lowlands of north-western Asia were almost certainly populated by wild horses. It is conceivable that domestication may have begun in such an area. Duerst (1908) found that masses of equine bones occurred at all levels, all from the same type of horse. In the lowest levels (Ia) they are associated with wild animals, but from Ib onwards they occur together with domesticated types.[1] At the same time, equine bones become more abundant compared with those of other animals, and this is considered by Duerst as evidence that *the horse had become tamed or domesticated*. He points out, however, that conclusive proof of domestication of this horse, which he called *Equus caballus pumpelli*, cannot be obtained since precise criteria, as present in the skeletons of cattle and sheep, are absent from the bones of horses.

Thus it is in any case not certain whether the equine from Anau was domesticated. But it is the more fundamental question whether this equine was *Equus caballus* that has to be answered in the negative. Admittedly the majority of archaeologists, as well as several palaeontologists, have accepted Duerst's identification. Both Hilzheimer and Antonius, however, regarded the Anau equine as a hemione. More recently, Lundholm has conclusively shown that the latter alternative is correct, using the first phalanx, a bone of which sufficient specimens for a comparison were available. The Anau horse has thus dropped out of the picture of the domestication of *Equus caballus*; it is a half-ass.

The second-earliest locality that is supposed to have yielded horse is Sialk in central Persia on the edge of the central basin. Only two molars are known, and they were assigned to *E. caballus pumpelli* by Vaufrey. The deposit, Sialk II, has been correlated with the Samara and Halaf phases of Mesopotamia, which are believed to be earlier than 3000 B.C. These equines, being identified with the Anau form, have now to be regarded as half-asses also.

From Shah Tepé on the shore of the Caspian Sea, i.e. north of the mountains, where wild horses are likely to have occurred, horse remains have been described by Amschler (1940a). Level III (about 3000–2500 B.C. according to Arne, the excavator) yielded a very spongy bone, regarded as domesticated for this reason, but it will be shown presently that it belonged to a domesticator rather than a domesticated beast. From Level II (2500–1500 B.C.) eleven bones of 'horse' were identified. The investigator again assigns the remains to *E.c. pumpelli*, the Anau 'horse'. This alone might be regarded as sufficient to assign the Shah Tepé form to the half-asses, but in fact the evidence is worth even less. From Level III, the oldest and therefore the most important, only one fragment of a long bone has been assigned to horse; but Lundholm has reinvestigated it and found it to be part of a *human* femur. Layer II is recent enough for horse to be present in any case, nevertheless the material could well belong to a hemione form. The jaw contains only teeth that have been ground down to the roots, and the pelvis is assigned to a horse because of its size

---

[1] Anau I-II is contemporary with Sialk I, and this is 4000 B.C. or earlier even on the most conservative estimate.

only. It must be stated, therefore, that there is no evidence for the true horse at Shah Tepé.

At Susa in ancient Elam (De Mecquenem and Scheil, 1943), an engraving on bone was found which is dated as coming from a level between Susa I and II, which would place it at the beginning of the third millennium B.C. It shows in a diagrammatic fashion a rider on horseback, and one must admit that Amschler (1935, 1936) is right in pointing to the short ears and untasselled tail as suggesting a horse and not an onager. On the other hand, Hančar stresses that the engraving is only 33 mm. high and that the specific identity of the animal cannot be established. If its stratigraphical position is beyond doubt, it would, however, prove that riding had been invented by the beginning of the third millennium B.C. Nevertheless it is strange that this custom did not spread south or west until some considerable time thereafter.

Another Elamitic illustration is a small bone plate showing nineteen heads of equids with varying profiles, which Amschler regards as representing various types of horses. Antonius, however, is satisfied that these were onagers.

In Mesopotamia the earliest evidence for domesticated horse-like animals is the Khafaje vase. It comes from a place about fifteen kilometres east of Baghdad and belongs to the Jamdat Nasr period, approximately 3000 B.C. Unfortunately the painting is extremely sketchy. The mane is shown upright, which speaks for onager or ass rather than domestic horse, unless these supposed horses had retained the 'wild' type of mane. One might, therefore, discard the Khafaje vase as an early representation of the onager, which was domesticated at Ur (p. 368), were there not a horse-like tail. It is shown on all three beasts drawing the cart. It is indeed lacking the tuft at the end of the tail (the sign of the onager), and this fact is quoted specifically (e.g. by Hermes, 1936) as demonstrating that the animals are horses. But the tails are shown by a single stroke of the brush, so that details cannot be expected anyway. The specific nature of the Khafaje animals thus remains uncertain.

Other evidence for the horse in the Mesopotamia of the third millennium B.C. is equally ambiguous, though acquaintance with northerly countries renders it likely that the horse was not unheard of and perhaps even occasionally brought into the country. Thus, Langdon (1924–1934) mentions that on a tablet found about seventeen miles north of Kish the ideogram of the horse appears. The animal is described as living on the mountains. This tablet is dated by Langdon at prior to 3500 B.C., which is certainly too early. The horse is further mentioned in a Babylonian liturgy of the third millennium (Langdon, 1913). This and other evidence is accepted by Hermes as proving that the horse was known in Mesopotamia at that time. It cannot, however, have played an important part in the economy of the people.

Some sites have yielded clay figurines that have been interpreted as model horses. From the third dynasty of Ur, some such figurines have been unearthed at Digdiggeh, near Ur, and others come from the palace of Naram-Sin at Brak (Akkadian period, *c.* 2300 B.C.). But these and statuettes from Tepé Gawra and Kish are quite indeterminate. If they are meant to represent equines they are best interpreted as hemiones, for which osteological evidence exists at Tell Asmar in the third millennium B.C.

The ancient civilizations of Mesopotamia thus may have become acquainted with the horse in the course of the third millennium B.C., though this is not certain. The animal was not used by the Sumerians, nor by the later, immigrating Semites. It is mentioned for the first time in the Chagar Bazar tablets, written in the reign of Samsi-Adad (*c.*1800 B.C.), though not frequently. One cannot be certain in this case of the specific identity, but the fact that chariots are mentioned, too, makes it likely that true horses are involved. Even in the days of Hammurabi (*c.* 1750 B.C.) the horse seems to have been of little economic importance, as it is not mentioned in his code of law. But a letter, apparently written during the reign of his successor, Samsulluna, says that about that time large movements of peoples took place, which brought many horses to Mesopotamia. The same movements would have brought it to Egypt in the west and to India in the east. About 1700 B.C., or slightly later, the horse was known in all countries of the Near and Middle East. According to Antonius (1918), this applies to Kassite Babylonia, Syria, Mitanni on the Upper Euphrates, the Hittite state in Asia Minor, the Amorite principalities of Palestine and the New Kingdom of Egypt. In this entire area the horse was at that time used exclusively to draw the two-wheeled chariot. Moreover, the breed appears to have been the same throughout.

The early Assyrian representations show a horse which, though belonging to the type of the Arab, appears to be more heavily built. But this is due to the artists' style, since other animals, and also men, are shown shorter and more muscular than they really may have been. If one makes allowances for this, the early Mesopotamian horse becomes a true Arab. Antonius is unable to agree with Hilzheimer who thinks he can recognize several races among the early Mesopotamian horses. In particular, Hilzheimer (1935) believed that the Assyrians possessed a heavy horse comparable with the modern Occidental. He was misled by the style, so far as the earlier pictures are concerned. But the horse of the time of Ashurbanipal (686–626 B.C.) (Fig. 12 : 11) was apparently indeed heavier and more muscular than that of earlier periods, as for instance in the time of Ashurnasirpal (884–816 B.C.). Antonius knows of only one representation which shows another breed alongside the typical Assyrian horse. It comes from Kuyunjik and shows the battle of Ashurbanipal against the Elamites. The horse of these opponents is distinctly a small animal which might be called a pony. The so-called hunting scenes from Kuyunjik, however, undoubtedly show onagers and not (as is commonly assumed) wild horses.

The Hittite representations of horses are too rough for the breed to be identified.

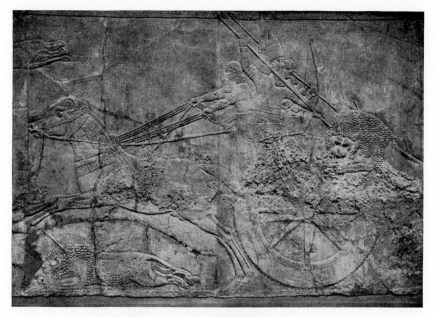

FIG. 12 : 11. Ashurbanipal's horses with bridle, reins and bit, 668–626 B.C., from Palace of Nineveh, Room C. British Museum No. 124859

But from Mitanni, of about 1360 B.C., a remarkable document is available. It is called the Kikkuli Text and was studied by Hrozný (1931). This treatise gives detailed directions for training and is apparently exclusively concerned with chariot-horses. Strangely enough, several technical terms used are reminiscent of Sanskrit expressions. Whilst this document provides a vivid picture of horse-breeding in the fourteenth century B.C., it is relatively late. Hrozný indeed argues in favour of an Aryan horse-equipped invasion which happened about 2000 B.C.

Egyptian art establishes the presence of the horse from the eighteenth dynasty onwards (c. 1580 B.C.) and it is commonly assumed that the Hyksos brought the horse to Egypt. Whilst this may still turn out to be the correct answer, Hyksos graves are so far lacking both horse bones and horse equipment.[1] In Palestine the Middle Bronze Age period (c. 1650 B.C.) representing the Hyksos shows very scanty evidence of the horse, though it appears to have been present. Tell-el-Yahudiyah is a Hyksos town excavated by Petrie, who found horse sacrifices buried as foundation deposits under the walls. The steep glacis, typical of Middle Bronze Age towns, is considered to be an anti-horse, or rather anti-chariot, device. At Tell-el-Ajjul horses were found buried in Middle Bronze tomb shafts. Only one of the Jericho tombs

[1] The tombs at Gaza in Palestine that contain horse remains are later than Hyksos.

319

(J3) has yielded bones of an *Equus*, but these belong to the onager, not the true horse (Grosvenor-Ellis, 1960).

Immediately after the expulsion of the Hyksos, reports about horses and pictures become plentiful. In the reign of Ahmes (*c.* 1580–1557 B.C.) the chariot is in evidence. A wooden statuette assigned to the seventeenth or early eighteenth dynasty and preserved in the Metropolitan Museum, New York, shows an Egyptian groom riding a black horse (Fig. 12 : 12). This is the earliest tangible evidence so far obtained and may take us back to the end of the Hyksos period itself, though its exact date is

FIG. 12 : 12. Figurine of a horse ridden by its groom (length 30 cm.). One of the earliest Egyptian representations of the horse. Early eighteenth dynasty, *c.* 1580 B.C. This picture is extraordinary in that it is evidence of riding, a practice almost unknown in early times

not certain. The early eighteenth dynasty was a period when plenty of horses were taken as war booty from the Syrians, and in the following centuries the Egyptians used the horse both for the drawing of chariots and for riding.[1]

Pictorial evidence is now plentiful (Fig. 12 : 13) and often well executed. It is, of course, once more necessary to consider the style of the pictures; otherwise one arrives, for instance, at the mistaken conclusion that the Egyptian horse was smaller and more graceful than the Assyrian. It is indeed shown as a slender animal with fine limbs and much like the modern Arab in the formation of head and body. It was small as evidenced by a preserved chariot, but Antonius points out that the same applies to the horse of the Assyrians.

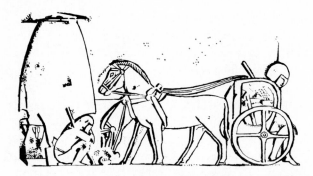

Fig. 12 : 13. Egyptian horses with chariot, Tomb of Chaemhet, eighteenth dynasty. The normal mode of use of the horse in the Bronze Age. After Boessneck (1953)

In Cyprus the horse was known at the latest by 1600 B.C., since its teeth occur in Kalopsida (Tomb 9; Myres, 1897) and Politiko (Tomb 3; Gjerstad, 1926). These tombs are of the Middle Bronze Age of Cyprus, which Dikaios dates at 2000–1600 B.C., whilst Schaeffer restricts it to 1800–1600 B.C. At Agia Paraskevi an Early Bronze Age tomb was found to contain horse, but the stratification was disturbed. It appears, therefore, that the horse was known in Cyprus about 1700 B.C., and possibly much earlier, though the evidence for earlier dates requires confirmation.

In Asia Minor a rein-terret from Boghaz-Köy with the representation of a horse has been assigned to the latter part of the third millennium by Rostovtzeff (1931) and others, but the objects cannot be dated reliably. There is also supposed, but unsubstantiated, evidence from the second level of Troy, the value of which lies mainly in the support it would give to Grahame Clark's view (1941) that the battle-axe people reached Troy about 2400 B.C. The American excavators did not find horse remains before Troy VI (1800 B.C.), as has been confirmed by Gejfall.

---

[1] Regarding riding, the evidence has been ably summarized by M. S. F. Hood (1953), but it appears that riding was not a mode of progression worthy of kings and other people of high rank. They used the chariot.

Crossing now into Europe, we encounter the horse early in the Bronze Age of Vardaroftsa in central Macedonia. No details appear to be available concerning this find except the lists published in 1926 by Heurtley and Hutchinson. Period A, correlated with Troy I-II, is reported to have produced the remains of ox, boar, horse, goat and elk; Period B, beginning about 2000 B.C., stag, ox, horse; Period C, red deer, boar, goat, dog, horse, ox and tortoise; and Period D, red deer, boar, horse, dog and 'cat'. It will be noticed that game animals are prominent, and there is no evidence that the horse was domesticated. If its domesticated status in Period A could be substantiated, this find would imply that man brought the horse to Macedonia, presumably from the Russian plains, some 500 years before it reached Asia Minor. This is conceivable, but it remains to be proved.

Even the picture of a horse on the silver cup of Maikop, in the Caucasus, is dated at 2000 B.C. and is thus later than the horse of Period A of Vardaroftsa.

The earliest picture of a domesticated horse on European soil[1] appears to be that on the capstone of the fifth shaft-grave of Mycenae (c. 1550 B.C.). It is shown drawing a two-wheeled chariot and appears in the same manner on contemporary weapons and ornaments. One sword, however, shows three horses running behind one another. They were domesticated since their manes are of the hanging type.

Two hundred and fifty years later riding was practised in Greece, for Sinclair Hood has described a small terracotta figurine from the Lower Helladic IIIb phase of Mycenae[2] (c. 1300 B.C.). This crude model (Fig. 12 : 14), however, provides no information about the characteristics of the breed of Greek horses. This can be deduced only from the sculptures of the later classical period, such as the Parthenon Frieze. From these it would appear that the Greek horse was derived from the same wild form as the Egyptian and Near Asiatic horses. Thus the entire eastern Mediterranean constituted a single hippological area.

In Crete chariots were used about 1400 B.C., according to the evidence provided by the palace of the Late Minoan II period at Knossos.

The picture that is emerging thus shows that the domesticated horse may have reached Macedonia about 2500 B.C. If so, it did not continue to spread, which is curious. By 2000 B.C. it was known in the Caucasus area and made its appearance in Asia Minor (Mitanni). By 1800 B.C. it had reached Troy, and within the century that followed it spread over the whole of the civilized Near and Middle East, in conjunction with the two-wheeled chariot.

In Greece it was established in the sixteenth century, and thereafter it must be regarded as a normal piece of equipment of Mediterranean economy (Figs. 12 : 15 to 12 : 17). It is almost certain that the reason why the horse appeared so suddenly

[1] Possibly except Tripolye, see p. 324.

[2] It should be noted that other similar riders appear in Cyprus in a much later context, c. 700 B.C. (see Jensen, 1958, Fig. 10, etc.). Almost identical ones came from Attica.

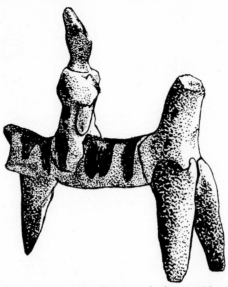

FIG. 12 : 14. Clay figurine of a horse with rider from the Lower Helladic IIIb phase of Mycenae, Greece, *c.* 1300 B.C. Another of the few instances of riding from the Bronze Age. After Sinclair Hood

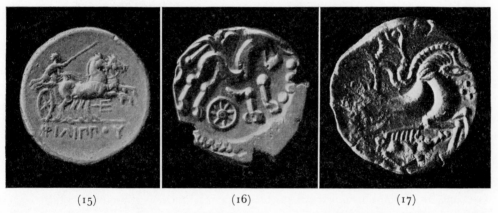

(15)   (16)   (17)

FIGS. 12 : 15 to 12 : 17. The story of the famous Philippoi of Philip II of Macedon, father of Alexander the Great, 359–336 B.C. The coins show a chariot with a pair of beautiful naturalistic horses with muscular bodies and small heads (Fig. 12 : 15). These coins were minted in large numbers and spread quickly throughout the Greek world. Merchants at Massalia (Marseilles) favoured them, and through this gateway they entered Gaul. Here they were copied, especially by the Arverni. Whilst some imitations were good, others were exceedingly crude. By the time they had reached Britain, little resemblance was left. Fig. 12 : 16 shows a gold stater of Regnum (Chichester) of the first century B.C. Only one dismembered horse is left, and a wheel probably representing the sun-wheel rather than the original chariot. Fig. 12 : 17 shows a billon stater probably derived from the same prototype (*c.* 56–51 B.C.), with a curious prancing horse. It was found in 1957, with other coins, at Grouville, Jersey, Channel Islands. All twice natural size; author's collection

was of a military nature. The chariot and later on the cavalryman were efficient weapons. The use of the horse for peaceful purposes was, at any rate in the initial stages, of secondary importance.

FIG. 12 : 18. Silver decadrachm of Syracuse, Sicily, late fifth century B.C. It shows a quadriga with two-wheeled chariot, Nike flying overhead. These coins may have been presented as prizes at popular races. Natural size. After Head (1959)

Eastern Europe

The evidence from the Near and Middle East and the Mediterranean thus suggests that about and after 2000 B.C. the horse arrived in that area from the north, where it had been domesticated at an earlier date. Though Vardaroftsa has not provided positive evidence for domestication in Period A, it must, on the other hand, not be ruled out as inconceivable that there were domesticated horses in Macedonia as early as 2500 B.C.

This problem is further illustrated, but not solved, by the evidence provided by the Tripolye culture of the chernozem lands of eastern Europe. This was divided by Passek (1949) into five stages, A, B_1, B_2, C_1 and C_2, the absolute chronology of which is, however, very uncertain. Unfortunately, this happens to be the crucial point. According to Passek, A (represented by Luka-Vrubleveckaya) is as early as 3000–2700 B.C.; B–C, dating from 2700–2000 B.C.; and C_2, the final phase represented by Usatova, from 2000–1700 B.C. Childe, however, placed the beginning at about 2100 B.C. and allowed the Tripolye culture to continue until 1400 B.C. Should Passek be right, the Tripolye complex would be the earliest to be considered in connection with horse domestication. Should, however, the shorter chronology be correct, eastern Europe would not have had domesticated horses earlier than western Asia.

Apart from the chronological problem there is another difficulty. Whilst bones of horse have been found in all Tripolye stages, they become frequent only in C_2. For this stage domestication is not disputed, so that eastern Europe would have had the domesticated horse at the latest between 2000 and 1700 B.C. on the long, and between 1600 and 1400 B.C. on the short, chronology. The status of the horse of stages A to C is more problematic. Its bones are rare in these stages, and it would be quite possible to regard them as those of game were it not that Gromova (1955) assigned these remains to the forest-horse group, and not to the tarpan as one would expect. On this morphological difference is based the view that the horses of the early Tripolye stages were domesticated.

This view in turn could be challenged. It is perfectly possible that the wild horse of the chernozem forest steppe belonged to the forest horse, and that the tarpan area lay originally farther east. Again, it might be replied that there are clay figurines of what appear to be horses, and that clay figurines usually represent domestic types.

It is thus evident that the Tripolye culture is of great importance in relation to the early history of the horse. Two questions remain to be settled, that of its chronology and that of the domestic character of the horse in stages A to C.

Quite recently, Hančar (1956) has chosen to accept both the long chronology and domestication from early Tripolye onwards. He thus finds himself in the happy situation of having an early focus of domestication of the horse in south-east Europe, whence the animal would have spread north-westwards. But it is to be feared that pottery experts familiar with the Danubian culture will find it difficult to accept such early dates.[1] And yet a date of the order of 3000 B.C. must be postulated for the beginning of horse domestication.

FIG. 12 : 19. Neolithic horse sculpture made of Prussian amber and found at Woldenberg, Friedeberg District, Neumark, East Germany. Late third millennium B.C. This sculpture need not represent a domesticated horse

Central and northern Europe

The difficulty of recognizing horse remains as domesticated hinders the elucidation of the prehistory of the horse everywhere. The statistical argument that large numbers of bones on a site suggest domestication is widely accepted. In this sense, Gromova regards small numbers as evidence of wild status and hunting. Nehring, however, regards the contrary as correct, and Lundholm says that the *large* number of bones in Baralda Cave (a Tripolye site) indicates that the horse was hunted. This may be true in the case of a cave. But one is left with the unpleasant feeling that less should be said and more osteological work done before conclusions are drawn.

Passing from Russia into central Europe, one encounters everywhere rare evidence for the presence of the wild horse. Only archaeological burials, therefore, afford a somewhat secure basis for arguments. The Danubian culture complex shows horse

[1] Childe held that the Tripolye culture is essentially the result of an expansion of the Danubian and correlated Tripolye A–C with Danubian II. He also regards the animal figurines as part of the Danubian heritage brought from the Middle Danube Basin.

burials at Bodzáspart in Hungary, Jordansmühl in Silesia[1] and the Złota culture of Poland. This group belongs to Danubian III and is thus, according to Gordon Childe, related to the early Tripolye. Setting aside the chronological problem, and if these horses were domesticated—as there is some reason to assume—such horses would have occurred in Europe in small numbers in the Copper Age. This is the time when battle-axes and corded pottery spread into central Europe, whilst the Michelsberg culture flourished in the Swiss lake-dwellings.

The late Neolithic corded-ware grave of Föllik in the Austrian Burgenland belongs to the same group. It contained the remains of four horses (one with foal), a cow with calf, a ewe with lamb and a goat with kid. This context would suggest domestication, but doubt has been cast upon the association of the bones with the artefacts and pottery. They may not be contemporary (Pittioni, 1954).

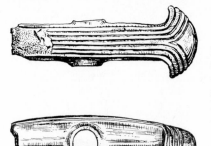

Fig. 12 : 20. Bronze battle-axe found in association with horse bones at the megalithic site of Dümmer Lake, north-west Germany. After Reinerth

Another interesting site is the Dümmer Lake, one of the three large lakes of north-west Germany (Reinerth, 1939). It is a megalithic village of rectangular houses with wooden floors. Stone axes and other equipment identify the culture, and there is also a battle-axe (Fig. 12 : 20). The fauna consisted mainly of hunted animals, namely beaver (most frequent), bear, badger, otter, wolf, fox, wild cat, aurochs, bison, red deer, elk, roe, wild pig (plenty), wild horse and birds. Of domesticated animals, Vogel identified the following: dog (a large form of the lake-dwellings' dog), pig (small form, plenty), sheep (turbary sheep, moderate numbers), goat (doubtful), cattle (both small and large forms) and horse. The horse is the most frequent of all hoofed animals and in order of frequency of all species ranges second after the beaver. Its bones, however, were all broken for the sake of the marrow. Horse, therefore, formed part of the normal diet at the Dümmer.

Vogel recognized three size-groups of horses. One he regarded as identical with the wild horse of the Schussenquelle. The second was smaller; it was the most abundant. The third was a large, heavy horse, represented by a few specimens.

[1] Copper ornaments correlate this site with the Danubian III, about 2000 B.C.

Vogel rightly considered this size distribution as suggesting domestication. It is indeed unlikely that three different forms of horse should have occurred wild in the area. But this does not rule out hunting, for as late as the eleventh century A.D., when domesticated horses were to be found everywhere, wild horses were still hunted in the Rhine Valley. The heavy horse from Dümmer may have been domesticated or wild, it links up with the large Scandinavian Bronze Age horses described by Lundholm and confirms that there was a heavy horse in Postglacial north-west Europe. The small form that constituted the bulk of the population would have been either a native wild horse that was hunted or a tarpan-derived herded horse imported from the East. The third form resembling the late Pleistocene horse from Schussenried cannot be interpreted without further information being made available. The most likely explanation is that the small horse was wild, hunted and eaten, whilst the other two were domesticated breeds, of which the heavy one may have been brought by the battle-axe users.

A number of contemporaneous local cultures have been collectively called the Baden culture; they cover the Middle and Upper Danube basins, Czechoslovakia and the Upper Vistula. That they had the horse as a domestic animal is certain, for a bit terminating in cheek-pieces of antler has been found (Childe, 1947, p. 113). Stone battle-axes complete the picture. In spite of the scanty evidence, it appears that by the end of Danubian III battle-axe-using Copper Age cultures had entered Europe with the horse, but the animal was still scarce and it may well have been regarded as more or less sacred.

It would appear, therefore, that the late Neolithic of Europe knew the domestic horse, though it was only occasionally used in quantity. At least the wild horse, if not all horses, appears to have been eaten, so that the taboo on horseflesh would have been created in the Bronze Age. What its economic use was otherwise is uncertain. There is no evidence that it replaced the ox as yet as a draught animal, nor is there any for riding. One should be careful regarding the last point, however. Horses can be ridden with a nose-string only, as is done by Arab bedouin today, and of such practice there would be no material evidence. They may also have served as pack-horses. Whether religious aspects played a part is not certain, though this is likely in later times (see p. 329).

With Danubian IV the early Bronze Age unfolds itself and spreads as far as the west and the north. The bell-beaker people established the new metal-working economy and developed trade everywhere. It may be due to the trade that the horse now became an important economic proposition, and that horse-breeding was begun on a large scale. Knowledge of this art had reached Europe during the preceding periods, but now the stock of local wild horses was taken advantage of, and local domestication, both of the forest horse and of the tarpan, became the fashion. Horse-bits have been found at Tószeg in Hungary and elsewhere.

The sudden expansion of the use of the horse cannot be understood without the assumption that it was used as a draught animal, or else for riding. Riding became important at a later date than drawing of carts, as has been pointed out.

In northern Europe the presence of the horse in Mesolithic levels has been studied particularly by Lundholm, who gives the revealing table here reproduced (Fig. 12 : 21). From it one cannot but conclude that the wild horse survived into the Neolithic (and possibly later) and that it was joined by the domesticated horse in the Bronze Age.

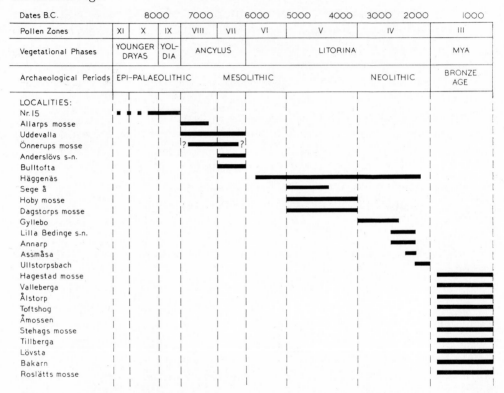

FIG. 12 : 21. The appearance of the horse in Sweden. Its presence in twenty-five localities shows clearly that the wild horse was supplemented by the domesticated at the beginning of the Bronze Age. After Lundholm (1949)

Mesolithic horses can therefore be dismissed as not domesticated even in northern Europe where this period is comparatively late.

At Assmåsa in Sweden the humerus of a horse was found associated with sherds that date it to the transition from the Dolmen period to that of the Passage Graves. It is, of course, not certain whether it was domesticated. Rydbeck (1934) held the view that the domestic horse entered northern Europe with the battle-axe people.

The records, however, are not ample. In Denmark the evidence is similar. The horse was present before the battle-axe invasion. But, after a careful scrutiny of the Scandinavian material, Lundholm still considers it possible that the battle-axe people knew horse-taming and used the local wild horses for the purpose. He and Degerbøl agree that from the Bronze Age onwards the horse is represented by so many bones that it must be regarded as domesticated. This confirms for northern Europe what is known from the central parts of the Continent, that everywhere the appearance of the domesticated horse coincided approximately with the beginning of the Bronze Age, and that local wild horses provided the stock from which breeding was started.

Gordon Childe (1951) successfully worked out the spread of wheeled vehicles into Europe. He believes that the wheeled cart and the potter's wheel are both inventions of the Uruk culture of southern Mesopotamia and that this happened before 3500 B.C. There is evidence that the wheeled cart was preceded by the sledge, and sledges have been found in the royal tombs of Ur which are at least 1000 years younger. The earliest evidence consists of script signs on late Uruk tablets (Childe, Fig. 1).

Whilst it is generally agreed that the earliest wheeled carts were drawn by oxen, onager bones were found in the chariot graves of the Y Cemetery of Kish, which is of Early Dynastic I date. Onagers were buried with the sledge of Queen Shub-ad, whilst the king's grave contained two ox-waggons. These finds are Early Dynastic III. From this and other evidence it is to be inferred that in Mesopotamia the ox was replaced by the swifter onager, though not universally, early in the third millennium B.C.

Childe held that this is the source of wheeled vehicles, that they reached the Indus Valley by about 2500 B.C., north Syria—2200 B.C., Crete—1900 B.C., Greece—1550 B.C., south Russia—1400 B.C., north Italy—1100 B.C., central and northern Europe—1000 B.C. and Britain—500 B.C. This sequence looks indeed convincing, though new finds are apt to modify it. In particular, whilst the use of the wheeled vehicle may thus have spread in this manner, there is enough evidence to suggest that the horse reached Europe earlier. The evidence from Danubian III sites is strongly in favour of domesticated horses entering Europe with battle-axe users. There is so far no evidence that they had waggons or carts.

It remains, therefore, obscure how these people used the horse. It may have been used for riding without bridle in the modern sense, or else it was used as just another source of meat supply. There is evidence that the horse was eaten in the Neolithic even though it may have been domesticated.

Thirdly, there is the curious aspect of the sacred character of the horse which is often present where the horse first enters the scene. It was an attribute of princes and kings from Europe in the west to China in the east. This exalted state can be explained only as due to some superior quality, most probably its swiftness, and possibly also its resistance to taming, which distinguishes it from the domesticated ruminants. A horse has to be 'broken in'.

The general use of the horse in the Bronze Age and later is almost certainly connected with its increased economic exploitation as a draught animal and for riding, most probably following the introduction of the war chariot.

The development of the central European horse in the Iron Age is indicated at Manching in Bavaria, where the vast majority of specimens was small, being only 120–130 cm. high (Förster, 1960; Liepe, 1958). In addition, a few up to 150 cm. high were kept. Haithabu in Schleswig is an example of medieval conditions. Here, Nobis (1960) found that the height of the horses varied a great deal, a pony of 135 cm. and a medium-sized horse of 145 cm. shoulder-height being discernible. He concluded that no systematic breeding was attempted and that the Vikings of that town were chiefly interested in getting physically efficient, broad-shouldered horses with modest food requirements.

Western Europe and North Africa
Ever since Antonius first suggested a separate domestication centre in Spain from which the modern heavy horse has emerged, a serious investigation of that area has been desirable, though little has been done. The most important analysis is that of Staffe (1944). He regards north-west Africa and Spain as one unit in this respect,

FIG. 12 : 22. One of the Greek bronze horses of St Mark's Church, Venice, illustrating the muscular, small-headed type popular in the Classical period of Greece.
Photo Liselotte Selbiger, Copenhagen

and quotes in support of the Western heavy horse of prehistoric times Iberian figurines from Despeñaperros (Jaén), Spanish rock engravings and representations on Carthaginian coins. There are also the well-known pictures from Canjorros (Jaén) showing horses on leads. Their age is uncertain, though probably Neolithic. North African graffiti, too, show the heavy horse according to Staffe, a view which is not convincing as the drawings are very inaccurate. According to Childe (1925, p. 114) Neolithic pits near Madrid contained bones of the horse, but no detailed research has been carried out.

The characteristic that would unite the Spanish/north-west African group of horses is the convex head-profile (ram's nose) (Fig. 12 : 23). Lundholm considers this a significant feature since, as was shown by Adametz, it is present in the foals also.

Assuming the West was indeed a separate centre of horse domestication, the chronological problem once more comes to the fore. If the domestic horse was present in the Neolithic of the Iberian peninsula, it must have been there considerably prior to 2000 B.C., at a time when the remainder of the Mediterranean had not yet received it. This implies several awkward complications, such as an independent centre of domestication, and dispersal of the idea across thousands of miles of land where it did not take root in spite of the presence of wild horses, either *via* temperate Europe or, even less probably, via the Mediterranean. Whilst it would be a mistake to reject this interpretation as impossible, it requires plenty of substantiation before it can be accepted.

It is evident, however, that if one allows the domestication of the Western horse

FIG. 12 : 23. Painting of a horse from the Magdalenian cave of Castillo in northern Spain. It is interesting to note the convex outline of the small head since this is one of the characteristics of the 'barb', the Spanish and North African breed of domesticated horse. After Breuil

(the 'barb') to be postponed until the Bronze Age, the theory of the independent Western centre can still be maintained, except in so far as the idea of horse domestication reached the western Mediterranean from the East. More intensive research on the osteological material from this area is much needed.

India and Pakistan

The wild horse that reached India early in the Pleistocene was long extinct when the domesticated horse was introduced. The earliest horse remains so far reported come from Rana Ghundai in northern Baluchistan (Ross, 1946). In Level RG I (Piggott's terminology (1950)), the date of which is regarded as earlier than 3000 B.C., four teeth of the 'domestic horse' have been found together with ass. This identification cannot be accepted as reliable unless it is carefully checked. The ass, being an African animal, cannot be right in this early period. The remains attributed to this species more probably belong to the hemione, which survives in north-west India to the present day. The four teeth are not sufficient to make a definite pronouncement. They may well belong to hemiones, too, and to recognize them as domesticated is, on the experience gained everywhere else, impossible. It appears, therefore, as if only hemiones existed at Rana Ghundai, and that they were hunted.

The same doubts apply to the rare finds of horses made in the Indus Valley culture. It is only with the Aryan invasion that the horse becomes frequent in India (Fig. 12 : 24), an invasion affording a parallel to those that occurred in the eighteenth and seventeenth centuries B.C. in western Asia and in Europe. The invasion of India, though perhaps to be dated slightly later, belongs to the same group; it was carried by tribes speaking Indo-Germanic languages. Ridgeway (1905) derived from the *Rigveda* descriptions of

FIG. 12 : 24. Sacrificial horse, northern Gujarat, India. Horse sacrifices were in places an important part of prehistoric religious rites from the Neolithic onwards. The Aryan tribes invading India about the middle of the second millennium B.C. appear to have practised them. In due course substitutes were adopted for the economically valuable animals, the smoke of the burnt sacrifice remaining the principal agent. In India, horses of burnt clay are used, the legs, tail and mouth of which form chimney-flues. The figure is stuffed with hay, which is lit and emits the required smoke. This completes the sacrificial act, and the figure is useless thereafter. Clay horses exist in remote districts, ranging from elaborate reproductions of the live beast through the type illustrated here to mere cylindrical bodies with a small central chimney (the original head). Of this most degenerate type the original meaning has almost certainly been lost.
Author's collection

these early Aryan horses which suggest that they were chestnut-coloured on the head and back, and dun below. The chestnut colour is not primitive, whilst the lighter belly may be so regarded. Nothing can therefore be said about their provenance. It goes without saying that in India, too, the Bronze Age horse was a chariot beast, and that riding was not practised until much later (Fig. 12 : 25), the earliest stirrup-loops appearing on the Sanchi stupa carvings in the second century B.C. Piggott stresses that chariot-racing was a favourite sport, and

Fig. 12 : 25. Silver coin of a Hindu king of Ohind, India, c. A.D. 875–900, showing a rider on horseback. Though the horse had reached India by 1500 B.C., it was soon eclipsed in importance by the zebu, which appears on the reverse of this coin. Horses are comparatively rarely depicted before the Moslem conquests. Twice natural size. Author's collection

that the races were run much as in later Greek and Roman events, the competitors having to turn round a marking post and to come back.

China

China occupies in the East the same position as Europe in the West.[1] The horse occurred wild in much of the country, though it was the subspecies *Equus caballus przewalski*. This local stock was domesticated under the influence of knowledge of horse-breeding that reached east Asia from the north and west. The ox-cart was evidently known at least since the beginning of the second millennium B.C., and the adoption of the horse followed later.

The Neolithic Lung-shan culture (between 2000 and 1500 B.C.) knew the horse, but the finds do not indicate so far the manner of use. Hančar considers them as domesticated here in China as he does in Neolithic Europe.

From 1300 B.C. (end of Shang and beginning of Yin dynasties) onwards, in the full Bronze Age, the horse was in use as a draught animal for chariots. It appears also as the steed of the archer, but the evidence does not suggest that it was economi-

---

[1] The chronological sequence adopted for the dynasties is as follows:

Han	246 B.C.—220 A.D.
Chou	1027 B.C.—246 B.C.
Yin	1300 B.C.—1028 B.C.
Shang-Hsia	1523 B.C.—1300 B.C.

cally important. China's farming was based on the pig, to which cattle, sheep and goat were added later in the Neolithic.

The horse of the Shang-Yin periods had, much as in Europe, the function to serve the nobility, and it retained a religious significance until much later.

At Wu-kwan-ts'un near Anyang in northern Honan a royal cemetery of the Yin period has recently been excavated.[1] The king's tomb was accompanied by 152 decapitated bodies of followers and servants, mostly in separate shaft-tombs. Horses, however, appeared in association with the royal tomb only, richly equipped with bits, buckles, plate and bell ornaments. Whether they were intended to draw the royal chariot to the land of eternity is not evident, however. Hančar considers it possible that a heap of rotted wood, some covered with red lacquer, is the remains of the royal cart.

At Lyn-li-ge, another site near Anyang, twenty graves of the Shang-Yin period yielded a very uniform equipment of tripods, wooden dishes and bronze vessels. Two of them contained in addition sets of horse harnesses and a chariot, as well as a lance, a sword and arrowheads. In addition, there were separate pits containing horses and chariots.

A third locality near Anyang, Hu-chia-chueng, may be described as a horse-and-chariot cemetery, with hundreds of horses buried in special graves. One was of particular importance (M. 020). It contained the remains of three men, three sets of weapons, four horses and a war chariot. This proves that the Bronze Age horse of China was essentially a means of quick attack. The burials accorded to the horses testify that they were regarded as comrades rather than slaves.

A sensational find was made at Hsiao-t'un. A small grave of the late second millennium B.C. (Yin period) contained the skeletons of a man, a horse and a dog side by side, with ornaments and equipment, suggesting that the man was a rider. It is by far the earliest evidence for horse-riding available in China, which in the course of the first millennium B.C. developed bow-and-arrow-using cavalry into an efficient weapon of attack. The rider of Hsiao-t'un, however, had his dog with him. He is likely to have been a hunter.

There is reason to believe that the development of cavalry in the first millennium was rendered possible largely by the presence of wild horses in parts of China. If the country had depended on supplies from abroad, these would have come precisely from those peoples whom the Chinese, with their insatiable desire for territorial expansion, wanted to subdue.

The story of the Heavenly Horses (Fig. 12 : 26) of Ferghana throws an interesting light on the situation of the Chinese horse in the second century B.C.

In 102 B.C. a military expedition was sent by Emperor Wu to Ferghana, which is now part of Russian Turkestan. Its object was to obtain 'superior horses'. The

[1] A report in German is available in Hančar, 1956, p. 269.

FIG. 12 : 26. 'Heavenly horse' emerging from the water; on a Chinese ink slab, A.D. 1620, in British Museum. These types of horses, different from local Przewalski horses, were much appreciated by the Chinese. They were probably regularly obtained from Turkestan

Chinese horses being descended from Przewalski's horse, whilst the Ferghana horses were derived from the tarpan, this would in any case have been a worth-while expedition, and it appears to have been successful, for by the middle of the second century A.D. the Chinese had, in addition to the Mongolian pony with its heavy head, a graceful horse with a small head (Fig. 12 : 27).

Waley, however, points out that Emperor Wu had something else on his mind when sending forth this expedition. He wished to acquire 'Heavenly Horses' of a type that would in due course carry him off to the other world. These Heavenly or superior horses were evidently rare. The expedition succeeded in collecting only thirty of them, but it took home some 3000 ordinary Ferghana horses also. Later, the King of Ferghana consented to make a present of two Heavenly Horses to the Emperor of China every year.

These animals must, as Waley argues, have been very superior indeed. Sacred poetry suggests that they 'issued from a pool', and that they were, therefore, 'dragon-horses'. Thus being invested with religious dignity, they were the kind of horses the emperor required for his funeral procession.

335

FIG. 12 : 27. Head of a Chinese horse in jade, illustrating the graceful head of the tarpan breed. Han dynasty (246 B.C.–A.D. 220), height 14·3 cm. Victoria and Albert Museum. (Crown copyright)

Among the physical characteristics of the Heavenly Horses is a curious one: they 'sweated blood'. This is no legendary attribute and mentioned repeatedly. The most likely explanation is that put forward by Dubs, that the sweating was due to wounds caused by a parasite.

The Heavenly Horses were not larger than the Chinese, and they sometimes had stripes, as they are met with in the tarpan. Large horses were known to the Chinese from Parthia only.

Conclusion

Taking into consideration the scanty character of the earliest evidence, and preferring for the Tripolye culture a chronology with comparatively late dates, the picture that emerges appears to be as follows: Between 3000 and 2500 B.C. a few debatable pictorial representations appear, including the rider from Susa and the Khafaje cart (giving it the benefit of the doubt), indicating that horse domestication was known. The bones from Rana Ghundai I are dated even earlier, but domestication cannot be proved. It is possible, and for theoretical reasons probable, that the original domestication of the horse had taken place by this time, and probably in areas north of the Persian mountains, i.e. mainly in Turkestan. Thence the horse spread slowly west and infiltrated into Europe in small numbers during the third millennium. It may, more or less simultaneously, have reached Asia Minor, and established itself there. By this time, the horse-chariot combination had been perfected and the first quarter of the second millennium witnessed an invasion of charioteers who brought the horse as far south-west as Egypt. A sequel of these movements was the general adoption of the horse in Bronze Age Europe.

On the whole, riding was less popular than the use of the chariot and it was adopted later. With the introduction of the horse as a companion in war, the prohibition of the eating of its flesh appears to have become widespread.

13

The Camels

SCIENTIFIC NAMES—PLIOCENE—*Camelus sivalensis* Falconer and *C. antiquus* Falconer (India).
PLEISTOCENE—*C. knoblochi* Nehring (south Russia), *C. alutensis* Stefanescu (Rumania) *C. thomasii* Pomel (Algeria).
RECENT—*C. dromedarius* L. (dromedary; north-west India, Arabia, North Africa).
C. bactrianus L. (Bactrian camel; central Asia).

Two kinds of camels exist today and are known to everybody: the dromedary, which is single-humped and occurs from North Africa to the Caspian Sea, and from Arabia to north-west India; and the Bactrian camel, which is two-humped and occurs from the Caspian Sea through central Asia to Manchuria. These two are regarded as different species by some authors, and as geographical races by others. Differences in the skeleton are few, and restricted mainly to the limb bones which are shorter in the Bactrian camel. The striking differences are in the soft parts, the double hump of the Bactrian appearing so radically unlike the single one of the dromedary. But Lombardini has found in the dromedary a vestigial anterior hump. It is present in the embryo as well as in the adult stage. Moreover, the low-set appearance of the Bactrian camel is emphasized by the long hair which hangs from the neck.

It had long been assumed that the two kinds of camels are unable to produce hybrids and this had been a strong argument in the hands of Hilzheimer (1913) and others who accept two distinct species. But it is not correct. According to Curasson (1947), hybrids are bred habitually in several countries, for instance in Turkey. The female is usually a dromedary, and the hybrids are single-humped,

heavier and considered more vigorous than the parents. The tendency is now, therefore, to describe our two camels as geographical races of one species. Yet, inter-
fertility is not always accepted as decisive evidence for co-specific status, for the lion
and the tiger interbreed without difficulty, and they are generally regarded as different species. It is certainly convenient to treat these borderline cases in this manner,
so long as one remains aware of their very close relationship.

The dromedary appears to be completely domesticated. The wild Bactrians
reported by Przewalski and later by Sven Hedin from the Lop Nor and the Tarim
Basin in central Asia are regarded by many as descended from domesticated specimens. Yet others are convinced that the Lop Nor camels belong to a wild core that
has survived, though feral individuals are likely to have joined them. Recent evidence
(Fig. 13 : 1) suggests that wild Bactrians still exist in the foothills of the Altai adjacent
to the Gobi Desert, where they were observed and photographed by Mongonial
scientists. A film was exhibited by Mr Ivor Montagu (1957) to the Zoological Society
of London, and it is stated that there are certain morphological differences char-
acterizing the wild beast, such as small humps and feet, slender build and short
hair.

Neither species of camel appears to have been much modified by domestication,
the reason being in all probability that under human control they have been allowed

Fig. 13 : 1. Wild Bactrian camels as observed recently on the Mongolian side of the Altai
Mountains

to continue their normal life. Camels are not stabled or penned. It is very curious, therefore, that there should be no, or so few, wild camels surviving, for only two other domestic species have lost their wild relatives completely, namely the dog and cattle. The cause of the disappearance of wild camels lies perhaps in the desiccation of their natural habitats; we shall return to this matter after the discussion of the history of their domestication.

Like the horses, the camels as a group are of American origin. In South America hump-less camels exist even today, namely the llamas, vicunas and guanacos. North America was the centre of camel evolution throughout the Tertiary. The earliest known ancestral camels are called *Protylopus*. They lived in the Upper Eocene and were no larger than hares. The Oligocene camel, *Poëbrotherium*, had the size of a sheep. *Protomeryx* of the Lower Miocene, *Protolabis* of the Middle Miocene, *Procamelus* of the Upper Miocene, and *Pliauchenia* of the Pliocene are further stages, and some of the later American camels were of very large size. In the Pleistocene of North America, including Alaska, the genus *Camelus* occurred. It is from such late source that the modern Old World camels appear to be derived, by way of migration to Asia across the Bering Straits, when these were dry land in late Pliocene or Early Glaciation times. Only one invasion of camels appears to have succeeded prior to this date; it brought to the Siwaliks of northern India *C. sivalensis*, a species which is believed to be not closely related to the living camels, and another smaller species (*C. antiquus*) which Falconer thought was perhaps related to the llama.

The Pleistocene wave of true camels spread rapidly west along the dry belt of the northern hemisphere. It reached eastern Europe, with *C. knoblochi* in Sarepta, south Russia, and *C. alutensis* in Rumania. They were not able to thrive farther west in Europe because of the unsuitable climate. Whilst these forms are supposed to have been closely related to the two-humped Bactrian camel, the dromedary became separated from the northern branch somewhere in western Asia and spread across Arabia (present in the late Pleistocene of Azraq Oasis, Clutton-Brock, 1961) and Palestine (where it was the contemporary of Levalloisian man at Sabha) into North Africa, reaching even Mauritania in the extreme west. The dromedary had arrived in North Africa in Acheulian times (see p. 356).

Arabia and Palestine
Everything points to the survival until recent times of the wild dromedary and to its eventual domestication in central or southern Arabia. Dr Stekelis and Dr Solomonica found a skull in a Pleistocene deposit in the Rishpan dunes[1] of Israel. Strabo and Diodorus Siculus mentioned wild dromedaries as occurring in Arabia about the commencement of the Christian era. Stekelis (1951) found its bones associated with those of sheep, goat, gazelle, wild boar and onager in the Neolithic of the Yarmuk

[1] Amer. J. Arch, **56** (2), p. 141, 1952.

River (northern Palestine), but whether it was a member of the wild or the domesticated fauna is uncertain. Vaufrey recorded it from the Levalloisian of Sabha (in
Neuville, 1951, p. 214). Its former presence as a wild beast in Palestine is thus certain.

The earliest record of its domestication is contained in the story of Rebekah in
the twenty-fourth and twenty-fifth chapters of Genesis. Abraham's servant goes to
Nahar in Mesopotamia, with ten camels, to find a bride for Isaac; he meets Rebekah
at the well, and she waters the camels. On the way to Palestine across the desert,
Rebekah rides a camel. In Chapter XXXI it is mentioned that Rachel, Jacob's
wife, is riding a camel which has a saddle (the 'furniture' (Fig. 13 : 2) of the
Authorized Version). From that time onwards camels are frequently mentioned
in the Bible. There is only one which is earlier, namely in Genesis, Chapter XIV,

FIG. 13 : 2. Rider on a saddled camel from Syria,
showing structure called 'furniture' in the Bible. One of
the orthostats found at Tell Halaf (*c.* 900 B.C.). After
von Oppenheim (1931, Pl. XXIa)

when on the occasion of Abraham's visit to Egypt the Pharaoh presents him with 'sheep, oxen, he-asses, male and female slaves, she-asses, and camels'. But in view of the obvious fact that Egyptians were unfamiliar with the camel (correctly drome-dary), the last two words of this enumeration may well have been added by a later Jewish writer who thought it inconceivable that the great Pharaoh would not have included camels in his present. The most probable date for the period of Abraham, his children and grandchildren is approximately 1800–1700 B.C. It is suggested by the relation of the movements of the Hebrews to events like the Hyksos invasion in Egyptian history, the presence of the Hittites and Mitanni in Palestine, and the resemblance of the marriage laws of Abraham's period to those of Hammurabi.

By 1800 B.C., therefore, the dromedary was a domesticated animal in the border-lands of Arabia, and used for traffic across the desert from southern Mesopotamia to Palestine. The Bible stories of Abraham and Rebekah receive confirmation by finds of Middle Bronze Age remains of camels in urban sites of Palestine. Four sites (Gezer, Megiddo, Taanerek and El Jisr), dating from about the sixteenth or seventeenth century B.C., are regarded as satisfactory by Isserlin (1951). The dromedary had found its way into the urban communities of Palestine at the latest in the sixteenth century.

About 1100 B.C. Palestine was invaded by the Midianites, tribes of camel-riders, coming from the south and east. Judges VI–VIII tells the story of the wars of the Hebrews against them. In Judges VI, v. 5, it is said of the Midianites that their camels were without number. Here then is evidence of the camel-riding tribes pouring in from the Arabian desert. The Arabian origin of the dromedary is again stressed by the reports on the Queen of Sheba, who brought her luggage on camels when she came to visit King Solomon in Jerusalem in 955 B.C. or thereabouts. From the sixth century B.C. a dromedary picture is known at Gerar and camel bones have been found associated with those of pig, dog and cattle in an ossuary at Tell Duweir (the ancient Lachish) in Palestine. Miss Olga Tufnell, to whom I am indebted for this valuable piece of information, reports that they accompanied a deposit of more than a thousand human skulls, and that it dates from about 700 B.C.

If one attempts to track down the early history of the dromedary in Arabia proper, one encounters little that suggests high antiquity. At Mount Horsfield near Kilwa, Kingdom of Jordan, Rhotert (1938) found a naturalistic camel engraving (Fig. 13 : 3) which in style and patination belongs to the earliest group (the author's 'Stone Age'). The later rock engravings of camels from the Kilwa district (Figs. 13 : 4 and 13 : 5) are associated with men and represent undoubtedly domesticated animals. Their geometrical style resembles that of the 'cameline period' of north-west Africa. Rhotert's engravings from Kilwa resemble closely those found by Euting in northern Arabia associated with Thamudenic writing. The former and some

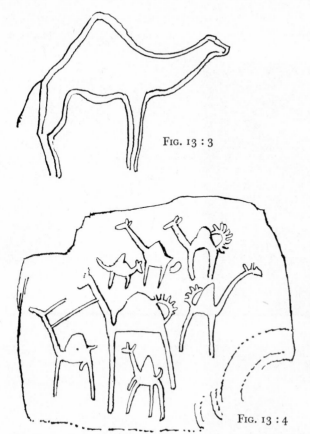

FIG. 13 : 3

FIG. 13 : 5

FIGS. 13 : 3 to 13 : 5. Rock engravings of camels recorded by Rhotert from the Kilwa area of southern Transjordan. Fig. 3 : From Mount Horsfield, in the naturalistic style. Fig. 4 : From Kilwa Site D, late geometric style. Fig. 5 : From Little Horsfield Mountain, another late style

FIG. 13 : 4

recently found near Azraq, Transjordan (Figs. 13 : 6, 13 : 7), are certainly pre-Islamic. Nabataean-Thamudenic inscriptions date them to the third century A.D. Nielsen (1927) considers that some of these inscriptions go back to pre-Christian times. That the Nabataeans, who lived in Jordan and on the north-east coast of the Red Sea, possessed the domesticated camel, is shown by a Roman coin illustrating the surrender of King Aretas in 8 B.C. (Fig. 13 : 8).

In south Arabia the Temple of Hureidha in the Hadhramaut, excavated by Caton-Thompson (1944), provides evidence for domesticated dromedaries in the sixth century B.C. or later (Fig. 13 : 9). Environmental reasons cause Mikesell (1955) to accept this area as the home of the domesticated dromedary. An inscription of Sargon II (*c.* 709 B.C.) relates that a tribute of camels was received from Arabia. There is also an undated, but possibly early, pecked drawing from the neighbourhood of Seiyun (Hadhramaut, Fig. 13 : 10). Other graffiti in the same area are associated with writing and certainly not earlier than the Moon Temple. A

343

Himyaritic bronze statuette of a dromedary acquired by Glaser and an altar with men on camelback from the Hadhramautic period (first century A.D.) are too late to be of interest in this context.

The material from south Arabia is thus scanty and does not take us further back than the eighth century B.C. Since local archaeological evidence as a whole does not go further back than this, however, the domestication of the dromedary may well have been practised in Arabia at a much earlier date. Another area where domesticated dromedaries might have originated is central Arabia, which is still unknown from the archaeological point of view and where ecological conditions might have been more suitable than in the urban civilizations of southern Arabia. It is certain that Mesopotamia was invaded by camel-using Arabs, at least from the ninth century B.C. onwards, so that by this time eastern and northern Arabia had fully entered the cameline age. The tradition of Abraham and some finds from Babylonia make it possible to push this date back by another 1000, if not 2000, years.

FIGS. 13 : 6 and 13 : 7. Pecking of camels on basalt blocks near Azraq oasis, eastern Transjordan, discovered by Mr R. R. Pannell of Rochester, Pennsylvania, U.S.A., c. third century A.D. Fig. 6: The chief block, with inscriptions resembling the northern semitic type of script. Fig. 7: A pecked camel with young, resembling the late style of Kilwa. Photographs by F.E.Z.

FIG. 13 : 8. Silver denarius showing King Aretas of Petra kneeling beside his camel. This coin commemorates the somewhat indecisive victory of the Romans over the Nabataeans in 58 B.C. Twice natural size. Author's collection

FIGS. 13 : 9 and 13 : 10. Two camel engravings from the Hadramaut, southern Arabia. After Caton-Thompson (1944). Fig. 9 from Hureidha and Fig. 10 from Wadi Djethma, Seiyun

FIG. 13 : 9

FIG. 13 : 10

Iraq and Syria

The first Semitic invaders of the lands around the Euphrates came from the south. There is some evidence that the domesticated dromedary was known in Babylonia before this event, for a damaged clay figurine of the Al Ubaid period was found in the precincts of the Anu ziqqurrat at Uruk. Semitic Akkad under Sargon (2400 B.C.) knew it, as testified by a copper amulet found at Lagash. By about 2000 B.C. dromedary-using Semites were settled in Chaldea on the south side of the Euphrates, if the story about Abraham can be regarded as reliable. But the dromedary was not adopted in the agricultural areas. When it appears in the records it is in connection with Arabs. The earliest pictorial representation is that on an orthostat of the palace of Tell Halaf, in northern Mesopotamia, described by Oppenheim (1931). It dates from about 900 B.C. and shows a camel-rider on his 'furniture' (Fig. 13 : 2).

The expansionist tendencies of the Assyrian Empire brought more frequent contacts with northern Arabs using dromedaries, who had established sheikhdoms in the steppes between the Middle Euphrates and Syria. On the other hand, it is conceivable that population movements had occurred in Arabia in the northward direction, movements which had brought the Midianites into Palestine a few centuries earlier. In any case, the Assyrians had plenty of quarrels with these Arabs, who evidently made full use of their ability to withdraw on their dromedaries into the desert where the horse-riding Assyrians could not follow.

The capture of the city of Dabigu in north Syria, illustrated on the bronze gates

345

of Shalmaneser III (858–828 B.C.) at Balawat, and a stele recording his victory over Ahab of Israel at Karkar mention Arab forces equipped with dromedaries. Reliefs from Nimrud illustrate fights with Arabs under Tiglathpileser III (745–727 B.C.). This king succeeded in obtaining Arab recognition of Assyrian domination (Fig. 13 : 11). Nevertheless, troubles continued until the final destruction of the sheikh-doms by Ashurbanipal (668–626 B.C.) (Fig. 13 : 12). He appears to have been the first to meet the Arabs on equal terms, equipping his officers with dromedaries, as evidenced by a picture on a wall of his palace in Nimrud. According to Meissner the booty obtained by the Assyrian soldiers in the Arabian campaign was immense. The

FIG. 13 : 11. Tribute of dromedaries being brought to Tiglathpileser III of Assyria (745–727 B.C.). Relief from the Palace of Nimrud. After Barnett

FIG. 13 : 12. Arabs fleeing and defending themselves against the army of Ashurbanipal, seventh century B.C. Note the technique of two riders sitting on the same camel. After King (1915)

whole of Assyria was inundated with camels (Fig. 13 : 13), and slaves, so that one could buy them for next to nothing. The adoption of the dromedary for military purposes was not, however, a permanent measure. For all we know, Nebuchadnezzar

FIG. 13 : 13. Loading of a dromedary. This illustration from Kuyunjik shows how the dromedary was being absorbed into the economic system of Mesopotamia

(604–561 B.C.) did not use them. It was the Persian conqueror of Mesopotamia, Cyrus, who first established and used camels in organized warfare against non-Arab nations.

Asia Minor and Greece
Passing on to Asia Minor, it may be mentioned that the domesticated dromedary was known in Neo-Hittite Carchemish (*c.* 700–500 B.C.). This is not surprising in view of the position on the northern edge of the north Arabian area of domestication. The dromedary appears to have spread into Asia Minor with the Persian conquerors.

Of the Battle of Sardes (546 B.C.) in which Cyrus defeated Croesus of Lydia, Herodotus (i, 80) says:

Assembling all the camels that followed his army bearing food and baggage, he took off their burdens and set men upon them equipped like cavalrymen. . . . The reason of his posting the camels to face the cavalry was this: horses fear camels and can endure neither the sight nor the smell of them. . . . So when battle was joined, as soon as the horses smelt and saw the camels they turned to flight, and all Croesus' hope was lost.

The transformation from pack-animal to living 'light tank' is here vividly described. But even then it was not adopted enthusiastically. When Cambyses went out to conquer Egypt he borrowed dromedaries from the Nabataean Arabs to carry water (Herod. iii, 4 ff., *c.* 525 B.C.). They were still merely used as baggage animals.

Darius, on whose table camel meat was served, introduced them for desert trade to the 'Oasis of the South', with its capital Hebt. It was only under Xerxes, *c.* 480 B.C., that Arab camel-riders were enrolled in the cavalry for frontier duty, in addition to the employment of the beast for transport purposes. Subsequently, camel corps became a feature of western Asiatic warfare. The Romans established one in Syria which, in the reign of Septimius Severus, was taken to north-west Africa in order to combat nomadic invaders from the interior (p. 354).

There are however a few records of camels reputed to be rather earlier than the Persian period. These are bones found on Cyprus by Cesnola (1877, p. 282) among the 'oldest cultures', a clay statuette from the Neolithic (which I have been unable to trace) and Gjerstad's (1926, p. 75) 'skeleton of a camel' from the Early Cypriote II (late Early Bronze Age, end of the third millennium B.C.) grave No. 69 at Katydhata. Miss J. du Plat Taylor has very kindly obtained for me from the Department of Antiquities, Nicosia, the relevant field notes by Markides. They are quoted here as an example of how positive statements can develop from vague factual reports:

Katydata Tomb 69. All vases smashed. Among the bones there are some which seem to be an animal—especially a backbone and one head—Cave fallen in and cleared from above—*Bronze Age*.
[Follows sketch showing diameter of pit—1.75m. and length of 'neck'—0.70m.] No. 1 and 2 and part of neck of 3 [pieces of pottery] have only preserved. The other all smashed. The animal seems to have a long neck. Some bones and backbones preserved—and animal's teeth.

The bones are no longer traceable, but the sketch shows that a whole camel would not have found room in the pit. The *Handbook to the Nicholson Museum* (Sydney, N.S.W., 2nd ed., 1948, p. 139) is slightly worried about the identification when considering the possible use of camels for the transport of copper. It can safely be said that this case is quite inconclusive. At best, parts of a camel were thrown into the pit at a time unknown, but more probably the animal was not a camel.

A small vase from a Late Helladic II chamber tomb of Mycenae (*c.* 1450 B.C.) shows an animal which, at a pinch, may be interpreted as a dromedary (Fig. 13 : 14). All these records are out of keeping with the remainder of the evidence and must for the time being be regarded with a great deal of suspicion.

India

In north-west India and Pakistan the dromedary is an important beast of burden at the present day. It was not known to the Aryan invaders, though Herodotus (iii, 102) mentions that the camels used by Indians were as swift as horses. This suggests that dromedaries, not Bactrians, were in use in the Indus Valley in the fifth century B.C. The country is indeed well suited for this animal. Herodotus further

FIG. 13 : 14. A small vase with animal frieze from a Late Helladic (*c.* 1450 B.C.) chamber tomb at Mycenae. The right-hand animal appears to be a dromedary. The middle picture has been interpreted as a cat but is too badly drawn to be certain. On the same grounds, the left-hand figure might be regarded as an octopus! After Wace (1932)

relates a strange story of how camels were used to recover gold sand from the Indian desert, where the chief obstacle was huge ants.[1] The dromedary was used for riding in the second century B.C., since one with its rider is sculptured on one of the stupa rails of Sanchi.

Bones of camels have been found both at Harappa and at Mohenjo-Daro, but whether they belong to the Indus Valley civilization or are later intrusions can no longer be ascertained. It is possible even to think of an original stock of wild dromedaries that existed in the Indian desert. The seals of the Indus Valley sites, however, show all manner of beasts, but no camels.

Nile Valley
The camel once occurred in the Arabian peninsula in the wild condition, and in the domesticated state from at least the eighteenth century B.C. onwards, and probably much earlier. In view of this, it is strange to find that Egypt lacks evidence for the existence of the camel almost entirely. The scarcity of pictorial representations and of actual remains of camels alone is surprising, but even more so the virtual absence of literary references (one exception to be mentioned later). There was no Egyptian word for the camel. Since the ancient records of the Nile Valley are singularly complete from the zoological point of view—*all* the larger species of mammals, most of the

[1] This story correctly describes the desert climate, the presence of large ants (though not as big as foxes), of burrows (those of rodents and foxes being erroneously attributed to the ants!), of the concentration of gold in such burrows and finally that the ants would attack when disturbed. But that a camel was left behind to distract the ants is, as Herodotus himself says, a 'tale' which he got from the Persians.

conspicuous birds and the common fish having been faithfully depicted—the absence of the camel must have some reason. The Egyptians depicted with great faithfulness every species they could lay hands on. Those, however, which were not caught or shot or brought as tribute are usually missing, such as elephant and giraffe after the predynastic period. Hence it is evident that wild camels did not occur in the Nile district, and if domesticated ones were known they must have been unclean or 'taboo'.

Nevertheless, there is evidence enough that the dromedary reached the Nile Valley from time to time, and yet there is (so far as the author is aware) only one Egyptian literary reference to the dromedary, in the *Travels of an Egyptian* written in the nineteenth dynasty and referring to Palestine. The beast appears under its Semitic name. It is inconceivable that the dynastic Egyptians did not know of the camel. No wonder that more than one author has suspected that the animal was unclean in Egypt, as it was for the Hebrews. Some support for this hypothesis may be derived from two facts, namely from the close contacts of Palestine with Egypt and the absence of the taboo against eating camel in Arabia and Assyria, at any rate from the Persian period onwards. The material and literary references (including the non-Egyptian) for the occasional presence of camels in the Nile Valley area are the following:

On one Amratian pot, of predynastic age, there appears a drawing of what may be intended as a dromedary (Childe, 1952, p. 51, Fig. 19). In the necropolis of Ezbet-el-Walda near Heluan, of first dynasty age, Zaki Saad has found what appears to be part of a camel, possibly to be interpreted as the burial of an animal servant with its master.

A receptacle for ointment having the shape of a sitting camel was found by Möller (1906) at Abusir-el-Melek, about sixty miles south of Cairo. It is made of limestone, is 6 cm. high and comes from a cemetery of over 1000 crouched burials of approximately first dynasty date. Its identification as a camel appears to be correct; the shape of the neck in particular suggests it.[1]

At Abydos, about 275 miles south of Cairo, Petrie found a pottery head 'which seems certainly to be that of a camel', of first dynasty or perhaps slightly earlier date (Fig. 13 : 17). Again, the identification is reasonably satisfactory, though a roughly made pottery head is precious little. Its profile, however, excludes other alternatives. At Hieraconpolis, some 250 miles south of Cairo, a fragment originally regarded as a donkey, and also of early dynastic date, has in recent years been interpreted as a camel's head (Fig. 13 : 16). If it is one, it confirms the Abydos find; if not, the value of the latter is not impaired.

---

[1] I have recently obtained a cast of the original in the former Staatsmuseum, Berlin (Fig. 13 : 15). There is no doubt that it is meant to be a dromedary, and one with a load at that. It puts its first domestication back into the fourth millennium B.C.

FIG. 13 : 15. Ointment jar in the shape of a sitting dromedary, Abusir-el-Melek, 2850–2650 B.C. (Length *c*. 11 cm.) Former Staatsmuseum, Berlin

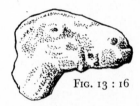

FIGS. 13 : 16 and 13 : 17. Two more early dynastic camel figurines from Egypt. For details see text. Fig. 16 from Hierakonpolis and Fig. 17 from Abydos

FIG. 13 : 16

FIG. 13 : 17

The most remarkable find was made by Caton-Thompson in the third or early fourth dynasty gypsum works of Umm-es-Sawan in the Fayum. It is a cord of camel hair, about 3 ft. 6 in. long. Dr M. A. C. Hinton compared it with ox, sheep, goat, horse, ass, man and other species. He was satisfied that it was made of camel hair. Was it the girdle of a labourer, and perhaps of an immigrant or slave who had come from Arabia? Or does it indicate that camels were used in the gypsum mines?

Schweinfurth (1912), a careful observer, described an engraving from Gezireh near Aswan which is combined with a hieratic inscription, both being heavily patinated and supposed to be of sixth-dynasty age (Fig. 13 : 18). Whether this date is correct I am not competent to judge, but the evidence for its considerable age deserves to be taken seriously.

There is a gap until the nineteenth dynasty.[1] From this period, from the northern cemetery of Deir Rifeh, near Asyut, about 200 miles south of Cairo, comes the pottery figure of a camel laden with water-jars found in a tomb (Fig. 13 : 19).

[1] Should the camel engraved with texts of the Middle Kingdom at Ouadi Hammamat really belong to the eleventh dynasty, the gap would in part be bridged. It was published in *Sapiski orient. Russ. archeol. Obshch.* 2, 1887, which I have been unable to see.

FIG. 13 : 18. Rock engravings near Aswan assigned by Schweinfurth (1912) to sixth dynasty. Note, however, that the style of the camel is reminiscent of the Late Geometric style both of north Arabia and North Africa

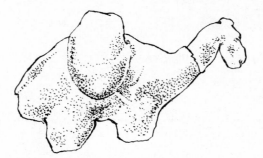

FIG. 13 : 19. Camel figure from Rifeh, Egypt, assigned to the nineteenth dynasty. After Petrie (1907)

Petrie (1907) stresses that there is no evidence of later re-use of the tomb, that the rough-fingered ware is characteristic of the nineteenth dynasty and quite unlike the moulded figures of the Roman period, and that the water-jars are of eighteenth-nineteenth-dynasty type and not of a form used in Greek or Roman times. This, too, appears to be a genuine specimen.

Another find referred to the same dynasty was mentioned by Lefébure (1906), a glazed dromedary figure with painted water-jars found at Benha. Its black painting on blue glaze is regarded as suggestive of an age prior to the twenty-sixth dynasty, and von Borsig assigns to it a Ramesside age.

The same period, *c.* 1300 B.C., has produced the remarkable story called *The Travels of an Egyptian* (Brit. Mus. Papyrus No. 10247) in which the camel appears as an animal of Syria and Palestine.

There is another gap of 600 years, after which several literary sources suggest that camels reached Egypt, first with the Assyrian inroads and later with the Persians. It cannot be said, however, that the animal became an integral part of the economic structure of the country which it has been since the Roman period. Lefébure mentions that camels appeared in the delta about 700 B.C. with Palestinians, and about 670 B.C. camels are said to have come into Egypt under Asarhaddon. Since it is known that the Assyrians did not normally use camels in their armies, allied Arab

352

troops may have imported them. Again, in 525 B.C. some camels would have reached upper Egypt under Cambyses, if one can trust Herodotus. Two hundred years later (331 B.C.) camels were present in the train of Alexander when he visited Siwah Oasis to consult the oracle of Zeus Ammon.

In the Ptolemaic period, probably as the result of the greatly increased commercial relations with the East, the dromedary appears to have come into more general use, at any rate for transport purposes. Under Ptolemy Philadelphus (285–247 B.C.), trade routes were established across the Eastern Desert, linking Coptus on the Nile with the Red Sea harbours of Berenice and Myus Hormus by a road and a chain of cisterns for the benefit of 'camel-merchants' (Strabo 17, 4. 45). The same road continued as a camel route for Arabian aromatics in the time of Augustus (Gallus's expedition to Arabia; Strabo, 16, 4. 24).

By the beginning of the Roman period the dromedary had acquired the place it holds in Egyptian trade today. Numerous figurines show it as a beast of burden (Figs. 13 : 20, 13 : 21). Whether it had already become popular with the peasant

FIGS. 13 : 20 and 13 : 21. Two figurines of working camels of the Roman period, Egypt

FIG. 13 : 20

FIG. 13 : 21

is another question. In southern Egypt, and especially the Eastern Desert and perhaps in Nubia and farther south also, the dromedary quite possibly appeared with invaders from Arabia across the Red Sea. There were many occasions of this sort, for several centuries in the pre-Christian era. Ethiopia was colonized from Arabia in the third century B.C., and the dry west coast of the Red Sea was occupied by Arabs who are unlikely to have left their dromedaries behind. In the third century A.D. the Blemyans enter the field of Egyptian history. They were a warlike people of camel-breeders and are associated with the hour-glass-shaped human figures on rocks (Fig. 13 : 22) as shown by Winkler (1939). Their late appearance in history, however, need not imply an equally late appearance in East Africa. Walz (1951, 1956) supposes that the dromedary reached East Africa from south Arabia about the middle of the first millennium B.C. and that it reached Egypt not only via Suez, but from the south also. This possibility deserves to be considered seriously, for it affords a southern route for the domesticated dromedary to reach north-west Africa, via the Saharan highlands and the oases. In Uweinat engravings of dromedaries

FIG. 13 : 22   FIG. 13 : 23

FIGS. 13 : 22 and 13 : 23. Rock engravings from Upper Egypt, possibly representing an invasion of camel-breeders in the last centuries B.C. See Winkler (1938 and 1939) for details

have indeed been found (Fig. 13 : 23). In this manner the domesticated dromedary may have become part of the equipment of Saharan desert tribes before it was adopted along the agricultural northern fringe of the desert from Libya to Morocco.

North-west Africa
Curiously enough, there is very little evidence for the presence of the domesticated dromedary in western North Africa prior to the Roman period, whilst there is plenty to show that the wild animal was there in the Pleistocene. Many workers have tried to bridge this gap, and two schools have come into being. One, represented by Gautier (1928, 1937) and Guey (1939), holds that the wild dromedary was extinct in North Africa when the Romans, mainly under Septimius Severus (193–211 A.D.), introduced it together with Syrian troops. Its subsequent adoption for agricultural purposes and peaceful transport would have occurred extremely rapidly. In the fourth century A.D. camel-riding nomads had become a serious menace to the provinces of Roman Africa. The other school is represented by Gsell (1913) and Leschi (1942), who assume that camel-using nomads existed in the south prior to the arrival of the Syrian troops, and that these were called in to combat such nomads who had been disturbing the southern provinces for some time.

The evidence that supports the latter view is briefly as follows: Caesar reports that he took twenty-two camels from Juba's army in 46 B.C.; dromedaries, therefore, were used at that time in Numidia. That Pliny and other Roman writers do not mention the dromedary in the first century A.D. appears to be due to the pushing-back of the nomads into the Sahara. Subsequently, a system of *limes* structures and forts was erected in order to keep these nomads out of Roman Africa. No other explanation can be considered as satisfactory regarding the organization of a considerable military display directed towards the south. But though the nomadic camel-riders or *meharistes* were thus temporarily excluded, the camel was not. It had been widely accepted as a domestic animal in the third century A.D. in the interior of Roman Africa (Fig. 13 : 24). There is good evidence for this, such as tombstones showing ploughing with camels (Fig. 13 : 25); the effigy of a camel found in a Christian church at Oued Rhezel, Algeria (Fig. 13 : 26); and a pottery lamp showing a person on camelback which I saw in the Temple Museum of Tebessa (Fig. 13 : 27). The reason why the dromedary was little known outside North Africa is that, then as today, this animal did not thrive in the mountainous and coastal districts which were the most densely populated and those in closest contact with the metropolis.

Fig. 13 : 24. An animal mosaic from the Roman city of Djemila, western Algeria. It shows a well-drawn dromedary and an elephant which is evidently based on a description only. By the fourth century A.D., therefore, the native elephant had disappeared, but the camel was well known

Fig. 13 : 25. Ploughing illustrated on a Roman tomb from Ghirza, Tripolitania, third to fifth centuries A.D. After Brogan

FIG. 13 : 26. Head of a
small figurine found in
Church No. 4 at Oued
Rhezel, Algeria

FIG. 13 : 27. Roman lamp
with a Cupid seated on a
camel, from Tebessa,
western Algeria, first
century A.D.

The palaeontological evidence for the presence of the wild dromedary (or possibly a very closely related ancestral form, *C. thomasii*) is sound, as I have convinced myself on a recent visit to north-west Africa. At Palikao (also called Ternifine), in western Algeria, it is associated with a hand-axe culture comprising cleavers and with a type of man called *Atlanthropus*. Contrary to its usual description in the literature as Chellian, the industry, preserved in the Oran Museum, is better classed as Acheulian. Hence it may be regarded as of Middle Pleistocene age. At Taza in eastern Morocco also, the dromedary was perhaps present in the Acheulian. This locality, however, has proved in addition the animal's association with Mousterian, and so have Ain-el-Turk and Saint-Roch-sur-Mer in western Algeria. At El Guettar (Tunisia) it occurred with a 'Mousterian' industry which includes one Aterian point. Since Aterian assemblages, if deprived of their tanged tools, are difficult to distinguish from Mousterian, this is perhaps evidence for the presence of the dromedary in the Aterian. In any case, however, it is known from the Oranian (Iberomaurusian) of Taza.

The continuity of the wild camel from the Middle Pleistocene to what may be as late as early Postglacial is thus evident. Fossil remains of dromedaries have even been recorded from 'Neolithic' sites by Pomel (1893) and other workers. Some localities, like Fort de l'Eau and Grand Rocher lie in Algeria (mentioned by Pomel), at least two others in Mauritania. Finally, the jaw of a dromedary, presumably domesticated, was found lying beside a human skull, at Ain-el-Hamara (Oued Itel, Algeria) near the Roman *limes*, together with bottles made of camel hide. These tombs are pre-Islamic and, according to Leschi, approximately contemporary with the *limes*.[1]

[1] The view that they are pre-Roman is unlikely to be correct.

If there was no evidence available elsewhere, one could accept this as proof of the continuity of the dromedary in north-west Africa and of its eventual domestication. The difficulties appear when the rock engravings are taken into consideration. Not one of the early groups of game and pastoral animals ever includes a camel and one wonders where the species managed to survive to be domesticated eventually.

The numerous engravings of dromedaries that exist have little or no patination, and are later than the bulk of the well-known pictures of game animals, including giraffes. Graziosi (1952) distinguishes in Libya a pre-cameline and a cameline age. Apart from partial contemporaneity with the Roman period, little can be said about the chronology of the cameline period. The animal had become the ordinary means of transport all over the Sahara and its northern fringe. It had reached Tibesti, whence both Dalloni (1935) and Monod (1947) have published engravings, and in view of the close adaptation of the modern Tuareg to the camel it has been suggested that these Berber people were responsible for the engravings of the cameline period. This reasonable hypothesis would imply two things, namely that the spread of the cameline nomads occurred *after* the hunting and pastoral peoples, who left innumerable engravings, had occupied North Africa, and that they have nothing to do with the chariot-using invaders either. The latter are more recent than the pastoral group. According to Graziosi they are not earlier than the middle of the second millennium B.C. A date in the second half of that millennium is indeed in keeping with the evidence and would make the charioteer invasion of North Africa west of Egypt a sequel to the arrival of the chariot in Egypt a few centuries earlier. Some authorities, however, place their appearance in the Saharan area as late as the first millennium B.C. That they were not yet present in the interior by that time is confirmed by Herodotus's description of the tribe of the Garamantes.

The evidence thus appears to suggest that the use of the domesticated camel in the Saharan area is later than the second half of the second millennium B.C., and perhaps later than the fifth century B.C., for the Garamantes did not have it. It is certain that it became popular only after that date.

Yet this does not exclude the possibility of some early camel-nomads existing in restricted areas. Some scraps of evidence can be interpreted in this manner. Thus Perret (1936) described an engraving from Oued Gerat, southern Algeria, which (if it is a camel) would be 'pre-cameline' according to style and patination. But one doubtful swallow does not make a summer, and there is no suggestion that this beast was domesticated. One would like to find evidence for the early use of the dromedary in north-west Africa. Above all, the question remains where in north-west Africa the wild camel would have survived. If it did become extinct before the arrival of domesticated animals, and only a short time before its introduction as a domesticated beast, we should be faced with one of those curious coincidences of history. But after all they do occur from time to time.

The later history of the dromedary in North Africa presents many parallels to Arabia. Again, the civilizations of the more humid coastal zone found it difficult to cope with the techniques of the dromedary-using nomads of the desert. Thus, even the Vandals, softened after a century of civilized life early in the sixth century A.D., were unable to defend themselves against the inroads of the Tripolitanian nomads under Cabaon (Julien, 1956), and about a decade later the Byzantine general Solomon encountered the fiercest resistance to his conquest of North Africa not from the Vandals but from the Berbers who used their dromedaries with the greatest dexterity. For the last time, the dromedary proved a decisive factor in the success of the conquest of the Mediterranean coastland by Islam (Hitti, 1956). Again and again the animal helped the nomads to conquer settled countries which, however, in due course proved unable to support an economy dependent on the dromedary, which had to content itself with a modest place in the farming systems of the subdued territories.

Europe

That the camel entered Europe during the Roman period is certain. But only a few individuals were imported, to be shown as curiosities or to be used in circus games. As it lacks fighting spirit one wonders what its function was in the circus; nevertheless, its bones were found in the theatre of Vindonissa (northern Switzerland, first century A.D.). Contrary to some authorities, however, it did not occur at the Saalburg *castellum* in western Germany.[1]

Representations of camels are occasionally found in the north on mosaics and works of art, for instance in an Orphean scene on a *patera* mould from Treves. But these do not prove the presence of the animal in the country; either the articles or the knowledge of the animal were imported, just as in the case of the lion in the European Middle Ages. This is obvious enough in northern Europe, but not so where the animal in question might have occurred. It is a mistake, therefore, to accept (as has been done) Roman mosaics as evidence of the local occurrence of animal species, for instance in Asia Minor or North Africa.

The Mahometans took the dromedary to Spain in A.D. 1019 and to Sicily in 1058. Some were produced at the wedding of Frederick II, Emperor of Germany, and Isabel, sister of Henry III of England in Worms on the Rhine in 1235. In 1622 Ferdinand II of Medici imported dromedaries to be used on the plains of Pisa, Italy. This herd was about 200 strong in the nineteenth century, but it was exterminated in the 1939–1945 war. I am informed that it was eaten up by the German occupation troops. Similar small herds were established to serve in the sulphur mines of Sicily and in southern Spain.

---

[1] Information from Dr Schleiermacher of the Römisch-Germanische Kommission, Frankfurt a.M.

The Bactrian camel

Little is known of the history of the Bactrian camel. In all probability it had a wide distribution as a wild animal in central and north-western Asia in prehistoric times. Whether the herds of Bactrians east of Lop Nor in central Asia, on which Przewalski reported in 1879, were wild stock or reconstituted by escaped domesticated specimens is difficult to say. The great Russian traveller regarded them as wild, though he stresses that domesticated beasts would have joined the herds from time to time. The recent observations of a Russian expedition have confirmed the view that wild Bactrians are still in existence (Montagu, 1957).

Remains of Bactrian camels have been found in two places, Shah Tepé (northern Persia) and Anau (Turkestan). The Shah Tepé specimen is a very large vertebra of a young animal. Amschler (1940a) assigns it to the Bactrian species. It comes from Level III, which is contemporary with Anau II (Neolithic) and Uruk in Mesopotamia, *c.* 3000 B.C. or a little earlier. The spongy texture makes Amschler believe that the animal was domesticated. This argument is, however, not trustworthy since the same texture occurs in wild specimens, especially females and young ones.

The other find comes from the uppermost levels of the second Copper Age stratum of Anau in Turkestan, which is approximately contemporary with the Jamdat Nasr period of Mesopotamia, about 3000–2800 B.C. Three fragments only were found, hence there is no evidence that the camel was domesticated at that time. It should not go without mention that Duerst (1908), who described them, assigned them to the Bactrian species for geographical reasons only, the bones in question (phalanges and vertebrae) being indistinguishable in the two species of living camels. Nevertheless, the large size of the Anau bones also favours identification as *C. bactrianus*.

Camels, presumably Bactrians, may have made an early appearance in south Russia. Two localities of the Tripolye culture (*c.* 2000–1400 B.C.) produced their bones. According to Childe, however, their antiquity is dubious and it is not known whether they were wild or domesticated. The occurrence of wild Bactrian camels in south Russia in Postglacial times is conceivable; they could have lived in the company of wild horses, saiga antelopes and other northern Asiatic steppe forms.

The earliest archaeological evidence for the presence of the Bactrian camel comes from Sialk III (*c.* 3000–2500 B.C.). A potsherd shows what may be a two-humped camel. It was the late Col. D. H. Gordon who drew my attention to this specimen. In spite of its sketchy execution, the curve of the neck, the outline of the back and the thickened knee are arguments in favour of a two-humped camel (Fig. 13 : 28).

FIG. 13 : 28. Potsherd possibly showing a two-humped camel from Sialk III. After Ghirshman (1938)

There is, of course, no evidence to show that the Bactrian camel was domesticated at this time.

At Khurab in Makran, near the border of Baluchistan, Sir Aurel Stein found an intriguing relief-model of a camel (Fig. 13 : 29) executed in bronze on a pick (Maxwell-Hislop, 1955; Zeuner, 1955d). Its age is probably second millennium B.C., judging from the accompanying pottery. There is no indication that this model is intended to depict a domesticated beast. The curious feature is that it combines the characters of the dromedary with those of the Bactrian camel, its head and heavily haired neck being exactly as in the latter species, whilst there is only a single hump shown. This hump (if it is one), however, is extremely slight and rests on the pelvis, not on the middle of the back as in the dromedary. In this respect also it reminds one of the Bactrian camel. The lack of the anterior hump is nevertheless a serious matter, as it raises the possibility of a distinct race of single-humped or even humpless camels having existed in Baluchistan and north-west India at an early date.

FIG. 13 : 29. Bronze pick from Khurab, Makran, second millennium B.C., showing a seated camel. After Maxwell-Hyslop (1955)

It is equally uncertain to which species the camels should be assigned that play a part in the religion of Zoroaster. In Persia both species overlap at the present day and the dromedary has spread, as a domesticated form, to the Caspian Sea and Afghanistan. It is likely, however, that much of this area belonged originally to the Bactrian, and Assyrian records refer to this form as being imported from the north. Zoroaster's name contains *ushtra*, the word for camel, and he asked Ahura Mazda to give him 'ten mares, a stallion and a camel'. In his time, about the eighth to the sixth century B.C. (the period is rather uncertain), the Bactrian was evidently domesticated in Persia, and well established. From there, and the adjacent countries, they reached Mesopotamia from time to time. Tiglathpileser I of Assyria (about 1125 B.C.) mentioned two-humped camels in the records of his expeditions (which included the hunting of elephants). On the bronze gates of Balawat (Shalmaneser, c. 850 B.C.) Bactrians appear that were brought to Assyria after the conquest of an Armenian city (Fig. 13 : 30). On Shalmaneser III's Black Obelisk (841 B.C.) several are depicted as tribute from the lands of Musri and Gilzami (Fig. 13 : 31). Musri lay north of Lake Urmia, in the neighbourhood of Mount Ararat and Dara Dagh, and Gilzami, too, is believed to have been situated in the mountainous districts of the north. By 670 B.C. the zoological gardens of Assur, the capital, contained camels.

It is evident that the Persians and their northern and eastern neighbours were familiar with the Bactrian camels and that this made them inclined to adopt the

Fig. 13 : 30. Men from Gilzami bringing tribute to Shalmaneser. A scene from the bronze reliefs of the Balawat gates in Mesopotamia, commemorating the king's campaign in Armenia, 857 B.C. An early record of the domesticated Bactrian camel from Armenia

Fig. 13 : 31. Bactrian camels in the booty collected by Shalmaneser III in Musri or some other northern country, as depicted on the black obelisk (841 B.C.) preserved in the British Museum

Fig. 13 : 32. A Bactrian camel from the Palace of Xerxes at Persepolis, 485–465 B.C. This tribute is said to come from the Bactrians

dromedary when they met it in their conquest of the West. The Bactrian is shown on the reliefs of Xerxes at Persepolis (485–465 B.C.) (Fig. 13 : 32), and it appears

361

on two Greek fifth-century gems of unknown provenance (perhaps from Asia Minor?) (Fig. 13 : 33). These gems are of considerable interest, since they suggest as a pos-

FIG. 13 : 33. Small Greek gem of fifth century B.C. of unknown origin. After Walters (1934)

sibility that the Persian transport camels were Bactrians, and not dromedaries as is commonly supposed. If so, the Persian armies would have had a well-organized

FIG. 13 : 34. Painting of a camel on an Ionic black figure vase antedating 530 B.C. and found by Mr J. N. Cook at Old Smyrna. It shows that camels had been heard of on the west coast of Asia Minor in Ionian cities in the sixth century B.C., but the drawing also shows that at that time there was little contact with the beast which is very inaccurately drawn. Drawing based on a photograph kindly supplied by Mr Cook

camel baggage-train which they brought from their homeland. Even the camels that chased Croesus's horses in the Battle of Sardis may then have been Bactrians. This is of course speculation, but worth while to remember when literary records only are available. A Parthian vessel from Teheran (Fig. 13 : 35), and various

FIG. 13 : 35. Parthian pot, third to fourth century A.D., found near Teheran, Persia, and now in the Metropolitan Museum, New York. After Pégard (1926)

figurines are evidence of the continued use of this hardy species in the third to fourth centuries A.D. But on the whole the dromedary gradually conquered the countries north of Mesopotamia also, once it had begun to spread, and this is the reason why

FIG. 13 : 36. Bronze coin of one of the Great Kushans of Bactria, Kadphises I, A.D. 50–85. Many of these coins show a Bactrian camel, with a zebu on the other side, indicating the economic importance of these species. Natural size. Author's collection

the use of the Bactrian is today mainly restricted to central Asia and Turkestan, where its hardiness enables it to survive the cold and frosty winter.

Summary and conclusions

The evidence discussed in this chapter is not complete, though the writer believes that the addition of further examples of archaeological camels would not substantially alter the picture. The evidence is satisfactory in so far as it points to certain conclusions to be listed later, and unsatisfactory as it points out the gaps in our knowledge. These are central Asia, central and south Arabia and the interior of north-west Africa where the dromedary appears to have survived, but where the older rock engravings do not show it.

(1) Unlike other domesticated animals, the camels are slow breeders, becoming mature only when five years old, and the females bringing forth single young every three years, or at even longer intervals. Moreover, both camels require long periods of pasturing during which they virtually lead their natural life, and they cannot be penned. Their low intelligence renders impossible any training comparable with that given to the horse. In addition, they are liable to be bad-tempered, and the males are apt to be dangerous, especially in the breeding season. Their smell is offensive. At Roman posts they were kept outside the walls for this reason.

It is understandable, therefore, that camels were not readily accepted as domesticated beasts in countries where other more tractable species, especially ox, horse and ass, could be bred, fed and watered easily.

(2) On the other hand, camels are a boon to tribes living in the borderlands of deserts. The close adaptation of their feet to walking on desert soils, their ability to subsist on vegetation growing on saline soils and to go without water for long periods, have enabled man to develop nomadic and semi-nomadic economic systems in areas that would otherwise be uninhabitable. As a means of transport in deserts, camels have been unique until quite recently when the desert motor truck appeared on the scene.

The use of the camel is primarily for transport of merchandise, household equipment and persons. Where nomads enter temporarily cultivable lands, ploughs are carried and, on arrival at a suitable place, the camels made to pull the plough. This practice, frequent in North Africa, led to their adoption in agricultural districts situated within reach of the desert, where small farmers who could afford only one animal preferred the dromedary because its superior strength is a real help in tilling the hard soil. A similar system, as observed today for instance in Morocco (where small farmers keep one dromedary and one donkey), appears to have existed in the interior of Roman Tripolitania. But such uses of the camels are secondary, and the animals do not thrive in damp climates.

(3) The wild stock appears to have been originally distributed as follows: The dromedary occurred sporadically on the borders of the Sahara, but not near the Nile Valley, and in the Arabian peninsula though not in Mesopotamia or Persia. Whether wild dromedaries, or an extinct race of one-humped camels, existed in the Indian desert and/or Baluchistan is uncertain. The Bactrian camel occurred possibly from as far west as south-east Russia, but certainly from the Iranian plateau and Turkestan through central Asia to northern China, where according to the most recent reports it may still survive.

(4) For the dromedary, only one domestication centre can be demonstrated, namely in Arabia. In all probability this means central Arabia, though the south is not ruled out. Concrete evidence from central Arabia is, however, still wanting, the material being supplied by adjacent countries. It is possible that its domestication had been achieved in the fourth millennium B.C. Successive waves of dromedary-breeders emanated from inner Arabia at least from the second millennium onwards.

The centre of domestication of the Bactrian is still obscure. It may have lain far to the east of Turkestan and the Iranian plateau. In the first half of the first millennium B.C., however, it appears to have been well established in Persia.

(5) The dromedary (and the same appears to apply to the Bactrian in central and east Asia) was not accepted by the ancient city civilizations and farming communities until the first millennium A.D., though its military value was recognized earlier. The reasons for this refusal are many, and chiefly economic: it is a slow breeder, bad-tempered and difficult to train, and subject to diseases in non-arid climates. Its unpleasant odour might have been forgiven in the ancient Orient, but the difficulty of keeping other domesticated beasts quartered with camels was a serious matter. It must not be forgotten that ancient cities were in a cramped condition for reasons of defence, and the agricultural land in the river valleys was parcelled out and used to capacity. Thus camels, which need pasturing on a large scale, are unpleasant to other beasts and reproduce but slowly, were not a feasible proposition.

They were admitted into the towns as vehicles of the desert trade. For other purposes they were not needed, and not wanted, since neither the city-dweller nor the cereal farmer could cope with them.

(6) Conditions changed profoundly, however, when the agricultural lands of the Near East and the southern Mediterranean began to show signs of deterioration. The causes were several, the one underlying all others being that the water tables of these areas, which reached a high level in the Last Pluvial, have not been sufficiently replenished under the less humid regime of the Postglacial. The scene was thus set for an increase in the aridity of the soil climate wherever man destroyed the natural vegetation cover either by ploughing or by grazing. The resulting 'soil erosion' by water and wind, and the abandonment of vast tracts of agricultural land that has lost all fertility, is today a well-known phenomenon. Whenever this happened, widespread shifts of populations were the result, and it is likely that many prehistoric and historic movements were caused in the first instance by soil wastage in zones of primitive agriculture.

From the camel's point of view, there were obvious advantages in this process. Not that it was allowed to enter such areas as a wild animal, but as a domesticated beast it became increasingly popular. The originally settled inhabitants, finding themselves compelled to lead a semi-nomadic life, adopted the camel. On the other hand, true camel nomads would invade such lands from, or across, the desert. The restriction of agriculture to a few localities left so much wasteland that the pasturing of the camel was no more a problem.

Apart from countries farther east, about which too little is known, Syria and the areas south of it were the first to be affected. The dromedary-using sheikhdoms of northern Arabia made their presence felt towards the end of the second millennium B.C. By the ninth century B.C. wars with the Assyrians who wanted to guard their lines of communication with the western sea became frequent. They ended with the subjection of the Arabs. The Assyrian, Syrian and Palestinian kingdoms thus came into close contact with the domesticated dromedary which, in the centuries between the seventh and the first, very slowly gained in popularity, notably in Syria.

Its most conspicuous spread, however, coincided with the first four centuries of the Christian era. The Romans had a hand in it in that they employed camel corps as troops in the dry borderlands. But this was not the only way by which the dromedary reached the extreme west of the Roman world in Mauritania.

(7) By the middle of the first millennium B.C. the dromedary appears to have obtained a foothold on the African coast of the Red Sea. Thence it entered the deserts of upper Egypt, and reached inner North Africa, spreading from oasis to oasis and reaching Numidia at the latest in the first century B.C. This move in all probability absorbed what little remained of the wild North African dromedary. Naturally, the beast soon became popular in the interior where growing soil desiccation, largely following the destructive practices of Roman agriculture, made plenty

of camel pasture available. It began to replace the horse in the countries away from the coast and the mountains.

The spread of the dromedary received a final impetus with the wars of Islam. This creed came to Africa with the Arabs who did not fail to bring their dromedaries, and with them they went as far as the climate would allow.

(8) The eastward spread of the dromedary began in the Persian and continued in the Hellenistic period. Since it is more sensitive to winter frost than the resistant Bactrian, it has succeeded in replacing the latter in parts of the Iranian plateau only.

14

The Onager

SCIENTIFIC NAMES—*Equus hemionus* Pallas (hemione, half-ass, or Asiatic wild ass).

Geographical races:

E.h. onager Boddaert (onager; Russian Turkestan, Persia, Afghanistan, localized). Very closely related and usually included with the onager: *E.h. khur* Lesson (Indian onager, wild ass; south-east Persia, Baluchistan, Cutch); *E.h. hemippus* Geoffroy (Syrian onager; Palestine, Syria, Iraq, now probably extinct. Domesticated in Sumerian times.)

E. hemionus hemionus Pallas (kulan, djiggetai; Altai, Mongolia). *E.h. kiang* Moorcroft (kiang; western Tibet, Ladak).

I T is not generally known that, prior to the introduction of the domesticated horse into Mesopotamia, the half-ass or hemione was domesticated by the ancient Sumerians. The half-asses, familiarly but incorrectly known as Indian wild asses, or correctly as kulan, kiang, onager and djiggetai, respectively, have nothing to do with the true wild ass of Africa. They are an Asiatic group of horses with a certain number of ass-like characters. They must be regarded as a separate species, or, better still, as a group of subspecies, in some respects intermediate between the true horse and the true ass. Geographically, too, they occupy a separate area, namely the dry belt from Mongolia through central Asia to Syria. West of this, and continuing it in Africa, lies the area of the true ass.

In the time of the famous naturalist Pallas, the kulan, one of the hemiones, occurred as far north-west as the European border, where it overlapped with the true horse. Being an animal of the steppe and capable of withstanding very cold winters, it is perfectly possible that at certain times in the Upper Pleistocene it was able to spread temporarily to central Europe. Remains of a hemione-like horse have been reported repeatedly from loess deposits and other steppe environments, for instance from the Mousterian site of Wallertheim, near Mainz in western Germany; the Mousterian site of Ehringsdorf near Weimar in central Germany; and the Magdalenian sites of Kesslerloch and Schweizersbild in Switzerland. But Stehlin has pointed out that these determinations are not based on sufficient material. The specimens might indicate either the presence of a second race of true horses or of a true ass such as *Equus hydruntinus*.

The onager is easily distinguished from the horse (Fig. 14 : 1); its ears are longer

FIG. 14 : 1. The onager, the best known of the half-asses.
This species still survives in north-west India on the dry
flats of the Rann of Kutch

than those of the horse but shorter than those of the ass. The front hoofs are narrow, there are chestnuts on the forelegs only, and (readily recognizable in pictures (Fig. 14 : 2)) the tail is short-haired for a long distance from its root, so that it appears tufted. In the horse the long hair starts almost immediately at the root of the tail.

The onager group comprises the now extinct hemione of Mesopotamia and Syria. Less than a century ago they were still fairly abundant and Layard, the great pioneer of Mesopotamian archaeology, saw them alive. The onager has been regarded as untamable. We owe to Sir Leonard Woolley the discovery that this view is mistaken. In the Royal Cemetery of Ur in Chaldaea (*c.* 2500 B.C.) pictures were found of animals drawing chariots. These animals looked somewhat like

Fig. 14 : 2. Mosaic from the Great Room of the Roman villa at Nennig, near Trier, West Germany, second century A.D. It shows a tiger slaying an onager. As both tigers and onagers are foreign to Germany, this mosaic illustrates the fallacy of regarding the species depicted as native to the country. This has been done repeatedly

horses, or perhaps more like mules. Woolley, however, recognized them correctly as onagers. This view was not generally accepted until Hilzheimer studied the bones found at Tell Asmar. At this place bones of the genus *Equus* were present in large numbers which, after careful examination, especially of the metapodials, proved to belong to the onager. In this way Woolley's identification was confirmed by osteological evidence.

By now quite a number of representations are known of onagers tamed by the Sumerians. The most characteristic is the electrum figurine from Queen Shub-Ad's chariot pole (*c.* 2500 B.C.) (Fig. 14 : 3). Another rein-ring carrying the model of an onager, but made of copper, has been described by Mallowan. It appears to date from about the same time. The animals drawing chariots on the war panel of the Royal Standard of Ur are almost certainly onagers, since they have the typical tufted tail. It appears, therefore, that in the third millennium B.C. the onager was used as a draught animal. It is, however, not certain whether the onager was truly domesticated at the time, so that its breeding was controlled by man. It is quite conceivable that the animals were obtained by catching foals (Fig. 14 : 4) and taming

Fig. 14 : 3. Silver rein-ring surmounted by an electrum onager, from the chariot of Queen Shub'ad of Ur in Mesopotamia. From the royal cemetery, c. 2500 B.C. For method of use see third register of War Panel, Fig. 14 : 6. Original in British Museum

Fig. 14 : 4. Capturing onagers with lassos. A scene from the Palace of Ashurbanipal at Nineveh, Room S, British Museum, No. 124882

them. In this case the Sumerian onager would have been employed, but not truly domesticated, much as the Indian elephant is today. With the introduction of the horse into Mesopotamia, early in the second millennium B.C., the onager disappears from the list of animals in the service of man.

It is not unlikely that the use of the onager was in the first instance a mere imitation of the use of horses in neighbouring countries. Quite apart from the question, however, of whether the horse was in the service of man already in the third millennium B.C., the method of bridling was different from that of the horse, for which the bit is the normal contraption used almost universally throughout the world. The Standard of Ur makes this evident. On it, the onagers are wearing rings in their noses (Fig. 14 : 5) when not harnessed (see the 'Peace' panel). When harnessed they wear in addition a strap tied round the jaws and connected with a further strap running round the head behind the ears (Fig. 14 : 6). Hilzheimer thinks that the jaw strap was the main means of bridling, whilst Woolley holds that the guide rein attached to the nose-ring was used for this purpose. In either case the method of bridling would have differed from that practised for the horse. This suggests that the use of the onager for traction was based by the Sumerians on the use of cattle for the same purpose, and not directly copied from the horse.

Whilst the evidence for the domestication of the onager about the time of the royal tombs of Ur is unambiguous, there is one doubtful record on a vase from Khafajeh which has already been discussed in connection with the horse (p. 317). If this fragment indeed depicts onagers, it would push their domestication back to at least 3000 B.C. Outside Mesopotamia the onager does not appear to have been used. There is a single exception, a scene from Thebes in Egypt, where a chariot drawn by two beasts resembling onagers is shown. They are not meant to be horses, for these are shown in the row above; their tails are tasselled and their ears too small for asses'. Maybe this scene depicts one of the many experiments in domestication that the Egyptians made, or else the idea was imported from Mesopotamia. Onagers were available to the Egyptians in nearby Palestine.

Whilst the use of the onager for traction in Mesopotamia was thus abandoned as soon as the horse became available, it may have played a part in the breeding of mules right into the Roman period. Many classical writers refer to the crossing of horses with wild asses in countries where no true asses ever occurred in the wild state. Tacitus mentions the *asini agrestes* of the Syrian desert. The mountainous highlands of Armenia, Phrygia and Lykaonia abounded in them, and they are expressly called onagri. From Asia Minor one continues to Persia, where hemiones are known to exist. In Turkestan we have an archaeological record from Anau, for the notorious Anau horse is a hemione, as was first established by Hilzheimer. In north-west India onagers still exist in numbers, and the few bones found at Mohenjo-Daro, which Sewell (1931) compared with the Anau horse, are likely to belong to Indian onagers.

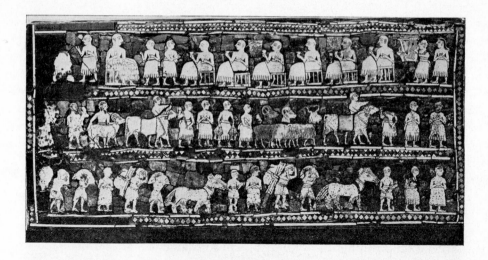

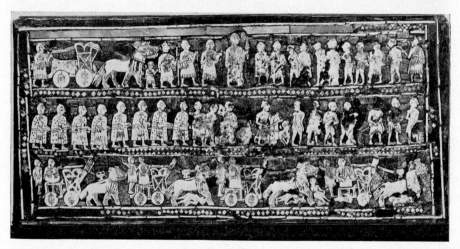

FIGS. 14 : 5 and 14 : 6. Peace and War Panels of the Standard of Ur, a box covered with mosaics measuring about 19 inches by 8 inches, first dynasty of Ur, Mesopotamia. The first and third registers of the War Panel show four-wheeled chariots drawn by onagers (note the tails!) The third register of the Peace Panel shows captured onagers. In the second there appear oxen, goat and sheep, as booty. Original in British Museum

I have had an opportunity to observe wild onagers in the Rann of Cutch. There they live mainly on the sparse vegetation of islands that rise above the salt flats of the Rann. Their number in this area must be at least a thousand. The herds number from a few individuals to about one hundred and they associate both with nilgai antelope and feral zebu. It was interesting to see that, when disturbed, the onagers would flee on to the open salt flats, where their progress was unimpeded, whilst

372

both nilgai and zebu would run into the scrub of the islands. This urge to escape from cover (which may hide dangerous enemies) must have done the species untold harm ever since the invention of long-distance projectiles, such as bows and arrows. The maximum speed at which these onagers could move was thirty-five miles per hour (about fifty kilometres), but they could not hold it for more than a few minutes in formation and would then disperse. All the time they were trying to look behind them to check on the movements of the pursuer (the jeep). On the occasion of these pursuits I was reminded of the reliefs of onager hunts from Kuyunjik.

Onagers, therefore, are extremely swift-footed. Since they are more difficult to guide than horses, they are less suitable for the drawing of chariots. They continued, however, to attract the attention of mule-breeders who wanted to improve the ass. Pliny maintains that they are easily tamed (contrary to the view now prevalent); and Columella (VI, 37) relates that male onagers were crossed with female asses. Petronius mentions mules bred from male onagers and female horses; they were regarded as particularly valuable. There are too many reports of this kind to discard them. On the other hand, since asses readily become feral, it is conceivable that some refer to true asses that had run wild.

Onagers were from time to time shown in circus games in Rome. They are very rarely mentioned, however, and thus do not appear to have been popular.

When the horse appeared in Mesopotamia early in the second millennium B.C. it replaced the onager in a very short time. The reason for this rapid change-over was undoubtedly the greater docility of the newcomer, its superior strength and the simultaneous introduction of the horse-bit and two-wheeled chariot.

15

Ass and Mule

SCIENTIFIC NAMES—*Equus hydruntinus* Reg. (Upper Pleistocene; small ass of Italy and other parts of Europe, also similar form in Palestine and Jordan. Possibly identical with the extinct North African wild ass.)

Equus asinus asinus L. (ass, donkey; domesticated form, probably derived from North African wild race, now extinct, to which this name would apply). *E.a. africanus* Fitz. (Nubian Ass; Sudan). *E.a. somaliensis* Noack (Somali Ass; Somaliland).

THE true asses, as distinct from the half-asses or onagers, are of purely African origin. Up to the Roman period there appear to have existed three wild races: one in north-west Africa; one in north-east Africa, where it occurred in the mountainous semi-deserts of Nubia and the eastern Sudan from the Nile to the shores of the Red Sea; and the third, the Somali race. The first is now extinct, the second almost exterminated. The North African race, known from rock pictures and Roman mosaics, was last seen in the Atlas Mountains and did not survive the Roman period. The Nubian wild ass was reported to be extinct in 1925, except for a few specimens surviving in zoological gardens, but some still appear to be roaming over the countryside (Fig. 15 : 1), though, of course, they may have been reinforced by domesticated escapees. It is possible that the original range of this race extended to the western Sahara. If Canon Tristram's description is correct (he is usually reliable) the pattern of stripes of the asses of the Hoggar Mountains in the Sahara agreed with the Nubian race in his day (*c.* 1870). The third wild ass is restricted to Somaliland, where it still survives under careful protection. There is no evidence that this third race has played a great part in the domestication of the species.

FIG. 15 : 1. Captured
Nubian wild ass, Abu
Hamad, northern Sudan.
Photo kindly supplied by
Mr Sadik Nur of the Sudan
Antiquities Service

No doubt the original area of distribution of wild asses was more or less continuous from Somaliland through the Libyan Desert to Morocco. Moreover, true wild asses occurred in southern Europe in the Upper Pleistocene. They were particularly common in Italy, but became extinct there long before domestication began. They have been named *Equus asinus hydruntinus*. Stehlin and Graziosi (1935) devoted to it a detailed study which has removed several uncertainties. This little ass was recognized and described from the Upper Palaeolithic cave called Grotta Romanelli in Apulia, by Regalia, who at first considered it as a relative of the hemiones. Later he changed his view and attached it to the *asinus* group. This interpretation has since been upheld, even by the latest authorities; it implies that the asses, now exclusively North and East African, had in the late Pleistocene spread to south-western Europe, either via Spain and France, or via Sicily,[1] and occasionally penetrated into Germany and England. This disposes of the many much-disputed fossils variously described as a small *Equus caballus* or as *E. asinus* or, most frequently, as *E. hemionus*.

Quite recently (Bökönyi, 1958; Necrasov and Haimovici, 1959, 1960) finds of *Equus hydruntinus* have been reported from the Azilian of the Crimea and the early Neolithic of Rumania, Hungary and north-east Yugoslavia. It remains to be seen whether this Postglacial *E. hydruntinus* is the same as the Pleistocene form.

The ass was first domesticated in the valley of the Nile. In Egypt it was known as a domesticated beast from at least protodynastic times onwards. It is depicted on the

[1] See Stehlin and Grazosi (1935).

Nagada palette as tribute from Libya and on a panel in the tomb of Sahure, fifth dynasty, *c.* 2650 B.C. (Fig. 15 : 2). Antonius, therefore, considers it as possible that the ass was first domesticated in Libya. Thence the practice would have spread to Egypt. On the other hand, the close connection which existed between Nubia and Egypt even in predynastic times renders it probable that the domesticated ass contains a fair amount of southern blood. In due course, the wild asses of the whole of North Africa must have contributed to the domesticated stock.

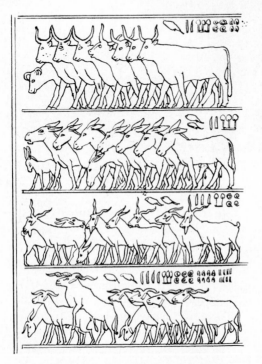

FIG. 15 : 2. Panel of domesticated animals from the tomb of Sahure, fifth dynasty, *c.* 2650 B.C. The second register shows asses. In the first register are cattle with rising horns, except for one specimen which has horns down-curved. Screw-horned goats are in the third register and the screw-horned sheep of the Old Kingdom in the fourth. After Hilzheimer

For long the ass remained an essentially African animal. Its spread into Asia was slow at first. Bones have been found in Early Bronze Age deposits at Tell Duweir in Palestine (*c.* 3000–2500 B.C.) and there is a pottery figurine from a tomb at Jericho, of Early Bronze Age III. From then onwards the ass is reported repeatedly from Palestine and Syria. Its bones occur at Gezer in the earliest layers, and clay figurines are known. Damascus is 'the town of the asses' in cuneiform. The ass is frequently mentioned in the Old Testament, and she-asses were popular for riding. The 'wild asses' mentioned in the Bible however were onagers, not true asses.

Whether the ass had reached Mesopotamia in the third millennium is uncertain and indeed unlikely. Bones claimed to be those of asses have been found in Meso-potamian sites, but most of them belong to onagers which were at that time domes-ticated by the Sumerians. The fauna of Tell Asmar, however, did contain a few bones which Hilzheimer considered as asses'. It is conceivable that asses were occasionally imported from the West, but for some reason unknown to us the species was then not generally adopted.

The tablets from Chagar Bazar in Mesopotamia (Gadd, 1940) mention asses. They were written about 1800 B.C. Three kinds of asses are distinguished, all domesticated, for their daily rations are specified. There is, however, no evidence of whether these creatures were true asses of African descent or hemiones. Their names do not reveal it, though they all begin with Anshe ... which reminds one of the Latin *Asinus*. The name of the horse which is mentioned also, though less frequently, has the same initial appellation. It is equally desirable to obtain more definite evidence for the identity of the horse. It is, however, mentioned in connection with a chariot, a point in favour of the true horse.

From the studies of Herre and Röhrs (1954), however, it appears that the ass had reached Asia Minor in the Hittite period, for they found that the small equids present in the tombs of Osmankayasi belonged to this species.

In biblical history the ass appears for the first time (Gen. XII, 16) when the King of Egypt presents Abraham with livestock including he- and she-asses. There is perhaps behind this the tradition of the importation of asses from Egypt into Palestine. The great spread of the ass across western Asia, however, coincides approximately with the period when the camel became frequent, and it seems connected with the increasing aridity of the Near and Middle East resulting from soil destruction.

Even less is known of the early domestication of the ass in Western countries. Rock paintings discovered in 1947 at Alacon in the province of Teruel, Spain, depict an animal which indeed looks like a domesticated ass. They are believed to be of Neolithic age, but the chronological position is uncertain.

The modern domesticated asses are mainly descended from the Nubian race, with which they agree in the presence of a stripe along the back and a vertical stripe on the shoulder. Races with stripes on the legs and the shoulder, however, are more likely to be derived from the extinct North African race. Some tropical African breeds, like the Masai donkey, which lack the shoulder stripe, may be descendants of the Somali race. But apart from many breeds that have retained the essential characters of the wild races, an astonishing variety of deviations is observed. The size varies from that of the Poitou ass, as large as a horse, to dwarf donkeys, hardly bigger than a sheep. In colour, though grey predominates, there are black, white and even piebald asses.

It appears that the ancient Egyptians did not use the ass for draught, and only from the Middle Kingdom onwards did they use it for riding (Erman and Ranke, 1923, p. 583). It was essentially a beast of burden, which was driven but never bridled. Only two ancient peoples practised riding on asses regularly, namely the

Jews and the Nubians. With the spread of the donkey in the last 2000 years, the practice of riding has been adopted almost everywhere, probably in imitation of horse-riding. Asses were, however, used for the treading of corn and for pulling the plough. In Arab countries one can today see peasants ploughing with a camel and an ass, two very unequal partners, but the only sources of kinetic energy available to them. The Bible deprecates the use of such unequal pairs, and says that ass and ox are not to be yoked together.

The ass is indisputably one of the most useful animals, and yet it is despised nearly everywhere. It is not fully understood why this should be so. In part, its stolid temperament has annoyed its master since time immemorial. By comparison with the horse and the mule it is inferior. Its food requirements are extremely modest, thistles and straw are sufficient, a diet with which the horse would not be satisfied. Modesty, however, was not in ancient times regarded as a quality of character worthy of admiration. In civilized countries the ass became the beast of the poor; of those who could not afford to buy and maintain the more pretentious animals. The patience of the ass likened it to the slave. It is probable that all these factors contributed to its low position in the social scale of domestic animals.

Originally, the ass was not despised. The Egyptians were proud of their white asses, and the large and graceful asses of Muscat have until recently served as processional mounts for the family of the Sultan of Zanzibar. Some Romans, too, appreciated the beauty of the well-bred asses. Varro relates that the Senator Q. Axius paid 400,000 sesterces for two pairs of draught asses, and Pliny that an ass from Reate in Sabinia was sold for 60,000 sesterces. This province was renowned for its excellent asses, as was Arcadia in Greece. Probably because of its association with corn and flour, the ass was the sacred beast of the goddess Vesta. In 260 B.C. a Gn. Cornelius Scipio Asina was consul, and his name is believed to be due to his large ears. If so, one might assume that at that time the ass had not yet been reduced as much in estimation as it was in later times.

The primary function of the ass was as a beast of burden, which it always retained (Fig. 15 : 3). In ancient Egypt it had to carry the harvest, and in time of war it transported war materials. In addition, the wealthy used it for conveyance, a saddle or litter being carried between two asses. Riding appears to have become popular only after the Greek civilization had contacted Egypt, though it was done occasionally before this (Fig. 15 : 4), such use of a medium-sized beast of burden being too obvious to be overlooked. After the introduction of the horse, asses may have been tried for traction. There are some pictures, but it is not clear whether they represent asses, hemiones or mules. In addition, donkeys were used for threshing, like cattle.

In ancient Greece and Rome the ass had become the beast of burden of the miller, the gardener and the smallholder. In the mill it was compelled to turn the stone, walking blindfolded in a circle. This was, of course, a very ordinary method of obtaining circular motion, and it is used today in many parts of the Orient, especially in connection with irrigation, both camel and cattle being used also. In Europe it

FIG. 15 : 3. Short-legged donkey used for transport in south Connemara, Ireland. It is curious that the donkey has retained a stronghold on that island up to the present day. Photo by J. Allan Cash

FIG. 15 : 4. Fifth-dynasty picture of a gentleman travelling on the back of an ass. This shows the early use of the beast for human transport. After Lepsius

was common practice in the Middle Ages in all kinds of factories and in mines, but small horses were employed as well (Fig. 15 : 5). An ass still draws water from a well at Carisbrooke Castle on the Isle of Wight (Fig. 15 : 6).

Curiously enough, the flesh of asses was eaten but rarely, and in Rome only by the very poorest. It is possible, though not certain, that the taboo on eating horse-

FIG. 15 : 5. Another example of the exploitation of animal energy: model of a horse-wheel of *c.* A.D. 1800 used for butter-churning. In Devon similar wheels were in use until recently to work cider presses. Science Museum (Crown copyright)

flesh was applied to it because of the close affinity of the two species. Nevertheless, the meat of wild asses (presumably hemiones or feral beasts) was highly esteemed in western Asia.

The milk of asses was regarded as a very valuable product and all sorts of properties ascribed to it. It was believed to be a remedy for ailments of the lung, liver, gall-bladder and the kidneys. This is not mere superstition. Ass's milk resembles in composition human milk and is therefore indicated in cases where cow's milk may cause digestive upsets. Until only a few years ago it was sought for to help cure cases of meningitis. Apart from strictly medical uses, the milk of asses was regarded as a very effective means of obtaining a white complexion. Poppaea, a wife of Nero, had 500 she-asses in whose milk she used to bathe. The large number was necessary as the yield is small.

Much use was made of asses' dung in classical medicine. Columella, however, was realistic enough to recommend this material as an excellent manure for the

FIG. 15 : 6. The ass used as a source of energy in a tread-wheel raising the bucket from the well at Carisbrooke Castle, Isle of Wight. Similarly, asses are used to work various types of wheels in the south, for instance in Tunisia. Elsewhere camels and cattle are used for the same purpose

garden, and for pomegranates in particular. From the skin of the ass parchment was made.

In ancient religion and legend the ass played its part, though it is often difficult to distinguish ass from mule and either from the hemione. King Midas I of Sardis was deified and shown in the shape of an ass. Keller offers the following interpretation: The River Pactolos near Sardis was full of sand containing gold. In order to obtain it, asses' skins were used. The legend subsequently appeared that Midas bathed in the river and gave it its abundance of gold, since everything he touched was converted into this metal. Behind it is apparently the simple fact that Midas organized alluvial gold mining in the sands of the Pactolos River.

The sex life of the ass is spectacular and full of temperament, hence it is only natural that there should be frequent allusions to it, and the beds of Roman married couples were often adorned with asses' heads. In the Hellenistic period the animal was associated with Priapus and Dionysos (Figs. 15 : 7 and 15 : 8). The large asses bred by the Karamanians,[1] which were used in wars, were sacrificed to their war god.

[1] I cannot locate this people. The reference is from Keller, p. 267.

The most remarkable association is that with Typhon, identified with the ass-headed Egyptian god Seth. He was able to do evil to others, and Greek and Roman competitors had his effigy engraved on small leaden tablets, together with some magical symbols. With these they hoped to cause accidents to rivals in the races, by throwing the tablets at them. Keller holds that the asinine crucifix of the third

FIG. 15 : 7. Greek silver coin from Mende showing an ass, 700–480 B.C.

FIG. 15 : 8. Another tetradrachm from Mende showing Dionysos riding an ass, 480–400 B.C. This scene was popular at the time and referred to the good quality of the Mendean wine which was evidently much enjoyed by Dionysos. The earlier coin, however, shows what is supposed to be a crow on the back of the ass, but the connection with wine is clear since grapes are indicated in the background. It may be that the animal was sacred in this town for reasons other than the Dionysian connections

century A.D., which was found on the Palatine and shows an ass-headed figure hanging on a cross, belongs to this Typhon-Seth complex and is not intended to deride Christ. The inscription says 'Alexamenos worships God'. It can be interpreted either way.

The ass was generally absent from northern Europe until presumably the Middle Ages. Curiously enough, even in the Roman period it did not strike roots except along the Mediterranean coast of France. Nevertheless it must have reached the north from time to time. Only Boessneck (1953) mentions three molars from Cambodunum (Kempten im Allgäu) which he regards as possibly asinine, and which date from the Roman Imperial period (c. A.D. 14–250).

The mule

The greatest contribution to animal husbandry that the ass has made is as pro-genitor of the mule. It is known that in earlier times crosses were attempted between hemiones and asses, as well as horses and asses, but of the several possibilities only one proved really successful, the hybrid between the male ass and the female horse, i.e. the mule. The product of the union of a male horse with a female ass is called hinny; it is on the whole rare. Pohlig found that hinnies were valued as good for riding in Persia, and Pallas mentioned them from China.

The mule, however, was and still is the normal cross in the lands surrounding the Mediterranean. It is strange to find that two species should be compelled to interbreed—they do not do so of their own free will—whilst the progeny is not even fertile. Pliny and Varro mention cases of fertile mules, and others have been reported since. Nobody, however, has tried to base the breeding of mules on these rare fertile specimens. Even the ancients were wondering how mule-breeding was invented though they were by no means unfamiliar with the crossing of species. After all, Leda is recorded as having interbred with a swan! Both Anakreon and Homer (*Iliad*, II) attribute the invention to the Myri and Eneti of Asia Minor. One wonders how much hemione blood went into these early mules. In the Bible (Authorized Version, Gen. XXXVI, 24), however, the Edomites and Hosites are stated to have invented mule-breeding. Mount Seir of Petra, where Genesis would place it, would indeed have been an admirable place for the use of the sure-footed mules. Unfortunately, translations other than the Authorized Version, including Moffat and Luther, substitute 'hot springs' for 'mules', which is equally possible in that area and rather spoils the use for the mules. Western Asia is in any case the likely place of origin, where horse-using peoples met the ass.

Mule-breeding is an art, and certain districts which specialized in it became famous in antiquity. First-class mules yielded high prices and were fit to be used by the imperial family. Empress Poppaea had golden sandals made for her mules, whilst Nero's had to be content with silver horse-shoes. It is quite probable that the mountainous nature of the Mediterranean countries made the mule so popular. It is sure-footed, careful and able to carry fragile loads on narrow mountain paths. Its gait is softer and more even than that of horse or ass, hence it was popular with the ladies for riding and drawing carriages. For the same reason it was used to draw the hearse. That of Alexander the Great was conveyed from Babylon to Alexandria by a team of sixty-four mules. Mules were also attached to the Roman army for the transport of weapons, and they were equally important in the imperial postal service.

On the whole, the same qualities render the mules useful in Mediterranean countries today and in other lands that have been colonized from the Mediterranean, and particularly from Spain.

GROUP IV

The Pest-destroyers

A N INTERESTING group of domesticated animals is the several small carnivores that have specialized in preying mainly on rodents. Since rodents became storage pests as soon as the problem of preserving a supply of grain from harvest to harvest was solved, these carnivores inevitably became the associates of man, both having the same goal. The chief species are the cat, the ferret and the mongoose. It is very probable that none of these was deliberately domesticated. An overlap of social media occurred, and since the animals were so obviously useful man cared for them or even regarded them as sacred. The cat and the mongoose entered into the human environment in Egypt, whilst the ferret appears to have originated farther east.

The history of the cat is the best known and must serve as the chief example.

16

The Cat

SCIENTIFIC NAMES—*Felis lunensis* Martelli (Villafranchian of Italy, possibly ancestral to following).

Felis silvestris Schreber (European wild cat; from Scotland and Spain to Causasus and Asia Minor; never domesticated).

F. libyca Forster (syn. *F. ornata* Gray, *F. ochreata* Gmel.; yellow cat, African wild cat, desert cat; from the Balearics, Corsica, Sardinia throughout Africa, Arabia to India; ancestor of domesticated cat).

F. manul Pallas (manul, Pallas's cat, steppe cat; northern Asia).

AMONG the domestic pets kept in the towns of England, the cat probably tops the list so far as numbers go. But, unlike other domesticated animals, its association with man has been relatively short and, in spite of the mouse-catching propensities of some breeds, domestication was in this case only in part guided by economic considerations.

The domestic cat belongs to the genus *Felis* in the narrowest sense, which has its chief representative in the wild cat (*Felis silvestris*), a species that has become extinct in many parts of Europe, though it is still found in some parts of Scotland. It belongs to a group of wild cats, often classified as distinct species, with a wide distribution and somewhat different habits. The European wild cat is the northern forest cat. It is found from Europe to the Caucasus and Asia Minor and is decidedly adapted to dense vegetation and the climbing of trees. The second member of the group is the manul (*Felis manul*), the steppe cat of central Asia. The third is the 'yellow cat' (*Felis libyca*) which occurs throughout Africa and extends to Syria and

Arabia. A race of this extends into India, where I have seen it roaming about in the dry scrub of Gujarat. In the Himalayas, however, other races occur which resemble the European wild cat, living in similar forest conditions. These 'species' replace one another geographically. Although each may be divided into a number of geographical races, they are hardly more than geographical and ecological sub-species themselves. This is confirmed by the fact that the domestic cat interbreeds with the European wild cat. Moreover, Dorothea Bate (1905) has shown that forms transitional between the yellow cat and the European wild cat exist on Mediterranean islands. According to Stehlin (1933), the wild cat may be the descendant of a cat from the Upper Pliocene of Olivola (Italy) called *Felis lunensis* Martelli. Only the fragment of a lower jaw is known, which agrees closely with the modern wild cat. A very similar fragment was described by Depéret from the Lower Pliocene of Perpignan in France. This was so much like the African wild cat that the author did not propose a special name for it. It is conceivable therefore that the ancestral line of our cat begins with Depéret's cat and passes through Martelli's species to the wild cats of the Pleistocene, though more material is required before definite pronounce-ments on phylogenesis can be made.

Remains of wild cats are known from a fair number of Pleistocene localities, such as Mosbach and Mauer in Germany, Hundsheim in Austria (all these are Lower Pleistocene); Grays on the Thames (Middle Pleistocene); Taubach–Ehringsdorf in Germany, Lunel-Viel in France, Kent's Cavern in England, the Grotte du Prince at Grimaldi and the Grotte de l'Observatoire at Monaco (both on the Italo-French Riviera) and Kesslerloch and Schweizersbild in Switzerland (all these of Upper Pleistocene age). In the majority of these places the cat was a contemporary of prehistoric man. There are many other localities.

Some of these fossil remains have been referred to the European wild cat, but others to the African cat or to the manul. Boyd Dawkins (Dawkins and Jackson, 1917), for instance, ascribed several European specimens, from Lunel-Viel in France, from Chokier in Belgium and from Bleadon in Somerset, to the African cat. The same was done by Scharff (1906) with certain Irish remains and by Boule (1910) with those from the Riviera caves mentioned in the last paragraph. On the other hand, Studer thought that the cats from the Kesslerloch and Schweizersbild in Switzerland belonged to the steppe species, the manul.

Whilst these cats are easily distinguished by the colour and length of their hair, it has been found by Stehlin, Pocock and other workers that one cannot distinguish them with certainty on characters of the skeleton. Extreme individuals may be identifiable, but there is so great an overlap in measurements and the relative proportions of the skull, the teeth and the bones of the extremities that the majority of specimens cannot be placed with certainty. All the fossil specimens known from Europe are likely to belong to the stock of the European wild cat, which perhaps

produced various ecological types according to the environmental conditions prevailing at certain times in certain areas.

The wild cats never played a part in the economy of Palaeolithic or Mesolithic
man. Finds made in the lake-dwellings of Switzerland (Neolithic and Bronze Age)
and even in the Iron Age lake-dwellings of Glastonbury, in Somerset, are now
regarded as belonging to the wild form. In Glastonbury, for instance, where animal
remains were identified by Dr Wilfred Jackson, bones belonging to five cats were
found associated with other small wild carnivores like fox, otter, marten, weasel and
polecat. There is thus no reason to suspect that the cats were domesticated.

Unfortunately, it is as difficult to recognize a domesticated cat from its skeletal
remains as it is to distinguish the wild races from each other. Domestication is
therefore often more easily established by the archaeological circumstances of a
find than by its osteological investigation. In the Roman town of Silchester the
remains of several cats were found. The investigator, H. Jones (1906), did not rely
on skeletal characters when he pronounced these as domesticated. He was merely
able to make a negative statement, namely that they showed no characters which
suggested that they belonged to the wild form. On the positive side, he refers to the
footprints of cats observed on tiles from Silchester. 'It is certainly more likely that
domestic cats should walk across tiles laid out to dry at their place of manufacture,
than that wild cats should do so.'

Nevertheless, it is possible in certain cases to make fairly definite pronounce-
ments as to the wild or domesticated condition of cats. Although there is a great overlap in all characters, certain extremes are confined to either the wild or the domesticated forms. Externally, tame cats with a colour and pattern of coat resembling the
wild form are distinguished by their slightly smaller average size and shorter hair.
In fact, it is the long fur and bushy tail which make the wild cat appear so much
stouter than the tame one; there are no corresponding differences in the skeleton.

Most of the differences in the skeleton which have been claimed as distinctive
are related to the differences in size already mentioned. It is, for instance, highly
probable that a cat's skull measuring less than 90 mm. from the incisors to the
condyles comes from a domesticated specimen, whilst one measuring more than
105 mm. is likely to belong to the wild race. Similar differences are observed in the
lower jaw. The bones of the body, however, are even less reliable, since there are
high-legged and low-legged domesticated breeds. Of the former, the Manx cat is
well known.

Some other characters found in the proportions of parts of the skull and of the
lower jaw are mainly the results of domestication. Some tame breeds have a shortened
face, hence their skulls are very broad across the eye-sockets and their premaxillary
bones rise more steeply than in the wild forms. The lower jaw of the tame cat has a
longer gap between the canine and the premolars than that of the wild one. This is

due to the smaller size of the teeth. The latter is most noticeable in the last tooth of the lower jaw, which is the first molar. Also, the anterior and posterior edges of the first molar of the lower jaw often rise more steeply in the European wild cat than in the domestic cat as well as the African. This character is not consistent either, perhaps because the European and domestic cats have interbred frequently, but for what it is worth it suggests that the tame cat was originally derived from the North African race. This has of course been put forward long ago on other grounds.

The names for the cat come from the Near East and from Africa. It is believed that 'puss' and 'pussy' are derived from the name of the Egyptian goddess Pasht, Bastet or Bubastis. 'Tabby' is apparently of Turkish origin, as there is a word *utabi*. On the other hand, Hitti (1956) says that it is derived from the name of a striped fabric first manufactured in the twelfth century and called after Attab, an Umayyid prince in Baghdad. 'Cat' itself is according to Keller of North African origin, where it appears in various forms in Berber languages. In Arabic it is *quttah*. Linguistics thus confirm the biological evidence for the origin of the domestic cat. The Latin word *cattus*, obviously derived from Berber or Semitic, was first used by Palladius in the fourth century; it is much later than *felis*, which apparently merely meant a yellowish carnivore and, therefore, is not diagnostic.

There are two records of cats from early prehistoric sites which have to be mentioned. The first is pre-pottery Jericho, where a single molar was found in a layer dating from about 6700 B.C. (Zeuner, 1958a). Since at that time only the goat was certainly domesticated, this single tooth may have belonged to a wild visitor. The same is the most likely explanation regarding the other early prehistoric locality, which is Harappa in the Indus Valley (*c.* 2000 B.C.), although Prashad (1936) thinks it was domesticated.

It is not known for certain whether or not the cat was domesticated in Egypt in prehistoric times. A fragment of a jaw found in predynastic Abydos belongs probably to the wild form, though Brunton (1937) thought they were already tamed at that time. No reliable records appear to be known from the Old Kingdom, whilst from Middle Kingdom times only wild representatives are known, such as that of a cat in a papyrus swamp from the tomb of Khnumhotep (twelfth dynasty, *c.* 1900 B.C.). In the New Kingdom (sixteenth century onwards), however, the cat appears as a domesticated animal, helping to hunt birds and sacred to Bastet or Bubastis, a goddess of the delta.

It is strange that the cat should have been domesticated at so late a period, since the ancient Egyptians used to tame all manner of animals from Old Kingdom times onwards. It is hard to believe that a people who kept hyaenas and monkeys and used the mongoose should have neglected the cat so long. Some archaeologists indeed hold that the cat was domesticated in Egypt from the first dynasties onwards (*c.* 3000 B.C.) but the evidence is ambiguous. Hilzheimer states that there is no evidence of any cats prior to the fifth dynasty. It is conceivable that the Egyptian cat was for a long time an intruder who entered human habitations in search of his usual prey, small rodents, and that it was suffered in the villages because of its usefulness, without being bred in captivity. But by eighteenth-dynasty times the cat had become popular and properly domesticated (Fig. 16 : 1). Its coloration still resembled the wild form, in other words it was a striped tabby. The Egyptians may have experimented

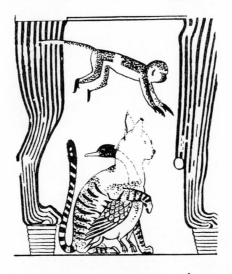

Fig. 16 : 1. Eighteenth-dynasty scene of cat holding a duck, and a monkey playing with them under a chair. Tomb of O-nen, Thebes. Metropolitan Museum, New York, No. 30.4.93

with other cats also, but without permanent results. A painted tile from Serabit-el-Khadem, which is in the Victoria and Albert Museum in London and of eighteenth-dynasty date, shows a serval cat, an imported species. The cat gradually became one of the most universally worshipped animals. When one died the owners went into mourning, shaving their eyebrows. Cats were not allowed to be killed. Herodotus relates that when a house was on fire the Egyptians were more anxious to save their cats than their property. Both Greek and Roman visitors suffered for having accidentally killed a cat. Dead cats were mummified and buried in consecrated places. The number of mummies in one of these cemeteries was so enormous that an enterprising merchant brought a whole shipload to Manchester, hoping to sell them as manure. Fortunately, they did not prove popular, and many ended up in collections, including that of the British Museum (Natural History).

The regular commercial relations between Egypt and Palestine brought the cat into the latter country, where an ivory statuette (*c.* 1700 B.C.) was found at Lachish (Fig. 16 : 2).

FIG. 16 : 2. Ivory carving of a cat from Lachish in Palestine, *c.* 1700 B.C. It is, of course, impossible to establish whether this cat was domesticated or wild, but in view of the close connections between Egypt and Palestine it is conceivable that Egyptians lived there and kept cats. Natural size

The Greeks knew the Egyptian cat, and Herodotus (fifth century B.C.) related the story of an unfortunate Greek who killed a cat on his visit to Egypt.

Following the intense traffic from Egypt across the Aegean Sea, however, cats actually reached Greece from time to time. The earliest record appears to be one from Crete, where a terracotta head of Late Minoan age has been interpreted as that of a cat by Bosanquet (1923, p. 54). It comes from Palaikastro and should be earlier than 1100 B.C. At that time domestic cats abounded in Egypt, and this find may provide another cultural link between that country and Crete.

On the Greek mainland cats were kept from the Archaic period onwards, though they were certainly scarce and curiosities rather than utilitarian animals. In the Athens Museum a marble block, the base of a couros of about 500 B.C., is exhibited (No. Ap. 3476). On one of its four sides it shows a scene of extraordinary interest (Fig. 16 : 4). Two seated men, with bystanders, have each an animal on a leash, and they allow them to sniff at each other. That on the left is undoubtedly a dog, and that on the right, with its short head, curved back and long tail, cannot but represent a cat. The intense interest displayed by the four men shows that the point was to see what would happen when a dog was confronted with a cat. I have examined the original with care and must admit that, unlike other supposed representations of cats from the classical world, this one most probably does show a cat. The block was found near the dipylon of Palestra and is of Attic workmanship. A very similar game of a man with a cat is shown on a coin from Tarentum in southern Italy, a didrachm dating from 440 B.C. (Seltman, 1955, Pl. XIX, fig 13)

FIG. 16 . 3. Bronze cat, height 17 cm., of the Saite period of Egypt, *c.* 600 B.C. Original in British Museum

FIG. 16 : 4. Greek marble relief from Poulopoulos, between Athens and Pyraeus, now in the Archaeological Museum at Athens, *c.* 480 B.C. It shows men trying to make a dog and a cat fight

Another cat, whose head is missing, is shown on a later funeral stele in the same museum, from Sounion (Fig. 16 : 5).

In the Etruscan necropolis of Cerveteri the tombs reproducing the interior of houses show reliefs of animals that have frequently been interpreted as cats. They

FIG. 16 : 5. Funeral stele of fifth century B.C. from Sounion, south tip of Attica, showing an animal which can only have been a cat

date from the fourth to second centuries B.C. and would therefore be of considerable importance.

I cannot, however, admit that this interpretation is correct. True enough, on one of the pillars of the Tomb of Reliefs there is an animal catching what appears to be a long-tailed rodent. But its body is short, its legs stiff and its tail comparatively short and curled as in many breeds of dogs. Hence I interpret this animal as a dog until somebody shows me a cat with a curled tail.

Another relief on a pillar depicts a very slim animal, standing on its hind legs but crouching with its forelegs, with a very slender tail curved in a circle. Any un-biased observer would regard this as a greyhound or whippet, especially as on the central bed of the same relief such greyhound appears as a mythical beast with three heads, possibly Cerberus. This alone shows that the Etruscans were familiar with greyhounds. There is thus no reason to assume that domestic cats were kept by them.

From Roman Imperial times onwards domestic cats reached Europe, though not in large numbers.[1] By the beginning of the Christian era it was well known to the Romans and it appears to have been kept fairly frequently (Fig. 16 : 7). With the

[1] The record from Vardaroftsa in Macedonia, Period D, well within the second millennium B.C., refers probably to a wild specimen, and finds made at the Iron Age lake village of Glastonbury in Somerset are regarded as wild by Dr. Jackson.

FIG. 16 : 6. Vase painting show-ing two ladies playing with a cat, using a bird and what appear to be balls of yarn. Exact origin not known; reproduced by Keller (1909, p. 78) and stated to come from Basilicata, south Italy, and to be fifth century B.C. If this is correct it would belong to the sphere of Greek culture in southern Italy. It may, however, be considerably later

FIG. 16 : 7. Mosaic in the Archaeological Museum of Naples showing a cat playing with a fowl. This cat has the characteristic spotted tabby markings of the wild specimens. Probably first century A.D.

Romans it spread to the outer parts of the empire, including Britain. Remains of domesticated cats were found in Silchester as mentioned earlier on, in the Villa at Dursley, in Hambledon in Buckinghamshire and recently at Lullingstone, Kent. The Lullingstone cat perished in a fire during the second half of the fourth century A.D., in a basement room of the house of a wealthy man. Most of its skeleton is preserved and shows both in the size of the body and structure of the skull, jaw and teeth evidence of domestication.

The Romans were responsible for the introduction of the cat into central Europe also. At Vindonissa in Switzerland remains have been found. Those of no fewer than eight individuals were reported by Nobis (1954) from Tofting in Schleswig. Unfortunately their date is not certain, as the finds range from the second to the tenth century A.D., though most belong to the Roman Imperial period. But the site lay outside the political boundaries of Rome, hence trade relations must have existed.

Remains of domestic cats were found at Haithabu, the important trading station near Schleswig of the tenth to eleventh centuries A.D. (Requate, 1960).

The comparatively late arrival of the cat in Europe was undoubtedly due to the embargo the Egyptians had placed on one of their sacred animals. Foreigners were occasionally killed for having caused the death of a cat, even in the Roman period according to Diodorus. Egyptians travelling abroad acquired any cats they might find kept in other countries and took them back to their homeland. It was only the spread of Christianity that caused these restrictions to collapse. The cat was no longer sacred. Roman visitors could buy them and take them home. There they began to replace their predecessor, the polecat or ferret. Late in the fourth century A.D. Palladius recommended the use of cats to cope with moles damaging artichoke beds, instead of the polecats used by some people. This is, incidentally, the first mention of the modern name of the animal (*cattus*).

It is virtually certain that whenever the domestic cat was spreading in Europe it would interbreed with the local race of the wild cat. In this manner, characteristics of the European wild cat entered the domestic stock, and the wild population became contaminated with some originally African features brought in by feral cats. Since the eighties of the last century Nehring's view has been widely accepted that the colour of the soles of the hind feet is black in the African and pale in the European wild cat. In this respect the domestic breeds agree on the whole with the African, but Pocock found that this character becomes unreliable when large series are studied. The cause is probably to be sought in interbreeding.

In the early Middle Ages the domesticated cat appears to have had a thin time. It emerges with the reputation of being the indispensable pet of all genuine witches, and the black cat became one of the symbols of Satan. Whether this was due to the nightly, silent expeditions of feral cats, their weird cries and their eyes shining in the dark, we do not know. In any case, another useful creature with similar habits, the owl, suffered the same fate of unpopularity in medieval times. But there were some who pleaded in defence of the cat. In A.D. 936 Howel Dda, a prince of southern central Wales, issued a law for the protection of the domestic cat.

The superstition with which the cat was regarded is well illustrated by the following report on a practice called *taghairm* or 'giving his supper to the devil' which I am quoting verbatim from Lewis Spence's interesting book entitled *The Magic Arts in Celtic Britain* (1945, p. 97).

The most celebrated case is that in which one Lachlan Oer and a companion, Allan, the son of Hector, shut themselves up in a barn near the Sound of Mull, and, impaling black cats on spits, roasted them alive by a blazing fire. Other cats entered the building, setting up an infernal caterwauling, which well-nigh daunted the men, but they remained inexorable until a greater cat of ferocious appearance entered and remonstrated with them, threatening them that if they did not desist from their horrid employment they would never see the face of the Trinity. Lachlan struck the hideous animal on the head with the hilt of his sword, whereupon the devil, for he it was, assumed his appropriate shape and asked the pair what it was they wanted of him. They replied that they craved prosperity and a long life to enjoy it. This was granted, and it is said that Lachlan, for his part, never relented of the dreadful act, even upon his deathbed.

Lent was a particularly hard time for medieval cats. They were killed and buried in Oldenburg, Westphalia, Belgium, Switzerland and Bohemia; burnt on Shrove Tuesday in the Vosges, and in Alsace at Easter. In the Ardennes they were thrown into bonfires or roasted on the ends of long poles, or in wicker baskets on the first Sunday in Lent (Howard, 1951). The connection with the idea of driving out the devil is evident.

The last three or four centuries have provided us with a sub-modern supply of mummified, or more precisely dried, cats about which M. M. Howard has reported (1951). Unlike the Egyptian mummies of cats, deliberately prepared and entombed because of their sacred associations, these British cats' mummies, found in the walls and under the floorboards of old houses, are either the results of accidents or of very utilitarian practices. Specimens like the one recently found in a seventeenth-century room of the Tower of London may have perished after having ventured too far into the crevices of an old building. But others, holding rats or birds in their mouths, as one from Southwark (Fig. 16 : 8), are likely to be prepared groups, perhaps intended to function as a kind of rat-scare. If so, they must have been manufactured and probably dried before being placed in the building. A more recent instance of a dried cat is from Christchurch Cathedral, Dublin, where a specimen, together with a mouse, was found behind the old organ. It must be later than A.D. 1698, the year when the old organ was put in. In a house about 200 yards away from the cathedral a cat was found in a partition wall. This house was new in 1786.

The custom of immuring cats continued even later. Miss Howard reports a find made in Värmland, middle Sweden, under the steps of a front door put in place about 1920.

This example and others show that the custom was not confined to Britain. In the Museum of Gibraltar I came across one dried cat in running position, and with wide-open mouth, and another that had been bricked up in a partition wall, an operation which Spanish masons believe brings luck.

Fig. 16 : 8. Dried cat with rat, from a house in Southwark, probably of seventeenth or eighteenth century A.D. and believed to have been used as a rat scare. For details see Howard (1951). Photo Mr Teulon-Porter

Little need be said about the outcome of the domestication of the cat. The divergence from the wild type has been very slight, except in the skin. Colour, pattern and length of the hair are thus the chief characters used in the distinction of modern breeds. Of these, the 'tabby' is closest to the wild form. Curiously enough, two types of tabbies exist, the striped and the blotched. In the striped tabby the vertical striation is often dissolved into rows of spots and its pattern is virtually that of the wild cat. The blotched tabby, however, has contorted bands of black arranged on the sides in a spiral or circle. This pattern does not occur in any wild race, nor in any other member of the cat family, and is therefore now believed to have arisen as an ordinary gene mutation. It was this type of cat that was named *Felis catus* by

Linnaeus. Hence this name applies to the domestic cat only, and the correct Latin name to be used for the European wild cat is *Felis silvestris* Schreber.

The other major breeds are known by geographical connotations, but their homelands are not known with certainty. The Abyssinian cat, which lacks the pattern and has a pronounced multicoloured hair like the wild rabbit, does not come from Abyssinia. It may well have arisen from a wild form resembling the Sardinian cat, in which the markings are disappearing. The Persians and Angoras, both long-haired, have been regarded as coming from the mountainous districts of the Middle East and as descended from the manul, without any scientific evidence being available. The length of the hair in these breeds is a product of selective breeding, and comparable with the similar condition in the Pekinese dog, the Angora goat, the Angora rabbit and the Angora guinea-pig.

In India cats have been domesticated for at least 2000 years, and feral Indian cats mingle frequently with the wild form, *Felis libyca ornata* Gray. The custom of keeping domestic cats may have reached India from Egypt by way of Babylonia, where it was known in the second century B.C. An exception is the cat from Harappa, of the Indus Valley civilization. If it was domesticated, which is unlikely, it would push the date back to 2000 B.C.

The Siamese cat, with its peculiar colour change from white in the young to smoky shading in the adult, first appeared in Britain in 1884. It is seriously believed by many to have originated in Siam, but some zoologists regard this as unproven and suggest that it is a comparatively recent mutation of the Indian cat. Some workers believe that it sprang from the golden cat (*Profelis temmincki* Vig.), but this is not possible, the latter being a different genus and not at all related to the domestic cat. The skull of a Siamese which I measured with care is in no way different from the skulls of African and European cats. There are two arguments in favour of an Eastern origin. One is that the so-called Himalayan rabbit has the same coloration, the other that the tails of Siamese cats are often abnormal, kinked or shortened.[1] This feature is common among the domestic cats of Burma, Siam and Malaya.

Finally, the Manx cat deserves to be mentioned. It is ideally completely devoid of a tail, a simple mutation apparently linked with high-leggedness. The Manx thus looks like a lynx in outline. Whether it originated in the Isle of Man is highly doubtful. Short tails are frequently encountered elsewhere, especially in the Far East, as has just been said, and one author has even gone so far as to say that Manx cats are common there and that the European Manx was imported. But tailless cats occur elsewhere, for instance in Japan and in the Crimea. It is likely, therefore, that the absence of the tail is a mutation that makes its appearance here and there.

Thus the history of the cat breeds is not yet satisfactorily known. It is an instructive example, however, of a species which is only in the first stage of domestica-

[1] Many have tails of only half the normal length, which are often contorted.

tion, perfectly capable still of becoming feral, and comparatively little altered. Changes are most conspicuous in hair length and colour, also in body size, which on the whole is reduced. In the skeleton, domestic feeding has resulted in changes in the lower jaw and the dentition, which however are still very plastic, so that the characters are not at all constant. The skull is beginning to be broader, with a shorter face in many individuals. This is a character favoured by fanciers. It is deliberately selected and will therefore become pronounced in the comparatively near future. Shortening of the face is a common feature of domesticated animals, well known in the bulldog and the pig, for instance. With the change of food many domestic cats are undergoing at present, from their original diet of live rodents and birds to cooked meals including fish, and to milk and biscuits, the rate of morphological change in the domestic cat is likely to increase in the future.

17

The Ferret

SCIENTIFIC NAMES—*Putorius putorius* L. (European polecat; Ural Mountains to Scandinavia, Britain and Spain).

P.p. furo L. (ferret, domesticated albinotic polecat). *P.p. eversmanni* Lesson (steppe polecat; western Asia). Other subspecies or closely related species to Amur region, China and (?) Morocco.

T HE ferret is one of the domesticated species the history of which is not evidenced by fossil remains. There is a fair amount of information about it from historical sources from the fourth century B.C. onwards. Nevertheless, it is considered to have been domesticated before this date, and if the interpretation of a Hebrew word in the Bible (Lev. XI, 29–30) is correct it was known in Palestine prior to 1000 B.C.

The ferret is closely related to the common polecat (Fig. 17 : 1) and is usually regarded as a domesticated form of this animal, which is widely distributed in western and northern Europe. The eastern limits of its range are, however, not precisely known. In the East there occurs a closely related species, the steppe polecat (*P. eversmanni* Lesson), which is distinguished by certain anatomical characters, most notably in the skull and the teeth. Miller (1912), however, pointed out that the characters of the ferret's skull are closer to those of the steppe polecat than to those of the original European species. This observation adds considerable weight to the theory that the ferret came into Europe from the East.

Aristotle, about 350 B.C., described a kind of polecat which may well have been the ferret, because he states that it 'becomes very mild and tame', although he did

not state the purpose for which this animal was kept. About a century earlier
Aristophanes used the same Greek word (*ictis*) in one of his comedies when alluding
to an animal used by the Boeotians. Thomson (1951) suggests that the Greek writer
would hardly have used an obscure animal in his ironical remarks about the Boeotians.
The fact that at the present day the ferret is used mainly for rabbit-hunting is no
argument against the interpretation of the *ictis* of Aristotle as a ferret, although the
rabbit did not exist in Greece at that time, for it could equally well be used to destroy
other rodents. In the first century A.D. Strabo described the intolerable situation that
had arisen in the Balearic Islands owing to a plague of rabbits, and he refers to the
breeding of Libyan ferrets which are muzzled and sent into the rabbit-holes. There
is no room for doubt that Strabo's statement refers to the ferret. A few years later
Pliny included in his *Naturalis Historia* a similar statement about the ferret, which he
calls *Viverra*, and it is possible that the modern European name of this animal is
derived from this Latin word, although today *Viverra* means a very different beast.
The only difficulty in accepting Strabo's ferrets is that he assigned to them a North
African origin, and it is not certain whether wild polecats existed in North Africa.
Strabo is the authority on which the popular view is based that the ferret was first
domesticated in northern Africa, but the text does not imply original domestication;
'Libyan ferrets' might well mean no more than a particular breed, much as we use
the term 'Belgian hares' to designate a breed of rabbits.

The evidence from Strabo and Pliny proves that Romans were familiar with the
use of ferrets in catching rabbits and presumably other rodents. It is a mistake,
however, to assume that the Romans brought the ferret to Britain. In spite of a

FIG. 17 : 1. Wild polecat in Wales. Photo A. Brook

remark to this effect which Whitaker made in his *History of Manchester* in 1773, there is no evidence either factual or historical that he was right. About A.D. 600 Isidore of Seville described an animal employed in rabbit-hunting which he called *furo*, a word supposed to be derived from the Latin *fur*, thief. This new name henceforth replaced the older *viverra*. Thomson has pointed out that from that period onwards the identification of the ferret is beyond suspicion; references to the use of ferrets occur in Britain from the fourteenth century onwards, when Richard II granted licences to hunt rabbits with ferrets and also prohibited their use on Sundays. There is reason to believe that ferreting was introduced into England by the Normans and that the animal was not used during the Anglo-Saxon period.

On the continent of Europe they were known prior to A.D. 1300. Albertus Magnus described them in the thirteenth century from Germany, and they are listed as one of the animals used by the Emperor Frederick II in 1245. About this time they were known as far east as Afghanistan where, in 1221, Genghis Khan made use of them. From the sixteenth century onwards the ferret is mentioned more frequently, and it was depicted by Gesner in 1551, by Aldrovandus and by others. Linnaeus in 1758 described as *Mustela furo* a species distinct from the wild polecat. He clearly had before him the domesticated race which is frequently albinotic, for he refers to its reddish eyes and its smallish size. Curiously enough, he makes no mention of its use and states that it lives in Africa, presumably on Strabo's authority, though without quoting him.

The ferret never became important in the economy of man. This is perhaps the reason why references have always been of a somewhat casual nature.

18

The Mongoose

SCIENTIFIC NAME—*Herpestes ichneumon* L. (mongoose or ichneumon; North Africa, Asia Minor, Spain).

LIKE the cat, the mongoose or ichneumon is likely to have found its way into the houses as a pest-destroyer. It did so, however, in Egypt only. Mongooses appear on many pictures, mainly hunting scenes, and are easily distinguished from the civet cat by the tail, which is bushiest at the base, giving the impression of a gradual tapering from the body towards the tip of the tail. The Egyptian species is large, about three feet from nose to tail. Whilst it feeds on all manner of prey, its most remarkable habit is the efficient way it deals with snakes, and this (as well as its ability to dispose of rats) has made it a useful and welcome visitor to the house, especially as, in spite of its natural fierceness, it is easily tamed. Its ability to cope with venomous snakes is not due to natural immunity, but to its thick fur and extraordinary swiftness. It is able to judge and to anticipate the movements of the snake and usually gets it by the neck or head immediately after the snake has struck.

In early Egypt the mongoose appears to have been allowed to roam about within the precincts of human dwellings. Whether it was ever domesticated, i.e. allowed to breed under human control, is doubtful. It became, however, a sacred animal which was kept in temples from New Kingdom times onwards, when mongoose mummies became frequent. In the Ptolemaic and Roman periods it was kept in large numbers.

Whilst the Egyptians are likely to have been familiar with the ichneumon's way of life, its story became taller with increasing distance. Pseudo-Aristotle, Strabo and Plutarch inform us that it rolls itself in mud before the battle, allowing it to dry and thus providing itself with impenetrable armour. It then seizes the snake and drowns it in the Nile. The original Aristotle knows nothing of this story, but relates correctly that the mongoose has as many young as a dog, that it eats the same food and attains an age of about six years.

In Martial's day it had become the fashion for Roman ladies to keep mongooses, though he considered them as dangerous. Diodorus relates that they were fed on bread and milk, and Herodotus that they received rations of fish from the Nile.

Especially in Letopolis and Heracleopolis the mongoose was regarded as sacred, and dedicated to Lato and Eileithya according to some, and to Heracles according to others. Oddly enough, the neighbouring town of Arsinoe venerated the crocodile, the supposed arch-enemy of the mongoose. Wild stories were circulating regarding this matter, or at least they were told to visitors from abroad, much as is still done today. Crocodiles have the habit of sleeping with an open mouth, and the clever mongooses were said to rush into the mouth and eat up the inside of the reptile before it realized what was happening and to escape through a hole made in the belly. If a mongoose ever did such a thing, which is unlikely, it is certain that the crocodile would have shut its mouth before it was completely gutted, and thus carried the day.

It has been mentioned already that there are many good representations of the mongoose on Egyptian paintings. In the Roman period it is shown in Pompeii on a mosaic of evidently Egyptian inspiration (Fig. 18 : 1). The British Museum has a

FIG. 18 : 1. Mongoose attacking a snake in an Egyptian delta scene. Mosaic from Pompeii

sculpture of one standing on its hind legs, and there is a Hadrianic coin from Panopolis on which the mongoose replaces the more usual crocodile as the symbol of Egypt.

In later times, with increasing density of population, the importance of the mongoose was eclipsed by that of the cat, especially as the danger from vipers receded. Some may still be kept today in outlying districts, and Europeans living in the tropics like them as pets. But the ordinary Arab dislikes the beast because it has become fond of taking poultry which, of course, was practically unknown in ancient Egypt. It is also very partial to eggs, and at Thebes and Memphis is often shown searching for eggs and young birds in the papyrus thickets. This is a natural propensity which at one time caused it to be regarded as holy, for it does not despise the eggs of the crocodile, according to Diodorus, and this may well have caused the antagonism between the cities of Heracleopolis and Arsinoe. The introduction of domestic fowl changed the situation, mainly from the Hellenistic period onwards, but the mongoose never lost its popularity entirely.

GROUP V

Various Other Mammals

T HE groups so far distinguished, i.e. the pre-agricultural herds and herders, the crop-robbers, the suppliers of labour and the pest-destroyers, are basic and natural. As man became familiar with domestication and realized its potentialities he began to capture and deliberately subdue many other species, only some of which have proved permanent gains. This group comprises the rodents, of which the most important is the rabbit, and some carnivores and ruminants, of which the most important appears to have been the gazelle.

In the New World the llama and its relatives were domesticated under conditions that are still obscure, and finally there are some pets pure and simple which are too modern to attract much attention in this context.

19

The Small Rodents

THE RABBIT

SCIENTIFIC NAMES—*Oryctolagus cuniculus* (L.) (originally in Spain only, now from Morocco and Algeria, the Azores, through Europe to Russia. Most recently introduced in Australia, etc).

HARES—*Lepus europaeus* Pallas (European hare; from France and Britain east throughout Europe, Asia, south to Syria and east to Kazakstan and Persia). *L. timidus* L. (varying hare; Ireland, Scotland, Alps, Scandinavia, Finland, northern Russia and Siberia to Manchuria and Japan).

I T IS virtually certain that after the end of the Last Glaciation the wild rabbit was restricted to the Iberian peninsula, though at the present day rabbits that are wild in the biological sense and have never passed through a phase of domestication are found from Algeria and the Azores to Russia, countries to which they have spread with the help of man. In several areas they have developed minor differences from the Spanish form and received scientific names, of which six are at present recognized. Three of these refer to rabbits from Algeria and Morocco, which are in all probability one geographical race (*Oryctolagus cuniculus algirus* Loche). The second race occupies the north-western Mediterranean region, the Canaries, Azores and Madeira. It is called *O.c. huxleyi* Haeckel, a name first given to the rabbit of Porto Santo which will be discussed presently. The Mediterranean rabbit is small, weighing only 1 to 1.25 kg.; in this race is included the Spanish rabbit. Whether the form that occurs around the mouth of the Rhône in southern France (*O.c. brachyotus*

Trouessart) deserves a separate name remains to be seen. Its ears are believed to be comparatively short. Finally, we are left with the north European race, of the remainder of France, Ireland, Britain, central and eastern Europe. It is much larger than the Mediterranean race, weighing 1.5 to 2 kg.

Fossil remains of rabbits are known from Gibraltar, northern Italy, France, Switzerland, Belgium, Germany and England, but in most cases their bones are not contemporary with those of the Pleistocene faunas with which they were found. They are intrusive, late specimens, and introduced by burrowing into deeper layers. There are a few exceptions, however. In Gorham's Cave, Gibraltar (Zeuner, 1953b), the rabbit is undoubtedly an Upper Pleistocene species. This is not surprising as the rabbit is indigenous in the Iberian peninsula. The only other area where it appears to occur as a genuine fossil is the Dordogne, France (Lacorre, 1937), whence it has been recorded from the Magdalenian V to the Azilian, but not earlier or later. This would correspond to the end of the Last Glaciation and the early Postglacial.

Fossil hares have been found in Miocene deposits in Oregon, the Pliocene of the Auvergne and of the Indian Siwaliks, and the Pleistocene of Europe and America. Some of these have occasionally been referred to as fossil rabbits, but this is a mistake. The rabbit is osteologically well differentiated from the hares, and hares and rabbits do not interbreed.

The rabbit entered the human orbit at a late date, at any rate as a domesticated animal in the strict sense not before the Middle Ages. It was, however, kept and reared in captivity long before this and became popular in Roman times.

As the rabbit is very adaptable and prolific, and today distributed over all the five continents, it is curious that its domestication should have begun so late. The reason is almost certainly geographical: the rabbit was in Postglacial times originally confined to the Iberian peninsula. There it is indigenous, for it occurs in large quantities in the Pleistocene deposits of Gorham's Cave, Gibraltar, as mentioned already, and elsewhere. During the Last Glaciation it appears to have spread to south-western France also, and it is conceivable that its presence in the Provence during the first centuries of the Christian era was due to natural migration.

On the whole, palaeontology suggests a restriction of the rabbit's area to the extreme south-west of Europe. The most obvious explanation is that this species is fond of open country and a temperate climate, and that the dense forests of the post-Pleistocene prevented it from spreading until man opened up northern Europe on a large scale. Even then, however, it did not spread naturally but was helped by man.

The rabbit entered the realm of history when the Phoenicians reached the Iberian shores about 1100 B.C. They were struck by the abundance of a small mammal that lived in burrows, somewhat like the hyrax of their own country which in Semitic tongues is called shephan (Arabic *thafan*, Hebrew *shofon*). They gave the newly discovered shore the name, i-shephan-im, of which the latinized form is Hispania.

Incidentally, the Hebrew word, *shofon,* which means the hyrax, was translated as coney or rabbit by several translators of the Bible. The correct identification was first pointed out by Tristram.

The fact that neither Aristotle nor Xenophon mentions the rabbit proves that it was unknown in the eastern Mediterranean in the fourth century B.C. Similarly, it was lacking in Italy, where the hare only was known In the second century B.C., however, the rabbit occurred in Corsica according to Polybios. How it reached that island is not clear, especially since it is difficult to believe that the Romans took it there without importing it into Italy.

This appears to have happened in the first century B.C. Varro, to whom we owe valuable information also about bees, is keen on the idea of keeping rabbits in *leporaria.* These were large gardens containing cover and surrounded by a white-washed wall into which were placed hares caught in traps, to be used in due course in the kitchen. Two species of hares were kept by the Romans in this way, the European hare and also the varying hare whose flesh is rather more like that of the rabbit. It is noteworthy that the leporaria should have functioned, for hares are difficult to keep in captivity. Evidently these hare-gardens were large, carefully laid out and well furnished with the necessary cover to keep the inmates comfortable. Varro, by suggesting that rabbits should be put into leporaria, became the father of the domesticated rabbit. The process was, however, more complicated than it would appear to have been at first sight. Firstly, rabbits and hares do not live on friendly terms, and it is usually the rabbit that remains victorious in a combat. Secondly, whilst hares are surface animals with open nests, rabbits are burrowers. Evidently the walls of the leporaria had to be continued below ground-level to some depth to retain the animals, and before experience in this respect had been gained it is likely that many rabbits escaped into the Italian countryside and started a wild population there. The third point is the most interesting, and it is Professor H. Nachtsheim (1949) who has made its significance clear in his book called *From Wild Beast to Domestic Animal.* It is the remarkable fact that, in a leporarium, selection would work in favour of wild characters and against domestication, since, owing to the necessity of catching or hunting the rabbits, the quickest and 'wildest' would have the best chances of survival, whilst the 'tamer' ones would be killed off. This state of affairs must have continued until the rabbits were no longer allowed to breed on their own. To this we shall return presently.

Some valuable information about the rabbit situation in the first century A.D. is due to Strabo and to Pliny. According to the former, a single pair of rabbits had been let loose in the Balearic Islands, and their progeny had multiplied to such an extent that the inhabitants implored the Emperor Augustus either to send military aid or resettle the inhabitants elsewhere. At that time the ferret was in use already to catch rabbits (see p. 402). Evidently the little beasts were spreading rapidly.

But their Spanish origin was still known in the days of Hadrian (A.D. 117–138), who had a rabbit pictured on some of the coins of Spain.

Whilst hares will not normally breed in captivity, and are unlikely to have done so in the leporaria, the rabbits kept in such enclosures would not have hesitated to do so. This must have greatly enhanced their usefulness and, though selection would have operated in favour of wildness rather than tameness, breeding in captivity was a necessary preliminary to domestication. The rabbit continued in this condition for several centuries. The Roman practice was not abandoned after the fall of the empire. Barbarian princes continued it, perhaps not so much for the sake of the meat but in order to obtain some much-wanted small game. A remarkable French manuscript dates from A.D. 1393. In it, rabbit gardens are shown, and it is the ladies who are seen hunting them with bows and arrows, with clubs and with lap-dogs (Fig. 19 : 1).

The difficulty of maintaining the walls of rabbit gardens in an escape-proof condition must at all times have suggested the use of small islands where the construction of the costly wall was not necessary. This may account for the many rabbit islands known both in antiquity and later. In A.D. 1407 an island in the Lake of Schwerin in Mecklenburg that had been made into a rabbit garden is mentioned in a treaty between the King of Sweden and the Duke of Mecklenburg. Queen Elizabeth of England had rabbit islands in the sixteenth century, and her contem-

FIG. 19 : 1 (a) and (b). Medieval French drawings of rabbits being hunted in a rabbit garden by ladies. Published in 1393, reproduced by T. H. Wright (1871) and Nachtsheim (1949)

porary, King Henry IV of France, kept them in enclosures at Clichy, which is now a suburb of Paris. In the neighbourhood of Berlin, the island now called Pfaueninsel was once called the *Kaninchenwerder* (rabbit island), where rabbit-keeping was started in 1683 by Frederick Wilhelm, the Great Elector of Brandenburg. Under these conditions the rabbit must have retained the characters of the wild form. Mutations are likely to have been wiped out rather than allowed to survive.

The actual domestication was probably accomplished by medieval monks. In their seclusion they would have esteemed a meat supply which is so easily obtained. Moreover, the need of finding a variety of foods suitable for the season of Lent caused them to fall back on an item once much relished by the Romans, namely the unborn or newly born young of the rabbit. They were called *laurices*. It appears strange to us that such food should not have been ranged with 'meat', but beavers were regarded as fish and thus were allowed, a fact which has sadly contributed to the extinction of that large rodent in Europe. Evidently natural history was still in its infancy.

In or about A.D. 590 Bishop Gregory of Tours relates with disapproval how popular these rabbit foeti were in Lent. Nachtsheim has pointed out that this pre-dilection, combined with the necessity of keeping pregnant does within the stone walls of the monastery, created the conditions that may have led to proper domestication. The prerequisite of rabbit domestication is that breeding must take place above the ground, otherwise selection is not possible. Pregnant does that had been caught and were brought in to obtain the newly born litter would, deprived of their warren, build a nest in any odd corner of the courtyard or even drop their young just anywhere, as some rabbit does do even at the present day. As it was uneconomical to kill the mother to obtain the foeti, whilst lost litters saved the life of the mother and made it possible to produce a succession of such litters from a small permanent stock, breeding must have been attempted very early. These first experiments in breeding appear to have taken place in French monasteries between the sixth and the tenth centuries.

Under such conditions, and unlike those obtaining in a rabbit garden, selection of 'domesticated' qualities of the stock became inevitable. While the wild rabbit is shy, and while the stock kept in a leporarium would remain shy, life in a monastery would put a premium on tameness. Also, selection for greater size would soon begin, and as always notice would be taken of colour mutations which might have been believed to be associated with other desirable qualities. But for several centuries the wild coloration was the rule, for it is not until the middle of the sixteenth century that black, white, piebald and other colour variants are mentioned by Agricola. The earliest picture of a white rabbit dates from 1530; it is in the 'Madonna with the Rabbit' by Titian preserved in the Louvre. Aldrovandi, a contemporary of Agricola, speaks of rabbits four times the normal size, which were bred in Verona.

The distinction of the domesticated rabbit kept in the monasteries, and the rabbit of the rabbit gardens which in its environment was encouraged to retain 'wild' characters, thus becomes clear and Nachtsheim is right in calling the latter 'wild rabbits'. The spreading of the two types across Europe was thus independent. Wild rabbits spread from rabbit garden to rabbit garden (or island) under the supervision of the princes interested in game, and there must have been innumerable escapes. These rabbits originally descended from the wild stock of Spain never had a chance to develop characters of domestication, and they are the ancestors of the wild rabbits of northern Europe. In many countries they arrived later than the domesticated form. The earliest document relating the presence of the wild rabbit in central Europe is a woodcut of St Christopher from Buxheim near Memmingen in south Germany. It dates from 1423. On the other hand, the first known importation of domestic rabbits is nearly 300 years earlier. In 1149 the abbot of the Benedictine monastery of Corvey on the Weser asked the abbot of Solignac in France to send him two pairs of rabbits. Nachtsheim comments on this that the abbot of Corvey was not yet acquainted with the breeding habits of the rabbit, otherwise he would have asked for one buck and three does. In the middle of the twelfth century, therefore, the domesticated rabbit was only beginning to appear in central Europe.

By the middle of the seventeenth century domestic rabbit-breeding was in full swing in England. Darwin quotes Markham (1631) as authority for the presence of a silver-grey rabbit with an even mixture of black and white hair. For the first time the rabbit appears here as a fur animal. Aldrovandi, too, figures an ash-grey variety, and he mentions that the wild rabbit, abundant in the Dutch province of Zealand, provided large quantities of pelts.

At that time Leeuwenhook, the inventor of the microscope, wrote a letter to the Royal Society in which he mentioned the practice of his compatriots of crossing white does with wild bucks. The market required wild-coloured rabbits, and this coloration is dominant over white. Evidently the domesticated breeds had by then been established and one had started to breed for colour. White, black, 'blue' and the white-collared Dutch had appeared. Most other breeds are more recent. The Angora, for instance, appeared about 1723 when British sailors are supposed to have brought long-haired rabbits to Bordeaux. They may have hailed from the Black Sea area, though it is open to doubt whether rabbits were known there at all at that time. The name, of course, does not imply a Turkish origin, it is derived from the Angora goat.

It now remains to discuss the reverse process, that of the return to the wild state. In this respect the rabbit has been more successful than any other domesticated mammal. The earliest report is concerned with the rabbit of Porto Santo, an island near Madeira. The Portuguese seafarers had the habit of colonizing desolate islands with goats and rabbits. This was done for the sake of shipwrecked sailors, but it resulted in far-reaching changes in the fauna and flora. Prestrello, the colonizer of Madeira, took domesticated rabbits to Porto Santo in 1418. They became feral in a short time, decreased much in size (the Porto Santo rabbit is the smallest of all rabbits, weighing not more than 600–800 grammes) and developed a slight colour variant. It became extremely shy. Both Darwin and Haeckel studied this animal and came to the conclusion that a new species had emerged here in the course of four centuries. It was named *Lepus huxleyi* by Haeckel, a name which is now generally applied to the Mediterranean wild rabbit. Since the Porto Santo rabbit is feral, i.e. descended from domesticated stock of Portugese origin and, therefore, not identical with the original wild Spanish race, the latter may, after all, require a name of its own.

As to the status of the Porto Santo rabbit, Nachtsheim (1941) has now established that it is not a species. He has succeeded in crossing a female with a buck which in turn was a cross of a Greek wild rabbit with a domestic Ermine.

The rabbits of Australia, too, are feral, and by no means the descendants of wild stock. They started their victorious expansion about ninety years ago. Many other examples are known from smaller islands; they show that the reversion to wild life soon leads to a uniformity of the population, though one that often retains features of domestic origin.

THE DORMOUSE

SCIENTIFIC NAME—*Glis glis* L. (syn. *Myoxus glis*), (the Fat Dormouse; wild from northern Spain through continental Europe to Asia Minor, Turkestan, Persia and Palestine.

Apart from the rabbit, one other rodent was in antiquity kept under conditions of domestication. This is the 'Fat' Dormouse, a species which is larger than British dormice and which occurs all over Europe in forests. It lives on trees and feeds on acorns and nuts. Like other dormice, it hibernates in hollow trees and begins this period of rest in a very fat state.

The Romans, who were always anxious to secure tasty tit-bits for the table, did not overlook this small rodent. *Gliraria*, enclosures with trees, were constructed by the end of the second century B.C., and the dormice were fattened in them with acorns, walnuts and chestnuts. Wealthy Romans had the ambition to confront their guests with the largest possible *glires*. Scales were even placed on the table in order to weigh them before they were consumed and, according to Ammianus Marcellinus, notaries were present to book and confirm the correct weight. In these circumstances it is not surprising that the dormice were placed in small earthenware pots, called *dolia*, in which they had little room to move about (Fig. 19 : 2). With ample food they thus became exceedingly fat. These containers had holes and ridges inside.

The practice of eating dormice was so evidently a luxury that it was from time to time branded as such, and the *Lex Aemilia* of 78 B.C. prohibited their consumption.

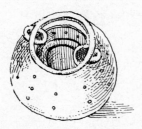

FIG. 19 : 2. *Dolia*, small pottery vessels with holes and a shelf inside, in which dormice were fattened by the Romans. After Keller

But this law had no lasting effect. In the days of Caesar they were well known, for Varro mentions them. Martial referred to them in the first century A.D. and they occur in many other historians' and poets' works. Whilst the keeping of rabbits in the *leporaria* continued into the Middle Ages, the *gliraria* disappeared. The tiny dormice were too much of a delicacy for the rich to be considered worth while as food in the turbulent period of the Migrations.

20

Experimental and Occasional Domestication

IN THIS group I have combined a heterogeneous assemblage of animals none of which has attained to a permanent and economically important position. They all are, however, relatively late cases of domestication, *except possibly the gazelle*, about which more evidence is required. But even its case would be due to the application of practices learned with the goat and sheep. All were thus systematically domesticated, mainly in that period of Old Kingdom Egypt when it was the fashion to try to domesticate everything that could be managed. The species here treated (the list is not complete) are:

> the cheetah, kept for gazelle-hunting;
> the hyaena, kept for food;
> the fox, kept for food;
> the elk, kept for transport;
> the fallow deer, kept possibly for religious purposes, and for food and sport;
> the gazelle, kept for food and sport;
> various other antelopes and the Nubian ibex.

Of these, only the cheetah is still used, and the fallow deer which has managed to spread over a wide area in Europe, but neither of them can be regarded as economically important.

THE CHEETAH

SCIENTIFIC NAME—*Acinonyx jubatus* Schreb. (Africa to India, now extinct over much of the area).

The cheetah (Fig. 20 : 1) with its spotted skin, high legs, long neck and small head is a well-known denizen of zoological gardens. Unlike the leopard, for which it has often been mistaken, it is a friendly animal and easy to tame. I have no records of its ever having been bred in captivity, but it has been tamed for several thousand years, to assist man in his hunting activities, sometimes alongside his dogs.

The cheetah is, unlike other cats, a runner. It is extremely fast and capable of catching gazelle, but it has little endurance and when the gazelle keeps on long enough it can shake off the cheetah easily. The element of surprise is therefore essential in its hunting.

FIG. 20 : 1. Cheetahs in Kenya. Photo J. S. Karurah

Cheetahs were tamed in ancient Egypt. In the tomb of Rekhmere it is clearly shown with its collar, being led (fifteenth century B.C.). There are a number of pictures of cheetahs from the eighteenth (Fig. 20 : 2) and nineteenth dynasties, for instance at El Amarna (Fig. 20 : 3). By this time, therefore, it was used abundantly, but apparently not much earlier. Whether it was first tamed in Asia is, therefore, a question worth considering. The Mesopotamian evidence points to a comparatively late employment of the cheetah, namely in the Assyrian period. One thus gains the impression that it was first tamed and used in Egypt, whence the practice spread to Assyria, and thence finally to India and central Asia.

Keller mentions some undated Greek period representations from Kyrena and Vulci. The Vandals in North Africa knew of cheetahs hunting together with dogs.

FIG. 20 : 2. Cheetah brought as tribute to Thothmes III (c. 1501–1477 B.C.)

FIG. 20 : 3. Cheetah brought to the King of Egypt as tribute from the south. Tomb of Meryra, Tell-el-Amarna, eighteenth dynasty, c. 1450 B.C.

Classical references to the Indian cheetah are somewhat uncertain, like those of Aelian and Arian, who speak of 'lions' and 'jackals' on leads. There are, however, a number of coins of Taxila, Bactria (Fig. 20 : 4) and of the Indo-Scythian period (Fig. 20 : 5), which show a high-legged beast with long neck and short head. It is usually regarded as a maneless lion, but the characteristics mentioned are typical of the cheetah, which is indigenous in that area.

The Mongol princes of the Middle Ages used the animal in large numbers, if one can trust the records, by the thousand. Marco Polo relates that Kublai Khan used them in the thirteenth century. The cheetahs sat on the horses behind their keepers, and were allowed to jump off and pursue the game when the chances appeared good.

Cheetahs are still tamed at the present day. The Indian race, however, has become extinct, and East African specimens have to supply the needs of Indian princes.

FIG. 20 : 4. Indo-Greek square bronze coin of Agathocles, 175–165 B.C., showing a cheetah. Natural size. Author's collection

FIG. 20 : 5. Indo-Scythian bronze coin of Azes I, 90–40 B.C., with cheetah. Twice natural size. Author's collection

419

THE HYAENA

SCIENTIFIC NAMES—GROUP OF THE SPOTTED HYAENA—*Hyaena crocuta* Erxleben (spotted hyaena; Recent, Africa), *H. spelaea* Goldfuss (cave hyaena; Pleistocene, Europe), *H. perrieri* Croizet and Jobert (Villafranchian, Europe).

GROUP OF THE STRIPED HYAENA—*Hyaena hyaena* L., syn. *H. striata* Zimm. (striped hyaena; Recent, India, western Asia, north-east Africa), *H. brunnea* Thunberg (brown hyaena; South Africa), *H. arvernensis* Croizet and Jobert (Villafranchian and Lower Pleistocene, Europe).

That hyaenas were the contemporaries of Old Stone Age man is well known. Their remains have come to light in many European caves which have yielded artefacts and bones of early man also. The 'cave hyaena' is indeed regarded as the counterpart of the cave bear and, to a minor degree, of the cave lion; the latter and the hyaena having been at one time regarded as sound evidence for a hot climate. That this view is thoroughly mistaken is now well known. Nevertheless, the hyaena has retained its romantic appeal for the archaeologist.

The cave hyaena of the Mousterian and Upper Palaeolithic was a relative of the spotted hyaena which survives in Africa south of the Sahara. The striped hyaena, however, now a denizen of India, south-western Asia and northern and eastern Africa, was present in Europe in the Lower Pleistocene, and hence known to the makers of the Abbevillian (or Chellian) hand-axes.

The spotted and striped hyaenas have similar habits. Their principal food consists of the carcasses of animals that have died or been killed by other carnivores. They kill their own prey to a very limited extent only. In devouring their food they do not stop at the bones, many of which are crushed and eaten. The floor of a hyaena's den, therefore, is strewn with smaller fragments of bones which are either sharp or, if they have passed through the intestines of the animal, corroded and rounded off. The excrements of hyaenas contain much bone matter, for which reason they are easily fossilized. Such excrements, called coprolites, have been found in many geological deposits containing hyaena remains. They are common in Palaeolithic caves, and they have also been found in some Bronze Age tombs at Jericho.

Hyaenas are efficient diggers. They make use of natural caves, shelters, crevices and of burrows of other animals. Such situations are excavated by the hyaenas to make dens which afford protection and in which the young are brought forth. Hence a comparatively large number of young specimens and even foeti have been discovered. This habit, however, renders the hyaena an awkward species from the stratigraphical point of view. Its burrows are liable to upset the stratigraphy of a site, particularly in narrow caves, and to introduce the remains of the species into horizons to which they do not properly belong. It is necessary, therefore, to study with special care the strata and artefact levels of caves containing hyaena remains.

FIG. 20 : 6. Striped hyaena (note the characteristic long tail) being stuffed with roast goose or duck (see also FIG. 20 : 17). In the lower register the hieroglyph bird which is commonly regarded as a chicken, but is almost certainly a quail. Old Kingdom Egypt, Mastaba of Gen-ni-ka, c. 2500 B.C.

FIG. 20 : 7. Striped hyaena being shepherded by a man. Evidence for regular keeping of hyaenas in Old Kingdom Egypt, sixth dynasty, c. 2750 B.C.

Of the three Recent species, the striped hyaena occurs from Africa north of the Sahara through Egypt, Arabia, Palestine and Mesopotamia to India. This beast is smaller than the brown hyaena, and it is less of a digger, preferring rocky districts, including rock tombs, as an abode. It is also less ferocious. The writer, when searching for prehistoric sites in the volcanic desert hills of eastern Jordan, once nearly stepped on one that was lying between the rocks. It proceeded to walk away apologetically, very different from the lively and aggressive interest that brown hyaenas in Kenya take in archaeological visitors. Yet in Palestine the striped hyaena is the most feared of all animals. It is conceivable that because of its practice of exhuming buried human bodies, and of making great efforts for this purpose, it is detested and feared for personal and religious reasons. This, however, does not deter at least some Palestinians from eating it, as did the workmen at the excavations of Qumran, the well-known Essene monastery of the Dead Sea scrolls.

This habit of robbing tombs of their carcasses is evidenced by the presence of coprolites in an Early Bronze Age tomb at Jericho. The striped hyaenas cannot have failed to do the same in ancient Egypt, a country where ancestor worship was so highly developed. But the Egyptians of the Old Kingdom not only ate hyaenas, they stuffed them with food (in Fig. 20 : 6 this resembles roast duck or goose) to fatten them. That this was the striped hyaena and not the spotted is shown by the manner of depicting the bushy tail. This is the best feature by which to distinguish hyaenas from other animals represented on reliefs and mural paintings (Fig. 20 : 7).

Obviously there is no proof that the striped hyaena was compelled to breed in captivity in Egypt and thus domesticated in the strict sense of the word. It is, however, perfectly conceivable, especially as some pictures show young animals accompanying the adults. In any case, it is unlikely that the operation of stuffing would be successful with captured adults. The beasts' legs had to be tied to immobilize them, and they were placed on their backs. Young hyaenas are known to be very tamable, according to Lydekker who knew them in India, and to become attached to their masters. Hence it is likely that the Egyptian practice of hyaena domestication was based on the taming of the young, either captured or bred.

A few Egyptian pictures show hyaenas associated with greyhounds. Keller thought that these were not hyaenas but Cape hunting-dogs, an African species, but this is not likely. The association suggests that hyaenas were used for hunting as well as for food, and in this respect they may be regarded as the predecessors of the cheetah.

The other two living species, the brown hyaena of South Africa and the spotted hyaena of Africa south of the Sahara, are not known ever to have been treated in this manner. It is only noteworthy that the hyaena which inhabited the caves of Europe, alternately with Palaeolithic man in the Upper Pleistocene, was the spotted one which is now absent even from North Africa.

THE FOX

SCIENTIFIC NAMES—Villafranchian—*Vulpes alopecoides* Major (extinct).
Recent—*Vulpes vulpes* L. (common fox; northern part of northern hemisphere), *V. corsac* L. (steppe fox; eastern Europe, Western Asia), *Alopex lagopus* L. (arctic fox; arctic portions of Europe and Asia).

The foxes are not likely to have played an important part in the economy of Palaeolithic man, though from the Upper Palaeolithic onwards it is conceivable that they were hunted for the sake of their pelts and perhaps eaten also. It is indeed noteworthy that their remains are rare in all deposits which antedate the Upper Palaeolithic.

Three species of foxes occur in the Pleistocene fauna of Europe: the common or red fox, the arctic fox and the steppe fox or corsac. Little is known about their ancestry, for of the several 'species' of *Vulpes* which have been described from the Pliocene of Italy and France only one, namely *V. alopecoides* from the Upper Pliocene of Tuscany, has to be regarded as a true fox. Although still imperfectly known, Stehlin considers it as closely related to the common fox. In Püspökfürdö in Hungary, Kormos found the remains of a fox which he was unable to distinguish from the common red fox. This deposit is regarded as Lower Pleistocene. The mandible which Newton (1880, 1882) described from the Bacton Forest Bed of East Anglia, however, should not be referred to the common fox without reservation. An upper jaw, incidentally, which Newton quotes from the Red Crag of Boyton in Suffolk, is regarded by Stehlin as that of a peculiar species of dog.

Whilst this evidence suggests that the lineage of the European common fox goes back to the European Pleistocene, the origin of the two other forms is entirely obscure. The few Villafranchian and Lower Pleistocene fragments which have been assigned to the lineages of the arctic fox or the corsac have been thus placed merely on account of their small dimensions. Body size is, however, an uncertain and variable character, and its use in the genus of the fox is very questionable since the common fox comprises a race of very small stature which occurs on Corsica and Sardinia.

From the Middle Pleistocene, only the common fox is known, as for instance from the Thames deposits of Grays and Ilford in Essex, and the species is also found in some Last Interglacial sites. But it becomes frequent in the first phase of the Last Glaciation, when it was the contemporary of the late Neanderthaler. In Magdalenian sites it is equally common. This sudden 'blossoming' of the species may, nevertheless, be fictitious and merely due to the fact that from the Mousterian onwards man frequently repaired to caves, which had been a popular abode of foxes since time immemorial.[1] Our search for cave man, therefore, inevitably produces fox remains from the same archaeological periods. On the other hand, the use of the fox as a supplier of flesh and fur cannot be excluded. Degerbøl records the species from Maglemose in Denmark, considering it as possibly domesticated.

In the Neolithic lake-dwellings of Switzerland remains of the common fox are more numerous than those of the dog. There is no doubt that the fox was eaten, for cut- and tooth-marks have been observed on many bones by Rütimeyer. Hauck (1950) even went so far as to suspect that the lake-dwellers had domesticated the fox, because arthritic ossifications are occasionally found which connect solidly the astragalus and the calcaneum. This fusion must have impaired the mobility of the hind feet and hence is unlikely to have occurred in nature. Another feature which can be quoted in support of Hauck's idea is the small size of most foxes from the lake-dwellings. They are smaller and more graceful even than the small Corsican race. This argument gains in strength by the fact that, apart from the small fox, a fox of normal size occurs, though rarely, in the lake-dwellings (see Hescheler and Kuhn, 1949). It is tempting to explain these as the wild form which was hunted, regarding the small foxes as domesticated or semi-domesticated. Whatever the truth, these small foxes from the lake-dwellings require a special explanation.

Whilst the common fox is on the whole an animal of the forests, the arctic fox is a denizen of the tundra, to which environment it is well adapted. In appearance it differs widely from the common fox, mainly because of its different coloration, long fur and rounded ears. But osteologically it differs little, except in its small size. Unlike the common fox, which feeds on all kinds of prey up to the size of lambs, the arctic fox has specialized in hunting lemmings and similar rodents of the tundra. It does not despise carrion. It is able to withstand famine and stores food in its hide-outs between rocks or under the snow. These provisions are collected and eaten by the tribes inhabiting the tundra, and Thévenin considers it possible that Upper Palaeolithic man may have done the same.

The arctic fox is not known from deposits antedating the Last Glaciation, when it appears with the cold Mousterian, as at Wallertheim in Rhenish Hesse, Sirgen-stein in Württemberg, at Hastière and La Naulette in Belgium and the Grotte de l'Observatoire in Monaco. The arctic fox from the Grotte de Cotencher in Switzer-land probably belongs to the same group. The species occurs furthermore in Aurignacian sites, and it becomes frequent in the Magdalenian of Czechoslovakia, Germany, Switzerland, Belgium and France. It has, however, never penetrated into either Italy or Spain.

The presence of the corsac in the Pleistocene of central and western Europe has been postulated repeatedly. The evidence, however, has to be treated with some

---

[1] It should also be noted that remains of the fox, a burrowing animal, will often be found in levels which are earlier than the time of its life activity.

reserve. It is, of course, quite conceivable that this small steppe fox, which lives mainly on gerbils and other small rodents, was able to extend its area westwards on the loess steppe in company with the saiga antelope. But the identification of its remains is not beyond doubt. Whilst the *Canis fossilis meridionalis* of Nordmann, which comes from Odessa, has perhaps rightly been assigned to the corsac, as also one from Quedlinburg in north Germany described by Dietrich, those described by Woldřich from Czechoslovakia are regarded by Stehlin as more probably belonging to the arctic fox. Kormos claims to have found several corsac-like foxes in the Lower Pleistocene of Hungary and Transylvania, and Stehlin considered it possible that some exceptionally small fox bones from Cotencher belong to the corsac.

THE ELK OR MOOSE

SCIENTIFIC NAMES—*Alces latifrons* Johnson (Villafranchian and Lower and Middle Pleistocene elk).
A. alces L. (Recent elk of Europe, moose of North America).

The elk (*Alces alces* L), or moose as it is called in North America, survives in the higher latitudes of Europe (Fig. 20 : 8), Asia and North America. It was more widely distributed right into the Middle Ages, but, being a large and much-coveted game and, moreover, dependent on forests, it had to yield before the advancing, extensive agriculture of medieval communities. An essential item in the diet of the elk is tree-bark. Experiments in zoological gardens have shown that it cannot live on a diet lacking bark or woody matter.

The earliest elk remains known are from the Villafranchian deposits of Senèze in France. This type is called *Alces latifrons*; it differed from the recent elk among other characters in the larger size and the longer beams of its antlers and the broader frontals. Apart from this difference it is likely to have resembled in appearance the modern moose of North America. *Alces latifrons*, is, however, supposed to have been a denizen of open country rather than of forest. On the other hand, the Interglacial specimen found by Schmidt (1934) near Göttingen had been living in an environment much like that preferred by the modern elk: coniferous forest with some birch, alder and oak, and some grass and heather on the margin of a lake. This is, on the evidence of an Etruscan rhinoceros found in association with this elk, a Lower Pleistocene deposit. It is thus possible that *Alces* changed its habits in the course of the early Pleistocene and became a forest-dweller, taking a trend opposed to that of many other Pleistocene mammals which adapted themselves to life in open country. That *A. alces* is the descendant of *A. latifrons* is, however, not strictly proven, though suggested by the chronological sequence and by their morphological resemblance. Reynolds is inclined to regard the differences as of little value and doubts that they were really different enough to be regarded as separate species. It has on the whole become the custom to call the remains of fossil elks *A. alces* from the Last Interglacial onwards. But there are exceptions, such as the *A. latifrons* of the Mousterian stations of Taubach and Ehringsdorf.

FIG. 20 : 8. Young male elk in Schorfheide Forest, Mark Brandenberg, Germany. Photo Lutz Heck

A. latifrons was the contemporary of Lower Palaeolithic man from the pre-Abbevillian to the Acheulian and Levalloisian. The species is known, for instance, from the Cromer Forest Bed ('First' Interglacial), and it occurs in Mauer together with Heidelberg man. It is altogether strange that the remains are rare in Pleistocene deposits, and this at localities where man was absent and where he undoubtedly did not interfere with the fauna. Very few pictorial representations of the elk by

Palaeolithic man are known. It is a mistake to argue from this that the elk was rare. In any case, it is likely that a large animal living in swampy forest was relatively safe. Palaeolithic man would not normally live or hunt in such an environment. If he did, as Neanderthal man appears to have done at Taubach and Ehringsdorf in the Mousterian, and long before this Heidelberg man at Mauer, he would have selected the weaker specimens, i.e. mainly the hinds and the young. Soergel found that, at the sites just mentioned, antlers are curiously rare (and at Mauer absent altogether, although the remains of fourteen specimens are known), and he explains this by pointing out that the elk-stag is a dangerous animal, which the Tungus of Siberia fear more than the bear. The fact, then, that the elk never played a great part in the economy of early man is due to the difficult environment in which he lived, and also to the difficult and dangerous chase. Nevertheless, man has tried to subdue this proud and intractable species.

Pictorial evidence for the elk is scanty. It appears to be mainly of Scythian origin. This people used the elk with its antlers in many ways as an ornament. The Pazaryk elk (Fig. 20 : 9) deserves special mention, and beautiful gold badges of elk were found at Maikop (*c.* 2000 B.C.; Fig. 20 : 10). At Memphis an Egypto-Roman collection of plaster-casts of silver vessels was found, dating from about 200 B.C. On one a woman is seen milking a deer, with a strong stag standing in front which is plainly

FIG. 20 : 9. Elk as shown by Scythian art.
From the frozen kurgan tombs of Pazaryk,
Altai Mountains, *c.* 500 B.C.

FIG. 20 : 10. Small gold casting of an elk from Maikop, Kuban area, east of Black Sea, length *c.* 3 cm. Early Bronze Age, *c.* 2000 B.C. The Scythian style which becomes typical of that area 1500 years later is already noticeable. Originals in Antikensammlung Berlin, and in Metropolitan Museum, New York

an elk (Fig. 20 : 11).[1] These vessels come, according to Rubensohn, from Olbia on the north of the Black Sea, which would once more point to Scythian origin.

Fig. 20 : 11. Egypto-Roman plaster cast of a scene of elks being milked, about 200 B.C., probably from north of the Black Sea. After Hilzheimer

Written records concerning the elk are equally scanty in the classical period. They improved only as northern countries became better known. Pliny (VIII, 39) relates garbled stories about two animals, one the *alces*, the other the *achlis*, but both evidently elks:

In the north there lives the *alces*, resembling an ox but with longer ears and neck. There also lives on the Scandinavian island a beast resembling the elk, of which much has been said though nobody has seen it in Rome, the *achlis*. It has no joints in the legs, wherefore, it sleeps leaning against a tree. This tree has to be cut down with a saw, if one wants to catch the animal.

The upper lip is described as very long, which is correct, but that it grazes walking backwards for this reason is nonsense. Whilst the descriptive details are reasonably accurate, the appended stories are inventions.

It is not generally known that the elk has been tamed and used for riding and as a draught animal. If one draws the line between taming and domestication by restricting the latter to cases of deliberate breeding of animals kept in captivity, the elk never was a truly domesticated animal. Karl XI, King of Sweden from 1660 to 1697, made his couriers ride on elks, which were able to cover greater distances in a shorter time than horses. Elks were used as draught animals in Sweden, and also in Estonia, where the city council of Tartu prohibited their use in the seventeenth century because they frightened the horses. And Pfizenmayer (1926), the excavator of one of the frozen mammoths in eastern Siberia, was told by old Yakuts that elks

[1] Hilzheimer was inclined to regard this as a reindeer. The stag, however, is an elk, and reindeer did not occur as far south as the Black Sea.

were used for riding as late as the beginning of the nineteenth century and that the Russian government stopped the practice in order to prevent Yakut criminals from escaping on these animals, which were evidently faster and more enduring than horses.

That the practice was at all known renders its antiquity probable. The evidence is, however, somewhat conjectural. On the rock engravings from the Zalavrouga River, north-west Russia, a man is shown on skis behind a bearded and long-eared stag. This appears to be an elk (Fig. 20 : 12). In other parts of this group of engravings, however, reindeer appear to be shown, and one of them is connected with a man by

FIG. 20 : 12. Bowman on skis behind an elk, either pursuing or being drawn. One of the rock engravings from the Zalavrouga River, north-west Russia, second millennium B.C. This is not a reindeer (as commonly stated) since the legs are high and the elk's 'beard' is plainly shown. After Clark

means of an engraved line. Hančar and others regard this as a spear or lasso. On the other hand, it is conceivable that hunters were drawn on skis by tamed elks or reindeer. The age of these engravings is, according to Hančar, early second millennium B.C.

These brief observations suggest that the elk was at one time important to northern peoples, but it never succeeded in competing seriously with the horse and the cow.

THE MINOR RUMINANTS

SCIENTIFIC NAMES—*Dama dama* L. (common fallow deer; wild in Asia Minor, introduced in the Mediterranean and Europe).
D. mesopotamica Brooke (Persian or Mesopotamian fallow deer; originally Palestine, Iraq, Persia. Now restricted to Persian Chouzistan).

Gazella dorcas L. (Dorcas gazelle, ghazal, afri, rhezel; North Africa from Rio de Oro to Egypt, Sudan, Abyssinia, Lake Chad; and from Sinai, Arabia, Palestine to Syria).
G. gazella Pallas (mountain gazelle, idmi, chinkara; distribution like that of *G. dorcas*, but extending east into India).

Addax nasomaculatus Blainville (addax or mendes antelope; from Rio de Oro through northern Sahara to Egypt and eastern Sudan).

Oryx tao H. Smith (= *O. algazel* Oken) (scimetar-horned oryx antelope; Sahara from Atlantic to Sudan).
O. leucoryx Pallas (Arabian oryx; Arabia and parts of Iraq).

For *Capra ibex* see Goats, p. 129.

In Old Kingdom times, when experimental domestication was at its climax in Egypt, many species of antelopes and other ruminants were kept under conditions of domestication. Very often they are shown with collars round their necks. It is impossible to ascertain, however, to what extent breeding took place in captivity. The species are mentioned here for a variety of reasons although they never attained economic importance. There is one possible exception, the gazelle of pre-pottery Neolithic Palestine, as will be shown presently. Apart from the Egyptian orbit, the western Asiatic area contributes a species to this group, the fallow deer.

FALLOW DEER

The fallow deer exists in two distinct forms which by some are regarded as species, the common fallow deer of Asia Minor with its spotted coat and large antlers terminating in a flattened shovel. This is the species which was at one time sacred to Hittite gods and later to Diana of Ephesus. In the wild state it occurs from the south-west end of the Sea of Marmora along the south coast of Asia Minor as far as Adana, and in the Taurus Range. This present-day distribution can be supplemented by localities of the Hittite Empire of central Asia Minor, though not with great accuracy as the deer may have been imported in many places. One of the Hittite gods is frequently shown standing on such a deer, the specific identity of which is borne out by the distal palmation of the antlers. Two Hittite localities, Zendjirli and Carchemish, if genuine, extend the area of the common fallow deer to the Euphrates. It appears also to have existed at Nimrud where the common fallow deer is known from a relief representing a winged human figure holding a deer in his arms.

The common fallow deer spread into the Western countries during the Roman period. It appears in mural paintings at Pompeii and in other places, and it is occasionally shown on coins of the Imperial period.

The ancient Greeks in all probability were familiar with the common fallow deer, since it occurred in the neighbourhood of their Asiatic colonies. Occasionally it appears in art, but usually in contexts that suggest importation from Asia (Fig. 20 : 13), as, for instance, in the Mycenaean tombs. The fact pointed out by Keller that the Greeks tended to take over the topics of the scene from Asiatic prototypes, replacing the fallow deer by European red deer, clearly indicates, however, that the latter kind was more familiar to them.

FIG. 20 : 13. Silver drachm of Eretria, Euboea, 369–336 B.C., showing a fallow deer being attacked by a lion. The race is clearly that of Asia Minor, and no wild fallow deer are known to have existed in Euboea. They must, therefore, have been imported. Lions were abundant in Macedonia shortly before this period, namely in the Persian wars. Twice natural size. Author's collection

Being sacred to Diana of Ephesus, the common fallow deer appeared on many coins of that city, as well as some others. One of the earliest of these is an electrum stater of the period 700–480 B.C. found at Halicarnassus, now in the British Museum. It shows a feeding stag and an inscription in archaic letters, 'φαννος (or φαενος) εμι σεμα', which has been read 'I am the badge of Phanes' (Head, 1959, Pl. 1, Fig. 9, pp. 2–3). Other readings are less likely, for Seltman (1955, p. 28) compares it with a scarab seal stone inscribed in archaic characters 'θερσιος εμι σαμα' and continuing 'do not open me', evidently to be used on letters. 'Phanes' has thus always been accepted as the name of a moneyer, a strange thing at that early period. Phanes is, however, the name of a local love-deity, too, who represented a buzzing bee and was regarded as the son of Artemis. The bee (see p. 499) indeed appears on the reverse of many Ephesian coins, the obverse of which has the stag, and I consider it most likely that this Phanes was not a moneyer at all, but the sacred bee which, in the days of incuse squares on the reverses, made his first appearance in writing on the obverse. A second coin of this kind, inscribed φανεος, has been added to the collection of the British Museum more recently. It is illustrated in the appendix to Head's monograph (1959, Pl. 51, Fig. 3) and confirms, in my opinion, the allusion to the sacred bee.

The second form of fallow deer is the so-called Persian, the antlers of which are not palmated (Fig. 20 : 15). On the contrary, they tend to become flattened in the lower part (Zeuner, 1957, 1958). This form was at one one time distributed south of the line Adana–Carchemish–Nimrud already mentioned, and it appears to have

Fig. 20 : 14. Gold rhyton in the form of a head of fallow deer from Panagurishte, Bulgaria. Period of Alexander the Great

been adapted to the dry woodlands and steppe scrub of southern Persia, Mesopotamia, Syria and Palestine. It is, for instance, depicted on many of the finds from Ur and many remains have been found in the Mount Carmel caves in a Palaeolithic context. From the Natufian onwards it must have rapidly reduced its area of distribution. In some cases, for instance in Syria, it appears to have been present as late as in Roman times according to an animal mosaic from Antioch-on-the-Orontes (Bate, 1939). For many years the Persian or Mesopotamian fallow deer was believed to be extinct. Quite recently, however, it has been rediscovered. In Persian Chouzistan, on the rivers Dez and Karcheh, at least a hundred individuals are still alive in floodplain forests (Haltenorth, 1959, 1961; Trense, 1959; Zukowsky, 1961). They are difficult to observe, but many shed antlers have been collected. In addition, two live fawns were caught and taken to the deer park of Herr von Opel at Kronberg in the Taunus Mountains, Germany (Figs. 20 : 15 and 20 : 16). Here they bred, but unfortunately the stag died suddenly a year ago. Observations by Haltenorth have confirmed that even here in the south the fallow deer is a woodland species.

A peculiar extension of this distribution area of the Persian fallow deer is Cyprus. Since this island is nearest to the coast of Asia Minor at Adana, where the common fallow deer occurs, one would expect the latter to be present on the island. Instead, the Persian fallow deer is found from the early Neolithic onwards. As localities Khirokitia and Erimi (King, 1953) must be mentioned. It is also present at Sotira and in the Late Bronze Age sanctuary at Pigadhes near Myrtou (thirteenth century B.C.) (Taylor, 1957). Here it appears that antlers and portions of skulls were offered as sacrifices, and apart from numerous other fragments two pairs of frontals and seventy-six single pedicles were available to the writer for investigation (Zeuner, 1958).

It might be held that the Persian fallow deer of Cyprus was an indigenous form which was kept in woods or otherwise herded in much the same way as this was done with the common fallow deer in Asia Minor.

The alternative view, however, that the Persian fallow deer reached Cyprus from Syria or Palestine for the first time in the Neolithic is equally tenable. The final decision in this interesting matter will depend on further careful collecting of osteological evidence.

FIG. 20 : 15. Mesopotamian fallow deer. Stag drawn from life on the Karcheh River, Persia, by Helmut Diller. Kindly supplied by Dr Haltenorth. Comparing this with the following figure, note the variability of the coat

FIG. 20 : 16. Mesopotamian fallow deer. Stag kept in captivity in the zoological park of Baron von Opel, Kronberg, Taunus, West Germany. Photo Gronefeld, kindly supplied by Dr Haltenorth

Fallow deer are very easy to keep in large enclosed areas as exemplified by our British deer-parks. This practice spread, probably with the aid of the Moors, into Europe during the Middle Ages where the animal has adapted itself well to northern climate. This is not surprising since the species was present in north-west Europe in all three interglacial periods. Of the fossil forms *Dama clactonianus* of the Great Inter-glacial of the Thames area is particularly well known.

GAZELLE

The gazelle is one of the most graceful animals that exist and has appealed to the imagination of man for thousands of years, and in the Orient it is still used as an epithet signifying loveliness. This, however, has never prevented man from hunting them, and many a scene of this type has been handed down to us by the ancient Egyptians. And, indeed, much earlier than in Old Kingdom times, in pre-pottery Neolithic Jericho, about 6935 B.C., gazelle formed an important part of the diet of the town. One wonders how this meat supply was organized. It is somewhat difficult to imagine that it was solely dependent on hunting, and the possibility that in those early days gazelle were herded like goats should not be refuted light-heartedly (Zeuner, 1955c). According to Brunton (Brunton and Caton-Thompson, 1928) it was tamed in Badarian times.

FIG. 20 : 17. Old Kingdom scene from a tomb at Saqqara, Egypt (*c.* 2500 B.C.), showing domes-tication of unusual animals. In the second register gazelle, addax, ibex and oryx all wearing collars, and in the bottom register hyaenas being stuffed (see also Fig. 20 : 7)

In Old Kingdom times gazelle were not only hunted but kept, as indicated by neck collars. In a tomb at Saqqara the occupant is stated to have owned 1135 pieces of gazelle in addition to 3988 cattle, and gazelle are shown on the tomb reliefs (Fig. 20 : 17). This statement suggests once more that gazelle were under fairly strict control, for how else could they be counted? If at that time, i.e. from the seventh to the third millennium B.C., gazelle were herded, or even to some extent domesticated, this practice was abandoned thereafter in favour of keeping the more ordinary stock, especially sheep.

In later times gazelle were kept by the Romans, who sold their meat in the butchers' shops as shown in a painting in Pompeii. Their skins were converted into leather and parchment and their horns worked into handles, mouthpieces for flutes and other articles. The astragalus of gazelle was used as dice in Africa and the Near East, especially in Roman times but also earlier. Besides all this, gazelle were used as luxury draught animals for children's chariots, as can be seen in the house of the Vetii in Pompeii, and for similar luxury displays. The animal appears occasionally on coins of the Imperial period.

The common species of gazelle in question is *Gazella dorcas*, the afri of Arabia.

ANTELOPES AND IBEX

In Old Kingdom times the Egyptians kept addax antelopes, oryx and a few rarer species (Fig. 20 : 17), as well as the Nubian ibex, in much the same way as gazelles. There is, however, no evidence that this practice was followed outside the Nile Valley, and it was abandoned at an early date. In fact, in early Old Kingdom times there was hardly a ruminant that the Egyptians had not attempted to draw into the orbit of domestication.

21

New World Species

SCIENTIFIC NAMES:

(a) Dogs. *Canis ingae* Tschudi.

(b) New World Camels. *Lama guanicoë* Muller (guanaco; Andes), *L. glama* L. (domesticated guanaco, llama), *L. pacos* L. (alpaca, paco, another domesticated guanaco), *L. vicugna* Mol. (vicuña; localized in Peruvian Andes), *L. elfridae* Krumbiegel (eastern Andes; doubtful).

(c) Guinea Pig. *Cavia porcellus* L. (a rodent; South America).

I T IS a curious and significant fact that at the time of the Spanish and Portuguese Conquest there were few domesticated animals in America. This is particularly remarkable in North America where a suitable wild fauna was in existence, and it can therefore be explained only by the cultural stage in which the first immigrants were. In other words, they appear to have been pre-agricultural, and any agriculture they had when the Europeans arrived must have been due to independent invention or later infiltration. No domesticated sheep, goats or reindeer reached the ancient Americas, though the dog did. This companion of Mesolithic man spread over both Americas.

In South America we encounter in ancient Peru a centre of domestication of at least one of the two species of humpless camels which are there available, and the process was certainly entirely independent of the domestication of Old World species. The llama and the alpaca were the result.

Only one other species was domesticated by the Indians of South America and this is the guinea pig, a small rodent nowadays regarded as a pet and an animal suitable for scientific experiment.

THE AMERICAN DOG

At the time of the discovery of the continent most American Indians owned the dog. On the whole, this animal occupied much the same position in the New World as in the Old, being the companion of man. In a few places man took to eating dogs, presumably because the meat supply was scarce. The practice was by no means universal. And the Incas despised the dog-eaters.

The breeds of dog of ancient America have not yet been studied in detail, to the best of my knowledge, with the exception of the Inca dogs investigated by Nehring (1884), Noack (1916b) and Ueck (1961). Four types are distinguished of which one is a primitive sheepdog which Antonius compares with the large form of *Canis palustris* of Europe. If it is correct to regard certain Mexican dogs as the descendants of this form, it would have had upright ears and a reddish-yellow coat of hair, and it would have resembled the pariah. It may be assumed that this form was nearest to the one originally introduced into the continent.

The first of the derived breeds is called by Nehring 'sheepdog-like', the second resembled a bulldog and the third a dachshund. Whilst the dachshund type also may be compared with the *Canis palustris* group of Europe, the third resembles a bulldog or boxer in the structure of its skull. These three types are known both from mummies and osteological material of the Inca Empire. What exactly their uses were remains to be discovered. Some were undoubtedly used like sheepdogs, whilst Mason (1957) mentions that black dogs were used in ritual sacrifices.

Greyhounds were reported as present soon after the conquest. Whilst some writers consider it possible that these were of native origin, there is much in favour of the assumption that they were the descendants of Spanish greyhounds imported at a very early date. The same happened in the Canary Islands, where the Spanish greyhound has established itself alongside the native prehistoric breeds.

LLAMA AND ALPACA

There are two wild species of 'camels' in South America, the guanaco and the vicuña. The former is the larger, with a shoulder height of 120 cm., whilst the vicuña attains 80 cm. only. The latter has a conspicuous ruff of long, white, silky hair. There are also two domesticated forms, the larger llama and the smaller alpaca.

Of these, the first is used mainly for transport, the second, however, for the production of wool (summary by Herre, 1958).

It was tempting, therefore, to derive the llama from the guanaco, and the alpaca from the vicuña. Antonius (1922) regarded this view as well supported by osteological and biological arguments. Some workers are still following Antonius unquestioningly. Others say that the alpaca, though descended from the vicuña, contains some llama blood. This Antonius considered unlikely, claiming that the two species do not interbreed voluntarily.

In recent years, the alternative that both domesticated forms are the descendants of the guanaco has gained considerable ground. Herre (1952, 1953a, b), in particular, has done much careful work in South America and arrived at the conclusion that this is the only interpretation that agrees with all the evidence, and in this he was followed by Röhrs (1957) and Fallet (1961). Osteological differences between llama and alpaca are now regarded partly as dependent on absolute size and partly due to domestication. Indeed, the skull of the alpaca shows unambiguous evidence for close relationship with the guanaco, a view held by several weighty authorities (for references, see Herre, 1952). The biological argument of Antonius also has been disproved. Llama and alpaca produce fertile hybrids, and, incidentally, so do guanaco and vicuña with each other and with either of the domesticated forms.

The differences between llama and vicuña, therefore, must be due to domestication, the llama having been bred predominantly to be a beast of burden, of great value to the natives in the thin air of the high altitude of the Andes. The wool of these large beasts, however, is too coarse to be spun, and the small alpaca is likely to have been developed as a supplier of wool. Several breeds exist, and Fallet (1961) has shown that the resemblance of alpaca wool to that of vicuña is due to convergence, and that thin-sections show up the true relationship.

Both llama and alpaca were domesticated by the Incas, or more probably by their predecessors, and bones of the llama have been found in a site of the early agricultural period (*c*. 2550–1250 B.C.) in the Virú Valley in Peru (Mason, 1957).

The llama (Fig. 21 : 1) has always been predominantly a beast of burden, although it is not capable of carrying more than about one hundredweight and it travels hardly more than fifteen miles a day. It was used in large caravans sometimes of several hundred each and driven by a man probably with the assistance of dogs. The alpaca on the other hand was chiefly kept for its fine wool, a most important textile fibre in the cold highlands of the Andes. Large herds of both breeds were owned by private individuals and commonly by the Inca state, and wealth was often counted by the number of llamas. It is a curious fact that the keeping of these domesticated beasts did not extend beyond the confines of the wild ancestors as is usually the case. On the contrary, the domesticated forms occur well within the distribution area of the wild guanaco. In any case, the lowlands of South America

Fig. 21 : 1. Llama, silver figurine from pre-Columbian Peru. Metropolitan Museum, New York

are climatically unsuited for the New World camels which are specialized high-mountain desert animals.

The vicuña is, according to several observers, difficult to bring under human control. It is a shy species, like many of the smaller ruminants. But it is not impossible to domesticate as the Jesuits were able to show, before their experiments came to an end when they were expelled from Spanish countries. Today, the wild species is exploited for hair. The herds are driven along stone fences into corrals where they are shorn and released again.

GUINEA PIG

The scarcity of large meat-providing animals in the Andean mountain range induced the pre-Inca natives to domesticate the guinea pig, a small South American rodent now well known to everybody. Many colour and fur types had already appeared by Inca times. The little animal served as an article of food as it would have been too expensive to eat the slow-breeding llamas and vicuñas unnecessarily. It was even worthy of being used as a sacrifice to the gods.

So far as is known, the guinea pig did not spread beyond the Inca Empire till after the Spanish Conquest when, being small and easily transported, it appeared at many places of the Spanish Colonial Empire within a century. It appears to have become known to the English-speaking world via West Africa, as is suggested by its name.

GROUP VI

Birds, Fishes and Insects

DOMESTICATED BIRDS

VERY little is known about the domestication of birds, as distinct from mammals. Being capable of flight, and on the whole extremely cautious, contacts or overlaps of their environments with those of man are few, though crop-robbing may have brought about encounters, all the important domestic birds being seed-eaters (pigeons, fowl), grazers (geese) or vegetable mud-eaters (ducks).

The idea of keeping birds, therefore, is not likely to be earlier than the Neolithic. Social propensities are present in those species that were to become economically important, especially in the fowl with its well-known pecking order. Geese and ducks are similarly gregarious, and show the beginnings of a social order in flocks. Pigeons are on a lower level, they associate in common nesting and feeding grounds and sleep together in the same trees. These propensities must have reduced the difficulties of domestication.

Birds have never played as important a part in human economy as have the mammals. They have been kept as substitute food, for pleasure and sport, and at a comparatively late stage as producers of eggs, a natural food reserve.

There is one possible exception, the Hallstatt culture of Europe. It shows so much evidence of the ritual and presumably economic importance of a bird which is either a goose or a duck that it may be inferred that these people had specialized in its domestication. It is more likely that this was a goose. On the whole, bronze figurines are not accurate enough to be certain, but many fit the goose better than the duck. Perhaps both species were involved. It may be noted that the goose (and the duck) plays a very important part in the farming stock of eastern Europe, especially in the Balkans up to Poland. Is this perhaps evidence for the survival of a goose economy from Hallstatt times to the present day?

22

Domestic Fowl

SCIENTIFIC NAMES—*Gallus gallus gallus* L. (Burmese fowl; Burma); *G. gallus murghi* Robinson (northern red jungle fowl; India from Kashmir south to Godavari); *G. gallus jabonillei* Delacour (Tonkin fowl; Indo-China); *G. gallus bankiva* Temminck (Bankiva fowl; Java, Bali).

Gallus sonneratii Temminck (grey or Sonnerat fowl; India south of Godavari). *G. lafayetti* Lesson (Ceylon fowl); *G. varius* (Shaw) (Gangegar; Java, and Lesser Sunda Isles to Allor).

O F THE four wild species of the genus *Gallus* the red jungle fowl (*Gallus gallus*) is the chief ancestor of the domesticated fowl. With its geographical races it occurs from Kashmir to Tonkin, and on the peninsula south to the Godavari. The other three species are, however, closely related and betray by their distribution that they are no more than somewhat divergent geographical races. They are known to interbreed with the red jungle fowl, especially *G. sonnerati*, according to Blyth and Marshall. That this grey species has contributed to the domesticated stock is also suggested by the appearance of its white-and-black pattern in some breeds. Hahn (1896) discusses the interbreeding of domestic fowl with wild birds, especially in Further India, and he regards it as almost impossible that the domestic stock should not have absorbed some blood from the other species.

The old-fashioned, multicoloured cock is hardly more than a large edition of the cock of the red jungle fowl which abounds in the woods of northern India, though it is not often seen because of its shyness. Its area of distribution happens to be the area from which the earliest evidence comes for man's interest in this species.

The Indus Valley civilization was familiar with the fowl. Among the seals from

Mohenjo-Daro, Mackay (1938) recognized one with two birds in the position of fight which he thought were Sonnerat cocks, whilst Gandert (1953) regards them as red jungle fowl. There are clay figurines from the same site which are intended for fowl. Most are fragmentary, but the evidence is cumulative. There is a cock in position of display, a fragment with a comb and one which Mackay interprets as a hen with a food dish. This would point to breeding in captivity. This is confirmed by Sewell's (Sewell and Guha, 1931) study of the bones which are larger than those of the wild bird. A femur from Mohenjo-Daro measures 103 mm. compared with 69 mm. in the wild bird. The femur of a modern table fowl (coll. Institute of Archaeology) measures 115 mm., which shows that the Indus Valley birds had been bred for size. Full domestication had therefore taken place, say, by 2000 B.C.

At Harappa the fowl is not absent, but there are only two clay figurines that appear to represent a cock and a hen. From Chanhu Daro clay whistles are known of a shape suggesting small gallinaceous birds. One is painted with vertical stripes, which pleads against domestic fowl. Perhaps they are intended for quail.

In the same millennium the Sumerian language has a word for the cock. It is conceivable that the Indus Valley people kept the fowl only for the purpose of sport, and that its breeding for flesh occurred later. When the Aryans invaded India, about the middle of the second millennium, the newcomers learned to admire the cock. The *Rig-Veda* does not mention him, but the *Atharv* and *Yajur* do. He is praised for his courage and pride, and as an indicator of time. By about 1000 B.C. it was forbidden to eat the fowl. Evidently the bird had assumed religious significance.

The coins of north-west India show that the cock continued in favour. It appears for instance on those of Sophytes (310 B.C.), a prince of the Punjab who submitted to Alexander the Great (Fig. 22 : 1). It is shown by Satyamitra (first to second century A.D.), together with a palm tree. This is a queer combination, and most probably symbolical.

It testifies to the far-reaching marine trade of the Egyptians that the fowl appears in the fifteenth and fourteenth centuries B.C. in Egypt. In the tomb of Tutankhamun, Carter found the painting of a cock (Fig. 22 : 2). This is proof that it was known about 1350 B.C. A century earlier the annals of Thothmes III mention birds that lay eggs daily, and this has been interpreted as a reference to hens. Without Carter's find,

Fig. 22 : 1. Silver coin of Sophytes, a prince of the Punjab who submitted to Alexander the Great, showing cock with large spurs, *c.* 300 B.C. Early cock coins of this type appear to celebrate the fighting spirit of the bird. Natural size. Author's collection

FIG. 22 : 2. Painting of a cock on a potsherd, from the tomb of Tutankhamun, Egypt, nineteenth dynasty (*c.* 1350 B.C.). After Carter (1923)

this text would be very doubtful; with it the interpretation appears less improbable. The fowl, however, disappears again from Egypt; perhaps because of its religious connections it was exterminated when after the Echnaton-Tutankhamun episode the old religion was re-established. It did not reappear in the country until the Ptolemaic period. The early introduction was almost certainly not the result of over-land connection, for the fowl had not yet spread through western Asia in the second millennium.

In the circumstances, the chicken hieroglyph presents a problem. Why should the chick be shown, but never an adult bird? It is highly probable that this hiero-glyph is derived from some other bird, or rather chick, not the domestic fowl. The quail has often been suggested.

The period of the rapid expansion of fowl-keeping was the first millennium B.C. From north-west India it evidently reached Persia at an early date. Whilst this is implied in the coin evidence from north-west India and its appearance on Assyrian seals around the eighth century B.C., there is substantial literary evidence in addition. In the religion of Zoroaster it plays an important part as guardian of the good against the evil. With his waking crow the cock became the symbol of the waking day and thus of the light in general. Hahn believes that the use of the cock as a 'time-piece' arose in Indo-Bactria.

From Persia the domestic fowl spread westwards to Mesopotamia and Asia Minor. It is possible that the Medes, who were subject to the Assyrians from the latter part of the ninth century onwards, brought it into the Euphrates-Tigris Basin.[1] A few seals from the eighth century B.C. show the bird. One found at Nimrud dates from 740–710 B.C. according to Mallowan.[2] Two others, dated about 700 B.C., are

[1] The Greeks occasionally called the fowl the Median Bird which may allude to this association. Persian Bird is, however, more commonly used.

[2] This is the date he gives in his publication (1950), but according to a personal communication, for which I am grateful, he now dates it about 800 B.C.

mentioned already by Layard (1853); they portray men in front of altar stones on which cocks are to be seen. The bird therefore appears to have had a religious significance, which is not surprising if it was received from the Medes, inhabitants of Iran, where the cock had by that time become connected with religious rites.

The earliest known pictorial representations from the Mediterranean are found on Proto-Corinthian pottery of the second half of the eighth century. Dumbabin (1948) studied this material. It is evident that the domestic fowl was becoming known by that time, but it appears not to have been really common before the sixth century. The bird had come from the East, but evidently it arrived ahead of the political expansion of the Persian Empire.

In Asia Minor the fowl became popular mainly in the course of the sixth century, though it had been known earlier. It was the Persians themselves who spread it as they expanded their empire. A combat of cocks appears on a vase from Klazomenai near Smyrna about 560 B.C. The fowl is mentioned by Theognis, a poet, about 530 B.C. About 500 B.C. it is shown on the Xanthos monument (Keller, 1909, p. 172), and from the period of the Ionian revolt against the Persian rule (500–494 B.C.) we have a beautiful Phoenician electrum stater, probably coming from Dardanus, on which a cock is depicted on the obverse.

By this time the domestic fowl was well known throughout the Greek world. It had reached the outlying coloniae in the West, too, for on the coins of Himera in Sicily, prior to 481 B.C., cocks figure in various attitudes. Himera must have been famous for its cocks, though in what capacity, whether as fighters or as health-giving birds (the town was a spa), as fertility symbols or as good food, is not known. On many of the coins the cock appears filling the obverse. One of particular interest is the silver drachma reproduced here (Fig. 22 : 3); it shows not only the customary cock on the obverse, but on the reverse a hen in an incuse square.

Another Sicilian town indulging in the display of cocks was Selinus. The issues

Fig. 22 : 3. Silver drachm of Himera in Sicily, showing cock on the obverse and hen in an incuse square on the reverse, prior to 481 B.C. Natural size. Author's collection

of 466–415 B.C. portray cocks. But here they are shown in a cage or similar contraption possibly representing an altar. The bird is evidently not being sacrificed, for on one coin the altar fire is burning above it and the bird appears very much alive. Beside the altar stands the river god, Selinus, holding forth a wreath. On the right a bull is shown with a 'Selinon' leaf, the parsley for which the town became famous after the draining of the marshes. A third coin (Head, 1959, pl. 16 : 53) depicts a similar scene, but this time a snake is crawling over the altar. This association clearly points to the worship of Aesculapius, and the substitution of the cock for the snake on some coins shows that it had become a symbol of health associated with the Greek deity of healing.

Head (1959) refers to the fact that the draining of the marshes relieved the town of Selinus of malaria and suggests that these coins were intended to commemorate the event.

Other Greek coins of the fifth century testify to the wide distribution of the cock. It is still popular in Dardanus in the Troas, and in Lycia it is used for fighting sports (Fig. 22 : 4). In that country it was even absorbed into the 'three-legged symbol',

FIG. 22 : 4. A silver coin showing two fighting cocks with spurs, from Lycia in Asia Minor, 480–400 B.C. Natural size. After Head (1959)

a coin with a pig on the obverse showing on the reverse an incuse square with three necks and heads of cocks arranged like the spokes of a wheel. Cretan coins from Phaistos likewise show our bird. In the literature of that period it is often mentioned. The Greeks were fully conscious of its Eastern origin and of its importation into the Western world by the Persians. Aristophanes alludes to it, as do many others. It is evident that the domestic fowl had been absorbed by the Greek world with the greatest readiness. After two centuries it was to be found everywhere. It was bred for fighting games which became so popular that they were at times organized by the Athenian government. It was accepted in its Eastern capacity as a divine symbol of light and health. Before taking poison, Socrates ordered a cock to be sacrificed to Aesculapius for recovery from an illness (399 B.C.). The cock also became an erotic symbol, because of its conspicuous wooing display. In Greece it became the fashion to present beloved boys with a live cock. In the museum at Olympia there is a terracotta figure of Ganymede with his cock being abducted by Zeus (Fig. 22 : 5), and similar pictures are found on vases. The modern word *cocotte*, incidentally, is derived from cock.

The adoption of the fowl as a symbol of fertility, however, is due to the prolific laying of eggs, and thus associated with the hens. The Jews carried a cock and a hen

FIG. 22 : 5. Statue of Zeus carrying
Ganymede, c. 480 B.C. Ganymede is
shown carrying a cock, possibly as a
symbol of sexual vigour. In museum
at Olympia

in front of bridal couples. It was in all probability the eggs that led to the economic exploitation of the species. The annals of Thothmes may be recalled with their birds that reproduced daily, and the Veneti were reputed to have had hens that laid a couple of eggs every day. This desirable condition is unlikely to have been achieved in reality, but that the ancients had breeds of fowl that laid prolifically is certain.

For the bird itself as an article of food there appears to have been little economic need. It was an important standby for the poor, but one would have avoided killing the producer of eggs until it had become too old. According to Aristophanes, every Athenian had his hen, even the poorest. Being cheap and easy to rear it became popular as a sacrificial animal for all sorts of gods, not Aesculapius only.

The evidence thus afforded for the keeping of chicken in comparatively close confinement raises the question whether modifications due to domestication existed in the Greek period. An interesting piece of evidence to that effect is supplied by an early-third-century B.C. tomb in Aphendrika on Cyprus (Dray and du Plat Taylor, 1951), in which fowls are included as gifts to the deceased. The birds were studied by Miss Bate and found to be small. Their metacarpals and ulnae, however, were too short for the size of the body, so that they must have been incapable of flying. Spurs

448

were not found either, hence Miss Bate concludes that this was a kind of table bird, and certainly not a fighting fowl.

Finally, the use of the cock as timekeeper was popular in Eastern countries and adopted by the Greek world. In the absence of mechanical alarm clocks a caller that rouses the sleeper before daybreak has an important function to perform. The cock is particularly efficient in the south where the dawn is short. Today we are apt to forget how much the ancient farmer relied on his cock to get him started in the morning.

Summing up the various uses of the domestic fowl, one begins to appreciate why it was regarded as such a remarkable bird. The Greeks had no taboos against eating it (such as existed elsewhere), which greatly enhanced its economic value. The first introduction occurred about the eighth century, and it spread during the sixth over the rest of the Greek world. At the end of that century, and in the one that followed, it was still sufficiently new to be regarded as important. It is frequently illustrated. But the fourth century already accepted its presence as a matter of course, and illustrations became rare. The bird had become part of the equipment of Mediterranean man.

A few words must now be said about the appearance of the domestic fowl in the Apennine peninsula. It is still a problem whether the Etruscans imported it at the time when it became popular in the Greek world. The Greek colony of Lokroi Epizephyrioi in Calabria shows it on terracotta reliefs about 500 B.C. It is also shown on a bronze coin from Cales in Campania (Fig. 22 : 6) after 268 B.C. Does this

FIG. 22 : 6. Bronze coin of Cales, Campania, after 268 B.C., with cock. Natural size. Author's collection

comparatively late date suggest that the introduction was relatively recent? This specimen appears to portray a fighting cock as is suggested by its proud posture. On the whole, however, it is unlikely in view of the numerous contacts with the Greek world that the introduction of the fowl into the states of Italy was long delayed. Again, it arrived with a reputation for its unusual qualities.

The Romans developed the remarkable method of prophecy called *oraculum ex tripudio*. Some hens were placed in a cage and their manner of feeding observed. If they ate greedily it was a good omen; if not, prospects were bad. This *oraculum* had the advantage of portability and was therefore very popular with the army. If the hens were starved beforehand, a general could always demonstrate to his troops that their enterprise was going to be crowned with success. No wonder that this practice was ridiculed even by many Roman writers. In the wars against the Samnites (second

half of the fourth century B.C.) L. Papirius Cursor used it abundantly. In the first
Punic war the consul P. Claudius Pulcher became angry with his prophetic birds
when they refused to eat their food with the alacrity required, and threw them into
the sea with the remark, 'May they drink if they won't eat.' His subsequent defeat
in the sea-battle of Drepana in 249 B.C. was attributed by the people of Rome to this
disrespectful act.

Much information is available about the economic aspects of poultry-farming
in Rome. Colour mutations existed in plenty. White birds, however, were not popular
because they attracted birds of prey. They did come in useful from time to time for
the purposes of sacrifice. The use of white fowl on such occasions was evidently taken
over from the Greeks. Anubis, worshipped in Rome, though of Egyptian origin,
required white fowl. Pythagoras had already forbidden his disciples to eat white
fowl because it was sacred to Zeus. King Pyrrhus of Epirus, well known for his use
of elephants in the Battle of Heracleia against the Romans, 280 B.C. (see p. 289),
had the habit of healing the sick by treading on their stomachs. Before these occasions he sacrificed a white cock. On the other hand, Ovid reports that black fowl
were required for the goddess of the night.

Elaborate treatises were written by Varro and by Columella on the art of
keeping poultry. Hens had to be fattened; they were stuffed like geese. The best
time for hatching eggs was when the moon was waxing, and an odd number of eggs
was to be placed under the hen. It was recommended to put the chicken-house near
the kitchen or a baking oven, so that the smoke would pass through it and kill the
lice. Columella describes the equipment of the chicken-house in detail. In his opinion,
red or brown hens with black wings and tail were the best layers and breeders.

Castration was practised in addition to fattening, and apparently invented by
the Greeks. The *Lex Famia sumptuaria* of 161 B.C. prohibited among other things the
eating of fattened fowl and permitted only one unfattened hen on the table. By
using castrated birds and cockerels, it was of course possible to circumvent the law.
Horace reports that fowl drowned in wine had a particularly choice flavour.

All this clearly shows that the fowl had become an economically important bird
and that it had come to play a conspicuous part in the menu of the Romans. Nevertheless, fighting cocks continued to be reared.

In many places, especially on islands, fowl escaped and became feral. One such
island off the Ligurian coast is specifically mentioned by both Varro and Columella.

North of the Alps, the domestic fowl is reputed to have appeared remarkably
early. There is even a find in an Upper Palaeolithic station, that of Salève near Geneva
in Switzerland. This must be regarded as intrusive, however, for the fauna comprises an improbable mixture of tundra and forest animals. In addition, the rabbit
is included in the list, a species which cannot have been present before the Roman
period, if not the Middle Ages. The Salève fowl, therefore, can safely be disregarded.

Another early find comes from Denmark, where Degerbøl reports the fowl from the 'Younger Stone Age' i.e. the Ertebølle culture, an age determination which is doubtful. It is perhaps intrusive, too.

The third group of early finds north of the Alps is of Hallstatt Age. Belt plating from Hallstatt Phase D (dated 600 B.C. on the long chronology, 450 B.C. on the short) was found at Ohlingen in Alsace by Schaeffer (1930) and at Koppel on the Upper Rhine by Wagner. Both were described as showing cocks, identifiable from their sickle-shaped tails. Schaeffer himself, however, withdrew the identification in the appendix to his publication, saying that these are riders on horseback. The illustrations bear out this correction. The punch-pattern of the belt is so highly stylized that the identification of animals from their portrayed characters is impossible. This evidence, too, has thus to be disregarded. A find that has been mistaken as of Hallstatt age comes from Hallstatt in Austria itself; it is Roman.

The fourth group is the Celtic fowl of the La Tène period. Enough is known to state that the bird had reached the Celts and was bred by them in the first century B.C., and perhaps a little earlier. In view of the close contacts of the northern Celts with Italy, it is likely to have been introduced into northern Europe from there, and not from the south-east.

In Switzerland the fowl appears in a settlement of the Rauraci at Basle Gas Works which, according to Hescheler and Kuhn (1949), must have been abandoned before 58 B.C. The evidence consists of bones.

Late La Tène tombs at Nauheim in Germany also contained bones. The pre-Roman Celts of Britain had the fowl. This is specifically mentioned by Caesar in *De Bello Gallico* and confirmed by its effigy on Belgic coins as well as two finds of bones. There is one record from Kingsdown Camp, near Wells in Somerset, where Jackson identified some bones of a small fowl. The more important site is pre-Roman Colchester, in Essex, where Bate found domestic fowl among the bird remains from the primary silt of ditch I (about A.D. 10–43). It may be assumed that the British fowl had not had a long history when the Romans encountered it. Caesar mentioned expressly that the Britons would not eat it, and the finds made so far show that the bird was not common.

An almost contemporary specimen comes from Hanging Langford Camp, Wylye, Wiltshire, where Belgic first-century occupation predominates, though Romano-British material occurs also. Here the fowl may be just prior to the Roman Conquest or just later. Several British caves have yielded remains of fowl, but nowhere could a pre-Roman date be proved. Among these sites are the Chudleigh Fissures in Devon, Gough's Cave in Cheddar Gorge, Somerset, Ravencliffe Cave in Derbyshire and Heathery Burn Cave in Durham.

From the time of the Roman Conquest appears to come a group of five contracted burials in High Street, Winchester. Two of these had the skeleton of a fowl between their legs. Whilst C. F. C. Hawkes was at first inclined to consider them as Bronze Age (which would be too early for the birds in any case), he later compared them with the crouched burials of Maiden Castle with their joints of mutton, and is now inclined to regard the Winchester burials also as of conquest date.

Roman sites in Britain, like London, Silchester and Caerleon, have produced bones of fowl, sometimes of larger size and with tarso-metatarsi equipped with large spurs, suggesting that the sport of cock-fighting was popular.

In central Europe, too, Roman sites contain remains of domestic fowl, for instance that of Niederbieber near Neuwied on the Rhine, Vindonissa in Switzerland, Stillfried on the March (Austria, on the border of Moravia) and Hallstatt-Lahn (Austria). The Romans evidently saw to it that the bird became popular (Fig. 22 : 7), and the people living outside the walls of the Roman Empire adopted it. Figurines of fowl occur in several places (Figs. 22 : 8 and 22 : 9). The Germanic tribes, therefore, must have taken over the fowl from the Romans. The spread of the species through northern-central Europe in the Middle Ages is summarized in Requate (1960).

An interesting discovery was made at Leuna in the province of Saxony, which was outside the Roman political sphere. The Germanic cemetery of Leuna comprises some very rich graves which have informed us about culinary practices more fully than many others. This matter has been discussed by Gandert (1954), both as regards the pig and the fowl. Three male and one female fowl were found. The female lay in Grave No. 2. It lacks the head and feet, but not the tibia. Gandert points out that these are just the parts that do not belong to a roasting chicken. Evidently a chicken prepared for the table looked in Roman times much as it does today. This is confirmed by a Roman bronze plate found at Mundelsheim near Marbach in Württemberg. According to Paret (1938), who described it, twelve roast chicken surround the edge. All heads are missing; five have wings, seven are without. Paret thinks that this is intended to indicate two kinds of birds. Whether this is so or not, the preparation for the table was essentially the same.

Returning to Leuna, excavation reports indicate that the cocks were not associated with the plates of food. Moreover, all three had retained their feet, and the cock of Grave No. 3 had spurs. The heads, however, were missing. This is interpreted by Gandert as evidence that they were sacrificed birds, killed by tearing off the head. This practice is used here and there even today. Saxo Grammaticus, the Danish chronicler who related the Hamlet saga and who died about A.D. 1210, describes a cock sacrifice of the Vikings carried out in this manner. And the Arab historian Ibn Fadhlan, who visited the court of the Khan of the Bulgars on the Volga in A.D. 921, witnessed the cremation of a prince in a boat. The female slave, his dog, two horses and two oxen, a cock and a hen accompanied him on his journey to eternity. It is expressly stated that the hen was killed by decapitation, and Gandert regards this

FIG. 22 : 7. Mosaic of Mercury with cock from Carnuntum, on the Danube, the Roman capital of the Pannonian Province, third century A.D.

FIG. 22 : 8. Enamelled bronze cock, early
Roman Imperial, from Cologne, West
Germany, part of a piece of furniture

FIG. 22 : 9. Roman pottery cock
from Reichenhall, Bavaria, about
first century A.D., probably a
toy. In the Landesmuseum,
Mainz

as another case that corroborates his theory that the cocks of Leuna were Germanic sacrifices to the dead.

FIG. 22 : 10. Chinese rice-paper painting of men selling poultry. A live cock being weighed and a duck are shown also. This scene illustrates the importance of poultry in the economy of densely populated China; an importance which the fowl acquired in Europe at a comparatively late period. Author's collection

Throughout the Middle Ages the fowl increased in economic importance. Since several distinctive breeds, in colour, size and egg production, existed in the Roman period already, the further development of special breeds may well have gone ahead. Nevertheless, it is remarkable that until the beginning of this century the primitive multicoloured cock still reigned almost uncontested over his hens from the dung-heaps of Europe.

23

Other Gallinaceous Birds

SCIENTIFIC NAMES—*Pavo cristatus* L. (peacock; India); *P. muticus* L. (Burmese peacock; Burma to Java).

Numida meleagris L. (Guinea fowl; West Africa).

Phasianus colchicus L. (pheasant; south-east Europe and western Asia, grading into *P. torquatus* Gmelin, the ringed pheasant of China).

Meleagris gallopavo L. (turkey; North America).

Coturnix coturnix L. (quail; Europe, North Africa, Asia).

PEACOCK

THE peacock occurs wild in India and Burma. Thence it was exported to the Western world, where it was admired as a marvel of nature and kept and bred in the precincts of temples and in the gardens of the rich. Needless to say, the Romans ate it, but it is reported that the flesh is exceedingly tough and not palatable. That it appeared again and again on the royal tables is probably due to the decorative value of the feathers.

From India the peacock reached Mesopotamia. There are Indian sources for this traffic. Moreover, Tiglathpileser IV received peacocks as tribute, and Diodorus mentions their presence in Babylon. It is strange, however, that the peacocks given as tribute came from Arabia. Is it perhaps conceivable that southern Arabia was in close contact with India and that the birds came thence? There are other indications

456

of such contacts in very early times, such as the species of cotton plant grown in western India, which is of Arab-African origin.

The Greeks received the peacock from Persia, Media and Babylonia. At first it was regarded as a sacred animal, as for instance on Samos in the Temple of Hera. The eyes on the feathers, especially in the erected 'wheel', were regarded as a symbol of the firmament, and thus of the goddess of the sky. The bird spread west along the Mediterranean and was occasionally depicted on ancient coins, for instance on an aureus of Julia Titi, A.D. 89, illustrated by Mattingly (1928, pl. 46, Fig. 5), on a billon tetradrachm of Antoninus Pius of A.D. 176 and a silver denarius of his wife (Fig. 23 : 1).

FIG. 23 : 1. Silver denarius of Faustina I, wife of Antoninus Pius, A.D. 141, with peacock walking. Natural size. Author's collection

The Romans specialized in peacock-breeding, and many sculptures, metal statuettes and pictures are known from this period.

In medieval times knights were keen to acquire peacock feathers, and they were occasionally required as tribute. After the Middle Ages its importance decreased rapidly, and the turkey took its place as a bird that was worth eating.

GUINEA FOWL

Guinea fowl occur in Africa, and appear at one time to have been frequent in North Africa. They reached Greece hardly before the fifth century B.C. The Greeks called the bird *melanargis* (black-white), which appellation was corrupted into *meleagris*, so that it became associated with Greek mythology. Klythos of Miletus, a pupil of Aristotle, gave an excellent description of the guinea fowl. The Romans knew they were of African origin. In Varro's time they were still expensive, and Pliny says they were the last poultry to be added to the Roman menu. The Emperor Caligula permitted them to be offered as sacrifices to his own majesty. Bones have been found at the Roman *limes* camp called Saalburg, in the Taunus Mountains, west Germany.

There are very few ancient pictures of the guinea fowl. Keller saw two in a mosaic in the thermae of Diocletian, and there is a poorly preserved fresco in the house of the Vettii at Pompeii.

In the Middle Ages the bird was forgotten, to be rediscovered by the Portuguese explorers of the African coast at the end of the sixteenth century, which explains its present English name.

QUAIL

The quail is a dwarf edition of the partridge. It is now rare in northern Europe, but in the south and in Egypt and western Asia it appears in enormous numbers in the season of migration and is then caught by every available means. They are pretty, have a peculiar call-note and the males often fight with each other. For these reasons quail were kept by the Romans. The Egyptians were familiar with the little bird and its picture denotes a hieroglyph (Fig. 20 : 6), often mistaken for a chicken, which was unknown in Egypt at the time when the hieroglyph was invented.

Quail are good to eat but, oddly enough, the Greeks and Romans did not care for them. They were believed to eat hemlock and other poisonous plants. It was not until Merovingian times that quail were esteemed as excellent food.

PHEASANT

The pheasant of the ancients was *Phasianus colchicus*, called after the River Phasis. It abounded in the Caucasus, and related races occur in Persia and Media. None of these has the white ring on the neck which today is often seen and is due to the presence of Eastern blood in our pheasants. The Mongolian and Chinese races show this character particularly well.

Martial maintains that the Argonauts brought it to Greece; in practice it must have been the flourishing Euxine trade of the Greeks. The bird did not play an important part in that country, however. The pheasant reached Italy later than the peacock, for Pliny, Statius (A.D. 49–96) and Martial are the first authors to mention it. In their day the birds were kept in enclosures in which they bred, and care was taken to fatten them. Prescriptions as to how to feed them were published by Palladius. The eggs were eaten, but considered inferior to hens' eggs.

From Italy the pheasant went with the Romans to all parts of the empire. It was established in the Rhineland, as witnessed by a relief preserved in the museum at Trier, and it is shown on a mosaic from Thysdrus in North Africa (Fig. 23 : 2) Curiously enough, it was never as completely domesticated as the fowl, and for this very reason never assumed the same economic importance. It remained a game bird of the rich, often bred and reared with care. Only in recent times has it become thoroughly established and feral in many parts of Europe.

TURKEY

The race of the turkey which has become domesticated is that of south-western North America. The first describers, of the early sixteenth century, mention the

Fig. 23 : 2. Cock, pheasants, white pigeon and (near foot of vase) two red-legged partridges (game birds). Musée du Bardo, Tunis, Roman Imperial period. Evidence that the pheasant was known. Photo F.E.Z.

presence of white hens; the birds were therefore domesticated already. This is corroborated by other evidence. In Mexico and Central America it was kept, apparently as the only domestic animal apart from the dog, and Cortez and others mention them as peacocks, without however wondering about their presence. It appears therefore that they were then well known in the domesticated state in the islands and countries conquered by Columbus and his successors.

The first introduction into Europe took place about 1523 or 1524. Only the males were shown at first, and Conrad de Heresbach says that before 1530 the birds were practically unknown, but by 1571 they were reared in flocks on the Lower Rhine. This rapid spread confirms that the birds were already domesticated when they arrived. In 1560 no less than 150 turkeys were eaten at Arnstadt in Germany at a wedding. Pennant tells us that the bird appeared on the English Christmas menu for the first time in 1585.

24

Non-gallinaceous Birds

THE PIGEON

SCIENTIFIC NAMES—*Columba livia* Gmelin (rock pigeon, wild form of domesticated pigeon; from Britain across Mediterranean to India). *C. oenas* L. (stock dove; Europe, etc., wild only). *C. palumbus* L. (wood pigeon; Europe, wild only). *Streptopelia turtur* L. (turtle dove; Europe to India, wild, sometimes bred in captivity).

Though the pigeons, as natural crop-robbers, are likely to have been domesticated in Neolithic times, the evidence is scanty until the classical period.

Their first impression on man appears to have been not as an economic proposition, but as a symbol of love and fertility. Their love display is particularly striking, and they are of a peaceful disposition. Moreover, the couples remain remarkably faithful to each other, and this in spite of a dissertation published by Riedlin about 1794, which tries to prove the contrary. Exceptions occur, it seems, even in the dove world. The bird thus became the symbol of the western Asiatic goddess of love, Astarte. They were popular both as temple birds, which were kept alive within the precincts, and as sacrifices. In the last-mentioned respect they were much used by the Hebrews.

Christianity transferred the symbol to heavenly love and, as a result, the domestication of the pigeon became more and more frequent in Europe, where the economic advantages of a small, self-sufficient table bird were appreciated in addition.

In spite of its antiquity and close association with religious beliefs, however, the pigeon has managed to continue leading a relatively independent life.

Many early pictures are difficult to interpret. But it was known in Mesopotamia from the Halafian period onwards (*c.* 4500 B.C.). Dove figurines have been found at Arpachiyah (Fig. 24 : 1). Assyrian reliefs show it frequently. Semiramis (*c.* eighth century B.C.) is reported to have changed into a dove upon her death, and the birds appear on some of the terracotta 'sheep boxes' of the Assyrian period. They were known in the Minoan and Mycenaean cultures.

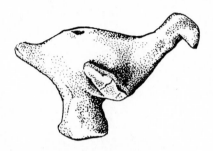

FIG. 24 : 1. Terracotta dove from one of the earliest Tell Halaf levels at Arpachiyah, Iraq, *c.* 4500 B.C. Length *c.* 12 cm. After Mallowan and Rose, 1935

In early times white pigeons (Fig. 23 : 2) were sacred and preferred because of the symbolism implied. Other types are due to mutations of very recent date. Attic comedies refer to the white pigeons from the sanctuary of Aphrodite on Mount Eryx in Sicily. It is said by Aelian that the introduction of white pigeons into Greece was due to the shipwreck of Mardonius on Mount Athos, which might mean that the Persians brought them to Europe.

The town of Sicyon on the Peloponnese shows pigeons on its coins from about 430 B.C. onwards for about 200 years (Fig. 24 : 2).

FIG. 24 : 2. Silver obol of Sicyon, Peloponnesus, Greece, *c.* 400–300 B.C. The pigeon was a symbol of Sicyon and is shown on many coins. On this one the reverse shows another, flying with both wings spread. 1.5 times natural size. Author's collection

That the Etruscans knew the pigeon is not surprising in view of their maritime connections. Oddly enough, however, it is nearly always the rock pigeon, or its domesticated descendant, that is in question. The much smaller turtle dove became somewhat the fashion in the Roman Imperial period, because of its peculiar sad-sounding call. Only rarely does the wood pigeon appear on the scene. This is perhaps so at Dodona in Epirus, where an oracle operated with pigeons living on oak trees. But even in antiquity some sceptics uttered the heretical opinion that priestesses worked the oracle whilst the pigeons were just living on the trees.

A remarkable practice is the erection of towers for the pigeons to build their nests in, which is still in vogue in the East. It provides protection and 'rocky' nesting places for the birds, and an easy way to collect the young for culinary purposes.

Many visitors to the East have mistaken the pigeon towers for ancient monuments, especially for tombs. Keller, however, relates an actual combination of these alternatives from Dama in Syria, third century A.D., where a large family tomb is crowned by a pigeon tower.

Whilst the Romans respected the religious qualities of the pigeons, they did not fail to eat them in quantity, and in a fattened condition. They had their *columbaria*, closed pigeon towers in which the birds were stuffed with chewed bread and other delicacies. To prevent them moving their wings were clipped, or the legs broken. Large sums were paid for first-class breeding stock.

The Romans developed, according to Pliny, a craze for pigeons, and this was extended to both the wood pigeon and the turtle dove, both being fattened and eaten.

One application of the pigeon that has not been mentioned is that as a carrier of messages. Its homing instinct was discovered early, and carrier pigeons were used in Egypt in Roman times. The messages were tied either to the leg or to the neck. Unfortunately, this kind of postal service, last used when Paris was beleaguered in 1871, is not very reliable, and it has apparently at all times been used in emergencies only. But the possibility had evidently been known for a very long time. At the coronation ceremony of Rameses III (1204 B.C.), four pigeons were sent out to announce the assumption of the crown. They were made to fly north, east, south and west, respectively, but it is unlikely that actual carrier pigeons existed at that time. Nero, the Roman emperor (A.D. 54–68), had them, however, for he used them to send the results of the sports to his friends and relations. The practice was handed down to later centuries, and the conquering armies of the Moslems used it, and the Crusaders learned it in the East and spread the custom in Europe. The Mamluks of Egypt (A.D. 1250–1517) perfected the pigeon post, and even under the Fatimids had their pedigrees kept in special registers (Hitti, 1956).

FALCONS

SCIENTIFIC NAMES—LONG-WINGED FALCONS—*Falco hierofalco* Kleinschmidt (gyrfalcon; Europe and Asia); *F. peregrinus* Turnstall (peregrine; Europe and Asia, mainly on cliffs); *F. columbarius* L. (merlin; Europe and Asia).

SHORT-WINGED FALCONS—*Accipiter palumbarius* L. (goshawk; Europe and Asia); *A. nisus* L. (sparrow-hawk; Europe and Asia).

Also various other species. *Aquila chrysaetus* L. (golden eagle; Europe and Asia; also other eagles).

The birds of prey used for hunting are not domesticated in the strict sense of the word, as none breed in captivity. Nevertheless, the subject is of sufficient interest to merit brief mention here.

Falconry is apparently of great antiquity. The Assyrians were familiar with it, certainly in Ahsurbanipal's time. The method of equipping the bird with a hood with a feather ornament and carrying it on a glove (Figs. 24 : 3 and 24 : 4) is of western Asiatic origin and still the fashion in Arabia.

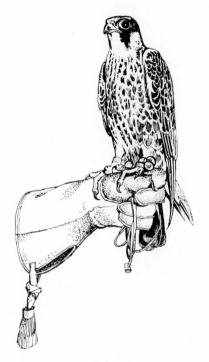

FIG. 24 : 3. A first-year peregrine falcon sitting on the glove. Original of a bird owned by Mr H. Pepper

FIG. 24 : 4. Hood as used in modern falconry, the property of Mr H. Pepper

Other methods prevailed elsewhere. Pseudo-Aristotle relates that in Thrace birds were hunted on a large scale with the help of falcons. The vast swamps of the country were chosen for this purpose. Beaters chased the small birds from the thickets, and as soon as they took to the wing the trained falcons were let loose, catching some of the birds. Most of them, however, settled on the ground for fear of the falcons, and were there killed with sticks.

This is not exactly the sport called falconry. Nor did the Romans practise it. That it became fashionable in medieval Europe was the result of the Crusades, though meanwhile the sport had spread from western Asia to India also.

In Europe falconry became the privilege of nobility. Only members of the royal family were permitted to use gyrfalcons. Peregrines were reserved for princes, dukes and earls, and sparrowhawks for the priests. In the course of time a complicated vocabulary developed, distinguishing young and old, male and female birds, which differ much in performance. Occasionally, eagles are trained also. In all probability the art reached northern Europe following the Crusades. Emperor Frederick II, who maintained an oriental court in Sicily, brought experts from Syria and experimented with the birds to find out whether they could find food by smell (Hitti, 1956).

The ancient art of falconry was thus practised with a number of different species. It was still very much alive in Kurdistan in the days of Layard, who gives a detailed description in his book on Nineveh and Babylon. A few abridged quotations from it are worth giving. Whilst the usual prey of falcons is other birds, including francolins, geese and other water fowl, the Houbara bustard and crane, a wide variety of mammals was hunted also, especially hares and gazelle. In order to hunt gazelle, it is necessary to train greyhounds and falcons so that they co-operate, as Layard explains:

In the first place, the bird is taught to eat its daily ration of raw meat fastened on the stuffed head of a gazelle. The next step is to accustom it to look for its food between the horns of a tame gazelle. The distance between the animal and the falconer is daily increased until the hawk will seek its meat when about half a mile off. A greyhound is now loosed upon the gazelle, the falcon being flown at the same time. When the animal is seized, which of course soon takes place, its throat is cut, and the hawk is fed with a part of its flesh. After thus sacrificing three gazelles, the education of the falcon and greyhound is declared to be complete. The chief art in the training is to teach the two to single out the same gazelle, and to ensure that the dog does not injure the falcon when struggling on the ground with the quarry. The greyhound, also, soon learns to watch the movements of its companion, without whose assistance it could not capture its prey.

The falcon, when loosed from its tresses, flies steadily and near the ground towards the retreating gazelles, and marking one, soon separates it from the herd. It then darts at the head of the affrighted animal, throws it to the ground, or only checks it in its rapid course. The greyhound rarely comes up before the blow has been more than once repeated. The falconer then hastens to secure the quarry. Should the dog not succeed in capturing the gazelle after it has been struck for the third or fourth time, the hawk will generally sulk and refuse to hunt any longer. I once saw a very powerful falcon belonging to Abde Pasha hold a gazelle until the horseman succeeded in spearing the animal. The fleetness of the gazelle is so great, that, without the aid of the hawk, very few dogs can overtake it, unless the ground be heavy after rain.

In ancient Egypt falcons were regarded with great respect; they appeared in the form of sculptures and paintings and played an important part in the cult of the dead (Fig. 24 : 5). Whether they were ever used for hunting is another matter and very little evidence exists. The bronze head of a falcon of the Late Period (after 850 B.C.) in the British Museum (Fig. 24 : 6) rather suggests an artificial hood, in which case it would indicate that the sport was known.

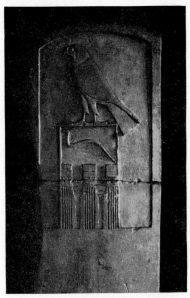

FIG. 24 : 5. Funeral stele of the 'Serpent King', Thinite period, Egypt, *c.* 3000 B.C., showing a falcon. Musée du Louvre E.51

FIG. 24 : 6. Bronze head of a falcon, Egyptian, later than 800 B.C. Possibly representing the hood of a trained bird

THE GOOSE

SCIENTIFIC NAMES—*Anser anser* L. (grey lag goose; Europe to Amurland north of 45° lat.); *A. albifrons* (Scopoli) (white-fronted goose; Europe, Mediterranean); *Cygnopsis cygnoides* (L.) (Chinese goose; China).
Alopochen aegyptiaca L. (Nile goose; Egypt, western Asia).

There is no doubt that geese were kept by man from the Neolithic onwards, but the evidence is on the whole deplorably scanty, largely because bird bones are neglected by excavators. The most important is the grey lag goose of temperate Europe, which breeds in northern and central Europe and Asia as far east as the Amur, but not south of 45° latitude. It does, however, migrate, and this explains why the northern species was important in ancient Egypt. Its original domestication must have taken place within the zone in which it naturally breeds, and one is tempted to suspect that it lay in south-eastern Europe. The grey lag goose has a strong tendency to leucism and white geese were regarded as of superior quality by the Romans. Gandert (1953) considers that Bronze Age representations of the Lausitz culture and the western Urnfield culture represent domesticated geese, and he quotes in particular two small clay figurines found at Biegen, Lebus district, eastern Germany.

The goose is easily domesticated if one starts with nestlings. Moreover, it is most willing to eat more than strictly necessary, a propensity which has been exploited since very early times both for the purpose of fattening and in order to render it too heavy to fly. On the other hand, tame geese cross with wild individuals wherever these are available, so that domestication has not resulted in the development of many divergent breeds.

Hahn (1926) regarded the goose as the oldest of all domesticated birds, but there is no evidence either for or against this assumption. We must assume that all Indo-Germanic tribes, as they entered Europe, had the goose. The word for it is the same in Latin (anser, old Latin hanser), Greek (chen), ancient Scandinavian (gas), ancient Prussian (sansy), Sanscrit (hamsa) and so forth. In pre-Roman Britain, however, the goose was considered a sacred bird which was not eaten, if one can rely on Caesar's statement regarding this matter.

The grey lag goose was domesticated by the ancient Greeks. It must be admitted that it is not mentioned in the *Iliad*, nor are there records from Mycenae, but it is mentioned in the *Odyssey*. Penelope, for instance, owned twenty geese. The Athenians obtained their geese mainly from Boeotia and Thessaly. The Greeks knew how to fatten them with soaked grain and Penelope is reported to have enjoyed the spectacle of her geese devouring greedily this wholesome food. It appears that goose eggs were appreciated also, as shown on a coin from Eion in Macedonia (Fig. 24 : 7).

Fig. 24 : 7. Silver obol of Eion in Macedonia, 500–437 B.C., showing a goose laying a (?golden) egg. Twice natural size. Author's collection

Both in Asia Minor and Greece the bird was sacred to Aphrodite for reasons which are not altogether obvious. The fertility of the goose does not exceed that of other domestic birds. In addition it was regarded as a symbol of plenty. According to Aesop's well-known fable, which in all probability originated in Asia Minor, the goose laid golden eggs on occasions.

The Romans were undoubtedly the foremost exploiters of the goose. They had it from early times onwards and ate it with pleasure. The anterior portion of the goose however was the only one regarded as wholesome by the imperial Romans. The posterior portion was therefore left to the household staff. The eggs of geese were generally eaten, but not in the hard-boiled condition, when they were considered indigestible. The liver was a great delicacy, and the Romans knew how to enlarge it by stuffing the bird with a mixture of flour, milk and honey. Following the practice of the Morini in Belgium, the down feathers were used by the Romans for cushions and upholstery, and geese were plucked twice a year to obtain them. The use of goose feathers for writing was first mentioned by Anonymous Valesii in the fifth century A.D. Goose lard was used abundantly in medicine against skin diseases, in ointments generally, but also internally against colic.

Nowadays, the goose is regarded as a stupid bird, but not so in ancient times. The Indians went so far as to believe that she instructed Brahma in the Vedas. The Romans, too, considered them as intelligent, no doubt largely because they saved Rome with their cackle from the Gauls, when the invaders were trying to climb the Capitol in 390 B.C.

These particular birds on the Capitol were kept in the Temple of Juno, to whom they were sacred. Juno, as the goddess of marriage, again shows some connection with fertility, but it is noteworthy that the Romans did not follow the Greeks in holding the goose sacred to Aphrodite or Venus. Instead the bird was associated with Priapus, again a fertility deity. It was also associated with Mars, the god of war, especially north of the Alps; this is probably due to the Capitolinian event. It thus symbolizes the vigilance of the soldier. Altogether, however, geese appear to have been bred in large numbers both in Gaul and in Germania. In Pliny's time excellent geese were imported from Gallia Belgica, but those from Germania, which were of a very pure white, were regarded as the best. These geese were apparently driven on foot across the Alps to Italy for sale. One wonders how much of their fat they lost in transit.

We must now consider briefly the position of the goose in ancient Egypt. The

Nile delta abounds in water fowl, and among them there are about half a dozen species of geese. Of these, the grey lag goose (Fig. 24 : 8) and the white-fronted goose (Fig. 24 : 9) were kept in captivity. It is difficult to decide whether these species were fully domesticated or kept captive, at any rate in Old Kingdom times.

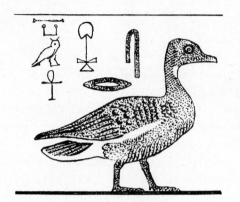 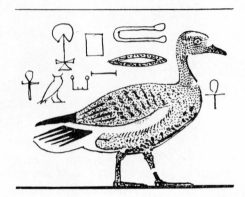

FIG. 24 : 8. Egyptian sixth-dynasty picture of a grey lag goose (left) from tomb of Kai-em-Anch. After Boessneck

FIG. 24 : 9. Egyptian sixth-dynasty picture of a white-fronted goose from tomb of Kai-em-Anch. Note white patch above the beak. After Boessneck

A fifth dynasty relief in the Berlin Museum shows the stuffing of geese, hyaena-fashion (see p. 421). This proves their exploitation. But it must have been easy to catch masses of these birds with nets, and such scenes are shown frequently. In addition, eggs were collected. By New Kingdom times, however, the grey lag goose had become completely domesticated (Boessneck 1960). It should be noted that the north of Europe had the domesticated goose at the same time. It is conceivable, therefore, that complete domestication of the grey lag goose in Egypt was due to influences from the north; on the other hand, the species may have been actually breeding in Egypt in antiquity.

Both species were much used not only for food—mummified roast geese are occasionally found in tombs—but for sacrifices also. As a sacrificial bird, however, the Nile goose was of greater importance, and it was often kept as a pet. It is a quarrelsome creature and was, perhaps, for this very reason not considered for domestic exploitation. Its character, on the other hand, may have inspired respect and induced nobles to adopt it as a pet. Only in the Old Kingdom phase of experimental domestication does the Nile goose appear in the company of other animals. In addition, a few other species of geese have been identified among those caught in the Nile swamps; yet they were never reduced to the state of domestication as far as is known.

Fɪɢ. 24 : 10. Geese being brought for inspection and registration at Thebes, *c.* 1400 ʙ.ᴄ. The presence of white geese in the lower flock is interesting since it suggests that these birds were domesticated. British Museum No. 37978

In Mesopotamia geese arrive in large numbers during the period of seasonal migration. It is not surprising, therefore, that they should appear on seals and other objects of art from the early dynastic period onwards. As with other species, however, it is often difficult to recognize the bird because of the poor draughtsmanship. A statuette from Ur which represents the goddess Ban seated on the backs of two geese, and with two more serving as a footstool, is the best-known example. There are in addition clay reliefs from Ur and cylinder seals showing geese associated with the goddess. Hilzheimer (1926) holds that many of the weights conventionally regarded as representing ducks are meant to be geese. These 'duck-weights', more correctly goose-weights, have survived in Burma into recent times.

Meissner reports that geese were kept in herds and they were used both for sacrifices and food in ancient Mesopotamia. They even appeared on the royal table. In Neo-Babylonian times they were kept by temple wardens or surrendered to breeders to be reared. These were required to deliver annually to the temple three times the original number of the birds, the surplus being the breeders' profit. The geese were fed with greenstuff as well as with grain.

The Chinese goose is a species closely related to the grey lag, but with a longer neck and a knob at the base of the male beak. It is thoroughly domesticated in China, where it is frequently white. In southern China, however, it is less important than the duck. Nothing is known about its early history, except that it is the descendant of the wild *Cygnopsis cygnoides* (L.), which does not have the knobbed beak.

THE DUCK

SCIENTIFIC NAME—*Anas platyrhyncha* L. (mallard; Europe, Mediterranean and eastwards in Palaearctic region. Many other species were hunted).

Provided that the numerous figurines of 'ducks' found in Mesopotamia are real ducks, interest in this species and perhaps domestication appear to have been centred there. In a house in Arpachiyah five miniature 'duck beads' were found, as well as elsewhere, according to Mallowan (1935). A clay vessel from Tepé Gawra shows a group of ducks, and there are many others. All, however, suffer from the lack of diagnostic details which are so typical of Egyptian art, and one is always left in some doubt whether ducks or geese are meant. This applies also to the well-known 'duck-weights', weights carved usually in hematite, and the large ones in stone, showing a 'duck' in the sleeping position, with head tucked away. They range from minute specimens to large ones weighing many pounds, and were used from Sumerian times onwards into the Assyrian period.

It appears that, unlike the goose, the duck was not domesticated in Egypt, though the mallard was hunted as much as several other species. But even as game it does not appear before the twelfth dynasty.

The Greeks and Romans (Fig. 24 : 11) rarely kept it as a domestic bird. The Roman *nessotrophia* were enclosures for ducks, but apparently usually for wild ones. But, even so, domestic ducks were not altogether unknown, if one interprets Aristophanes correctly. On Cyprus and Rhodes, famous for their cult of Aphrodite, ducks must have been kept. These islands have produced curious duck-shaped vases, sometimes with a Venus or an Eros on them.

Another strange group of objects are the fibulae adorned with ducks or heads of ducks, from Rhodes and Etruria, but also from Hallstatt-La Tène graves in Sigmaringen, Germany (Keller, p. 232). There are other representations that have been interpreted, rightly or wrongly, as ducks. Whether the Germanic tribes were duck-breeders is still uncertain, but one of the breeds mentioned in the late Roman period was known as the German duck. A mosaic in Cologne shows a drake associated with other domestic animals (Fremersdorf, 1941, pl. 58). Excavations have not yet, however, produced unambiguous bones with domestication characters. On the other

Fig. 24 : 11. Mallard (right) and pochard (left) in a Roman-mosaic still-
life preserved in the National Museum at Naples

hand, a chariot model with ducks was found at Hart near Altötting in Bavaria,
dating from the Urnfield culture, and thus from the Bronze Age.

Another centre of domestication of the duck was China. Archaeological evidence
is lacking, but the biological points clearly to a great age of the domestic duck in the
Far East, where lakes and canals make it a valuable and easily reared item on the
menu.

PELICAN

SCIENTIFIC NAMES—*Pelecanus onocrotalus* L. (pelican; Italy, Mediterranean); *P.
crispus* Bruch (Greece).

The pelican was never domesticated for the purpose of helping man to fish. The
ancient Egyptians, however, esteemed its eggs. That they kept pelicans in enclosures
and collected their eggs is suggested by a remarkable painting in the tomb of
Haremhab at Thebes, who lived in the days of Thothmes IV, 1420–1411 B.C. I owe
this reference (to Wilkinson, 1897) and the illustration (Fig. 24 : 12) to Dr Charles
Singer.

Otherwise, the pelican is rarely mentioned in pre-Christian literature and
depicted only casually. It was not until the early Christian period that the bird
assumed religious significance. Fishermen had long observed its habit of feeding the
young with the huge open beak pressed against the chest. The half-digested fish
thus regurgitated gave rise to the legend that the pelican feeds its young with its
own blood. Similarly, its habit of scraping body and legs with the beak resulted in

471

FIG. 24 : 12. Pelicans and their eggs in Egypt. Drawn and restored from the copy of the original painting by Nina M. Davies from the tomb of Haremhab at Thebes (reign of Thothmes IV, 1420–1411 B.C.)

the story that it tears flesh from its legs to feed the young. Subsequently, even more fantastic tales were invented, such as that it ruminates its food. The supposed blood sacrifice, however, rendered the bird sacred in the eyes of the early Christians, who regarded it as a symbol of self-sacrificing love.

CORMORANT

SCIENTIFIC NAMES—*Phalacrocorax carbo* L. (cormorant; Europe to Asia and Mediterranean), *Ph. carbo sinensis* Shaw and Nodder (common Chinese cormorant; India and China), *Ph. capillatus* Temminck and Schlegel (Temminck's cormorant; Japan and Korea).

The cormorant was known to the ancient Mediterraneans. It would have been strange if the Egyptians had not depicted it. It appears, for instance, on the fishing scene from the tomb of Mera, of the sixth dynasty, associated with a pelican, but evidently as a wild bird. Aristotle was familiar with it and so were the Romans.

The idea of domesticating the cormorant, however, first occurred probably to the Japanese. In Japan it appears to have been used from the fifth century A.D. onwards, and in China fishing with cormorants is mentioned in the annals of the Sui Dynasty (A.D. 590–617) with reference to Japan. Today, however, it is centred in the Lower Yangtse Basin.

The eggs are hatched by domestic fowl, so that the Chinese cormorant is truly domesticated. The birds are taken out by the fishermen sitting on the edge of the boat (Fig. 24 : 13) and usually, though not always, restrained from swallowing the fish by a leather ring round the neck. A sign from the fishermen makes them take the plunge, and they soon return with the fish they have caught. They are rewarded with food according to their catches. The food, incidentally, comprises mashed

Fig. 24 : 13. Japanese in a boat, fishing with cormorants by night. Modern Japanese painting by Gyokudo

beans apart from fish. Many of these cormorants have irregular white patches. This may or may not be evidence of domestication; wild specimens are also said to show this character.

Oddly enough, cormorants were trained in the same manner in seventeenth-century England. According to Pennant (1776, p. 610), Charles I had a 'master of the cormorants', Mr Wood. Hahn (1896) went to the trouble of ascertaining the exact date when this man was working, and found him not only mentioned in 1660–1661, but also that he had served under James I already. Tame cormorants were owned by Louis XIII of France who kept them in Fontainebleau about 1625. It is further recorded that these tame cormorants stemmed from Flanders. This suggests a connection with China, since the Jesuits from the Spanish Netherlands went as missionaries to that country.

CRANES

SCIENTIFIC NAMES—*Grus grus* L. (common crane; Europe to Siberia, migrating to tropical Africa); *G. virgo* L. (demoiselle crane; Spain, North Africa, south Russia); *Balearica pavonina* L. (crowned crane; North and West Africa).

The cranes deserve brief mention. They were exceedingly popular birds, partly because of their conspicuous migration habits, when they fly in wedge-shaped formation uttering their weird cries, and partly because of the queer wooing dances performed by the males. In Egypt, however, a more utilitarian view was taken, and cranes were caught and kept captive to be fattened and sacrificed (Figs. 24 : 14 and 24 : 15). It is possible that they were induced to breed in captivity like geese. In

Fig. 24 : 14. Demoiselle crane with bill tied to neck. A sacrificial gift to the Temple of Hatshepsut, eighteenth dynasty, *c.* 1450 B.C. After Boessneck

Fig. 24 : 15. Common crane being brought as a sacrifice to the Temple of Hatshepsut at Deir-el-Bahri, eighteenth dynasty, *c.* 1450 B.C. After Boessneck

pictures, Egyptian herdsmen are seen driving the birds across the fields, in others they are stuffing them like geese.

Wealthy Romans kept tame crowned and demoiselle cranes for the sake of their women and children. But these were certainly tamed, not domesticated, birds. Mattingly believed that a crane shown on a Roman coin was a demoiselle crane.

CANARY

SCIENTIFIC NAME—*Serinus serinus canariensis* Vieill. (Canary Islands).

The canary was domesticated as a pet and it has no economic value whatever except to the breeders themselves. The bird belongs to the finches and is derived from a greenish-brown wild form which lives in the forests of the Canary Islands. It is somewhat smaller than the domesticated bird, and its song in the natural surroundings is as pleasant as it is conspicuous. For this reason it is quite conceivable that the Guanche, the prehistoric inhabitants of the Canary Islands, caught the birds and kept them prior to the Spanish Conquest, which took place in the fifteenth century. Otherwise it is difficult to understand why the Spanish trade in these birds developed as rapidly as it did.

The conquest of Gran Canaria was not completed until 1483 and that of Tenerife until 1494. But the first half of the sixteenth century already witnessed a lively trade in these birds ranging over Europe and even reaching America and India. It is mentioned in a scientific publication for the first time by Gesner in 1555.

The Spaniards were careful to export male birds only. Whether this was due quite simply to the value of the male being the singer, or whether they intended to maintain a breeding monopoly, cannot be decided. It is a fact, however, that the birds were not bred abroad until a Spanish ship carrying a canary-breeding-cage with many birds foundered off the Italian island of Elba. The birds escaped and became feral on the island. As by that time (sixteenth and early seventeenth centuries) the bird was popular, bred in Spain and captured in the Canaries for export, one cannot be surprised that the Italians took advantage of this windfall and began breeding the bird on a large scale.

Italy became the centre of canary-breeding in the seventeenth and early eighteenth centuries. From there the small Tyrolean township of Imst obtained supplies, and it soon became the most famous centre of canary-breeding. Records give the year 1776. By that time, however, the art was spreading fast in Europe, and in 1782 no fewer than 1600 singing birds were imported into England, whilst other birds from Imst were sold to Germany, Russia and even Turkey.

In the course of the nineteenth century some small towns in the Hartz Mountains in Germany became the most famous centres of breeding. It is an odd fact that the bird is not now much bred in the Canary Islands, which are full of canaries kept in cages, but many of these are now imported from the Hartz Mountains.

OSTRICH

SCIENTIFIC NAME—*Struthio camelus* L. (ostrich; Africa, Arabia, Syria, Mesopotamia, formerly south Russia and central Asia, and possibly Baluchistan).

The ostrich aroused the imagination of the ancients from the earliest times onwards. It was hunted where it occurred, but more important still were its eggs, used as vessels or broken up and converted into beads. Eggs were traded all over the Mediterranean. One, with animal paintings, was found in the Isis Grotto at Vulci and silvered and gilt eggs were imported by the Etruscans, presumably from Carthage. In ancient Sparta an egg was on exhibition which Leda had laid following her affair with Zeus in the shape of a swan and from which the Dioscuri had hatched. Unbelievers maintained that this was the egg of an ordinary ostrich.

FIG. 24 : 16. Billon tetradrachm of Antoninus Pius, A.D. 144, of the Alexandria mint. This is clearly an ostrich, though in numismatic catalogues it is commonly called a 'Numidian crane'. Natural size. Author's collection

The bird was shown in the circus in Rome. The Emperor Commodus had the heads of ostriches cut off, and the public was amazed to see the birds running about for a while before they collapsed. Occasionally, ostriches were used for riding and

FIG. 24 : 17. Ostrich on a mosaic of the Roman Imperial period, from the Musée du Bardo, Tunis. Photo F.E.Z.

476

pulling small carts. Ptolemaeus Philadelphus used a chariot drawn by eight ostriches in a procession. His queen had a statue on the Helikon which showed her riding an ostrich. On the whole, however, ostriches are not strong enough to carry adult riders, and the performance was largely a show-piece. These ostriches were tamed, and almost certainly not bred. There was, at that time, still too abundant a supply of wild ostriches available both in Arabia and North Africa (Fig. 24 : 17). Their capture is depicted in the mosaic of the corridor of the great hunting scene in the famous fourth-century villa of Piazza Armerina in Sicily.

Ostrich feathers, too, were in great demand, and they had a regular market in the large cities. The actual breeding of ostriches in captivity, i.e. under conditions of complete domestication, is an invention of the nineteenth century. It was first achieved by the French in Algeria in 1856, though ostrich-farming is now restricted to southern Africa. But attempts had been made earlier, for Emperor Frederick Barbarossa, whilst in Sicily, tried to hatch ostrich eggs by using the heat of the sun (Hitti, 1956).

25

Fishes

SCIENTIFIC NAMES—*Muraena muraena* L. (Roman eel, moray or murena; Mediterranean and other seas).

Cyprinus carpio L. (carp; Europe to east Asia).

Carassius vulgaris Nils. (Crucian carp; Europe to east Asia) with *C. auratus* (domesticated goldfish).

Macropus viridi-auratus Lacepède (paradise fish; south-east Asia).

ONLY four species of fish have ever been domesticated: the Roman eel, the goldfish, the carp and the paradise fish. Strictly speaking, many modern aquarium fishes would have to be added to the list, but their status is of no great antiquity, though several already show definite domestication characters. Other species have been kept in captivity and bred under such conditions for generations, but the effects were not permanent and there is no evidence of selection. In fact, the knowledge the ancient Greeks and Romans had of the propagation of living things, except mammals and birds, was scanty and often fantastic. Of the *muraena* or Roman eel it was believed that this fish was female and that for the purpose of reproduction she mated with a viper that came to visit the sea-shore. This fable was repudiated by some educated Romans, but everybody took it for granted that certain lowly creatures could be generated from dust, mud and the like. The eggs of the murena were certainly known to Pliny (IX, lxxiv).

As fishes have at all times made a substantial contribution to the diet of man, it is only natural that the early civilizations tried to organize this food supply by changing over from 'hunting' to 'production'. At any rate, though it may have been found difficult to induce fish to breed in captivity, at least they could occasionally be 'herded' and then stored. Artificial fishponds were known in ancient Mesopotamia as well as Egypt. Reliefs from Assyria show artificial fishponds. In Egypt, Plato saw the royal fishponds, and he mentions the 'taming' of fishes.

That the Romans should have developed this system was a matter of course. They may have inherited the idea from the Sicilians, who had a fishpond about 500 metres square at Agrigentum. This remarkable pond had been constructed by Carthaginian prisoners-of-war. Its maintenance appears to have been somewhat difficult and costly; in the days of Diodorus (first century B.C.) it had already been filled in.

In Italy fishponds became a great fashion in the first century B.C. They were called *piscinae*, a word from which our word 'basin' was derived, not to mention the modern use of the word for swimming pools in the Mediterranean area. Every wealthy family had one, and a particular point was made of owning a pond near the sea, where the highly esteemed Roman eels could be kept. These eel-like fishes, which incidentally have a beautifully marbled skin, were fattened for the table. It is possible that they bred in these large basins. The Romans were very fond of their murenas, and some were kept as pets.

Antonia, the daughter of Drusus, had such a pet which was adorned with golden ear-rings, and people travelled to her country house at Baiae to admire this beautiful creature. Marcus Crassus, too, owned a murena which wore ear-rings and a be-jewelled necklace; it obeyed the call of the great triumvir and fed from the hand. When it died he wept bitterly over it and had it buried. In these circumstances it cannot surprise that there is a story of murenas being fed on the flesh of slaves. But Keller points out that this refers to a single incident and that the slave was after all not thrown into the pond. The earliest version of this story is found in Seneca's *De re* (II, 40). When Orgastus was dining with his friend Oedius, Pollio, a slave, dropped a precious vessel. The host in his anger ordered him to be thrown into the fishpond to be devoured by the voracious murenas, but the emperor eventually prevailed on him and the slave was saved.

It is indeed probable that murenas were bred, for imperial Rome required quantities that could hardly be obtained by fishing. A man called Hirrius gave Julius Caesar 6000 for his triumphal dinner. He did not however present them to him, he only lent them, and one wonders whether, and if so how, Caesar returned the lot.

The Romans kept other species of fish in fishponds, among them mullets and wrasses. They also had freshwater ponds, one of which was found in Roman Trier (west Germany) in 1892. In addition, natural lakes and ponds were used for the breeding of freshwater fish by the Romans, and it is maintained that the German word *Weiher* for pond is derived from the Latin *Vivarium*.

It is not known whether these fishponds of the Romans contained the carp

(Fig. 25 : 1). Its Latin name is *Cyprinus* and some writers have been tempted to link it either with the island of Cyprus directly or the cult of Aphrodite, in which case the carp would have been a symbol of fertility. It is unfortunate, however, that no carps occur on Cyprus.

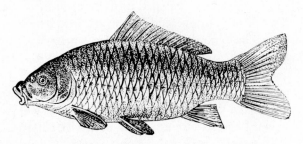

FIG. 25 : 1. The carp. One of the few domesticated
fishes. Original drawing by Mr H. Pepper

The wild carp appears to have been originally an inhabitant of the Danube system, and Rütimeyer (1862) reported it from the Swiss lake-dwellings. This find alone proves that the carp is not a comparatively recent importation from China, although it is a native of Far Eastern rivers also (Fig. 25 : 2). As a large fat fish which thrives in muddy water and can be fed on kitchen offal, it must have recommended itself to the monasteries. It is conceivable that the carp was thus first domesticated in the fishponds of European monks and that its breeding by the Chinese was a completely independent invention.

The carp has developed definite domestication characters. Apart from the normal dark-grey coloration, red, white and mottled carps occur. The cover of scales may be normal, or there may be only a few rows of very large scales, or the fish may be devoid of scales altogether.

Medieval and later sources mention the carp as nothing new. The earliest record is probably that of the Ostrogoth king Theoderic (A.D. 475–526), whose secretary Cassiodorus was compelled to issue a circular to the provincial governors to improve the supply for the king's table. From various sources, dating from the fifteenth to the eighteenth centuries, it emerges that the carp would not breed successfully in northern countries.

Hahn (1896) paid attention to the question of its introduction into the British Isles. The rhyme that

> Turkey, carps, hops, pickerell and beer,
> came into England all in one year,

by which year is meant 1514, is nonsense throughout. The turkey arrived later, and the other items earlier. As to the carp, Dame Juliana Barnes mentions it in the *Book of St Albans*, printed in 1468 as one of the first English books. From her words it is evident that the fish was not very popular, because it does not provide good sport as it does not easily take the hook. Her words are worth repeating:

The carp is a dayntous fisshe, but there ben but fewe in Englonde, and therfore I wryte the casse of him. For he is too stronge enarmyd in the mouthe that there may noo weke harnays hold hym. And as touchyne his baytes, I have but lytyll knoolege of it, and we were loth to wryte more than I know and have prouyd. But well I wote that the redde worm and the menow ben good baytyn for him at all tymes, as I have herd saye of persones credyble, and also founde wryten in bokes of credence.

Carps are extremely tenacious of life. Pennant in his *British Zoology* (1776) tells the remarkable story that carps placed in a net well wrapped in wet moss and hung up in a cellar will remain alive, providing the moss is kept wet. He asserts that they are frequently fed with white bread and milk and become exceedingly fat

Fig. 25 : 2. Japanese woodcut of a carp leaping above the surface of the water, by Taito (early nineteenth century A.D.). Original in Victoria and Albert Museum (Crown copyright)

and far superior in taste to those that are immediately killed when taken from the pond. This is conceivable, as the fish might well lose their muddy taste as a result. Thus the art of stuffing is applied not only to birds and to the hyaena already mentioned, but even to a fish, an amusing illustration of the labours that go into improving the taste of food of civilized peoples.

The European area of the domesticated carp has never been extended permanently to southern Europe or Russia. In Polish Galicia it is reared in numbers, but around the Black and Caspian Seas it has remained a wild fish in spite of the efforts of Tsar Peter the Great.

The goldfish is one of the most highly domesticated of all animals. Not only are there colour varieties, apart from the normal grey, black, red and colourless, monstrosities have been bred for centuries which one can only describe as pathological mutations. Among them are eye-balls outside the cranium, lack of a dorsal fin, doubling of the tail and the anal fin and lengthening of all fins present. The wild ancestor is the Crucian carp, a relation of the carp, which does not attain a weight of much more than three pounds in the wild state. It is a native of temperate Europe and Asia. This species is capable of breeding in small pools and survives even in water poor in oxygen. It is therefore easy to breed in artificial containers and this desirable quality must have appealed to the Chinese in their densely populated country at an early date. That fancy breeding far outstripped economic breeding is a different matter and could not be expected at the outset.

Nevertheless, specimens weighing up to ten pounds have been reported. It is stated by Mayers that breeding of goldfish began in China about A.D. 960 under the Sung Dynasty. From China the species soon spread to Japan where they were seen by a scientific observer. Hahn suspects that, because of the difficulties of transporting live fish from the East to Europe in sailing ships, an intermediate station has to be assumed, which he suggests was Batavia, a place visited by rich Chinese merchants as well as the Dutch. Thence they may have reached St Helena, and from this island the first goldfish were taken to England in 1691, according to Pennant. From that time onwards they reached Europe repeatedly, the first to breed being fish imported by the Lord Mayor of London in 1728. In the course of the eighteenth century the goldfish became known and popular as a curiosity throughout Europe. Madame Pompadour was presented with some. Strangely enough, the first goldfish to reach Europe appear to have been long-tailed, according to the description given by Linnaeus.

Only one other fish must be mentioned here, the paradise fish, which is of no economic value whatsoever. It is not more than two inches long and equipped with long fins and is beautifully coloured. The Chinese must have bred it for centuries.

In the earlier literature it is stated that the wild ancestor of the paradise fish is unknown and that the fish is the product of domestication. Since then the ancestor has been discovered in the rice-swamps of Formosa and Canton, and it appears to occur near Singapore also. If these are truly wild populations, the claim that the paradise fish has been much changed by domestication would have to be dropped. On the other hand, it is impossible to say to what extent feral specimens are present in the rice-swamps, especially as the Chinese like this fish because of its beautiful mating display, the foam nest it builds and the way the male cares for the young.

26

The Silk-moths

SCIENTIFIC NAMES—FAMILY BOMBYCIDAE—*Bombyx mori* L. (Chinese silk-moth; China, domesticated where mulberry grows); *B. textor* Hutton (the boropooloo; Bengal); *B. sinensis* Hutton (Chinese monthly silkworm; China and India); *B. croesus* Hutton (Madrasi worm; India); *B. fortunatus* Hutton (Desi worm; India); *B. arracanensis* Hutton (Burmese worm; Burma). All mulberry feeders.

FAMILY SATURNIIDAE (tusser silk-moths)—*Antheraea mylitta* Drury (India, on bher tree, *Zizyphus jujuba*); *An. assama* Westwood (Mezankooria moth; Assam); *An. pernyi* Guér. Mén. (Mongolia and thence to China, on oak, chief tusser producer); *An. yamamai* Guér. Mén. (Japan, on oak); *Attacus atlas* L. (India); *Philosamia cynthia* Drury (Ailanthus moth; China, on Tree-of-Heaven, *Ailanthus*); *Ph. ricini* Boisol (Arrindi moth; Bengal and Assam, on castor-oil plant, *Ricinus*). The Ailanthus worm of Europe is a cross between *Ph. cynthia* and *Ph. ricini*.

FAMILY LASIOCAMPIDAE—*Pachypasa otus* (L.) (Cos silk-moth; eastern Mediterranean, on cypress, oak, etc.).

CURIOUSLY enough, even an insect has become fully domesticated in the sense that it has lost the ability to live without the help of man. This is the silk-moth, *Bombyx mori* L. (Fig. 26 : 1), which is today, as it has been in the past, the chief producer of natural silk. There are, however, about a dozen other species belonging to the families Bombycidae, Saturniidae and Lasiocampidae whose cocoons yield commercially usable silk. Most of these species inhabit the Indo-Chinese region, but one is found in the eastern Mediterranean, where it had given rise to an industry in classical times, before *Bombyx mori* had reached the

Fig. 26 : 1. The Chinese silk-moth, *Bombyx mori*. Natural size. Fig. 26 : 2. *Bombyx huttoni*, north-west Himalayas. This species is possibly ancestral to one or several of the domesticated *Bombyx* species. It is brown and has a pattern and it therefore seems possible that *Bombyx mori*, the domesticated silk-moth, is a white form bred under conditions of domestication. Hutton succeeded in crossing this species with *B. mori*. Natural size

western world. This species is *Pachypasa otus* L. (Fig. 26 : 3); it will be discussed later on.

It is nevertheless virtually certain that sericulture began in China and was based on *Bombyx mori*. According to Chinese legend, it is said to have been invented by an emperor called Fu-shi, who may have lived about 3000 B.C. On the other hand, the

Fig. 26 : 3. *Pachypasa otus* (L.), an eastern Mediterranean moth which produced the famous Coan silk. Half-size

spinning and weaving of silk is definitely later than the invention of spinning and weaving of vegetable fibre and wool, and it appears that in China these fibres were gradually replaced by silk and to a minor extent by cotton.

If one can trust the dates, the Emperor Huang-ti encouraged his subjects to take up the rearing of silkworms about 2630 B.C. His wife, Hsi-ling-shi, was ordered to teach the art to the common people, as tradition has it, because he wanted them to have clothes that prevented chapped skin and frostbite. Under Emperor Yu (*c.* 2220 B.C.) vast areas were drained for mulberry plantations, mulberry trees were planted and silkworm eggs distributed to the population. By about 1000 B.C. the ritual side of sericulture had been fully developed. Hsi-ling-shi was worshipped, and the empress of the time had to start silkworm-rearing ceremonially each year. A treatise on sericulture was first published in A.D. 1210 and has since gone into many editions.

Up to the beginning of the Christian era it appears that China succeeded in retaining a complete monopoly of *Bombyx mori* silk. It is conceivable that elsewhere the art of spinning caterpillar silk had been invented independently. It is after all an obvious thing to try, once spinning of fibres is at all practised. The chief difficulty is not the conception of the idea but the ungluing of the threads (Fig. 26 : 4). As this is done with hot water, it is likely to have been discovered sooner or later.

FIG. 26 : 4. Chinese rice-paper painting of a lady reeling silk threads off the cocoons. Author's collection

In India, in particular, the art of using native silk may well have been developed independently, since that country harbours several silk-producing species. No fewer than five belong to the same genus *Bombyx* (see the list at the head of the chapter, and Fig. 26 : 2); they occur from Burma and Bengal throughout the peninsula. It appears, however, that the earliest silk industry of India was located in the Brahmaputra Valley. According to Sanscrit writings, it would have been in existence about 1000 B.C. Later on it would have spread into the Ganges Valley. This might indicate an influx of the practice of silk-rearing from China by way of the Brahmaputra Valley.

In addition to *Bombyx* silk there are several species of Saturniidae, producers of the coarser and harder tusser silk, which is still used. The chief species are *Antheraea mylitta* of India, *Antheraea pernyi* of China, and *Antheraea yamamai* of Japan. Two species of large size, *Attacus atlas* and *Philosamia ricini* (Fig. 26 : 5) are used also. All these species feed on oak and other trees, not on mulberry.

Fig. 26 : 5. *Philosamia ricini*, the Arrindi moth of Bengal. Much reared in the East for a coarser variety of silk. Half-size

It appears that even in the eastern Mediterranean silk production began independently of China. In the island of Cos the species *Pachypasa otus* L. was reared several centuries before Christ and mentioned by Aristotle. A gauze-like tissue was made of it, famous for its transparency under the name of *Coa vestis*.

Coan silk and its manufacture is described by Pliny (XI, xxvi–xxvii). It is a fantastic and garbled story. 'Small butterflies are produced that are devoid of down, and as they cannot endure the cold they grow shaggy tufts of hair and equip themselves with thick jackets against winter, scraping together the down of leaves with the roughness of their feet. This is compressed by them into fleeces . . . and wrapped round their body in a coiled vest. They are taken away by a man, put in earthenware vessels and reared with warmth . . . but tufts of wool plucked off are softened with moisture and thinned out into threads with a rush spindle.' No doubt Pliny's informant had seen a silk farm, as he describes the pupae, the vessels, the reeling-off of the silk threads. But he had not grasped the process, and Pliny did not quite trust him either, for twice he adds the remark, 'it is said'.

Pliny is much more precise regarding the final product. Of the 'luxurious material for women's dresses, called silk', he says that the process of unravelling the threads made by the caterpillars and weaving them again 'was first invented in Cos by a woman named Pamphile, daughter of Plateas, who has the undeniable distinction of having devised a plan to reduce women's clothing to nakedness' (XI, xxvi). 'Nor have even men been ashamed to make use of these dresses, because of their lightness in summer: so far have our habits departed from wearing a leather cuirass that even a robe is considered a burden! All the same we so far leave the Assyrian silk-moth to women' (XI, xxvii). But silk found its way into Rome, though it had to be paid for heavily. The transparent variety from Cos was often criticized as indecent by Roman satirists. In A.D. 222 the Emperor Heliogabalus shocked his subjects by wearing a thin silken garment.

It is very unlikely that (as is assumed by some writers) the inhabitants of Cos unreeled imported woven pieces of Chinese silk. Aristotle, however, already knew of the horned caterpillar of the true *Bombyx* also, a piece of knowledge which is likely to have reached Greece in the wake of Alexander's Indian and Bactrian campaigns, and of its metamorphosis. He said the products of the metamorphosis were the *bombykia*, by which term the cocoons or the silk threads appear to be meant. Subsequently, this information was forgotten.

Unlike the Chinese, who were acquainted with the life-cycle of their silk-moths in every detail (Figs. 26 : 6 – 26 : 8), and who, in order to control the insects' food supply and prevent predators from reaching them, had taken to breeding them in houses, the post-Alexandrine Graeco-Roman world knew little about the biology of moths. It is to be hoped that on the Isle of Cos people were better acquainted with the way in which silk is made by the caterpillars than was Pliny, whose story is so full of fanciful errors. In his time some even thought that silk was made from the hairs

Fig. 26 : 6. Modern Chinese painting of silk-moth caterpillars and cocoons

of the leaves which were scratched off by the moths with their claws. Another widely accepted view was that silk grew on trees as a fleece—evidently a confusion with cotton.

As a finished article, silk cloth was one of the most valuable articles of export that

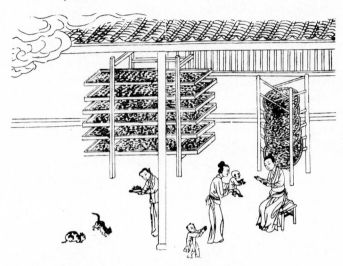

FIG. 26 : 7. The breeding of silkworms on open trays. The caterpillars are sufficiently domesticated not to leave the trays of their own accord. From an ancient Chinese work on sericulture

FIG. 26 : 8. Trays holding cocoons. A basketful of cocoons being sorted according to quality

China produced. It first became fashionable in Rome in the days of Julius Caesar. The emperors, however, tried to suppress the use of silk from time to time as an effeminate luxury. Their real reason was probably its excessive price, which was too much of a drain on gold reserves, since the East Indian trade was by that time in full swing. In Aurelian's time Chinese silk materials still fetched their weight in gold. In A.D. 273 he turned a completely deaf ear to his empress who wanted to buy just one single robe of purple silk. It is likely that about this time the practice was developed of unreeling imported Chinese silk materials and of reweaving them in various patterns appealing to Western taste, perhaps after dyeing the threads. A silk tapestry panel, about four inches square, is in the textile collection of the Victoria and Albert Museum and of Romano-Egyptian provenance. Its topics are so obviously Roman that the use of imported thread has to be inferred. Silken materials were traded in Syria, as evidenced by finds made in Palmyra and Zenobia by Pfister (1951). It is conceivable that the overland silk-trade route from China to Rome passed through Syria at that time. There is no doubt that silken goods gradually became cheaper. In A.D. 380 Ammianus Marcellinus stated that they were sufficiently inexpensive to be bought by ordinary citizens.

For very obvious reasons the Chinese were interested in exporting their silk, though by doing so they aroused the interest of all foreigners in the method of silk production, which they were trying so hard to keep as an exclusive secret to themselves. Commercial silk had reached the Altai Mountains, and possibly Persia, by the fourth century B.C., for the Pazaryk carpet, a piece of equipment of a princely grave found in a frozen condition, contains silk. It dates from the Achaemenid period and is Persian in style. In 139 B.C. trade in silk cloth was established with Turkestan by a Chinese general, Chang-Kien.

It was at about this time that the Chinese silkworm monopoly was broken, perhaps because the Chinese emperors themselves allowed the industry to spread to tributary countries. According to some authors, sericulture spread to Korea and to Japan in the second century B.C., though according to others it did not reach Japan until A.D. 300.

The custom of marrying Chinese princesses to the rulers of other oriental states turned out to be another gap in the wall of seclusion surrounding the silk production of the ancient Chinese. It is related that about 140 B.C. a Chinese princess who went to Khotan in the northern Kwen-Lun mountains took eggs with her which she hid in her hair. After all, one could hardly blame her for doing so, for ever since the days of the Lady Hsi-ling-shi royal ladies had specialized in silk-rearing. The princess evidently did not see why she should give up her hobby just because she was to be married to a prince in a faraway land. From Khotan silk-rearing rapidly spread to Turkestan. From that country silk was supplied to the nomads who in later centuries invaded Europe. The silken tents of Attila made a great impression on the inhabitants of central Europe, for whom at that time silk was almost a mythical material.

The first *Bombyx* silkworms were seen by ambassadors of the Roman emperor Marcus Aurelius Antonius when they visited the Emperor of China, Loyang, in A.D. 166. The description, however, which Pausanias obtained from these ambassadors was very inaccurate. It was only in the year A.D. 536 that eggs were successfully imported into the Mediterranean region. According to Procopius, Syrian monks succeeded in bringing them to Byzantium, hidden in a cane. In some reports these monks are called Persian, which may suggest the provenance of the eggs. It appears certain that sericulture had by this time spread to Persia, presumably from Turkestan.[1]

Silk production spread quickly throughout Syria, and the then reigning emperor, Justinian, realizing the commercial value of the new industry, monopolized it forthwith. This action prevented its spread westwards for some centuries.

In the meantime the Islamic world had come into being. From Persia and Syria the production of silk spread as far west as Spain, where it flourished for a time. In

[1] Marco Polo, in the thirteenth century A.D., remarks upon the flourishing silk-farming practised in Georgia, Armenia and around Tabriz in Persia.

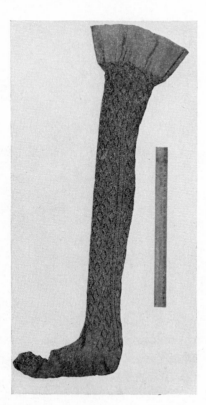

FIG. 26 : 9. A silk stocking of Elizabeth I, preserved at Hatfield House, Hertfordshire. Reproduced by permission of the Marquess of Salisbury

the ninth century it reached Sicily with the Arab Conquest (Palermo fell in A.D. 831). When this island was reconquered by the Normans in A.D. 1060, under Roger I, an opportunity was at last given for the spread of the Chinese silkworm in Europe as far as the mulberry tree could be cultivated. Sericulture established itself quickly in northern Italy. Attempts were made repeatedly to spread it in France and elsewhere. Silk trade began in Lyons and Tours in the thirteenth century. In 1253 a thousand knights wore silken garments at the marriage of the daughter of King Henry III of England, and in the fourteenth century English silk merchants were established as a guild. Queen Elizabeth I began to wear silk stockings, a pair of which are on exhibition in Hatfield House (Fig. 26 : 9). Owing to the inclement climate of England, however, breeding of silkworms never proved a lasting success in this country. Its most northerly and most recent outpost is the silk farm of Lullingstone in Kent which provided the silk for the wedding dress and the coronation robe of Queen Elizabeth II.

27

The Honey-bee

SCIENTIFIC NAME—*Apis mellifera* L. syn. *A. mellifica* L. (honey-bee; Old World).

IT BEFITS a book on the domestication of animals that the last creature to be discussed should be the honey-bee, a member of the order Hymenoptera, which has provided most instances of complex social organization apart from man himself. The bees—like the ants—can claim to have invented the division of labour, artificial domestic environment and warlike attitude towards neighbouring communities some thirty million years before man thought of them. We shall return to this matter later on.

The honey-bee has at all times, including the Palaeolithic, been of the greatest economic importance. In the age of cane and beet sugar, one is apt to forget that until but a couple of centuries ago honey was the only major source of sugar available to man.[1] That the ancient Egyptians considered the bee as sacred is therefore not surprising.

There are several species of bees providing honey of some sort. The bumble-bees, the stingless bees (*Melipona* and *Trigona*) of the tropics,[2] and the three species of the genus *Apis* all do. All these must since time immemorial have been the targets of food-collectors. The collecting of wild honey is a normal occupation of primitive communities even at the present day. Where it is done it is an act of straightforward robbing, with or without extermination of the colony. Indeed, where food-collecting is practised in forests, the extermination of whole colonies of bees remains a comparatively rare event, and the survival of the species is not impaired. The usual method of getting rid of the bees has always been to smoke them out. Whether they

---

[1] Except in the East Indies, where sugar-cane was collected and grown.
[2] The Veddas of Ceylon still keep *Trigona* species in inhabited caves, according to Seligman (1911).

are merely made unconscious or killed was irrelevant, so long as man could get at the comb.

This, however, was a matter of considerable inconvenience, not only because of the aggressiveness of the bees, and of the smoke that was liable to asphyxiate the collector with the bees, but because of the combs being often in places very difficult of access, in hollow trees, on branches high up, in fissures of cave roofs and rock shelters.

A scene that vividly depicts the difficulties of getting the honey was drawn by the presumably Neolithic originators of the eastern Spanish rock-shelter art,[1] at the Cueva de la Araña (Fig. 27 : 1). This famous picture has been interpreted in various

[1] The bag or vessel held by the collector is of a shape that suggests Neolithic affinities, though a Mesolithic age cannot be excluded. A Palaeolithic age as postulated by some archaeologists is most unlikely.

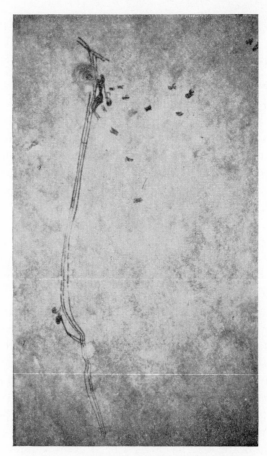

FIG. 27 : 1. The prehistoric honey-collector from the Cueva de la Araña. Eastern Spanish rock-shelter art. Photo Dr E. Ripoll

ways, but all are agreed that it shows a person, male or female, in the act of collecting combs, while the bees are furiously buzzing around. The difficulty lies in the correct interpretation of the three vertical lines. Are they trees, perhaps pines? Or are they intended to indicate ropes, so that the bee colony would have been in a recess of a cliff? The position of the knees of the collector favours the second view. But why then are there three 'ropes' where one would suffice? This question will not be answered unless similar pictures are found elsewhere. In this context the precise interpretation matters little; it is evident that collecting honey was no easy job. Much is known of the methods used by modern natives in Africa and Asia which bear out the difficulties of the enterprise.

It cannot have escaped the attention of the collectors that the honey-bee forms swarms from time to time, which then look for a suitable abode to found a new colony. Since wild bees often live in hollow trees, the idea of offering an artificial abode was so obvious that the keeping of bees in containers of some kind may well be extremely old. It survives in many forms in tropical countries (Fig. 27 : 2).

Fig. 27 : 2. Beehives made from hollow tree-trunks and suspended from an Euphorbia tree, near Longonot volcano, Kenya Rift. Photo F.E.Z.

It is of course possible, as Fraser (1951) suggests, that bees first settled voluntarily near man in an old disused pot. More likely still, they may have settled in a cave used by man, an event common in India today.

How exactly man became acquainted with the habits of bees is not very relevant —it is the offering of an abode to the swarm that constituted the first step towards domestication. That this had happened by the end of the Neolithic is certain, for in Egypt the bee was an important member of the economic-religious pantheon from the first dynasty onwards.

In East and central Africa log-shaped cylinders are made from tree-bark, closed completely at one end, whilst at the other a small entrance is left open. They are embalmed with substances to attract flying swarms and then suspended in trees. When the owner thinks the bees have collected enough honey and wax the bees are killed and the produce collected. This is not domestication, but simple exploitation of the guests by the host species.

The history of the hive is interesting. The warmer parts of the Old World, south of the great mountain ranges, all had the horizontal, 'tubular' hive, derived from the hollow branch, which in its developed form could be opened at the back in order to blow smoke in. This would drive the bees out through the flight-hole, the honey could be taken without difficulty and the bees would return. If mounted in walls, as was done in Egypt, for instance, this was a most efficient contraption. The materials used varied a great deal. Clay was popular in hot countries but considered too cold in winter and too hot in summer by the Romans, hence they recommended wicker, bark and other materials, sometimes smeared with cow-dung. The cow-dung had the disadvantage of catching fire easily when smoking was carried out. North of the great mountains, however, the skep was developed—a vertical hive derived from the hollow tree—evidently because wild bees nest commonly in hollow oaks. Bears knew this, incidentally, which accounts for the many folk-tales of bears emerging from hollow trees. The vertical hive is known all over the belt of mixed oak forests.

Egypt

The first step towards proper domestication was taken when provision was made for the survival of the bees, and especially of their brood. Smoke had been used to drive away wild bees. If smoke was blown into the log hive from one end, the bees would fly out at the other. The honey could then be taken and the brood saved. This technique was known in ancient Egypt (Fig. 27 : 3). Though the illustration here shown is relatively late, the practice must go back a long time. The recovery of honey is shown also on a relief from the Temple of Ne-Usere-re at Abusir, of fifth-dynasty age (*c.* 2600 B.C.), now in the Egyptian Museum, Berlin.

In Egypt, where wood was scarce and suitable bark still more so, clay cylinders were substituted for the earlier bark hive. These cylinders were piled up to form walls, with the flight-holes on one side and the plug end (from which the bee-keeper would operate) on the other. The practice has continued in the Near East to the present day.

Elsewhere in the Old World, too, from the western Mediterranean to eastern Siberia, primitive hives were all derived from the hollow log. In many places, however, oblong wooden boxes replace the normal cylinder.

The importance of bee-keeping in Egypt is illustrated by the fact that with the union of Lower and Upper Egypt by the first dynasty the bee appears as the symbol

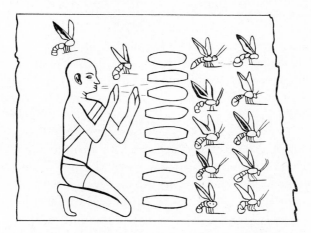

FIG. 27 : 3. Egyptian bee-keeping scene from tomb of Pa-bu-sa (625–610 B.C.) Bees are being driven out of their conical clay hives by means of smoke.
After Fraser

of the former country. It was the emblem of the king, and it remained so until imperial Rome abandoned it.

The bee is so frequently depicted on Egyptian monuments that its economic importance is beyond doubt. It was used as a hieroglyph, too, and it was a symbol of industrious activity. The eagerness with which bees pursue their various jobs must have made a great impression on man from the beginning, and solicited comparison with human life.

Mesopotamia

Curiously enough, the domesticated bee was introduced into Mesopotamia at a comparatively late date. What the Babylonians called honey was syrup of dates, and this is confirmed by Herodotus. The later Assyrians, however, were familiar both with honey and with wax. As they came from the mountainous regions of the north, where wild bees occur in the forests, this is not surprising. The credit for the introduction of the domesticated honey-bee into the land of Sukhi on the Middle Euphrates goes to Shamash-resh-ussur, who claimed:

I, Shamash-resh-ussur, governor of Sukhi and Ma'er, have brought from the mountains of the people of Khabkha into the land Sukhi the bees that collect honey and which since the days of my ancestors nobody has seen. I settled them in the gardens of the city of Gabbarini, so that they should collect honey and wax. The manufacture of honey and wax I understand, and the gardeners understand it also. Whosoever wishes to raise his voice, may he ask the elders of his country: Is it the truth that Shamash-resh-ussur, Governor of Sukhi, introduced the honey-bees into the land of Sukhi?

This text, which dates from about 1100 B.C., is of great interest. It shows that, unlike Egypt, bee-keeping was not indigenous in Mesopotamia. On the other hand, the report implies that the art was of long standing in the mountains adjacent to the north, and it was brought, fully fledged, with bees and technique, down into the Euphrates-Tigris Basin.

The produce of the bee that was regarded as the most valuable in Mesopotamia was perhaps the 'plastics' rather than the honey. In a country that used bitumen on a large scale for the manufacture of articles, wax and propolis were highly esteemed. In the seventh century B.C. the writing tablet covered with wax had made its appearance, as shown by a magnificent specimen excavated by Mallowan at Nimrud (Howard, 1955). It antedates the destruction of the city in 612 B.C. Wax had the advantage over baked clay, commonly used for cuneiform writing, that the letters could easily be smoothed out again. Wax tablets therefore were eminently useful as notebooks, for temporary messages or information. Their survival into the Roman period is well known.

In spite of the scarcity of evidence for the domesticated bee in Mesopotamia, the insect with its peculiar social organization must have been known, for wild bees are indigenous. It is conceivable that several, if not most, representations listed by van Buren (1939) as flies are meant to show bees. The fly is hardly a creature to be regarded as worthy of being depicted or converted into an amulet. If this is right, the bee would have been used as an amulet or on seals from Uruk III and the Halafian onwards.

Asia Minor, Syria, Palestine

Palestine, which was in close contact with Egypt, knew bee-keeping. The settled Philistine population practised it, whilst the nomadic Hebrews did not. When the latter were moving into the country they were promised a land flowing with milk and honey, which was a great attraction for desert tribes invading agricultural

lands. It is very probable that the Hebrews up to the time of Joshua confined themselves to the recovery of wild honey only. That bees are apt to be furious when their
honey is taken is mentioned in Deut. i, 44, but references to the actual keeping of
bees are absent from the Old Testament. The honey which Samson found in the
carcass of a lion again suggests wild honey, for a swarm may well have established
itself in the dried body, or even the skeleton.

The use of earthenware hives shaped like cases is reported by Armbruster to
continue with the Druz in Syria (Fraser, p. 97).

In Asia Minor, Ephesus became closely associated with the bee. The reasons for
this are not known. Artemis or Diana of Ephesus, a fertility deity who appears to
have come into existence in the form of a meteor with numerous protuberances
that were interpreted as breasts, became a many-breasted goddess of the Greek type,

FIG. 27 : 4. Silver coin of Ephesus with the
two emblems of the Ephesian Diana. Bee
on the obverse, fallow deer on the reverse,
c. 400–336 B.C. After Head (1959)

clad in a garment covered with fallow deer and bees. Coins of the city show the bee
very frequently (Fig. 27 : 4) on one side, and the fallow deer on the other. On two
early coins (probably seventh century B.C.), the bee is represented by the name of
'Phanes' (see p. 431).

Crete

The honey-bee was well known in Crete and its existence attributed to ancient
times. It was here that Zeus, the ruler of Olympus, was said to have been born and
concealed from his father Cronos in the Dictean Cave, the same where so many
double-axes had been deposited as votive gifts (see p. 233). The father had been told
by an oracle that his son would depose him, hence he devoured the children he had
from his wife, Rhea. On this occasion, however, he was served with a stone instead
of a child, and Zeus was reared on goat's milk and honey by the daughters of King
Melissus, one of whom had discovered the uses of honey and brought her hive along
to the cave. Her name was Melissa, *honey*. This is unlikely to be connected with the
modern use of the word as a substitute for 'sweetheart'. Hers and her father's names
emphasize the importance of bee-keeping in early Crete.

An amusing scene of a swarm attacking some men is depicted on a Cretan vase
in the British Museum (Fig. 27 : 5). It is conceivable that bee-keeping in Crete was
connected either with Egypt or with Asia Minor.

FIG. 27 : 5. A Greek vase from Volci depicting men being attacked by bees; probably referring to a Greek legend. British Museum No. B.177

Greece

In early Greece, bee-keeping was not important. Homer mentions the robbing of honey from wild bees on several occasions, but only one reference in the *Odyssey* (xiii) has been interpreted as evidence for apiculture of some sort. It is doubtful. The Naiads live in a cave in which there are 'mixing bowls and jars of stone, and there, moreover, do bees hive'. This cannot be regarded as proof, since wild bees establish themselves so frequently in caves without the help of man.

In Greek legend Aristaeus is connected with bees. He was believed to be a son of the Cretan lady Melissa. Under the tuition of the Horae, he learned three major farming activities of ancient Greece, namely the growing of olive, making cheese and constructing beehives. Many variants of the Aristaeus legend exist. In one, related by Nonnus, he is dressed in a linen frock to protect him against stings. Fraser considers that this may be the first reference to the use of a veil.

In the days of the city states, however, bee-keeping was practised on a large scale. Solon made it a law that between the hives of two owners there should be a distance of at least 300 feet.

The works of Aristotle, written about 343 B.C., contain numerous references to bees, including a good description of their anatomy. It is evident that he was familiar with the inside of a hive, of which he knew many details. He found it difficult, how-ever, to disentangle the problem of their reproduction, not knowing the sexes of queens, workers and drones. Queens are called 'rulers' and were generally regarded as males in Roman times. It is certain that Aristotle never saw the laying of an egg, though he was familiar with the grubs of all stages.[1] He quotes the popular view that they collect their young from flowers, but eventually comes to the conclusion that rulers produce rulers and workers, workers only drones, whilst drones do not reproduce. This is a remarkable approximation to the truth.

The ninth book of the *Natural History of Aristotle* was written by another author commonly called Pseudo-Aristotle who lived early in the third century B.C. and who was a professional bee-keeper. He was the first to know something about the division of labour among the workers of a hive. Many correct observations are made, but they are often wrongly interpreted because he thought that young bees were hairless and old bees hairy, whilst the opposite is true.

Rome

The attitude of the Romans was essentially practical. Their writers were not interes-ted in the bee's anatomy but in the mass production of honey. Hence most treatises deal with this aspect and provide us with much interesting information. The earliest mention of bees is in Cato, who followed Pseudo-Aristotle in the latter half of the third century (234–149 B.C.). Wax is mentioned as one of the constituents of a cement for pot-mending. In his time slaves called *mellarii* were the bee-keepers. The owner and the writer therefore had often only indirect knowledge of what was going on. This accounts for many of the mistakes in Roman books dealing with apiculture.

Varro's book, *De Re Rustica*, appeared in 37 B.C. This author refers to the social life of the bees and compares it with that of man, a matter to be taken up a few years later by the great poet Virgil. Position of the apiary, shapes and mode of construction of the hives, the planting of bee flowers and even winter feeding are discussed. For the first time the requeening of a weak colony is recommended.

The very detailed practical knowledge the *mellarius* must have had did not, how-ever, prevent Varro and Virgil from accepting that most curious story of bee-generation from carcasses of cattle, called the *bugonia*. It obviously had a popular appeal and continued to have it until it was published for the last time in A.D. 1842 by one Mr Carew. Its origin is in remote antiquity, for it was known to the Greeks; possibly it is to be sought in North Africa. There are slight variants of the story. Essentially it is as follows:

Bees are generated either from bees or from dead oxen. If you wish to raise them in the second manner, put a very fat and fleshy bullock two and a half years old into

---

[1] The chief discussion is to be found in Aristotle, *Generation of Animals*, III, x.

a small house or room ten cubits square, beat it with bludgeons rather carefully until all bones are broken and, incidentally, the animal is dead. On no account must blood flow, for bees are not generated from this substance. (Evidently this refers to the belief of the classical world that insects have no blood. Their colourless blood was not recognized.) Then stop all natural openings with rags and place the carcass on a bed of thyme. Leave the house, closing all windows and the door, stopping cracks with clay.

In the third week you have to return, open the house on all sides except the one from which a strong wind may be blowing, and admit pure air. (On this occasion, flies must have been admitted in quantity which would lay their eggs on the carcass forthwith.) The airing completed, the house is closed again as before.

When it is opened again, on the eleventh day thereafter, the carcass will be found covered with masses of bees. It is believed that 'kings' are produced from the brain, workers from the flesh. The first indication that the process is going on well is provided by small white things on which wings and legs appear gradually. (The larvae and pupae.) As bees suffocate easily, the windows should be opened every second day, the hives prepared near the house and fumigated with thyme and other fragrant herbs to invite the bees in. (This would surely not work but was an ancient practice generally.)

This story is readily explained by any naturalist. The fly produced in this circumstantial manner is *Eristalis tenax* L., the 'drone fly', which mimics a bee with great success both in appearance and buzzing. Other flies would be bred also.

Of course, this story was easily accepted for many reasons. It appealed to the ancients, being a prescription fraught with difficulties. It could always be said that it did not work because some mistake was made, and the chances were many. The bloodless smashing of the bones of an ox, alive at the beginning of the procedure, must have required supreme skill. The purifying of the air may not have been completed. Indeed it couldn't, with the decomposing body in the small house. No wonder the bees did not turn out to be the right quality, and that flies and beetles were generated instead. And if proper 'bees' appeared (the *Eristalis* being mistaken) one would have done the thing very nearly correctly, only they would not produce honey.

It was, moreover, far more economical to catch swarms or to buy stock, instead of killing oxen. So the experiment was probably carried out but rarely. One feels pity not only for the ox, but for the slaves who had to carry out the work and were no doubt severely punished for the failure.

It is thus easy to understand that the story was willingly believed. One wonders, however, how it could have originated. The observation that drone flies breed on the liquid issuing from carcasses may have been interpreted as generation of false bees that do not swarm and make no honey. Quite recently, however, I came across a report that real honey-bees were attracted by a corpse and that it was difficult to fight them off. It was published in a most reputable bee journal in this country (*Bee World*, 1958).

In any case, there is no doubt that even in antiquity all honey-bees were 'generated' from honey-bees.

Virgil, in his *Georgics*, a teaching poem on agriculture, gives much sound advice on practical matters. It becomes clear that he had first-hand knowledge, unlike most of his predecessors, and that he loved his bees. It is a pleasure to read the fourth book of the *Georgics*, in which the countryside, the flowers and the activities of the bees are beautifully put into words, mixed on many occasions with apicultural instructions.

Whilst the Greeks were greatly interested in the anatomy of the bee and the organization of the beehive in general, and most Roman authors on the subject emphasize the practical side, there appears in Virgil a philosophical interest for the first time. This poet was intensely interested in the meaning of the bee state. He came to the conclusion that Jupiter had endowed the bees with all their gifts and made them live a life of toil and production in order to set an example to mankind. The bee had always been associated with divinity by the Greeks, and the gods on Mount Olympus were believed to have included large quantities of honey, preferably mixed with milk, in their daily rations. Evidently the bees came from the gods, and their organization was of necessity perfect.

If one studies the fourth book of the *Georgics* in some detail, one discovers that, quite apart from giving good advice to the farmer, which is almost the sole purpose of the first three books, the poet is using metaphorical language with exceptional skill. Everything the bees do has a hidden application to human life. Their activities are described in the order of the seasons: it begins with the birth of a young bee in the spring, their toil on a summer day is described, the fighting of swarms as an example of how human wars should be conducted (a misinterpretation), it continues with the harvest of the honey and finishes with sickness and death. In point of fact, of course, bee colonies hibernate, but this was not relevant to Virgil's context. The vocabulary used is an apicultural one only where this is strictly necessary. Elsewhere words are drawn from the human sphere. If one neglects the wealth of technical information which Virgil can only have obtained first-hand, one is apt to think that he was completely out of touch with the animal world. But what mattered to him really was the ulterior significance of bee life. In this respect he was one of the first Roman writers who refused to accept the animal world merely as an object of exploitation, and he was trying hard to discover the secrets of life.

The *Georgics* appear to have influenced contemporary thinking considerably. Virgil died in 19 B.C. In A.D. 55 Seneca, the tutor of the young Emperor Nero, presented to him the two books entitled *De Clementia*. In them the author applies the thoughts of Virgil to the monarchy. Nature, he says, invented the king, and it is demonstrated by the bee. He lives in the largest cell in the middle of the hive. He does not work, and when the king dies the hive organization disintegrates. The king is larger and more beautiful than the other bees, and there is only one in each hive. The king is of a mild disposition, and does not sting. It is the others, his armies, that have the weapons and wage war on his behalf. This philosophical exploitation of the bee is the most interesting episode of the history of the bee in antiquity.

There are many other Roman writers on bees, among them Pliny (A.D. 23–79), Columella (about A.D. 60) and Palladius (fourth century A.D.). Knowledge of the bee did not improve greatly during this time. Pliny was still convinced that honey fell from the heavens and collected like dew on the leaves.[1] This is evidently due to a perfectly correct observation, in so far as the sugary exudations of greenfly cover the leaves of many trees. They are of course collected by bees where there is an opportunity. But other theories were in vogue too, for instance that honey was the sweat of trees and that bees obtained it from flowers. Whilst the first two theories were more popular with educated writers, one can read between the lines that the last was popular with the actual bee-keepers. Why else should they have planted bee flowers in the neighbourhood of the hive? It appears that only Seneca put forward the correct idea that nectar was collected from the flowers and converted into honey by the bees.

Exploitation of the Products of the Bee

The bee provides man with four useful items, namely honey, wax, propolis and the hives themselves. To take the last item first, they have from time to time come in useful as weapons of war, whole hives being hurled into the lines of the enemy, who were thus kept busy defending themselves against the insects and became an easy target for arrows. In the third Mithradatic war (74–66 B.C.) the army of Lucullus was thus inconvenienced. The last occasion when hives were used this way which is known to the writer was in the Thirty Years' War (A.D. 1618–1648).

Honey is mainly a foodstuff; in addition it was, and still is, used for the manufacture of drinks. Varro described a drink called *mulsum* which was a mixture of honey and wine. The fermentation of honey produces mead, a liquid which was much in vogue in all northern countries where grape-vines would not grow. Its taste is somewhat insipid, though I suppose one would get used to liking it if one knew of nothing better. This undoubtedly applied to the ancient Germans before the Migrations period, which brought them in contact with wine. That mead was popular in Germania is reported by Pytheas from the mouth of the River Ems. In the eighth century A.D. it was the national drink of the Baltic countries. Almost everywhere it has

---

[1] See *N.H.* XI, xii. But in XI, viii, he clearly says that bees depend on flowers, and 'when the flowers in the vicinity have been used up they send scouts to further pastures'. A correct observation.

by now been replaced by other beverages, but some mead is still made even in Britain, as well as in Russia and Siberia and in East and South Africa.

In view of the attention paid by the ancients to honey as a foodstuff, it is only to be expected that they distinguished with care various qualities. The honey coming from Mount Hymettus near Athens was believed to be the best.[1] Pliny (*N.H.* XI, xiii–xv) mentions others. Many kinds were distinguished according to the flowers they were derived from and the season of collecting. Oddly enough, heather honey was regarded as inferior (Pliny, *N.H.* X, xv), perhaps because the kind known to Pliny was somewhat granular or, as he calls it, 'sandy'.

Certain types of honey were regarded as poisonous and liable to cause insanity. One was derived from rhododendron flowers in the region of the Black Sea, and there were many others. According to Xenophon, the Ten Thousand suffered from honey poisoning. Fraser states that these reports must not be regarded as fabulous.

Honey was the chief supplier of sugar throughout the prehistoric periods and in antiquity, and as such added to many kinds of meal. Honeycake was made regularly. This particular delicacy had some ritual importance also, since it was the custom to supply the dead with a portion, which they were to throw to Cerberus, the dog guarding the entrance to the underworld. A competitor of honey arose in the Western countries of the Old World as cane sugar was becoming known. It was apparently not known in ancient Mesopotamia and the Levantine countries. In the course of the ninth century A.D. it reached Arabia, and it was a novelty in Venice in A.D. 996, coming from Alexandria in Egypt. After the crusades it came to be cultivated in many parts of southern Europe, but it was always expensive. Colonial mass production followed, until the discovery of the sugar content of the beet by Marggraf in 1747 made the northern countries independent.

As has been stated before, wax was of the greatest technological importance in antiquity. It was used for light and for writing tablets. In addition, it was an important ingredient of many medicines, and was used for embalming purposes. The sculptor used it, and last but not least the *cire perdue* process of bronze-casting has made use of it ever since Bronze Age times. Accordingly, many different kinds of wax were distinguished, and its purification was an important matter which Pliny discussed in detail. The best wax was called the Punic, but it probably came from Spain. Its manufacture was described by Pliny (*N.H.* XXI, xlix). How important wax was in Roman times is shown by the imposition of a tribute of 100,000 pounds of wax, which was doubled two years later, on the island of Corsica in 181 B.C. Whether the Romans succeeded in collecting such huge quantities is however doubtful.

There were other uses of wax. The Greeks used it in their technique of encaustic painting, and plasters were made of it (*ceroma*). Athletes rubbed themselves with a

---

[1] It is indeed the most aromatic honey I have had occasion to taste.

mixture of oil, wax and earth, and the Roman ladies used similar concoctions in their beauty parlours.

Finally, a few words must be said about propolis. This is a resinous substance which the bees use to fill gaps and cracks, and to adjust cavities so as to hold the wax on combs. In the Palaeolithic period, and perhaps the Stone Age generally, it must have been one of the materials serving as cement for the hafting of tools and similar purposes, and it was still of some importance in the Bronze Age of the Mediterranean. In the countryside it was probably used rather longer.

Propolis is gathered from bleeding trees, nowadays mainly pine and horse-chestnut, carried by the bees like pollen on the hind legs into the hive and there used. In addition, it commonly serves to adjust the size of the flight-hole, and even to immobilize intruders, such as the Death's Head hawk moth and sometimes slugs. It is only natural that early man should have been interested in this useful substance, which he obtained as a by-product of honey-gathering. Later on propolis was generally replaced by resins collected directly from the trees. Pliny describes propolis, stating that it is mainly derived from 'willow, elm and reed' and from gum-producing trees in general (*N.H.* XI, v). Its varieties were of great use for medicines (*N.H.* XI, vi), and as a substitute for the Persian gum-resin called galbanum.

The Self-domestication of the Honey-bee

The reason why ancient and modern writers, among the latter Maeterlinck and Bonsels, have been so fascinated by the bee is the many parallels that exist between it and man. Both have complex social organizations with castes, division of labour, sacrifice or restriction of sex for the sake of the community, permanent settlements and food production. One major difference is that bees do not use tools (though ants do).

The common background of both animals of such different organization—one an insect, the other a mammal—is that they have undergone a process of self-domestication. By this term I intend to describe that remarkable condition of some members of a species living at the expense of others, the whole forming a social unit in which all benefit from the division of labour. The term is, therefore, not synonymous with slavery, which also occurs among man and ants.

In the bees the process of self-domestication has gone much further than in man. Individual bees cannot exist without the support of other members of the hive, whilst men can do so though they might not like it. Furthermore, the bees have introduced the division of labour into their sex-life to an infinitely greater extent than man has. Only one female (normally) produces all the progeny, the others doing the chores both at home and outside. The males are suffered only until the young queen has mated, thereafter they are all thrown out or killed. Had Virgil and his contemporaries known of this custom they might not have praised the perfection of the bee state so eagerly. But they thought of the queen as a king, and of the workers as labourers and soldiers. That the drones do not work was unknown at that time.

With the development of division of labour goes, in the bees as in the case of man, the appearance of 'language', or a means of communication. This fact, long claimed and doubted, has now been established by Roesch and von Frisch (1955). The means of communication of information used by bees are special types of movements ('dances') which are correctly interpreted, understood and acted upon by the other bees.

This is not the place for a discussion of the social life of the Hymenoptera in general and of the honey-bee in particular. It is, however, worth while to point out what periods of time were involved in this case of evolution of a complex type of society which in the case of the ants has led to both domestication and slavery. For ants, palaeontological evidence is less informative than for the bees, of which well-preserved fossils are known from the Eocene onwards.

This fossil evidence suggests that considerable morphological changes took place from Eocene to Oligocene times, between forty and thirty million years ago, i.e. in a period of perhaps not more than ten million years (Zeuner and Manning, in the press). The Eocene ancestors (*Electrapis*) were in many respects like bumble-bees. But the Oligocene bees were already essentially equipped like honey-bees and very close to the modern *Apis mellifera*. Since that time thirty million years have elapsed with hardly any morphological evolution. That the Oligocene bee was already a social insect is highly probable, since the structure of the legs, tongue and abdomen are like those in modern worker bees. The Eocene bee, however, can hardly have had a social life higher than that of the bumble-bees. On the other hand, at the latest in the Miocene, true swarming occurred, implying the social structure of a modern hive. There is fossil evidence for this (Zeuner, 1931, 1951).

Now, the sequence of social evolution represented by the series of morphologica changes is the following:

(1) Mother building cells, laying eggs and providing food, but dying before offspring emerges.

(2) Mother still building cells and laying eggs when first daughters have become adult. These follow their instinct of building and looking after offspring instead of (or before) mating and founding their own colonies. This is said to occur with unfertilized queen bumbles in the autumn at the present day, and it may be connected with the males appearing later than the females.

(3) Helping daughters become 'exhausted' before leaving the nest for the mating flight. They thus give up normal reproduction, and become *workers*, though some may act as subsidiary mothers.

(4) Production of queen by ample feeding. Increasing care for young generally. In temperate climates the workers die off in the autumn; in the tropics they possibly survive. *Bombus* (bumble) stage.

(5) Queen produced by different feeding. Workers hibernate, heating the hive. Complicated division of labour, 'gesture language', food production. *Apis* (honey-bee) stage.

The palaeontological evidence at present available suggests that stage (1) was normal in the Eocene, and that by the end of the Oligocene, ten million years later, stage (5), that of complete self-domestication, including food production, had been reached. As has been said, not much more has happened in the succeeding thirty million years. This is one of the many instances of *explosive evolution* observed in biology, in which, after a period of a few million years of rapid changes, stability is attained. I have given some examples of this phenomenon in the last chapter of my book, *Dating the Past*.

In spite of all modern developments of human technology, man is still subject to the laws of evolution. There is no doubt that he is in his phase of explosive evolution and it must not be assumed that the rate of change will continue to be as fast as it has been for the last million years or so. The adoption by man of the practice of self-domestication as well as of the domestication of other animals is so recent that one cannot predict future developments, but the examples from the animal world show that in successful species stabilization is invariably achieved. It appears that so far as animal domestication itself is concerned this stage has already been reached. Man's self-domestication, however, is likely to continue for a long time to come.

Bibliography

ABEL, O., 1927. Lebensbilder aus der Tierwelt der Vorzeit.—2nd edn., 714 pp.—Jena. (Horse)

ADAMETZ, L., 1914. Untersuchungen über *Capra prisca*, einer ausgestorbenen neuen Stammform unserer Hausziegen.—Mitt. landw. Lehrk. Hochsch. Bodenkultur, Wien, **3** (1): 1–21. (Goat)

——, 1937. Über die Rassenzugehörigkeit des 'ziegenförmigen Torfschafes' der neolitischen Schweizer Pfahlbauten und seiner Abkömmlinge.—Züchtung, Berlin, (B) **38** (2): 113–129. (Sheep)

AGACINO, E. M. [N.D.] El conejo de monte.—Serv. Extension Agricola, Conejo No. 10, Madrid, 32 pp. (Rabbit)

ALLAN, J., 1936. Catalogue of the Coins of Ancient India.—318 pp., 46 pls.—London (Brit. Mus.). (Elephant)

AMSCHLER, W., 1931. Beitrag zur Rassen- und Abstammungsfrage der Hausziege und der Haustierwerdung.—Biol. Gen. Wien, **7** (3): 445–468. (Goat)

——, 1935. The Oldest Pedigree Chart.—J. Heredity, Washington, **26**: 233–238. (Horse)

——, 1936. Die Ältesten Funde des Hauspferdes.—Wien. Beitr. Kulturges. Linguistik, **4**: 497–516. (Horse)

——, 1937. Goats from Ur and Kish.—Antiquity, London, **11**: 226–228, pls. 5–6. (Goat)

——, 1940 (a). Tierreste der Ausgrabungen von dem 'Grossen Königshügel' Shah Tepé, in Nord-Iran.—Rep. sci. Exped. N.W. Prov. China (Sino-Swedish Exped.), No. 9: 35–129, pls. 14–26. (General)

——, 1940(b). Der illyrische Haushund von Bludenz.—Umschau, Frankfurt-a.-M., **44**, (22): 347–359. (Dog)

——, 1949. Ur- und frühgeschichtliche Haustierfunde aus Österreich.—Archaeol. Austr. Wien **3**: 1–100, 12 pls. (General)

ANTONIUS, O., 1918. Die Abstammung des Hauspferdes und Hausesels.—Naturwiss., **6**. (Horse)

——, 1922. Stammesgeschichte der Haustiere.—377 pp.—Jena. (General)

——, 1937. On the Geographical Distribution in Former Times and Today of the Recent Equidae.—Proc. zool. Soc. London, **107**: 557–564. (Horse)

ANUTSCHIN, D. N., 1882. Zwei Rassen des Hundes aus den Torfmooren des Ladoga.— Moscow. (Dog)

ARAVAMUTHAN, T. G., 1949. Notes on Punch-marked Puranas.—J. numism. Soc. India, **10**(1): 1–14, pl. 1. (Elephant)

ARISTOTLE. History of Animals.—Transl. by A. L. Peck.—Loeb Classical Library. (General)

AURIGEMMA, S., 1940. L'Elephante di Leptis Magna.—Riv. Africa Ital., **7**: 67–86. (Elephant)

BAIERSDORF, T., 1937. Studien über die zur Gruppe der Zackel gehörenden Landschafe Siebenbürgens.—Züchtung, Berlin, (B) **38**: 153–198. (Sheep)

BAILEY, F. M., 1948. Yaks.—Geogr. Mag., London, **21** (5): 176–179.

BAKER, A. L. L., 1954. Wild goats in Wales.—The Field, London, Sept. 2nd: 1 p.

BANTJE, O., 1958. Über Domestikationserscheinungen am Bewegungsapparat des Kaninchens.—Zool. Jahrb. (Phys.), Jena, **68**: 203–260. (General)

BARNETT, R. D., 1939. Phoenician and Syrian Ivory Carving.—Palestine Expl. Quart. London, 1939: 4–19, pls. 1–11. (Elephant)

——, 1960. Assyrian Palace Reliefs.—36 pp., 173 pls.—London. (General)

BATE, D. M. A., 1905. On the Mammals of Crete.—Proc. zool. Soc. London, 1905 (2): 315–323. (Cat)

——, 1934 (a). The Fauna.—In: CATON-THOMPSON, G., AND GARDNER, E. W. The Desert Fayum.—167 pp., 107 pls.—(R. anthrop. Inst.) London. (General)

——, 1934 (b). The domestic fowl in Pre-Roman Britain.—Ibis, April, 1934: 390–395.

——, 1937 (a). The Fossil Fauna of the Wady El-Mughara Caves.—In: GARROD, D. A. E. AND BATE, D. M. A. The Stone Age of Mount Carmel I.—240 pp., 55 pls. Oxford. (General)

——, 1937 (b). In: GARDNER, E. W. AND BATE, D. M. A. The Bone-bearing Beds of Bethlehem: Their Fauna and Industry.—Nature, London, **140**: 143. (General)

——, 1939. Note on an Animal Mosaic from Antioch-on-the-Orontes.—Bull. Honolulu Acad. Arts, **1**: 26–31. (Fallow Deer)

——, 1941. The Bone-Bearing Beds of Bethlehem.—Nature, London, **147**: 783. (General)

——, 1953. Report on the Vertebrate Fauna of Shaheinab.—In: ARKELL, A. J. Shaheinab. —Oxford: 10–19. (Various)

BAUME, W. LA, 1909. Beitrag zur Kenntnis der fossilen und subfossilen Boviden.— Schriften Naturforsch. Ges. Danzig (n.s.) **12** (3): 45–80, 7 pls., 10 tables. (Cattle)

——, 1947 (a). Hat es ein wildlebendes Kurzhorn-Rind (*Bos brachyceros*) gegeben?—Ecl. geol. Helvetiae, Basel, **40** (2): 308–316. (Cattle)

——, 1947 (b). Diluviale Schädel vom Ur (*Bos primigenius* Bojanus) aus Toscana.—Ecl. geol. Helvetiae, Basel, **40** (2): 299–308. (Cattle)

BIEBER, M., 1944. Two Attic Black-figured Lekythoi in Buffalo.—Archaeol. Notes. Amer. J. Archaeol. 2nd ser. **48**: 121–129. (Fowl)

BLANFORD, W. T., 1891. Mammalia. Fauna of British India.—617 pp.—London. (General)

BLYTH, E., 1840. An amended List of the species of the genus *Ovis*.—Proc. zool. Soc. London, **8**: 62–81. (Sheep)

BOBRINSKOY, N. A., 1944. Key to the Mammals of U.S.S.R.—Moscow. (Sheep)

BOESSNECK, J., 1953. Die Haustiere in Altägypten.—Veröff. zool. Staatssamml. München, **3**: 1–50. (General)

——, 1957. Tierknochen. In: KRÄMER, W. Cambodunumforschungen 1953.—Hefte bayer. Vorgesch. München, **9**: 103–116. (Cattle and other species)

——, 1958. Herkunft und Frühgeschichte unserer mitteleuropäischen landwirtschaftlichen Nutztiere.—Züchtungskunde Stuttgart, **30**, 8 pp. (General)

——, 1960. Zur Gänsehaltung im alten Ägypten.—Wiener Tierärztl. Monatschr. 1960 (Festschrift Schreiber): 192–206. (Birds)

BOGORAS, W., 1904–1909. The Chukchee.—Mem. Amer. Mus. Nat. Hist., Jessup North Pacific Exped. **7**: 4 ff. (Reindeer)

BOHLKEN, H., 1958. Vergleichende Untersuchungen an Wildrindern.—Zool. Jahrb. (Phys.), Jena **68**: 113–202. (Cattle)

——, 1960. Remarks on the Stomach and the Systematic Position of the Tylopoda.—Proc. zool. Soc. Lond., **134**: 207–215. (Camel)

BÖKÖNYI, S., 1952(a). Die Wirbeltierfauna der Ausgrabungen in Tószeg vom Jahre 1948.— Acta archaeol. Budapest, **2** (1/3): 71–113, pls. 27–36. (General)

——, 1952(b). Les chevaux scythiques du cimetière de Szentes-Vekerzug.—Acta archaeol. Budapest, **2** (1-3): 173–183. (Horse)

——, 1958. Zur Urgeschichte der Haustiere und der Fauna der archäologischen Urzeit in Ungarn.—Z. Tierzücht. Züchtungsbiol., Hamburg, **72**: 239–249. (General)

BOLTZ, C. L., 1955. The camel riddle answered.—Discovery, London, **16** (8): 338.

BOSANQUET, R. C. AND DAWKINS, R. M., 1923. The unpublished objects from the Palaikastro Excavations 1902–1906.—Brit. Sch. Athens Supplement. Pap. No. 1, 160 pp., 34 pls. (Cat)

BOUCHUD, J., 1954 (a). Le renne et le problème des migrations.—L'Anthrop., Paris, **58** (1/2): 79–85. (Reindeer)

——, 1954 (b). Dents de rennes, bois de rennes et migrations.—Bull. Soc. préhist. franç., Paris, **51** (7): 340–345. (Reindeer)

——, 1955. Deux espèces rares au Moustérien découvertes au Pech de l'Azé.—Bull. Soc. préhist. franç., Paris, **52** (1/2): 89–93. (Sheep)

——, CHEYNIER, A. AND GUILLIEN, Y., 1953. Dents de renne et migrations.—Bull. Soc. préhist. franç., Paris, **50** (3): 127–132. (Reindeer)

BOULE, M., 1899. Observations sur quelques équidés fossiles.—Buli. Soc. géol. franç., **3**: 27. (Horse)

——, 1910. Les Grottes de Grimaldi (Baoussé-Roussé). Géologie et Paléontologie.—Vol. 1 (3): 157–236—Monaco. (Dog and Cat)

BOURDELLE, E., 1938. Essai d'une étude morphologique des équidés préhistoriques de France d'après les gravures rupestres.—Mammalia, Paris, **2**: 1–11. (Horse)

BOYE, H., 1956. Vergleichende Untersuchungen über die arterielle Gefässversorgung des Uterus von Wild - und Hausschweinen.—Z. Tierzücht. Züchtungsbiol., **67**: 259–296. (Pig)

BRAESTRUP, F. W., 1960. Kouprey-Oksen Opdaget 1933–1937—er det en slags urokse?—Nat. Verden Copenhagen: 37–44. (Cattle)

BRAIDWOOD, R. J., 1951. From Cave to Village in Prehistoric Iraq.—Bull. Amer. Sch. orient. Res., Baltimore. No. 124: 12–18. (Sheep and Goat)

——, 1958. Near Eastern Prehistory.—Science, **127** (3312): 1419–1430. (Sheep and Goat)

—— AND L., 1953. The earliest village communities of Southwestern Asia.—J. World History, **1**: 278–310. (Sheep and Goat)

—— AND REED, C. A., 1957. The Achievement and early consequences of Food-production. A consideration of the archaeological and natural-historical evidence.—Cold Spring Harbor Symposium on Quantitative Biol., **22**: 19–31. (General)

BRANDT, J. F. AND WOLDŘICH, J. N., 1887. Diluviale europäisch-nordasiatische Säugethierfauna und ihre Beziehungen zum Menschen.—Mém. Acad. Sci. St Petersbourg. (7), **35** (10): 162 pp. (Sheep)

BRAUNER, A., 1933. Contributions to the investigation of domestic animals in U.S.S.R. from the point of view of natural history and especially osteology.—Trans. orig. dom. anim. Ac. Sci. U.S.S.R. (Horse)

BRINKMANN, A., 1924. Canidenstudien V-VI.—Aarb. Bergens Mus., naturv. R., **7**, 57 pp., 4 pls. (Dog)

BROGAN, O., 1954. The Camel in Roman Tripolitania.—Pap. Brit. School, Rome (n.s.), **9**: 126–131.

——, 1955. The Fortified Farms of Ghirza, Libya.—Illustrated London News, Jan. 22nd and 29th, 1955: 138–142 and 182–185. (Camel)

BROOKS, C. E. P., 1926. Climate through the Ages.—439 pp.—London. (Chapter 1)

BRUNSCH, A., 1956. Vergleichende Untersuchungen am Haarkleid von Wildcaniden und Hausehundes.—Z. Tierzücht. Züchtungsbiol., **67**: 205–240. (Dog)

BRUNTON, G. AND CATON-THOMPSON, G., 1928. The Badarian Civilization.—121 pp., 85 pls.—London (Brit. Sch. Archaeol. Egypt). (Goat)

—— AND MORANT, G. M., 1937. Mostagedda and the Tasian Culture.—163 pp., 84 pls. —London. (Goat)

BUREN, E. D. VAN, 1930. Clay Figurines of Babylonia and Assyria.—Yale orient. Ser. Research, **16**: 287 pp. (Camel)

——, 1939. The Fauna of Ancient Mesopotamia as represented in Art.—Analecta Orientalia, Rome, **18**: 113 pp. (General)

BURKITT, M. C., 1940. Explorations in Cilicia. Nielson Expedition: 1938–39. The Earlier Culture at Mersin.—Ann. Archaeol. Anthrop. Liverpool, **26**: 51–72. (General)

BUTLER, C. G., 1956. The Adaptable Honeybee.—Countryman, Burford, **53** (2): 337–338.

BUTZ, H. AND HEINMÜLLER, W., 1937. Beobachtungen über das Verhalten verschieden pigmentierter Rinderrassen bei Kreuzung bezw. Rückkreuzung.—Z. Züchtung, Berlin, (B) **38**: 131–152. (Cattle)

CAIUS, J., 1570. De Canibus Britanicis, Liber Unus.—London. (Dog)

CAMPANA, D. DEL, 1913. I Cani Pliocenici di Toscana.—Palaeont. Ital., Pisa, **19**: 189–254, pls. 13–22. (Dog)

CAPART, J., 1905. Primitive Art in Egypt.—304 pp.—London. (Elephant)

CAPITAN, L., BREUIL, H. AND PEYRONY, D., 1924. Les Combarelles aux Eyzies (Dordogne). 192 pp., 58 pls.—Paris. (Horse)

CARRINGTON, R., 1958. Elephants. A short account of their Natural History, Evolution and Influence on Mankind.—272 pp.—London.

CARTER, H., et al., 1900. Beni Hassan. Part IV.—Archaeol. Surv. Egypt (edit. F. L. Griffith), 9 pp., 27 pls. (Dog)

——, et al., 1923. The Tomb of Tut-Ankhamen.—3 vols.—London. (Birds)

CATON-THOMPSON, G., 1934. The Camel in Dynastic Egypt.—Man, London, **34** (24): 21.

——, 1944. The Tombs and Moon Temple of Hureidha (Hadhramaut).—Rep. Res. Comm. Soc. Antiq. London, **13**: 191 pp., 81 pls. (Camel)

CESNOLA, L. P. DI, 1877. Cyprus: its ancient cities, tombs and temples.—448 pp.—London. (Camel)

CHARDIN, T. DE, AND PIVETEAU, J., 1930. Les mammifères fossiles de Nihowan (Chine).—Ann. Paléont. Paris, **19**: 135 pp., 23 pls. (General)

CHILDE, V. G., 1925. The Dawn of European Civilization.—1st edn.—London. (Horse)

——, 1944. Progress and Archaeology.—119 pp.—London (Thinker's Libr. No. 102). (General)

——, 1947. The Dawn of European Civilization.—4th edn.—362 pp.—London. (General)

——, 1951. The first waggons and carts from the Tigris to the Severn.—Proc. prehist. Soc. (n.s.), **17** (3): 177–194, pls. 8–9. (Horse)

——, 1952. New Light on the Most Ancient East.—255 pp., 39 pls.—London. (General)

——, 1957. The Dawn of European Civilization.—6th. edn., 368 pp.—London. (General)

CLARK, G., 1941. Horses and Battle-Axes.—Antiquity, **14**: 50–70.

CLUTTON-BROCK, J., 1962(a). Near Eastern Canids and the affinities of the Natufian Dogs. Intern. Symp. Problems Domestik. Frühgeschichte Haustiere (1961). (In the press.)

——, 1962(b). An analysis of the mammalian remains from three prehistoric sites in India and western Asia.—Doctoral Thesis, Univ. London. (Various species, including Dog, Goat and Camel)

COLE, S., 1959. The Neolithic Revolution.—60 pp.—London (Brit. Mus. Nat. Hist.). (General)

COOK, J. M. AND AKURGAL, E., 1953. Excavating Old Smyrna, City of Homer and Mimnermus: The discovery of the oldest known Greek house and light on the birth of Greek Civilization.—Illustrated London News. 28th Feb., 1953: 328–329. (Camel)

COOLIDGE, H. J., 1940. The Indochinese Forest Ox or Kouprey.—Mem. Mus. comp. Zool. Harvard, **54** (6). (Cattle)

COON, C. S., 1951. Cave explorations in Iran 1949.—Pennsylvania Univ. Mus. Mon., 124 pp., 15 pls. (Goat and Sheep)

COOPER, B. A., 1942. Silkmoth Rearer's Handbook.—Amateur Entom., **6** (39): 72 pp.

CORBEL, J., 1952. Contribution ethnologique à la connaissance de la Civilisation du Renne. —Bull. Soc. préhist. franç., **49** (11-12): 639-644. (Reindeer)

COULONGES, L., 1935. Gisements préhistoriques de Sauveterre-la-Lémance (Lot-et-Garonne).—Arch. Inst. Paléont. hum., Paris, Mém. 14: 54 pp., 6 pls. (Chapter 1 and Sheep)

CRISLER, L., 1956. The Wolves in Our Tent.—Saturday Evening Post, Philadelphia, 228: 34-35, 90-92. (Dog)

——, 1959. Arctic Wild.—274 pp.—London. (Chapter 2 and Dog)

CRONIN, B., 1953. Pariah of Our Wild Creatures.—Walkabout, Austr. geog. Mag., Jan. 1953: 10-14. (Dog)

CURASSON, G., 1947. Le chameau et ses maladies.—462 pp.—Paris. (Camel)

DAHLMANN, H., 1954. Der Bienenstaat in Vergils Georgica.—Akad. Wiss. Lit. Mainz Abt. Geist. Socialwiss. K1., No. 10: 547-562. (Bee)

DAHR, E., 1942. Über die Variation der Hirnschale bei wilden und zahmen Caniden.—Ark. Zool. Stockholm, 33A (16): 1-56. (Dog)

DALLONI, M., 1935. Mission au Tibesti (1930-1931).—Mem. Acad. Sci. Paris, 62. (Camel)

DARWIN, C., 1859. The Origin of Species.—1st edn. London. (Chapter 1 and general)

——, 1868. Variation of animals and plants under domestication.—2 vols.—London. (Chapter 3)

——, 1871. The Descent of Man.—1st edn.—London. (Chapter 1)

DAVIES, N. DE G., 1901. The Rock Tombs of Sheikh Said.—Archaeol. Surv. Egypt, London, Mem. No. 10: 34 pls. (Sheep)

——, 1903. The Rock Tombs of El Amarna, I. The Tomb of Meryra.—Archaeol. Surv. Egypt, London, Mem. No. 13: 56 pp., 42 pls. (General)

——, 1905. The Rock Tombs of El Amarna, II. The Tombs of Panehesy and Meryra II.—Archaeol. Surv. Egypt, London, Mem. No. 14: 47 pp., 47 pls. (Cheetah)

——, 1908. The Rock Tombs of El Amarna, V.—Archaeol. Surv. Egypt, London.—37 pp., 11 pls. (Cattle)

—— AND GARDINER, A., 1926. The Tomb of Huy.—Egypt. Expl. Soc. Theban Tombs Ser. 4: 42 pp., 40 pls. (General)

DAWKINS, W. B. AND JACKSON, J. W., 1917. The remains of the Mammalia found in the Lake-Village of Glastonbury.—Chpts. XXV and XXVI in: BULLEID, A. AND GRAY, H. ST. G., 1911 and 1917. The Glastonbury Lake Village.—724 pp.—Glastonbury. (Cat)

DAWSON, W. R., 1925. The Earliest Records of the Elephant.—Ann. Mag. Nat. Hist., London, (9) 16 (96): 656-660.

DEGERBØL, M., 1933. Danmarks Pattedyr i Fortiden i Sammenligning med recente Former I.—Vidensk. Medd. Dansk naturh. Foren., Copenhagen, 96 (2): 641 pp., 24 pls., (General)

——, 1939. Dyreknogler fra Bundsø, en yngre Stenalders Boplads paa Als.—Aarb. Nord. Oldkyndigt. Hist. Copenhagen, 1939: 85-198, 3 pls. (General)

——, 1942. Et Knoglemateriale fra Dyrholmen-Bopladsen, en aeldre Stenalder-Køkkenmødding.—Kgl. Danske Vidensk. Selsk. Arkaeol.-Kunsthist. Skr. 1 (1): 129-131. (Cattle)

DERANIYAGALA, P. E. P., 1950. The Elephant of Asia.—Pres. Add. 5th Sess. Ceylon Assoc. Sci., 1949, 18 pp.

——, 1951. *Elephas maximus*, the elephant of Ceylon (Part II).—Spolia Zeylanica, **26** (2): 161–176, 8 pls.

DIGGES, I. G., 1944. The Practical Bee Guide.—12th edn., 305 pp.—Dublin.

DIKAIOS, P., 1953. Khirokitia.—447 pp., 152 pls.—Oxford. (Sheep and Goat)

DOTTRENS, E., 1946. Déterminations des phalanges osseuses de *Bos taurus* dom.—C. R. S. Soc. phys. hist. nat. Genève, **61** (1): 46–49. (Cattle)

——, 1947. La Faune Néolithique de la Couche Profonde de St Aubin II.—Rev. Suisse zool., **54**: 459–544. (Cattle)

——, 1948. Le Grand Bos des quatre couches néolithiques d'Auvernier et de Saint-Aubin.—Eclogae geol. Helv., **40**: 360–366. (Cattle)

DRAY, E. AND TAYLOR, J. DU PLAT, 1951. Tsambres and Aphendrika, two classical and Hellenistic cemeteries in Cyprus.—Rep. Dept. Ant. Cyprus, 1937–1939: 24–123. (Fowl)

DUBOIS, A. AND STEHLIN, H. G., 1933. La Grotte de Cotencher, station moustérienne.—Mém. Soc. Paléont. Suisse, **52-53**: 291 pp. (Cattle)

DUBOIS, E., 1922. Hat sich das Gehirn beim Haushunde, im Vergleich mit Wildhundarten, vergrössert, oder verkleinert?—Bijdr. Dierkunde, 'Natura ortis Magistra', Amsterdam, **22**: 315–320. (Dog)

DUELL, P., 1938. The Mastaba of Mereruka.—Univ. Chicago Orient. Inst. Publ. **31**: 18 pp., 103 pls. and **39**: pls. 103–219. (General)

DUERST [DÜRST], J., 1899. Die Rinder von Babylonien, Assyrien und Aegypten.—Berlin. (Cattle)

——, J. U., 1900. Notes sur quelques Bovidés préhistoriques.—L'Anthrop., Paris, **11**: 129–158 and 655–676. (Cattle)

——, 1908. Animal Remains from the Excavations at Anau.—Ch. XVI-XVIII: 341–399 in: PUMPELLY, R., Explorations in Turkestan. Expedition of 1904.—Publ. Carnegie Inst. Washington, No. 73, 2 vols., 494 pp. (General)

——, 1908. The Horse of Anau in its Relation to History and to the Races of Domesticated Horses.—Ch. XIX-XX: 401–442 in: PUMPELLY, R., Explorations in Turkestan. Expedition of 1904.—Publ. Carnegie Inst. Washington. No. 73, 2 vols., 494 pp. (Horse)

—— AND GAILLARD, C., 1902. Studien über die Geschichte des ägyptischen Hausschafes. Rec. Trav. philol. archéol. Egypt, Paris, **24**: 44–76. (Sheep)

DUMBABIN, T. J., 1948. The Early History of Corinth.—J. Hellenic Stud., **68**: 59–68. (Birds)

DYSON, R. H., 1953, Archaeology and the Domestication of Animals in the Old World.—Amer. Anthrop. **55** (5): 661–673. (General)

EHIK, J., 1938. Jackal or Reed-Wolf from Hungary.—Ann. Mus. nat. Hung., Budapest, **31**: 11–15. (Dog)

——, 1938. Was versteht man unter dem 'Rohrwolf'?—Zool. Garten, Leipzig (n.s.), **11** (6): 232–238. (Dog)

EHRSTRÖM, C. R., 1852. Djurvandringar i Lappmarken och Norra Delen af Finnland Åren 1839–1840.—Notiz. Sållfk. Fauna och Flora Fenn., **2**: 1–8. (Reindeer)

EICKSTEDT, E. F. VON, 1952. Die Sauhatz von Valltorta.—Homo, **3** (3): 123–130. (Pig)

ELLERMAN, J. R. AND MORRISON-SCOTT, T. C. S., 1951. Checklist of Palaearctic and Indian Mammals, 1758 to 1946.—810 pp.—Brit. Mus. (Nat. Hist.) London. (General)

ELLIS, A. G., 1960. The Equid in the Shaft of Tomb J 3.—In: KENYON, K. M. Excavations at Jericho I.—Appendix C, 535–6. (Horse)

ELWES, H. J., 1913. Guide to the Primitive Breeds of Sheep and their Crosses.—44 pp., 43 pls.—Edinburgh.

EPSTEIN, H., 1954. Le dromadaire dans l'Ancien Orient.—Rev. Hist. Sci., Paris, **7** (3): 247–268. (Camel)

ERMAN, A., 1927. The Literature of the Ancient Egyptians.—Transl. by A. M. Blackman, 318 pp.—London. (Camel)

ERMAN, A. AND RANKE, H., 1923. Ägypten und ägyptisches Leben im Altertum.—J. C. B. Mohr (P. Siebeck), Tübingen. (Ass)

EVANS, A., 1921–1936. The Palace of Minos at Knossos.—5 vols.—London. (Cattle and Birds)

EWART, J. C., 1913. Primitive and Improved Breeds of Sheep.—Trans. Highland agri. Soc. Scotland, (5) **25**.

FALCONER, H., 1868. Palaeontological Memoirs. I: Fauna Antiqua Sivalensis.—590 pp.—London. (General)

FALCONER, H. AND CAUTLEY, P. T., 1869. On the Fossil Camel of the Sewalik Hills.—Pal. Mem. Hugh Falconer, **1**: 227–246, pl. 18.

FALLET, M., 1961. Vergleichende Untersuchungen zur Wollbildung südamerikanischer Tylopoden.—Z. Tierzücht. Züchtungsbiol., **75**: 34–56. (Llama)

FALZFEIN, F. VON, 1919. Über das letzte Auftreten des Wildpferdes in Südrussland, Taurisches Gouvernement.—S. B. Ges. naturf. Fr. Berlin, **1**. (Horse)

FELTEN, H., 1957. Der australische Wildhund.—Natur und Volk, Frankfurt, **87** (11): 389–392. (Dog)

FIRBAS, F., 1949. Spät- und nacheiszeitliche Waldgeschichte Mitteleuropas nördlich der Alpen.—Vol. 1: 480 pp., vol. 2: 256 pp. (Chapter 1)

FITZINGER, L. T., 1860. Über die Racen des zahmen Schafes.—Sitz. Akad. Wiss. Wien, **38**: 141–222; **41**: 151–246. (Sheep)

FLAMAND, G. B. M., 1907. De l'introduction du chameau dans l'Afrique du Nord.—Act. XIV Congr. intern. Orientalistes, **2**: 7. (Camel)

FÖRSTER, U., 1960. Die Pferdephalangen aus dem Keltischen Oppidum von Manching.—Stud. vor- und frühgesch. Tierresten Bayerns, Tieranat. Inst. Univ. München, **8**: 36 pp. (Horse)

FRANKE, O., 1913. Keng Tschi Tu. Ackerbau und Seidengewinnung in China.—Abh. hamburg. Kolonialinst., **11**: 194 pp., 102 pls. (Silk Moth)

FRANKFORT, H., 1936. A new site in Mesopotamia: Tell Agrab.—Illustrated London News, Sept. 12th, 1936: 432–436. (Cattle)

——, 1939. Sculpture of the third millennium B.C. from Tell Asmar and Khafajeh.—87 pp., 115 pls.—Chicago. (General)

FRANKFORT, H., 1939. Cylinder Seals.—328 pp., 47 pls.—London. (Elephant, Cattle and Sheep)

FRASER, H. M., 1951. Beekeeping in Antiquity.—145 pp.—London.

FREMERSDORF, F., 1941. Das neugefundene Kölner Dionysos-Mosaik.—Germania, **25**: 233–238. (Birds)

FRISCH, K. VON, 1955. Die Sinne der Bienen im Dienst der sozialen Gemeinschaft.—Nov. Act. Leop. Halle (n.s.), **17** (122): 472–482. (Honey-bee)

GADD, C. J., 1940. Tablets from Chagar Bazar and Tall Brak, 1937–1938.—Iraq, **7**: 22–66. (Ass)

GAILLARD, C., 1901. Le Bélier de Mendes ou le mouton domestique de l'ancienne Égypte. —Bull. Soc. Anthrop. Lyon, 1901: 69–102. (Sheep)

——, 1934. Contribution à l'étude de la faune préhistorique de l'Égypte.—Arch. Mus. Hist. nat. Lyon, **14** (3): 1–125, pls. 1–12. (General)

GANDERT, O. F., 1930. Forschungen zur Geschichte des Haushundes. Die Steinzeitrassen in Nordosteuropa.—Leipzig, Mannus-Bibliotek **46**: 93 pp. (Dog)

——, 1953. Zur Abstammungs- und Kulturgeschichte des Hausgeflügels, insbesondere des Haushuhnes.—Deutsch. Akad. Landwirtschaftswiss. Berlin, **6** (1): 69–81. (Birds)

——, 1954. Die Säugetier- und Vogelreste aus den Gräbern von Leuna.—Leuna, Berlin, 1954: 1–10, pls. 39–40. (Pig and Birds)

GANS, H., 1915. Banteng und Zebu und ihr gegenseitiges Verhältnis.—Kühn Archaeol., Halle, **6**. (Cattle)

GARDINER, A. H., 1911. Egyptian Hieratic Texts. I: The Papyrus Anastasi.—42 pp., 99 pls. —Leipzig. (Camel)

GARDNER, E. W. AND BATE, D. M. A., 1937. The Bone-Bearing Beds of Bethlehem: Their Fauna and Industry.—Nature, London, **140**, p. 431. (General)

GARRETSON, M. S., 1938. The American Bison.—254 pp.—New York (Zool. Soc.). (Cattle)

GARROD, D. A. E., 1952. A transitional industry from the base of the Upper Palaeolithic in Palestine and Syria.—J. R. anthrop. Inst., London (1951) **81** (1-2): 121–130, pls. 1–4. (General)

——, 1957. The Natufian Culture: The Life and Economy of a Mesolithic People in the Near East.—Proc. Brit. Acad., London, **43**: 211—227, pls. 1–9. (Chapter 1)

—— AND BATE, D. M. A., 1937. The Stone Age of Mount Carmel.—Vol. I, 240 pp.— Oxford. (General)

GAUTIER, E. F., 1928. Le Sahara.—129 pp.—Paris. (Camel)

——, 1937. Le passé de l'Afrique du Nord, les siècles obscurs.—188 pp.—Paris. (Camel)

GEE, E. P. 1950. Wild Elephants in Assam.—Oryx, London, **1** (1): 16–22. (Elephant)

GEJVALL, N. G., 1938. The Fauna of the Different Settlements of Troy. Preliminary Report, 1937–1938.—K. Humanist. vetenskap. fundet Lund, 1937–1938: 51–57. (Horse)

——, 1939. The Fauna of the Successive Settlements of Troy. Second Report 1938–1939.— K. Humanist. vetenskap. fundet Lund, 1938–1939: 1–8. (Horse)

——, 1946. The Fauna of the Different Settlements of Troy. Part I. Dogs, horses and cattle. Stencil MS, Stockholm.

GENTILI, G. V., 1956. The Imperial Villa of Piazza Armerina.—Guide-books Mus. Monu. Italy, 86 pp.—Rome. (Ostrich)

GHIRSHMAN, R., 1938–1939. Fouilles de Sialk, vols. 1 and 2.—Sér. Archaeol. Départ. Antiquités orient. Mus. Louvre, 4 and 5: 152 pp., 96 pls. and 259 pp., 101 pls. (General)

GIFFEN, A. E. VAN, 1929. On the Oldest Domestic Animal and its significance for Palethnology.—Kon. Akad. Weten., Amsterdam, 32 (3): 321–329. (Dog)

GJERSTAD, E., 1926. Studies on Prehistoric Cyprus.—Arsskr. Uppsala Univ. (fil.-hist) 1: 342 pp. (Camel and Horse)

GLANVILLE, S. R. K., 1926. Egyptian Theriomorphic Vessels in the British Museum.—J. Egypt. Archaeol., 12: 52–69, pls. 12–16. (Elephant)

GMELIN, S. G., 1768–1769. Reise durch Russland.—Moscow. (Horse)

GOWERS, W., 1948. African Elephants and Ancient Authors.—Afr. Affairs, July 1948: 173–179. (Elephant)

—— AND SCULLARD, H. H., 1950. Hannibal's Elephants Again.—Numism. Chron., (6) 10 (39–40): 271–283. (Elephant)

GRAZIOSI, P., 1933. Sull'*Equus* (*Asinus*) *hydruntinus* Reg.—Riv. Ital. Paleont., Firenze, 39 (11, pt. 1): 35–39. (Ass)

——, 1941. L'Arte Rupestre della Libia.—322 pp., 160 pls.—Naples. (Elephant)

——, 1952. Les Problèmes de l'Art Rupestre Libyque en Relation à l'Ambiance Saharienne. —Bull. Inst. Fouad 1er Désert, 2 (1): 107–113. (General)

——, 1956. L'Arte dell'antica età della pietra.—289 pp., 300 pls.—Firenze. (General)

GRIFFITH, F. L., 1896. Beni Hassan Part III.—Archaeol. Surv. Egypt.—London, 42 pp., 10 pls. (Sheep)

GROMOVA, V., 1931. Zur Kenntnis des Ures im östlichen Europa und südlichen Asien.— Ann. Mus. zool. Acad. U.S.S.R., 32. (Cattle)

——, 1955. Le genre *Equus*.—Ann. Centre Etud. Document. paléont., Paris—No. 13, 202 pp., 20 tables, 8 pls. (Horse)

GRZIMEK, B., 1940. Die Gedächtnisleistungen eines Wolfes und zweier Hunde.—Z. Tierpsychol., 4: 311–326. (Dog)

——, 1943. Weitere Vergleichsversuche mit Wolf und Hund.—Z. Tierpsychol., 5: 59–73. (Dog)

GSELL, S., 1913. Histoire ancienne de l'Afrique du Nord I.—544 pp. Paris. (Elephant and Camel)

GUENTHER, W., 1953. Fossile Elefantenfunde aus Schleswig-Holstein.—Schrift. Naturwiss. Ver. Schleswig-Holstein, 26 (2): 160–169. (Elephant)

GUEY, J., 1939. Note sur le limes romain de Numidie et le Sahara au IVe siècle.—Mélanges Archéol. hist. École franç. Rome: 178. (Camel)

HÄGLER, K., 1945. Das Bündneroberländerschaf im Lichte der Haustierforschung.— Jahresber. Naturf. Ges. Graubündens, 79: 3–21. (Sheep)

HAHN, E., 1896. Die Haustiere und ihre Beziehungen zur Wirtschaft des Menschen.— 581 pp.—Leipzig. (General)

HAHN, E., 1926. Gans. In: EBERT, M., Reallexikon der Vorgeschichte, **4**: 167—Berlin. (Goose)

HALL, H. R., 1930. A 'Mascot' rein-ring from Boghaz-Koyi.—Ann. Archaeol. Anthrop. Liverpool, **17**: 3, pls. 1–2. (Horse)

HALTENORTH, T., 1958. Rassehunde-Wildhunde.—216 pp.—Heidelberg. (Dog)

——, 1959. Beitrag zur Kenntnis des Mesopotamischen Damhirsches.—Säugetierk. Mitt. München, **7**: 1–89. (Fallow Deer)

——, 1961. Lebensraum und Vorkommen des Mesopotamischen Damhirsches, *Cervus mesopotamicus* Brooke, 1875.—Säugetierk. Mitt. München, **9**: 15–39. (Fallow Deer)

HAMILTON, E., 1896. The Wild Cat of Europe.—99 pp.—London.

HAMMOND, J., 1932. Growth and development of mutton qualities in the sheep.— Edinburgh. (Chapter 3)

——, 1947. Farm Animals. Breeding, growth and inheritance.—London. (Chapter 3)

HANČAR, F., 1952. Stand und historische Bedeutung der Pferdezucht Mittelasiens im ersten Jahrtausend v. Chr.—Wien. Beitr. Kulturgesch. Linguistik, **9**: 465–483. (Horse)

——, 1956. Das Pferd in prähistorischer und früher historischer Zeit.—651 pp., 30 pls., 63 tables.—Wien and München. (Horse)

HASEBE, K., 1924. Über die Schädel und Unterkiefer der steinzeitlich-japanischen Hunderassen.—Arb. anatom. Inst. Kaiserl.-japan. Univ. Sendai, **10**. (Dog)

HASKINS, C. P., 1945. Of Ants and Men.—244 pp.—London. (Chapter 2)

HATT, G., 1919. Notes on Reindeer Nomadism.—Mem. Amer. anthrop. Ass., **6**: 75–133. (Chapter 2 and Reindeer)

HAUK, E., 1950. Abstammung Ur- und Frühgeschichte des Haushundes.—Prähist. For- schungen, Wien, **1**: 164 pp. (Dog and Fox)

HEAD, B. V., 1959. A Guide to the Principal Coins of the Greeks from *c.* 700 B.C. to A.D. 270.—108 pp., 52 pls.—London (Brit. Mus.). (General)

HEBERSTAIN, S. VON, 1549. Rerum Moscoviticarum commentarii.—Various later editions published. (Cattle)

HECK, H., 1951. The Breeding Back of the Aurochs.—Oryx, London, **1** (3): 117–122. (Cattle)

HECK, L. [N. D.] Die Rückzüchtung ausgestorbener Tiere.—10 pp. (Cattle)

——, 1934. Über die Neuzüchtung des Ur oder Auerochs.—Ber. intern. Ges. Erhaltung Wisents, **3** (4): 225–294, pls. 17–30. (Cattle)

——, 1950. Schwarzwild, Lebensbild des Wildschweins.—48 pp.—Munich (Bay. Landwirtschaftsverlag). (Pig)

——, 1952. Über den Auerochsen und seine Rückzüchtung.—Jahrb. Nassau. Ver. Naturk., **90**: 107–124. (Cattle)

HEINRICH, E., 1937. Uruk-Warka. V Die Grabung im Planquadrat K XVII.—Abh. preuss. Akad. Wiss. (Phil-Hist.) 1936: 27–55. (Camel)

HELBAEK, H., 1953. Archaeology and Agricultural Botany.—Rep. Inst. Archaeol. Univ. London, **9**: 44–59, (1951–1952). (General)

HEPTNER, W., 1934. Notiz über den Südrussischen Tarpan.—Z. Säugetierk., Berlin, **9**:
431–433. (Horse)

HERMES, G., 1935, 1936(a). Das gezähmte Pferd im neolithischen und frühbronzezeitlichen
Europa. I and II.—Anthropos, Wien, **30**: 803–823 and **31**: 115–129. (Horse)

——, 1936(b). Das gezähmte Pferd im alten Orient.—Anthropos, Wien, **31**: 364–394.
(Horse)

———, 1937. Der Zug des gezähmten Pferdes durch Europa.—Anthropos, Wien, **32**:
105–146. (Horse)

HERNÁNDEZ-PACHECO, E., 1953. La Caverna de la Peña de Candamo.—Com. Investig·
Paleont. Prehist., Madrid, No. 24, 281 pp. (Horse)

HERODOTUS. Histories. Transl. by A. D. Godley, 1950.—London (Loeb Classical Libr.).
(General)

HERRE, W., 1935. Ein Schnurrbart bei einem Pferde.—Zool. Anz., **109**: 39–44.
(Horse)

——, 1938. Zum Wandel des Rassebildes der Haustiere.—Kühn Archiv, **50**: 203–228.
(Pig)

——, 1943. Beiträge zur Kenntnis der Zwergziegen.—Zool. Garten, Leipzig, (n.s.) **15**:
26–45. (Chapter 3)

——, 1948. Zur Abstammung und Entwicklung der Haustiere: I. Über das bisher älteste
primigene Hausrind Nordeuropas.—Verh. deutsch. Zool. Kiel. (Cattle)

——, 1950. Neue Ergebnisse zoologischer Domestikationsforschung.—Verh. deutsch.
zool. Ges., Mainz: 40–54. (Chapter 2)

——, 1952. Studien über die wilden und domestizierten Tylopoden Südamerikas.—Zool.
Garten, Leipzig, **19**: 70–98. (Llama)

——, 1953 (a). Die Herkunft des Alpakka.—Säugetierk. Mitt., München, **1**: 176–177.
(Llama)

——, 1953 (b). Studien am Skelet des Mittelohres wilder und domestizierter Formen der
Gattung *Lama* Frisch.—Act. anat., Basel & New York, **19**: 271–289. (Llama)

——, 1953 (c). Wie sah der Auerochse aus?—Kosmos, Stuttgart, **49** (11): 4 pp. (Cattle)

——, 1954. Domestikation und Stammesgeschichte.—In: HEBERER, G., Die Evolution
der Organismen.—2nd edn.: 801–856—Stuttgart. (General)

——, 1955 (a). Fragen und Ergebnisse der Domestikationforschung nach Studien am
Hirn.—Verh. deutsch. zool. Ges., Leipzig: 144–214. (General)

——, 1955 (b). Das Ren als Haustier.—324 pp.—Leipzig. (Reindeer)

——, 1958. Züchtungsbiologische Betrachtungen an primitiven Tierzuchten.—Z.
Tierzücht. Züchtungsbiol., **71**: 252–272. (General)

——, et al., 1960. Die Haustiere von Haithabu.—152 pp., 10pls.—Neumünster. (General)

——, 1961. Grundsätzliches zur Systematik des Pferdes.—Z. Tierzücht. Züchtungsbiol.,
75: 57–78. (Horse)

—— AND LANGLET, J., 1936. Untersuchungen über Haut-, Haar- und Lockenbildung des
Karakulschafes.—Z. Tierzücht. Züchtungsbiol., **35**: 299–422. (General)

HERRE, W. AND RABES, I., 1937. Studien an der Haut des Karakulschafes.—Z. mikr.-anat. Forsch., Leipzig, **42**: 525–554. (Sheep)

—— AND RÖHRS, M., 1954. Die Tierreste aus den Hethitergräbern von Osmankayasi.—Wiss. Veröff. Deutsch. Orient. Ges., **71**(2): 60–80. (Ass)

—— AND STEPHAN, H., 1955. Zurr postnatalen Morphogenese des Hirnes verschiedener Haushundrassen.—Moph. Jb., Leipzig, **96** (2/3): 210–264. (Dog)

—— AND WIGGER, H., 1939. Die Lockenbildung der Säugetiere.— Kühn Archiv, Halle, **52**: 233–254. (General)

HESCHELER, K. AND RÜGER, J., 1939. Die Wirbeltierreste aus dem neolithischen Pfahlbaudorf Egolzwil 2 (Wauwilersee) nach den Grabungen von 1932 bis 1934.—Vierteljahrsschr. naturf. Ges., Zürich, **84**: 307–330. (General)

—— AND RÜGER, J., 1942. Die Reste der Haustiere aus dem neolithischen Pfahlbaudörfern Egolzwil 2 und Seematte-Gelfingen.—Vierteljahrsschr. naturf. Ges., Zürich, **87**: 383–486. (General)

—— AND KUHN, E., 1949. Die Tierwelt.—In: TSCHUMI, O., Urgeschichte der Schweiz. —pp. 120–368—Frauenfeld. (Cattle)

HEURTLEY, W. A. AND HUTCHINSON, R. W., 1926. Report on excavations at the Toumba and Tables of Vardaróftsa, Macedonia, 1925–1926.—J. Brit. Sch. Athens (1925–1926), **27**: 1–66. (Horse)

HILZHEIMER, M. [N.D.] Geschichte unserer Haustiere.—100 pp. Leipzig. (General)

——, 1909. Wisent und Ur im Kgl. Naturalien-kabinett zu Stuttgart.—Jahresheft. Ver. vaterländ. Naturk. Württemberg, 1909: 241–269. (Cattle)

——, 1910. Wie hat der Ur ausgesehen?—Jahrb. wiss. prakt. Tierzucht, **5**: 42–93. (Cattle)

——, 1913. Überblick über die Geschichte der Haustierforschung.—Zool. Rundsch., Würzburg, **5** (4): 233–254. (Camel)

——, 1926. Natürliche Rassengeschichte der Haussäugetiere.—233 pp.—Berlin and Leipzig. (General)

——, 1935. The Evolution of the Domestic Horse.—Antiquity, London, **9**: 133–139.

——, 1936. Sheep.—Antiquity, London, **10**: 195–206, 8 pls.

——, 1941. Animal Remains from Tell Asmar.—Orient. Inst. Chicago Stud. Ancient Civ., **20**: 52 pp. (General)

HITTI, P. K., 1956. The Arabs.—212 pp.—London. (General)

[HOLLAND, J.], 1835. The History and Description of fossil fuel, the colleries and coal trade of Great Britain.—485 pp.—London. (Sheep)

HOOD, M. S. F., 1953. Mycenae 1939–1952. Part V: A Mycenaean Cavalryman.—Ann. Brit. Sch. Athens, No. 48: 84–93. (Horse)

HOOIJER, D. A., 1949. Observations on a Calvarium of *Equus sivalensis* Falconer et Cautley from the Siwaliks of the Punjab, with craniometrical notes on Recent Equidae.—Arch. Néerland. Zool., **8** (3) : 1–24. (Horse)

——, 1961. The fossil vertebrates of Ksâr 'Akil, a Palaeolithic rockshelter in the Lebaonn.—Zool. Verh. Rijksmus. natuur. Hist. Leiden, No. 49, 67 pp.

522   BIBLIOGRAPHY

HOPWOOD, A. T., 1936. The Former Distribution of Caballine and Zebrine Horses in Europe and Asia.—Proc. zool. Soc. London, 1936 (4): 897–912, pls. 1–2.

——, 1942. Notes on Recent and Fossil Equines. I. Anatomical Features of Certain Limb-bones.—Ann. Mag. nat. Hist. (11) **9**: 73–94.

HORNBLOWER, G. D., 1927. A Humped Bull of Ivory and Some Predynastic Carvings.— J. Egypt. Archaeol., **13**: 222–225., pl. 55. (Cattle)

HORNITSCHEK, H., 1938. Bau und Entwicklung der Locke des Karakulschafes.—Kühn Archiv, Leipzig, **47**: 81–174. (Sheep)

HOUGHTON, W., 1890. Was the camel known to the early Egyptians?—Proc. Soc. bibl. Archaeol. London, **12**: 81–84.

HOWARD, M. M., 1951. Dried Cats.—Man, London, **51** (252): 149–152.

——, 1955. Technical description of the ivory writing-boards from Nimrud.—Iraq, London, **17** (1): 1–7. (Honey-bee)

HOWCHIN, W., 1925–30. The building of Australia and the Succession of Life.—750 pp.— Adelaide. (Dog)

HROZNÝ, B., 1929. L'invasion des Indo-Européens en Asie Mineure vers 2000 av. J.-C.— Archiv. orientálni, Praha, **1**: 273–299, pl. 9. (Horse)

——, 1931. L'entraînement des chevaux chez les anciens Indo-européens d'après un text: mîtannien-hittite provenant du 14ᵉ siècle av. J.-C.—Archiv. orientálni, Praha, **3**e 431–461. (Horse)

HUGHES, T. MCKENNY, 1896. The more important breeds of cattle which have been recognized in the British Isles.—Archaeologia, **55**: 125–158. (Cattle)

——, 1902. On the Remains of the Dog, Prehistoric, Roman and Mediaeval, found near Cambridge.—Cambridge Antiquarian Soc. Commun., **10**: 245–249.

ISSERLIN, B. S. J., 1951. On some possible early occurrences of the camel in Palestine.— Palestine Expl. Quart., 1950–1951: 50–53. (Camel)

JACKSON, J. W., 1939. Discovery of Remains of the Celtic Short-horned Ox, *Bos longifrons* Owen, at Whitepart Bay, Co. Antrim.—Irish Naturalists' J., **7** (6): 189–192.

——, 1943(a). Animal Bones from Maiden Castle.—Rep. Res. Comm. Soc. Antiq. London, **12**: 360–371. (General)

——, 1943 (b). Report on Animal Remains from the Late Bronze Age site at Minnis Bay, Birchington, Kent.—Proc. prehist. Soc. (n.s.) **9**: 41–44. (Cattle)

—— AND BATE, D. M. A., 1939. Animal Remains from Camulodunum.—Rep. Res. Comm. Soc. Antiq. London, No. 14: 350–355. (General)

JACOBI, A., 1931. Das Rentier.—Zool. Anz. Beil.—B., **96**: 264 pp., 6 pls. (Reindeer)

JAESCHKE, L. AND VAUK, G., 1951. Studien am Blut verschiedener Haustierarten und einiger ihrer Stammformen.—Zool. Anz., **147**: 121–129. (General)

JANIKOWSKI, T., 1942. The Wild Horse of Poland.—Nature, London, **150**: 681–682.

JARDINE, W., 1833–1843. Mammalia: Goats, Sheep, Oxen, etc.—12 vols.—Edinburgh (Naturalists' Library).

JEITTELES, L. H., 1872. Die vorgeschichtlichen Altertümer der Stadt Olmütz und ihrer

Umgebung.—Mitteil. anthrop. Ges. Wien, **2**: 18–32, 53–62, 86–91, 130–136, 162–182, 211–224, 233–248, 278–288. (Dog)

——, 1873. Zur Geschichte des Haushuhns.—Zool. Garten, 1873: 55ff., 88ff., 130ff. (Fowl)

JENSEN, K. W., 1958. Om Louisianas graeske samling.—Louisianas Årb., Copenhagen: 10–28. (Horse)

JETTMAR, K., 1952. In den Anfängen der Rentierzüchter.—Anthropos., **47**: 737–766. (Reindeer)

JOLEAUD, L., 1931. Succession des faunes de mammifères quaternaires en Berberie.—C.R. 15th Congr. intern. Anthrop. Archaeol. préhist., Paris, 1931: 220–226. (Camel)

JONES, F. W., 1921. The Status of the Dingo.—Trans. R. Soc. S. Austr., Adelaide: 254–263. (Dog)

JONES, H., 1892 (–1906). Animal Remains found during the Excavations (at Silchester).—Archaeologia, London, **53**: 23–26; **59**: 333–370; **60**: 149–168. (Cat and general)

JULIEN, C. A., 1956. Histoire de l'Afrique du Nord.—333 pp.—Paris. (Elephant and Camel)

KAGELMANN, G., 1954. Der Ur in den letzten zeitgenössischen Darstellungen der mitteleuropäischen Kunst.—Kosmos, Stuttgart, **50** (2): 570–575. (Cattle)

KEIMER, L., 1929. Über die Darstellung eines Kamelreiters aus der ägyptischen Frühzeit. —Kemi, Cairo, **2**: 85–90. (Camel)

KELLER, O., 1909 and 1913. Die Antike Tierwelt.—vol. 1, 434 pp., vol. 2, 617 pp.—Leipzig. (General)

——, 1919. Geschichte der Schweizerischen Haustierwelt.—84 pp.—Frauenfeld. (General)

KELM, H., 1938. Die postembryonale Schädelentwicklung des Wild und Berkshireschweins. —Z. Anat. u. Entwicklungsgesch., **108**: 499–559. (Pig)

——, 1939. Zur Systematik der Wildschweine.—Z. Tierzücht. Züchtungsbiol., Berlin, **43**: 362–369. (Pig)

KENYON, K. M. 1952–1957. Excavations at Jericho.—Palestine Expl. Quart., London, 1952: 4–6 and 62–82; 1953: 81–95; 1954: 45–63; 1955: 108–117; 1956: 67–82; 1957: 101–124. (General)

——, 1957. Digging up Jericho.—287 pp., 65 pls.—London. (General)

KING, J. E., 1953. Mammal Bones from the Neolithic Sites of Khirokitia and Erimi.—Khirokitia Final Rep., Cyprus Dept. Ant.: 431–437. (Goat and Sheep)

KING, L. W., 1915. A History of Babylon.—340 pp.—London. (General)

KLATT, B., 1954. Das Säugetiergrosshirn als zoologisches Problem.—Zool. Anz., **153**: 1–15. (Chapter 3)

KLEBS, L., 1915. Die Reliefs des alten Reiches.—Abh. Heidelb. Akad. Wiss. (phil.-hist.) **3**, 150 pp. (General)

KONO, T., 1934. Kodai no inu.—Dolmen, **3** (1): 31–35. (Dog)

KOSSACK, G., 1954. Pferdegeschirr aus Gräbern der älteren Hallstattzeit Bayerns.—Jb. Römisch-German. Zentralmus. Mainz, **1**: 111–178. (Horse)

KRUMBIEGEL, I., 1947. Von Haustieren und ihrer Geschichte.—84 pp., 18 figs.—Stuttgart. (General)

KUHN, E., 1946. Die Tierreste der La Tène-Siedlung Bonaduz (Kt. Graubünden).—Bündner Monatsbl., Chur, **6**: 165–176. (Pig)

LACAM, R., NIEDERLENDER, A. AND VALLOIS, H. V., 1944. Le gisement mésolithique du Cuzoul de Gramat.—Mém. Arch. Inst. Paléont. hum., Paris, **21**, 92 pp., 8 pls. (Sheep)

LACORRE, F., 1937. Utilité de tableaux synoptiques de faune pour les gisements paléolithiques.—Congr. préhist. France, **12**: 824–831, 1 pl. (Rabbit)

——, 1951. Les migrations des rennes dans la province préhistorique des Eyzies.—C. R. S. Acad. Sci., Paris, **232**: 1702–1704. (Reindeer)

LAMB, W., 1938. Excavations at Kato Phana in Chios.—Ann. Brit. School Athens, **35**: 138–164, pls. 27–37. (Birds)

LANE, Y., 1946. African Folk Tales.—240 pp.—London. (Chapter 2 and Dog)

LANGDON, S. [N.D.] The Excavations at Kish with special reference to the Conclusions reached in 1928–1929.—9 pp. (Horse)

—— (Ed.) 1924–1934. Excavations at Kish.—4 vols.—Paris. (Horse and Sheep)

——, 1913. Babylonian Liturgies.—151 pp., 75 pls.—Paris. (Horse)

LARTET, E. AND GAILLARD, C., 1907. La Faune momifiée de l'ancienne Égypte.—Arch. Mus. Hist. nat. Lyon, **9** (2): 1–130, 184 figs. (Cattle)

LAUFER, B., 1917. The Reindeer and its Domestication.—Mem. Amer. anthrop. Assoc., **4**: 91–147. (Reindeer)

——, 1931. The Domestication of the Cormorant in China and Japan.—Publ. Field Mus. nat. Hist. anthrop. ser. **18** (3): 201–263., pls. 13–16. Chicago. (Birds)

LAVIE, P., 1954. L'enregistrement thermique continu dans les populations d'*Apis mellifica* au cours de l'hivernage.—Insectes Sociaux, Paris, **1** (1): 39–48. (Bee)

LAWRENCE, B., Cave Fauna.—In: FIELD, H., 1956. An Anthropological Reconnaissance in the Near East, 1950.—Peabody Mus. Pap., Chicago, **48** (2): 80–81. (Dog)

LAYARD, A. H., 1853. Discoveries in the ruins of Nineveh and Babylon.—686 pp.—London. (General)

LECOMTE, J., 1954. Essai d'une analyse causale du comportement agressif des ouvrières d'abeilles.—Insectes Sociaux, Paris, **1** (1): 49–58. (Bee)

LEFÉBURE, E., 1906. Le Chameau en Egypte.—Act. XIV Congr. int. Orientalistes Alger, 1905, **2** (Sect. 7): 24–62. (Camel)

LEGRAIN, L., 1930. Terra-Cottas from Nippur.—Publ. Univ. Pennsylvania, Babylonia Sect., **16**, 52 pp. 77 pls. (Elephants)

——, 1936. Ur Excavations III. Archaic Seal Impressions.—Publ. Brit. Mus. and Univ. Mus. Pennsylvania, 49 pp., 58 pls. (Sheep)

——, 1951. Ur Excavations X. Seal Cylinders.—Publ. Brit. Mus. and Univ. Mus. Pennsylvania, 56 pp., 43 pls. (General)

LEHMANN, V., 1949. Der Ur im Diluvium Deutschlands und seine Verbreitung.—N. Jahrb. Min., Abh. (B), **90**: 163–178. (Cattle)

LEISNER, G. AND V., 1951. Antas do Concelho de Reguengos de Monsaraz.—Inst. Alta Cultura, Lisbon, 322 pp. (Rabbit)

LEITHNER, O. F. VON, 1927. Der Ur.—Ber. intern. Ges. Erhaltung Wisents, **2** (1) 1–139. (Cattle)

LENGERKEN, H. VAN, 1955. Ur, Hausrind und Mensch.—Wiss. Abh. deutsch. Akad. Landwirtsch. Berlin, **14**, 191 pp. (Cattle)

LEONARD, A. G., 1894. The Camel.—335 pp.—London.

LESCHI, L., 1942. Rome et les Nomades du Sahara Central.—Trav. Inst. Rech. Saharien., Alger, **1**: 1–16. (Camel)

LEY, W., 1951. Dragons in Amber.—328 pp.—London. (Camel)

LHOTE, H., 1953. Le cheval et le chameau dans les peintures et gravures rupestres du Sahara.—Bull. IFAN, Dakar, **15**: 1138–1228. (Camel)

LIEPE, H. U., 1958. Die Pferde des Latène-Oppidums Manching.—Stud. vor- u. frühgesch. Tierresten Bayerns, Tieranat. Inst. Univ. München, **4**: 32 pp., 3 pls. (Horse)

LORENZ, K., 1942. Die angeborenen Formen möglicher Erfahrung.—Zeit. Tierpsychol., **5**: 235–409. (Chapter 3)

LORENZ-LIBURNAU, L. VON, 1899. Die Wildziegen der griechischen Inseln und ihre Beziehungen zu anderen Ziegenformen.—Wiss. Mitt. Bosnien Hercegovina Wien, **6**: 851–886, pls. 26–28. (General)

Low, D., 1842. The breeds of domestic animals of the British Isles.—2 vols. (General)

LOWE, P. R., 1934. Animal Bones from Silchester.—Ibis, London, (13) **4**: 378–382. (Fowl)

LÜDIKE-SPANNENKREBS, R., 1955. Studien über die Anzahl der Eizellen von Wildkaninchen und verschiedenen Hauskaninchenrassen.—Z. mikr.-anat. Forsch., Leipzig, **61**: 454–486. (Chapter 3 and Rabbit)

LUNAU, H., 1956. Vergleichend-metrische Untersuchungen am Allocortex von Wild- und Hausschweinen.—Z. mikr.-anat. Forsch., Leipzig, **62**: 673–698. (Pig)

LUNDHOLM, B., 1949. Abstammung und Domestikation des Hauspferdes.—Zool. Bidrag. Uppsala, **27**: 1–288. (Horse)

LYDEKKER, R., 1898. Wild Oxen, Sheep and Goats of all lands, living and extinct.—318 pp.—London.

——, 1912 (a). The Horse and its Relations.—286 pp.—London.

——, 1912 (b). The Ox and its Kindred.—271 pp.—London.

——, 1912 (c). The Sheep and its Cousins.—315 pp., 24 pls.—London.

——, 1913–1915. Catalogue of Ungulate Mammals.—5 vols.—London (Brit. Mus.). (Hoofed mammals)

MACKAY, E. J. H., 1938. Further Excavations at Mohenjo-Daro.—718 pp., 146 pls.—New Delhi. (General)

——, 1943. Chanhu-Daro Excavations 1935–1936.—338 pp., 96 pls.—New Haven. (General)

MALLOWAN, M., 1936. The Excavations at Tall Chagar Bazar and an archaeological survey of the Habur Region 1934–1935.—59 pp., 28 figs.—Oxford and London. (General)

MALLOWAN, M. E. L., 1946. Excavations in the Balih Valley, 1938.—Iraq, London, **8**: 111–159. (General)

——, 1948. A copper rein-ring from Southern Iraq.—Iraq, London, **10**: 51–55. (Onager)

——, 1950. Excavations at Nimrud (Kalhu).—Iraq, London, **12**: 147–183. (Birds)

——, 1956. Twenty-five Years of Mesopotamian Discovery.—81 pp.—London (Brit. Sch. Archaeol. Iraq). (Cattle)

—— AND ROSE, J. C., 1935. Prehistoric Assyria. The Excavations at Tall Arpachiyah, 1933.—Iraq, London, **2** (1): 178 pp., 22 pls. (Cattle, Sheep and Pigeon)

MARKHAM, G., 1631. A Way to get Wealth.—London. (Rabbit)

MARSHALL, J., 1931. Mohenjo-Daro and the Indus Civilization.—716 pp., 164 pls.—London. (Elephant, Cattle and Camel)

——, 1951. Taxila.—3 vols., 895 pp., 246 pls.—Cambridge. (Elephant)

MASON, J. ALDEN, 1957. The Ancient Civilizations of Peru.—330 pp.—London (Pelican). (General)

MATTINGLY, H., 1928. Roman Coins.—300 pp., 64 pls.—London. (Elephant and Peacock)

MAXWELL-HYSLOP, K. R., 1955. Note on a Shaft-hole Axe-pick from Khurab, Mesopotamia —Iraq, London, **17** (2): 161. (Camel)

MECQUENEM, R. DE, et al., 1943. Archéologie Susienne.—Mem. Miss. arquéol. Iran, **29**: 207 pp., 12 pls. (General)

MEISSNER, B., 1920. Babylonien und Assyrien I.—466 pp.—Heidelberg. (Bee and Onager)

——, 1926. Könige Babyloniens und Assyriens.—Heidelberg. (Elephant)

MERLA, G., 1949. I *Leptobos* Rütim. Italiani.—Palaeontogr. Ital., Pisa, **46**: 41–155. (Cattle)

MERTENS, R., 1936. Der Hund aus dem Senckenberg-Moor, ein Begleiter des Urs.—Natur u. Volk, Frankfurt a.M., **66** (1): 499–562. (Dog)

METZDORFF, H., 1940. Untersuchungen an Hoden von Wild- und Hausschweinen.—Z. Anat. Entwicklungsg., **110**: 489–532. (Pig)

MEUNIER, K., 1959. Die Grössenabhängigkeit der Körperform bei Vögeln.—Z. wiss. Zool., Leipzig, **162**: 328–355. (General)

MICHENER, C. D., 1944. Comparative external morphology, phylogeny, and a classification of the bees (Hymenoptera).—Bull. Amer. Mus. nat. Hist. New York, **82** (6): 151–326. (Bee)

MIDDENDORFF, A. TH. VON, 1851. Reise in den äussersten Norden und Osten Sibiriens 1843–1844.—2 vols.—St. Petersburg. (Reindeer)

MIKESELL, M. K., 1955. Notes on the dispersal of the Dromedary.—S. W. J. Anthrop., New Mexico, **11** (3): 231–245.

MIKULICZ-RADECKI, M. VON, 1950. Vergleichende Musterstudien an Wildleporiden und Hauskaninchen.—Neue Erg. Probl. Zool., Leipzig: 588–601. (Rabbit)

MILLAIS, J. G., 1906. The Mammals of Great Britain and Ireland.—Vol. **3**, 384 pp.—London. (General)

MILLER, G. S., 1912. Catalogue of the Mammals of Western Europe.—1019 pp., Brit. Mus. (Nat. Hist.) London. (General)

MIVART, ST G., 1881. The Cat.—557 pp.—London.

MOHR, E., 1960. Das Przewalski-Pferd, seine Zuchten und Bestände.—Natur u. Volk, Frankfurt a.M., **90** (4): 101–111. (Horse)

MÖLLER, G., 1906. Ausgrabung der Deutsch. Orient-Gesellschaft auf dem vorgeschichtlichen Friedhofe bei Abusir-el-Meleq im Sommer 1905.—Mitt. Deutsch. Orient Ges. Berlin, No. 30: 28 pp. (Camel)

MONOD, TH., 1947. Sur quelques gravures rupestres de la région d'Aozou (Tibesti).— Riv. Sci. preist. Firenze, **2** (1): 30–47. (Camel)

MONTAGU, I., 1957. The wild camels of the Gobi Desert.—The Times, Oct. 9th, 1957: 18.

MONTAGU, M. E. A., 1942. On the origin of the domestication of the dog.—Science, Philadelphia, **96** (2483): 111–112.

MORRISON-SCOTT, T. C. S., 1947. A revision of our knowledge of African Elephants' teeth, with notes on Forest and 'Pygmy' Elephants.—Proc. zool. Soc., London, **117** (2-3): 505–527. (Elephant)

MURRAY, G. W., 1952. Early Camels in Egypt.—Bull. Inst. Fouad 1er Désert, **2** (1): 105–106.

MYRES, J. L., 1897. Excavations in Cyprus in 1894.—J. Hellenic Stud., London, **17**: 134–173. (Horse)

NACHTSHEIM, H., 1941. Das Porto-Santo Kaninchen.—Umschau, Frankfurt, 1941 (10): 4 pp. (Rabbit)

——, 1949. Vom Wildtier zum Haustier.—123 pp.—Berlin and Hamburg. (Chapter 3 and Rabbit)

NARR, K. J., 1959. Frühe Hundevorkommen und ihr kulturgeschichtlicher Ort.—Berliner Beitr. Vor- u. Frühgesch., **2**: 119–125. (Dog)

NASONOV, N. V., 1919. O 'perverzii' v rogakh dikikh daranov *Ovis vignei* Blyth, *gmelini* Blyth i *urmiana* (Guenther).—Bull. Acad. Sci. Russie, 1919: 1215–1246. (Sheep)

——, 1924. Distribution géographique des moutons sauvages du monde ancien.—255 pp., 20 pls.—Petrograd (Russian only). (Sheep)

NECRASOV, O. AND HAIMOVICI, S., 1959. Sur la présence d'une espèce pléistocène d'Equidés, *Equus hydruntinus* Reg., dans le Néolithique Roumain.—An. Ştint. Univ. Al. I. Cuza Iaşi (n.s.), **5**: 137–148. (Ass)

—— AND HAIMOVICI, S., 1960. Nouvelle contribution à l'étude de *Equus* (*Asinus*) *hydruntinus* Reg.—An. Ştinţ. Univ. Al. I. Cuza Iaşi (n.s.), **6**: 355–376. (Ass)

NEHRING, A., 1884. Über Rassebildung bei den Inkahunden.—Kosmos 1884:94–111. (Dog)

——, 1887. Die Sohlenfärbung am Hinterfusse von *F. catus*, *F. caligata*, *F. maniculata* und *F. domestica*.—Sitz.-Ber. Ges. naturf. Freunde, Berlin, 1887: 26–27. (Cat)

——, 1891. Diluviale Reste von Cuon, Ovis, Saiga, Ibex und Rupicapra aus Mähren.— Neues Jb. Min., 1891 (2): 107–155, pls. 2–3. (Sheep)

NELSON, H. H., 1932. Later Historical Records of Rameses III. Medinet Habu II.—Univ. Chicago Orient. Inst. Publ. **9**: 55–130. (General)

NEUVILLE, R., 1951. Le Paléolithique et le Mésolithique du Désert de Judée.—Mem. Arch. Inst. Paléont. hum. **24**, 270 pp., 20 pls. (Horse and Camel)

NEWBERRY, P. E., 1893 and 1894. Beni Hassan. Parts I and II.—Archaeol. Surv. Egypt, London (Edit. F. L. Griffith), 85 pp., 47 pls. and 85 pp., 37 pls. (General)

NEWTON, E. T., 1880. Notes on the Vertebrata of the Pre-Glacial Forest Bed Series of the East of England III.—Geol. Mag., London, (2) **7**: 442–452. (Sheep and Fox)

——, 1882. The Vertebrata of the Forest Bed Series of Norfolk and Suffolk.—Mem. geol· Surv. Engl. Wales, 143 pp., 19 pls. (Sheep and Fox)

——, 1921. Bones other than Human.—Appendix III in: COCKS, A. H., A Romano-British Homestead in the Hambleden Valley, Bucks.—Archaeologia, London, **71**: 141–198. (Cat)

NOACK, T., 1916 (a). Über die Schädel vorgeschichtlicher Haushunde im Römermuseum zu Hildesheim.—Zool. Anz., **46**: 75–94. (Dog)

——, 1916 (b). Über den mumifizierten Kopf eines Inkahundes.—Zool. Anz., **46**: 62–70. (Dog)

NOBIS, G., 1954. Die Haustiere von Tofting.—Offa-Bücher, Neumünster, **12**: 114–134. (Cat)

——, 1954. Zur Kenntnis der ur- und frühgeschichtlichen Rinder Nord- und Mittel-deutschlands.—Zeit. Tierzücht. Züchtungsbiol., **63** (2): 155–194. (Cattle)

——, 1955. Beiträge zur Abstammung und Domestikation des Hauspferdes.—Zeit. Tierzücht. Züchtungsbiol., **64** (3): 201–246. (Horse)

——, 1960. Das Hauspferd.—In: Die Haustiere von Haithabu. pp. 73–79—Neumünster. (Horse)

NÖLDEKE, A., HALLER, A. VON, LENZEN, H. AND HEINRICH, E., 1937. Uruk-Warka.—Abh. preuss. Akad. Wiss., Berlin (phil.-hist.) 1936 (13), 61 pp., 60 pls., (Cattle and Sheep)

OBERDORFER, F., 1959. Die Hunde des Latène-Oppidums Manching.—Stud. vor- u. frühgesch. Tierr. Bayerns, Tieranat. Inst. Univ. München, **7**, 43 pp., 7 pls. (Dog)

OBERMAIER, H. 1924. Fossil Man in Spain.—495 pp., 23 pls.—London. (Pig)

OLMSTEAD, A. T., 1923. History of Assyria.—695 pp.—London. (Elephant)

——, 1948. History of the Persian Empire.—576 pp., 70 pls.—Chicago. (Camel)

OPITZ, G., 1958. Die Schweine des Latène-Oppidums Manching.—Stud. vor- u. frühgesch. Tierr. Bayerns, Tieranat. Inst. Univ. München, **3**, 40 pp. (Pig)

OPPENHEIM, M. VON, 1931. Tell Halaf. A new Culture in Oldest Mesopotamia.—337 pp., 68 pls.—London. (Camel)

OSBORN, H. F., 1916. Craniometry of the Equidae.—Mem. Amer. Mus. nat. Hist., (n.s.) **1**: 3. (Horse)

OWEN, R., 1846. A history of British Mammals and Birds.—560 pp.—London. (Cattle)

PALLADIUS, 4th cent. A.D. De Re Rustica. 9, 14. (Cat)

PARET, O., 1938. Der römische Bronzedeckel von Mundelsheim.—Germania, **22**: 104, pl. 23. (Fowl)

——, 1946. Das neue Bild der Vorgeschichte.—232 pp.—Stuttgart. (Goat)

PASSEK, T. S., 1949. Periodizatsiya Tripolskikh poselenii.—247 pp., 1 pl.—Moscow (Akad. Nauk). (Horse)

PENNANT, T., 1776. British Zoology.—Vol. 2, 4th. edn.—London. (Cormorant and Fish)

PÉQUART, M. AND ST J., BOULE, M. AND VALLOIS, H., 1937. Téviec. Station-nécropole mésolithique du Morbihan.—Mem. Arch. Inst. Paléont. hum., Paris, **18**; 227 pp., 19 pls. (Sheep)

PERICOT, L., 1950. El Arte Rupestre Español.—56 pp.—Barcelona (Argos, S.A.). (Bees)

PERRET, R., 1936. Recherches archéologiques et ethnographiques au Tassili des Ajjers (Sahara central). Les gravures rupestres de l'oued Djaret, la population et les ruines d'Iherir.—J. Soc. Africanistes, **6**: 41–64, pls. 1–19. (Camel)

PETRIE, W. M. FLINDERS, 1903. Abydos. Part II. 1903.—Mem. Egypt. Expl. Fund, London, 50 pp., 64 pls. (Camel)

——, 1907, Gizeh and Rifeh.—Brit. Sch. Archaeol. Egypt, 13th year.—49 pp., 40 pls.—London. (Camel)

——, 1953. Ceremonial Slate Palettes.—Brit. Sch. Archaeol. Egypt, 1953: 1–23, pls. A–K. (General)

PFISTER, R., 1951. Textiles de Halabiyeh.—Serv. archéol. Beyrouth, **18**. (Silk-moth)

PFIZENMAYER, E. W., 1926. Mammutleichen und Urwaldmenschen in Nordost-Sibirien.—Leipzig. (Horse and Elk)

PHILLIPS, D. W., 1948. Ancient Egyptian Animals.—Metr. Mus. Art, New York, 24 pp. (General)

PIGGOTT, S., 1950. Prehistoric India.—293 pp.—London (Pelican Books). (Horse)

PILGRIM, G. E., 1939. The Fossil Bovidae of India.—Palaeont. Indica (n.s.) **26** (1): 356 pp., 7 pls. (Cattle)

PIRA, A., 1909. Studien zur Geschichte der Schweinerassen, insbesondere derjenigen Schwedens.—Zool. Jahrb., Jena, **10**: 233–426. (Pig)

PITTIONI, R., 1954. Urgeschichte des Österreichischen Raumes.—854 pp.—Wien. (Horse)

PLACZEK, DR, 1893. The Weasel and the Cat in Ancient Times.—Trans. Soc. Bibl. Archaeol. London, **9**: 155–166.

PLINY. Natural History.–Transl. by H. Rackham.—London (Loeb Class. Libr.). (General)

POCOCK, R. J., 1907. On the English Domestic Cat.—Proc. zool. Soc. London, 1907 (1): 143–167, pls. 8–10.

POLHAUSEN, H., 1949. Der Gebrauch der Rentiere zum Reiten. Zugleich ein Beitrag zur Frage nach dem Ursprung der Herdentierzucht.—MS. Kandidatenaufsatz, Stockholm. (Reindeer)

——, 1953. Nachweisbare Ansätze zum Wanderhirtentum in der niederdeutschen Mittelsteinzeit.—Zeit. Ethnol., Berlin, pp. 64–82. (Reindeer and Horse)

——, 1954 (a). Das Wanderhirtentum und seine Vorstufen.—Braunschweig. (Reindeer and Horse)

——, 1954 (b). Die Stangenschleife im Rentiergebiet.—Manuscript. (Reindeer)

PÖLLOTH, K., 1959. Die Schafe und Ziegen des Latène-Oppidums Manching.—Stud. vor- u. frühgesch. Tierr. Bayerns, Tieranat. Inst. Univ. München, **6**, 53 pp., 3 pls. (Goat and Sheep)

POMEL, A., 1893 (a). *Bubalus antiquus.*—Paléont. Mon. Carte géol. Algérie, **1**: 94 pp., 10 pls. (Buffalo)

——, 1893 (b). Caméliens et Cervidés.—Paléont. Mon. Carte géol. Algérie, **2**: 52 pp., 8 pls. (Camel)

——, 1897. Les Carnassiers.—Paléont. Mon. Carte géol. Algérie, **9**: 42 pp., 15 pls. (Dog)

——, 1898. Les Ovidés.—Paléont. Mon. Carte géol. Algérie, **13**: 33 pp., 14 pls. (Sheep)

POMMEROL, F., 1879. Le Mouflon quaternaire.—Assoc. franç. Av. Sci., Montpellier, 1879: 600-609, pl. 3. (Sheep)

——, 1881. Le quaternaire ancien de l'Auvergne.—Assoc. franç. Av. Sci., Montpellier. (General)

PORADA, E., 1948. The Collection of the Pierpont Morgan Library.—Corpus of Ancient Near Eastern Seals in North American Collections.—Bollingen Series, Washington, **14**: 187 pp., 176 pls. (Cattle)

PORTIS, A., 1907. Di alcuni avanzi fossili di grandi Ruminantia principalmente della Provinzia di Roma.—Palaeogr. Ital., **13**. (Cattle)

POTTIER, E., 1926 and 1931. L'Art Hittite.—2 vols, 100 pp. and 80 pp.—Langres (France). (General)

PRASHAD, B., 1936. Animal remains from Harappa.—Mem. archaeol. Surv. India, **51**, 62 pp., 2 figs., 7 pls. (General)

PRELL, H., 1939. Skandinavische Wildrinder in historischer Zeit.—Zool. Anz. Leipzig, **125**: 203–208. (Cattle)

PRITCHARD, J. B., 1950. Ancient Near Eastern Texts relating to the Old Testament.— Princeton. (Elephant)

RAHIR, E., 1921. L'habitat tardenoisien des grottes de Remouchamps, Chaleux et Montaigle.—Bull. Soc. Anthrop., Bruxelles, **35**: 31–89. (Goat)

RANDALL-MACIVER, D. AND MACE, A. C., 1902. El Amrah and Abydos, 1899–1901.—108 pp., 60 pls.—London (Egypt Expl. Fund). (General)

RAUDONIKAS, W. J., 1938. Les gravures rupestres des bords du lac Onéga et de la mer Blanche.—Moscow. (General)

RAWIEL, F., 1939. Untersuchungen an Hirnen von Wild- und Hausschweinen.—Z. Anat. Entwicklungsgesch., Berlin, **110**: 344–370. (Pig)

REED, C. A., 1959. Animal domestication in the Prehistoric Near East.—Science, **130**: 1629–1639. (General)

——, 1960. A review of the archaeological evidence on animal domestication in the prehistoric Near East.—Stud. ancient orient. Civil. (Orient. Inst.), Chicago, **31**: 119–145. (General)

REICHENAU, W. VON, 1915. Beiträge zur näheren Kenntnis der fossilen Pferde aus dem deutschen Pleistozän.—Abh. Hess. geol. Landesanst. Darmstadt, **7**: 1–156. 16 pls. (Horse)

[REINDEER] The Reindeer Council of the United Kingdom. Annual Reports from 1946 onwards.—Cambridge.

REINERTH, H., 1939. Ein Dorf der Grossteingräberleute. Die Ausgrabungen des Reichsamtes für Vorgeschichte am Dümmer.—Germanen-Erbe, **4** (8): 227–242. (Horse)

REITSMA, G. G., 1935. Zoologisch Onderzoek der nederlandsche Terpen. II. Het Varken.—Publ. Sticht. Fonds Landbouw Exp. Bur. 1916–1918, Wageningen, **14**: 58 pp., 90 figs. (Pig)

REMÉNYI, K. A., 1952. Canidenreste aus den Ausgrabungen bei Tószeg.—Acta archaeol., Budapest, **2** (1–3): 115–124. (Dog)

REQUATE, H., 1957. Zur Naturgeschichte des Ures (*Bos primigenius* Bojanus 1827), nach Schädel- und Skelettfunden in Schleswig-Holstein.—Z. Tierzücht. Züchtungsbiol., **70**: 297–338. (Cattle)

——, 1959. Federhauben bei Vögeln.—Z. wiss. Zool., Leipzig, **162**: 191–313. (General)

——, 1960 (a). Das Hausgeflügel.—In: Die Haustiere von Haithabu: 136–146.—Neumünster. (Birds)

——, 1960 (b). Die Hauskatze.—In.: Die Haustiere von Haithabu: 131–135.—Neumünster. (Cat)

REVERDIN, L., 1927. Recherches sur les mandibules de chien du niveau inférieur néolithique lacustre.—Verh. schweiz. naturf. Ges., Basel, **108**: 215–216. (Dog)

REVILLIOD, P. AND DOTTRENS, E., 1946. I. Étude préliminaire: Les phalanges osseuses du *Bos taurus domesticus*.—Rev. Suisse Zool. Genève, **53**: 739–774. (Cattle)

—— AND DOTTRENS, E., 1947. II. Les ossements de *Bos taurus brachyceros* Rütim. et de *Bos primigenius* Boj.—Rev. Suisse Zool. Genève, **54**: 459–544. (Cattle)

REYNOLDS, S. H., 1939. British Pleistocene Mammalia. The Bovidae.—Palaeontogr. Soc., **3** (6): 65 pp., 5 pls.

RHOTERT, H., 1938. Transjordanien.—251 pp., 30 pls.—Frankfurt (Forschungsinst. Kulturmorphol.). (Camel)

RICE, D. TALBOT, 1955. Mosaics of the Great Palace of the Byzantine Emperors.—Ill. London News, March 12th, 1955: 462–463. (Camel)

RIDGEWAY, W., 1905. The Origin and Influence of the Thoroughbred Horse.—538 pp.—Cambridge.

RITCHIE, J., 1920. The influence of Man on Animal Life in Scotland.—550 pp.—Cambridge. (Reindeer)

ROBERTS, E. J., 1950. The Story of Our Cattle.—Young Farmers' Club Booklet, No. 22: 48 pp.

ROBINSON, A. E., 1936. The Camel in Antiquity.—Sudan Notes and Records, **19**: 47–69.

ROBINSON, E. S. G., 1927. Catalogue of the Greek Coins of Cyrenaica.—154 pp., 47 pls.—London (Brit. Mus.). (Elephant)

——, 1951. The Coins from the Ephesian Artemion Reconsidered.—J. Hellenic Stud., **71**: 156–167, pl. 38. (Fowl)

RÖHRS, M., 1957. Beobachtungen an wildlebenden Tylopoden Südamerikas.—Verh. deutsch. zool. Ges., Graz. (Llama)

——, 1959. Neue Ergebnisse der Allometrieforschung.—Z. wiss. Zool., Leipzig, **162**: 1–95. (General)

—— AND HERRE, W., 1961. Die Tierreste der neolithischen Siedlung Fikirtepe am kleinasiatischen Gestade des Bosporus.—Z. Tierzücht. Züchtungsbiol., **75**: 110–127. (General)

Ross, E. J., 1946. A Chalcolithic Site in Northern Baluchistan.—J. Near Eastern Stud., Chicago, **5**: 284–316. (Cattle and Horse)

Rostovtzeff, M., 1931. Dieux et Chevaux. À propos de quelques Bronzes d'Anatolie, de Syrie et d'Arménie.—Syria, Paris, **12**: 48–57. (Horse)

Rothmaler, W. and Padberg, W. (Ed.), 1953–1957. Beiträge zur Frühgeschichte der Landwirtschaft I-III.—Wiss. Abh. Deutsch. Akad. Landwirtsch. Berlin. (General)

Rowe, A., 1930. The Topography and History of Beth-Shan.—Publ. Palestine Sect. Mus. Univ. Pennsylvania, **1**: 62 pp., 58 pls. (Elephant)

Rumjancev, B. T., 1936. Origin of the Domestic Horse.—Bull. Acad. Sci. U.S.S.R., **2-3**.

Rust, A., 1937. Das altsteinzeitliche Rentierjägerlager Meiendorf.—144 pp., 57 pls.— Neumünster. (Horse and Reindeer)

——, 1943. Die alt- und mittelsteinzeitlichen Funde von Stellmoor.—240 pp., 107 pls.— Neumünster. (Horse and Reindeer)

Rütimeyer, L., 1862. Die Fauna der Pfahlbauten der Schweiz.—Neue Denkschr. Schweiz. Ges. Naturw. Zürich, **19**, 248 pp. (General)

——, 1867. Versuch einer natürlichen Geschichte des Rindes, in seinem Beziehungen zu den Wiederkäuern im allgemeinen.—Neue Denkschr. Schweiz. Ges. Naturw., Zürich, **22** (1): 102 pp., 2 pls.; (2): 175 pp. 4 pls. (Cattle)

Rydbeck, O., 1934. Das Pferd als Transport- und Kampfmittel in den Völkerwanderungen der Ganggräberzeit.—Medd. Lunds Univ. hist. Mus., 1933–1934: 77–98. (Horse)

Ryder, M. L., 1960. Sheep breeds in history.—Nat. Sheep Breed. Ass. Yearb.: 17–25.

Saad, Z. Y., 1947. Royal Excavations at Saqqara and Helwan (1941–1945).—Suppl. Ann. Service archéol. Égypte, Cairo, **3**: 258 pp., 102 pls. (Camel)

Sauer, C. O. 1952. Agricultural Origins and Dispersals.—Bowman Mem. Lect., ser. 2 (Amer. Geogr. Soc.) New York, 110 pp. (General)

Schaeffer, F. A., 1930. Les Têtres funéraires préhistoriques dans la Forêt de Haguenau. II. Les Tumulus de l'Age du Fer.—332 pp.—Haguenau. (Fowl)

Scharff, A., 1927. Grundzüge der Ägyptischen Vorgeschichte.—Morgenland, Leipzig, **12**: 69 pp. (General)

Scharff, R. F., 1906. On the former occurrence of the African wild cat (*Felis ocreata* Gmel.) in Ireland.—Proc. R. Irish. Acad., Dublin, **26** (B): 1–12, pl. 1. (Cat)

Schmidt, H., 1934. Ein Skelett vom Riesenelch.—Forschungen u. Fortschritte, Berlin, **10** (15): 198–199. (Elk)

Schneider, F., 1958. Die Rinder des Latène-Oppidums Manching.—Stud. vor- u. frühgesch. Tierr. Bayerns, Tieranat. Inst. Univ. München, **5**: 33 pp., 2 pls. (Cattle)

Schwarz, E., 1935. On Ibex and Wild Goat.—Ann. Mag. Nat. Hist., London, (10) **16**: 433–437.

Schweinfurth, G., 1912. Tierbilder und Felsinschriften bei Assuan.—Z. Ethnol., **44**: 627–658. (Camel)

Seligman, C. G. and B. Z., 1911. The Veddas.—463 pp., 71 pls—Cambridge (U.P.). (Honey-bee)

SELTMAN, C., 1955. Greek Coins.—2nd edn., 311 pp., 64 pls.—London. (General)

SETHE, K. 1916. Die älteste Erwähnung des Haushuhns in einem ägyptischen Texte.—
Festschr. F. C. Andreas, Leipzig: 109–116. (Fowl)

SEWELL, R. B. SEYMOUR AND GUHA, B. S., 1931. Zoological Remains.—In: MARSHALL, J.,
Mohenjo-Daro and the Indus Civilization II.—pp. 649–673. London. (General)

SICKENBERG, O., 1930. Eine Wildziege der *Capra prisca*-Gruppe aus dem Pleistozän
Niederösterreichs.—Palaeobiol. Wien, 3: 92–102. (Goat)

SIEWING, G., 1960. Das Hausschwein.—In: Die Haustiere von Haithabu: 81–114.—
Neumünster. (Pig)

——, 1960. Das Hausrind.—In: Die Haustiere von Haithabu: 19–71.—Neumünster.
(Cattle)

SIMONDS, J. B., 1854. The Age of the Ox, Sheep and Pig.—118 pp.—London. (General)

SIMPSON, G. G., 1951. The Story of the Horse Family in the Modern World and through
Sixty Million Years of History.—247 pp., 32 pls. Oxford. (Horse)

SINGER, C., HOLMYARD, E. J. AND HALL, A. R., 1955. A History of Technology. Vol. I.—
830 pp., 36 pls.—Oxford. (General)

SIRELIUS, U. T., 1916. Über die Art und Zeit der Zähmung des Renntiers.—J. Soc. Finno-
Ougrienne, 33 (2). (Chapter 2 and Reindeer)

SISSON, S. AND GROSSMAN, J. D., 1953. The Anatomy of the Domestic Animals.—4th edn.,
972 pp.—London. (General)

SLIJPER, E. J. 1948. Mens en Huisdier.—410 pp.—Zutphen. (General)

——, 1951. On the Hump of the Zebu and Zebu-crosses.—Hemera Zoa, 58 (1/2): 6–47.
(Chapter 3 and Cattle)

SPENCE, L., 1945. The Magic Arts in Celtic Britain.—London. (Cat)

STAFFE, A., 1938. Über einen Hausschweinschädel aus dem frühdynastischen Ägypten.—
Zeit. Tierzüchtg. Züchtungsbiol., 41: 107–115. (Horse)

STAPLETON, H. E., 1953. Origin of Short-horned Cattle.—Bull. Soc. Jersiaise, 16: 100–102.

STEHLIN, H., 1933. In: DUBOIS, A. AND STEHLIN, H. La Grotte de Cotencher, station
moustérienne.—Mem. Soc. paléont. Suisse, Bâle, 52–53, 292 pp. (General)

—— AND GRAZIOSI, P., 1935. Ricerche sugli Asinidi fossili d'Europa.—Mém. Soc. paléont.
Suisse, Basel, 56: 73 pp., 10 pls. (Horse, Ass, Onager)

STEIN, A., 1937. Archaeological Reconnaissances in north-western India and south-
eastern Iran.—267 ppl., 34 pls.—London. (Camel)

STEINDORFF, G., 1913. Das Grab des Ti.—12 pp., 143 pls., 20 plans—Leipzig. (General)

STEINHAUSEN, J., 1951. Die Waldbienenwirtschaft der Rheinlande in ihrer historischen
Entwicklung.—Rhein. Viertelj. Bl., Bonn, 15–16: 216–257. (Bee)

STEKELIS, H., 1951. A New Neolithic Industry: The Yarmukian of Palestine.—Israel Expl.
J., Jerusalem, 1: 1–19, pls. 1–7. (Sheep and Camel)

STONOR, C. R., 1950. The Feasts of Merit among the Northern Sangtam Tribe of Assam.—
Anthropos, 45: 1–12. (Cattle)

——, 1953. The Mithan of Assam.—Geogr. Mag., London, 26 (6): 332–335.

STONOR, C. R., 1957. Notes on Religion and Ritual among the Dafla Tribes of the Assam Himalayas.—Anthropos, **52**: 1–23. (Cattle)

STORER, J., 1877. The Wild White Cattle of Great Britain.—384 pp.—London.

STRESEMAN, E. 1924. Zur Geschichte des Haushuhns.—Ornith. Monatsber., **32**: 105–106. (Fowl)

STUDER, T., 1901. Die prähistorischen Hunde in ihrer Beziehung zu den gegenwärtig lebenden Rassen.—Abh. Schweiz. pal. Ges. Zürich, **28**: 1–137, 8 pls. (Dog)

SUTCLIFFE, A. J., 1957. Cave fauna and cave sediments.—Ph.D. Thesis, Univ. London, 477 pp. (Reindeer)

TAYLOR, J. DU PLAT, 1957. Myrthou-Pigadhes.—118 pp., 71 pls.—Oxford (Goat and Fallow Deer)

TENNENT, J. E., 1860. Ceylon.—2 vols.—London. (Elephant)

TERMER, F., 1951. Die Hühner der Azteken.—Z. Ethnol., **76**: 205–215. (Fowl)

THÉVENIN, R., 1943. La Faune Disparue de France.—323 pp. —Paris. (General)

THOMPSON, R. C. AND MALLOWAN, M. E. L., 1933. The British Museum Excavations at Nineveh, 1931–1932.—Ann. Archaeol. Anthr. Liverpool, **20**: 71–186, pls. 35–106. (Cattle)

THOMSON, A. P. D., 1951. A History of the Ferret.—J. Hist. Med. Sci., New Haven, **6** (4): 471–480. (Ferret)

TOBIEN, H., 1952. Die Prämolarverluste bei Haushunden im Lichte der Stammesgeschichtlichen Entwicklung der Canidengebisses.—Der Terrier, 1952 (12): 2 pp. (Dog)

TOLMACHOFF, J. P., 1929. The Carcasses of the Mammoth and Rhinoceros found in the frozen ground of Siberia.—Trans. Amer. phil. Soc., Philadelphia, **23** (1): 1–74. (Elephant)

TÖMÖRDY, F., 1936. Der Föllik bei Gross-Höflein, ein neuer ur- und frühgeschichtlicher Fundplatz im Burgenland.—Bgld. Heimatblätter, **5**.

TRENSE, W., 1959. Der Mesopotamische Damhirsch (*Cervus mesopotamicus*) und sein Lebensraum.—Jahrb. Georg v. Opel Freigehege f. Tierforsch., Frankfurt: 18–22. (Fallow Deer)

TSCHERSKI, J. D., 1892. Wissenschaftliche Resultate der von der Kaiserlichen Akademie der Wissenschaften zur Erforschung des Janalandes und der Neusibirischen Inseln in den Jahren 1885 und 1886 ausgesandten Expedition. IV Beschreibung der Sammlung posttertiärer Säugethiere.—Mém. Acad. imp. Sci. St. Pétersbourg, **40** (1): 511 pp., 6 pls. (Horse)

TUDOR-WILLIAMS, V., 1954. Basenjis. The Barkless Dogs.—2nd edn., 79 pp.—London.

UECK, M., 1961. Abstammung und Rassebildung der vorkolumbianischen Haushunde in Südamerika.—Z. Säugetierk., **26**: 157–176. (Dog)

ULMANSKY, S., 1913. Untersuchungen über das Wild- und Hausschwein des Pfahlbaues im Laibacher Moor.—Mitteil. Landw. Lehrk. Hochsch. Bodenkultur. (Pig)

URBAIN, A., 1937. Le Kou-Prey ou Bœuf sauvage du Cambodge.—Bull. Mus. Hist. nat. Paris, **11** (6). (Cattle)

URE, A. D., 1951. Koes.—J. Hellenic Studies, London, **71**: 194–197, pl. 42. (Fowl)

VAUFREY, R., 1939 (a). L'Art rupestre nord-africain.—Mem. Inst. Pal. hum. Paris, **20**: 127 pp., 44 pls. (General)

——, 1939 (b). Faune de Sialk.—In: GHIRSHMAN, R., Fouilles de Sialk II.—Ser. archéol. Mus. Louvre, Paris, **5**: 195–202. (Horse and Sheep)

——, 1951. Mammifères.—In: NEUVILLE, R., Le Paléolithique et le Mésolithique du Désert de Judée.—Mém. Inst. Paléont. hum., Paris, **24**: 198–217. (Horse, Goat and Camel)

VESEY-FITZGERALD, B., 1947. Origin of the Domestic Cat.—The Field, London, July 5th, 1947: 10–11.

VOGEL, R., 1932. Die Tierreste. In Führer zur Urgeschichte. (Goat) (Not seen)

——, 1933. Tierreste aus vor- und frühgeschichtlichen Siedlungen Schwabens. I. Die Tierreste aus den Pfahlbauten des Bodensees.—Zoologica, Stuttgart, 109 pp., 14 pls. (Goat)

——, 1955. Die Tierknochen.—In: PARET, O., Das Steinzeitdorf Ehrenstein bei Ulm (Donau), 64–71. (General)

VOLKMER, D., 1956. Cytoarchitektonische Studien am Hirn verschieden grosser Hunde.— Z. mikr.-anat. Forsch., Leipzig, **62**: 267–314. (Dog)

VOSS, G., 1952. Rassenanalytische Untersuchungen an Eierstöcken von Schafen.—Zool. Jahrb. (Anat.) **72**: 438–467. (Sheep)

WACE, A. J. B., 1932. Chamber Tombs at Mycenae.—Archaeologia, **82**: 242 pp., 57 pls. (Camel)

WAECHTER, J. D'A., 1951. Excavations at Gorham's Cave, Gibraltar.—Proc. prehist. Soc., (n.s.) **17** (1): 83–92. (Goat and Rabbit)

WALEY, A., 1955. The Heavenly Horses of Ferghana. A New View.—History Today, February 1955: 95–103.

WALTERS, H. B., 1934. The Art of the Greeks.—3rd edn., 285 pp., 112 pls.—London. (Camel)

WALZ, R., 1951. Zum Problem des Zeitpunkts der Domestikation der altweltlichen Cameliden.—Zeit. Deutsch. Morgenländ. Ges., Wiesbaden, **101**: 29–51. (Camel)

——, 1956. Beiträge zur ältesten Geschichte der altweltlichen Cameliden unter besonderer Berücksichtigung des Problems des Domestikationszeitpunktes.—Act. IVᵉ Congr. intern. Sci. Anthrop. Ethn., Vienne, 1952, **3**: 190–204. (Camel)

WATSON, D. M. S., 1943. Note on the Skeleton of a Dog from the Eastern Entrance of Maiden Castle.—Rep. Res. Comm. Soc. Antiq. London, **12**: 371–2. (Dog)

WEBER, M. AND ABEL, O., 1928. Die Säugetiere.—2nd edn., 2 vols.—Jena. (Camel)

WELTEN, M., 1944. Pollenanalytische, Stratigraphische und Geochronologische Untersuchungen aus dem Faulenseemoos bei Spiez.—Veröff. Geobotan. Inst. Rübel, Zürich, **21**: 201 pp. (Dog)

WERTH, E., 1930. Zur Abstammung des Hausesels.—Sitzungsber. Ges. naturf. Berlin, 1930: 342–355. (Ass)

WEST, R. G., 1956. The Quaternary Deposits at Hoxne, Suffolk.—Phil. Trans. R. Soc. London, (B) **239** (665): 265–356. (Chapter 1)

WHEELER, W. M., 1928. The Social Insects: Their Origin and Evolution.—378 pp.—
London. (Chapter 2)

WHITEHEAD, G. K., 1953. The Ancient White Cattle of Britain and their Descendants.—
174 pp.—London.

WIARDA, H., 1954. Über Wuchsformen bei Haustieren.—Z. Tierzücht. Züchtungsbiol.,
63: 335–380. (Pig)

WILCKENS, M., 1888. Beitrag zur Kenntnis des Pferdegebisses.—N. Acta Leop. deutsch.
Akad. Naturf., **52**: 5. (Horse)

WILKINSON, J. G., 1897. Manners and Customs of the Ancient Egyptians. 3 vols.—London.
(Pelican)

WILLS, L. J., 1951. A Palaeogeographical Atlas of the British Isles and adjacent parts of
Europe.—22 pls.—London. (Chapter 1)

WINDELS, F., 1948. The Lascaux Cave Paintings.—159 pp.—London. (Cattle and Horse)

WINKLER, H. A., 1939. Rock-drawings of Southern Upper Egypt I, II.—Egypt Explor.
Soc., London. (Camel)

WINLOCK, H. E., 1955. Models of daily life in ancient Egypt from the tomb of Meket-Rēʿ
at Thebes.—Publ. Metr. Mus. Harvard.—106 pp., 86 pls. (General)

WOLFGRAMM, A., 1894. Die Einwirkung der Gefangenschaft auf die Gestaltung des Wolf-
schädels.—Zool. Jahrb. (Syst.), **7**: 773–822. (Dog)

WOOLLEY, L., 1934. Ur Excavations. II: The Royal Cemetery.—604 pp., 273 pls.—London
(Brit. Mus.) and New York. (Onager)

——, 1948. Excavations at Atchana-Alalakh, 1939.—Antiq. J., **28**: 1–19. (Elephant)

YALOURIS, N., 1950. Athena als Herrin der Pferde.—Mus. Helvet. **7**: 19–64. (Horse)

YEIVIN, S., 1934. A New Egyptian Source for the History of Palestine and Syria.—J.
Palestine orient. Soc., **14** (3): 194–229. (Elephant)

ZAMMIT, T., 1930. Prehistoric Malta. The Tarxien Temples.—127 pp.—Oxford. (General)

ZEUNER, F. E., 1931. Die Insektenfauna des Böttinger Marmors.—Fortschr. Geol. Palaeont.
Berlin, (9) **28**: 160 pp., 19 pls. (Bees)

——, 1945. Fossil Honey-Bees.—Rep. Brit. Beekeepers' Ass. (1944): 10.

——, 1950 (a). Archaeology and Geology.—South-east. Naturalist and Antiquary, **55**:
5–16. (General)

——, 1950 (b). The Cat.—Oryx, London, **1** (2): 65–71.

——, 1951 (a). Archaeological Dating by Radioactive Carbon.—Sci. Progress, No. 154:
225–238. (General)

——, 1951 (b). A Discussion of Time-rates in Evolution.—Proc. Linnean Soc. London,
162 (2): 124–130. (Honey-bee)

——, 1952 (a). The Microlithic Industry of Langhnaj, Gujarat.— Man, London, **52** (182):
4 pp. (General)

——, 1952 (b) On the Lascaux rhinoceros.—Man, London, **52**: 111. (Chapter 2)

——, 1953 (a). The colour of the Wild Cattle of Lascaux.—Man, London, **53** (98):
68–69.

ZEUNER, F. E., 1953 (b). The Chronology of the Mousterian at Gorham's Cave, Gibraltar.—Proc. prehist. Soc. (n.s.) **19** (2): 180–188. (Goat and Rabbit)

——, 1953 (c). Das Problem der Pluvialzeiten.—Geol. Rundschau, Stuttgart, **41**: 242–253. (Chapter 1)

——, 1955 (a). Radiocarbon Dates.—Rep. Inst. Archaeol. Univ. London, **11**: 43–50, 1953–1954). (Chapter I)

——, 1955 (b). Domestication of Animals.—In: SINGER, C., HOLMYARD, E. J. AND HALL, A. R. A History of Technology. I—Oxford: 327–352.

——, 1955 (c). The Goats of Early Jericho.—Palestine Expl. Quart., April: 70–86.

——, 1955 (d). The identity of the camel on the Khurab Pick.—Iraq, London, **17** (2): 162–163, pl. 36. (Camel)

——, 1956 (a). Domestic Cattle and Aurochs.—Oryx, London, **3** (6): 319–322.

——, 1956 (b). The Domestication of Animals.—Scientia, (6) **50** : 6 pp. (General)

——, 1956 (c). The Radiocarbon Age of Jericho.—Antiquity, **30**: 195–197. (General)

——, 1957. Animal Remains from Pighades, Cyprus.—In: TAYLOR, J. du PLAT, Myrtou-Pigadhes. A Late Bronze Age Sanctuary in Cyprus.—pp. 97–101—Oxford. (General)

——, 1958 (a). Dog and Cat in the Neolithic of Jericho.—Palestine Explor. Quart., London, Jan.–June 1958: 52–55.

——, 1958 (b). Dating the Past.—4th edn., 516 pp., 27 pls.—London. (Bee and general)

——, 1959. Some domesticated animals from the prehistoric site of Guayadeque, Gran Canaria.—El Mus. Canario, Las Palmas: 31–40, 2 pls. (Dog, Goat and Pig)

——, 1960. On the origin of the cinder-mounds of the Bellary District, India.—Bull. Inst. Archaeol. Univ. London, No. 2 (1959): 37–44. (Cattle)

——, 1961. Animal Remains from a Late Bronze Age Sanctuary on Cyprus and the Problem of the Domestication of Fallow Deer.—J. Palaeont. Soc. India, Lucknow, (1958), **3**: 131–135.

——, 1962 (a). The history of the domestication of Cattle.—R. anthrop. Inst. Symp. Cattle, London, 1960. (In the press.)

——, 1962 (b). Summary of the Symposium on Man and Cattle.—R. anthrop. Inst. Symp. Cattle, London, 1960. (In the press.)

——, 1962 (c). Further notes on the radiocarbon age of Jericho.—(In the press.) (Goat, Dog and Cat)

——, AND MANNING, F. J., 1962. Fossil Bees. (In the press.)

ZUKOWSKY, L., 1961. Der Geweihabwurf von *Cervus* (*Dama*) *mesopotamicus* in der Hagenbeckschen Trophäensammlung.–Säugetierk. Mitt., München, **9**: 69. (Fallow Deer)

Index